Second International Symposium

CONCRETE BRIDGE DESIGN

This symposium was compiled under the sponsorship of ACI Committee 443 and contains 44 papers on subjects ranging from methods of theoretical structural analysis to examples of unique bridge designs and construction techniques. Twenty-three of these papers were presented at the 65th ACI Annual Convention, Chicago, April 2, 1969.

ACI PUBLICATION SP-26
AMERICAN CONCRETE INSTITUTE
DETROIT, MICHIGAN

DISCUSSION of individual papers in this symposium may be submitted in accordance with general requirements of the ACI Publications Policy to the Secretary, Technical Activities Committee, at the ACI address given below. Closing date for submission of discussion is January 1, 1972. All discussion approved by the Technical Activities Committee will be published in the July 1972 ACI JOURNAL together with appropriate closing remarks by the authors.

P. O. Box 4754, Redford Station
Detroit, Michigan 48219

Printed in the United States of America

The papers in this symposium are the sole responsibility of the authors. Institute authority attaches only to standards adopted as provided in the Bylaws.

LIBRARY OF CONGRESS CATALOG CARD NUMBER 71-155481

PREFACE

This volume embodies a collection of the 44 selected papers out of those proposed for presentation to, and publication by, the ACI Second International Symposium on Concrete Bridge Design as held in Chicago on April 2-3, 1969. Not only were the proposed synoptic summaries first judiciously weighed through a referral process, but also all the final versions were likewise prudently re-examined by the Paper Review Panel of ACI Committee 443 - Concrete Bridge Design. Altogether, the 44 chosen papers were authored or co-authored by 63 contributors from 4 continents. It is their brain work and their unselfish sharing of knowledge and experience with others that had made the Second International Symposium on Concrete Bridge Design as significant as the First held in Toronto, Canada, in April 1967.

To facilitate future reference, this volume has been edited and grouped into 12 sections in the following sequence: Live Loads and Load Factors; Analysis and Design of Slab Bridges; Skew Concrete Bridges; Box and Cellular Girder Bridges; Ultimate Strength and Limit Design of Concrete Bridges; Service Load Analysis and Working Stress Design; Design and Construction of Prestressed Concrete Bridges; Precast Concrete Bridges; Fatigue of Concrete Bridges; Concrete for Bridge Members; and Bearings and Substructures for Concrete Bridges. Thus, the contents published herein represent an excellent cross-section of the ever advancing stature of concrete bridge technology, complementing the First International Symposium Volume as well as indicating the trend for the 70's decade.

As chairman of ACI Committee 443 - Concrete Bridge Design, during the preparation of the Second Symposium as well as the First, and as General Chairman of both Symposia, the writer had the privilege and pleasure to work with the contributing authors from overseas and within the U.S. It will be to the credit of their lasting effort, if this volume may endure the test of time. To the ACI and ACI-TAC, the Symposium was due for its having been held at the right time, and, additionally, to the ACI Staff, this volume is due for its having been published and disseminated among the concrete bridge engineering communities throughout the world. It is only appropriate to dedicate this volume to "Progress through knowledge" as the ACI motto indicates.

The writer is especially appreciative of the enduring and diplomatic effort of Leonidas T. Delyannis, Program Committee Chairman of the Second Symposium as well as the first. The task involved was enormous and exacting, requiring courteous acts to all authors. Throughout the two-day Symposium, 6 sessions were held, conducted by 6 Session Chairmen, 6 Co-Chairmen, and 6 Secretaries. It was due to their utmost efficiency in conducting the Sessions that the Symposium ran to the entire satisfaction of all stimulating contributors and the untiring audience.

Unconventional methods of aggregate grading, innovative cementing materials, exciting treatment of concrete, and new methods of design, fabrication and erection, and construction are being rapidly evolved. ACI Committee 443 is planning further specific Symposia on Concrete Bridges. True as "Progress through knowledge" it can be certain that more rapid progress will always come forth through periodic sharing of knowledge among all concerned with concrete bridges which man is bound to continue to use in his ground transportation for an indefinite future.

For uncontrollable reasons, this volume has not been able to come off the press earlier as we all had planned and expected on the second day of the Symposium. We do regret the unavoidable delay.

And finally, as is usually the case in this kind of publication, notwithstanding the fact a review was exercised, neither ACI, nor its Committee on Concrete Bridge Design, nor the Program Committee, is responsivle for any statement made in the papers, but it is the respective author who is responsible for his statement and to whom credit is due.

Shu-t'ien Li
General Chairman of the Symposium

ACI COMMITTEE 443

Concrete Bridge Design

Chairman

DAVID A. VANHORN

Vice-Chairman

WILLIAM C. CORLEY

Secretary

TI HUANG

ARTHUR R. ANDERSON
RAYMOND ARCHIBALD
LAURENCE CAZALY
LEONIDAS T. DELYANNIS
JOSEPH DUDRA
NOEL J. EVERARD
JOHN J. FIALA
C. L. FREYERMUTH
BEN C. GERWICK, JR.
HANS GESUND
AMIN GHALI
MAXIMIL GRIETENS
THOMAS T. C. HSU

JOHN J. KOZAK
SHU-T'IEN LI*
T. Y. LIN
ROBERT G. LIUM
A. M. LOUNT
ROBERT LEE PARE
E. G. PAULET
V. RAMAKRISHNAN
GEORGE S. RICHARDSON
LUIS P. SAENZ
A. C. SCORDELIS
GEORGE SOMERVILLE
K. G. TAMBERG**

W. J. JURKOVICH

*Chairman, ACI Committee 443, 1966 to 1969
**Chairman, ACI Committee 443, 1969 to 1970

The Program Committee wishes also to express its gratitude to the following distinguished engineers who served as officers of the six sessions in Chicago and especially to the Chairman of each session for their Highlight Introduction at the Symposium:

Session on Loads, Skew Decks, and Fatigue --	Arthur R. Anderson, Chairman J. Dudra, Co-Chairman Robert G. Lium, Secretary
Session on Slab Bridges	T. Y. Lin, Chairman Ben C. Gerwick, Jr., Co-Chairman John J. Fiala, Secretary
Session on Box and Cellular Girder Bridges	Anthony R. Cusens, Chairman Laurence Cazaly, Co-Chairman Karl G. Tamberg, Secretary
Session on Ultimate Load Analysis and Ultimate Strength Design	Noel J. Everard, Chairman Frederic Roll, Co-Chairman A. Murray Lount, Secretary
Session on Service Load Analysis and Working Stress Design	V. Ramakrishnan, Chairman W. Gene Corley, Co-Chairman Thomas T. C. Hsu, Secretary
Session on Composite Bridge Design	George S. Richardson, Chairman D. A. VanHorn, Co-Chairman R. Green, Secretary

The editing of this volume would not have been possible without the efforts of the following members of the Reviewing Committee:

Raymond Archibald, Laurence Cazaly, W. Gene Corley, Leonidas T. Delyannis, J. Dudra, Noel J. Everard, John J. Fiala, C. L. Freyermuth, Hans Gesund, Thomas T. C. Hsu, W. J. Jurkovich, Shu-t'ien Li, T. Y. Lin, Robert G. Loum, A. Murray Lount, Luis P. Saenz, Karl G. Tamberg.

Their suggestions and advice to the authors contributed to the success of this Symposium Volume.

Leonidas T. Delyannis
Chairman, Program Committee

FOREWORD

The Second International Symposium on Concrete Bridge Design, held in Chicago from April 2 to 3, 1969.

An unprecedented attendance of many hundreds of bridge enginee from four continents participated, and shared the design and practi experience of outstanding authors. The experience gained by the Fi International Symposium, which was held in Toronto in April, 1967, s that this exchange of views and new ideas among bridge engineers at international level is advantageous to all participants and will hope result in better, safer, and more economical bridges.

This volume contains 44 papers; 23 of these papers were presente orally in Chicago, and the rest, due to time limitations, were selecte for publication. Discussions received for certain papers are also inc in this volume. The papers of this Symposium have been classified int groups covering the following areas of bridge design:

- Live Loads and Load Factors
- Analysis and Design of Slab Bridges
- Skew Concrete Bridges
- Box and Cellular Girder Bridges
- Ultimate Strength and Limit Design of Concrete Bridges
- Service Load Analysis and Working Stress Design
- Design and Construction of Prestressed Concrete Bridges
- Precast Concrete Bridges
- Composite Bridges
- Fatigue of Concrete Bridges
- Concrete for Bridge Members
- Bearings and Substructures for Concrete Bridges

The sixty-one authors and co-authors represent distinguished bridge designers from Canada, England, Hong-Kong, India, Israel, Japan, Sweden, the Union of Soviet Socialist Republics, the United Arab Republic, the United States of America, and West Germany.

The Program Committee feels indebted to these authors and co-authors for their deep interest in the Second International Symposium; for their significant contributions to the art of bridge design; and for their co-operation before, during, and after the Symposium.

Special appreciation is extended to Dr. Shu-t'ien Li, Chairman of ACI Committee 443 at the time of the Symposium and General Chairman of the Symposium. His tireless efforts and devoted guidance are gratefully acknowledged by all those who had the privilege to work with him.

CONTENTS

SKEW CONCRETE BRIDGES

BOX AND CELLULAR GIRDER BRIDGES

ULTIMATE STRENGTH AND LIMIT DESIGN OF CONCRETE BRIDGES

SERVICE LOAD ANALYSIS AND WORKING STRESS DESIGN

DESIGN AND CONSTRUCTION OF PRESTRESSED CONCRETE BRIDGES

PRECAST CONCRETE BRIDGES

COMPOSITE BRIDGES

FATIGUE OF CONCRETE BRIDGES

CONCRETE FOR BRIDGE MEMBERS

BEARINGS AND SUBSTRUCTURES FOR CONCRETE BRIDGES

COMPARISON OF LIVE LOADS USED IN HIGHWAY BRIDGE DESIGN IN NORTH AMERICA WITH THOSE USED IN WESTERN EUROPE

By ALFIO SENI

SYNOPSIS

The author first discusses the advantages resulting from having all Live Load Specifications approved and enacted by a State Administration, prior to their publication.

The main provisions for live loads in United States, Canada, Great Britain, and France are then defined.

These specifications are afterwards compared: first a quantitative comparison of moments and reactions for different cases, the results being shown in tables and charts.

There follows a qualitative comparison of these specifications in regard of their simplicity and ease of application. In conclusion, the author suggests that North American specifications for Highway Bridge Loadings should be revised.

Keywords: bending moments; bridge decks; bridges (structures); girder bridges; girders; highway bridges; moving loads; standards; structural design.

ACI member ALFIO SENI is a senior structural engineer with Lalonde, Valois, Lamarre, Valois & Associates, consulting engineers, Montreal. He is also a lecturer for Bridge Engineering at the Ecole Polytechnique, University of Montreal, Canada.

In Canada for 9 years, Mr. Seni was in charge of the design of several important bridge structures in the Montreal region. He is also designer of some subway stations and tunnels for the Metro of Montreal.

Mr. Seni is member of the Corporation of Engineers of Quebec (CEQ), of ACI and ASCE. He is author of several papers appeared in American and European technical publications.

1- Introduction

In all the countries, there are specifications which establish the loads which have to be taken in consideration in the design of bridges. In this article, we will deal only with those concerning the highway bridges and only with the live loads.

In Europe, the live loads are generally established by a State organization and are rendered compulsory by a law or a government decree. In North America, the specifications for loadings are issued by non-government organizations and have not the same binding power as in Europe. These are only recommendations for the designers, and the public administrations may approve them, or may leave the designers the freedom to apply them as issued, or to modify them according to their own judgment.

That is why in countries like U.S.A. or Canada, each state or province may use the specifications issued by the "American Association of State Highway Officials" (AASHO), or by the "Canadian Standards Association " (CSA) but they may also issue their own specifications.

The European system seems to the author to be better from this point of view, because it obliges the designers to use the same loads and the same methods of design and thus to obtain an uniformity regarding the bridges in the respective country. If, concerning the methods of design, this advantage may be questionable, it is indisputable that concerning the live loads, it would be better if they were established in each country by a state administration. To leave the designers or the local administrations, the latitude to decide on the live loads to be used, leads to the construction of bridges having various capacities, in different places and even on the same highway, which is surely not desirable.

To give an example, in Canada, the code CSA S6-1966 provides as maximum live load the HS20-44 loading (the same as AASHO). However, some provincial or municipal authorities, ask the designers, with good reason as it will be seen later on, to increase this loading by 25%. Others, for instance the Province of Quebec, use a quite different truck loading than the one recommended by the CSA.

It should therefore be desirable that the live loads, once established by an organization, be approved and enacted by the central government of the respective country, like in Europe, so to avoid the above mentioned disadvantages. As far as the author knows there is neither in U.S.A., nor in Canada, at this time any law or government decree prescribing the loads to be taken in the design of highway bridges.

The question of having compulsory loadings is important, because in this case, the government takes the responsibility for the loadings used, and therefore their values have to be established with great care.

2- Presentation of Loadings used in some Countries of North America and Western Europe

In the following, we shall outline the main previsions of the specifications on live loads used in North America (USA and Canada) and Western Europe (Great Britain and France).

A) United States

In this country, the "Standard Specifications for Highway Bridges 1965" of the AASHO are generally used. It must be mentioned that the loadings, there provided, have not been changed since 1944.

This code provides more classes of loadings, the heaviest being designated by the indication HS20-44. The Code provides also another system of loads: The H loads (truck without trailers) the corresponding heavier loading being H20-44.

For the design of highway bridges, for each class of loading, two types of loadings are considered: the truck loading and the lane loading, and the one will be adopted which leads to maximum stresses (Fig. 1).

For the truck loading, on each traffic lane, one single truck is considered on the whole length of the lane. This is very important for the further comparison.

The lane loading is supposed to be the equivalent of a train of H15 trucks, with one H20 truck, the trucks being spaced at 30 ft. one from the other. It will be shown thereafter that this loading is much lighter than the European loadings; one of the causes is evidently that the truck loads which served to establish the equivalent are much lighter than HS20-44 and at long distances one from the other.

The AASHO code provides that all the live loads shall be increased by an impact factor. It also provides reduction factors for members affected by loading simultaneously more than two traffic lanes.

B) Canada

The specifications of the Canadian Standards Association (CSA) designated as CSA S6-1966, Design of Highway Bridges, are generally used in Canada. The CSA, like the AASHO, is a non-government organization, and the issued standards are not compulsory for the designers in Canada. The live loads for highway bridges, according to the CSA specifications, are exactly the same as those of the AASHO.

C) Great Britain

The loads are designated by the appellation "Standard Highway Loadings" and are established by the British Standards Specification B.S. 153: Part 3A: 1954 (amended in 1959, 1961 and 1966). This loading is issued by the British Standard Institution and was enacted by the Ministry of Transport of Great Britain (Memorandum No. 771 of 1961) so that it is obligatory in the country.

a) The normal loading called type HA loading, is of one single class and is given as an equivalent uniform load per linear foot on a 10 ft. wide traffic lane. In addition, a concentrated (knife-edge) load of 27,000 lbs. is provided for one 10 ft. lane (Fig. 2a). The uniform load is not constant but is varying with the loaded length. The values of this load are given in the specification both in tabular and graphical way. In table 1 are shown the values of the uniform load for a loaded length varying from 3 ft. to 3,000 ft. The loads include an impact factor of 25%. This loading represents approximately the effect of 3 vehicles each 22 tons in weight closely spaced, followed by 10 ton and 5 ton vehicles.

b) The specifications provide also for an abnormal loading called type HB loading, consisting of a very heavy vehicle. The vehicle has 4 axles, having each one a weight expressed in units (1 unit = 1 ton) (Fig. 2b). The bridge must be checked for this loading only if it is required and if the load of an abnormal vehicle exceeds 20 units (80 tons). In this case, an overstress of 25% is allowed.

The specifications provide a reduction for loading of more than two traffic lanes.

D) France

The live loads are provided in a decree of August 1960 of the Ministy of Public Works, Transports and Tourism:

The loadings are of two sorts: The system A and the system B, the second being the only one used for the design of the slabs and of the floorbeams.

The system A consists of an uniform load of an intensity A in kg per sq.m., which is given by a formula in terms of the loaded length (Fig. 3a). The load varies from 1,772 kg/sq.m. (354 lbs./sq.ft.) for 1 m length to 350 kg/m = (78 lbs./sq.ft.) for 200 m. (655 ft.) length. The load includes the impact factor.

The system B, comprises 3 types of loadings:

a) type Bc consists of two trucks of 33 tons each, closely spaced (Fig. 3b).

b) type Be consists of a single axle of 22 tons applied on a 2.50 m. (7.4 ft.) width

c) type Br consists of a single wheel load of 11 tons applied on a square area of 1 ft. side

The system B loadings do not include an impact factor, which is given by a very complicated formula.

No reductions for more than two loaded lanes, are allowed.

3. Comparison of the Load Specifications

A) Quantitative Comparison

For comparing the specifications, from the quantitative point of view, seeing that these are basically different, moment and reactions (shears) were calculated for different elements of various spans.

In table 2 are indicated the values of bending moments for slabs with simple spans between 7 ft. and 12 ft. The values are represented graphically in the chart Fig. 4. The values include the impact, and for each span three values are given, according to AASHO & CSA loading, British HA normal loading, and French A loading.

In table 3, and in the chart Fig. 5 are given the 3 values for bending moments in simple spans of 50 ft. to 150 ft.

In table 4 and chart Fig. 6 are given the maximum positive bending moments in two equal continuous spans of 40 ft. to 120 ft.

The values of end reactions in simple spans of 50 ft. to 150 ft. are given in table 5 and in chart Fig. 7.

In table 6 and in chart Fig. 8 are given the values of the reactions at middle support of two equal continuous spans of 40 ft. to 120 ft.

All the values include the impact factor, as provided by each of the 3 specifications.

If we examine the values given in the tables and the charts above shown, the following conclusions may be drawn:

a) The values found by applying the British and the French specifications are generally very close to each other, although the loading systems used are quite different.

b) These values are, in all cases, much higher than those found by applying the AASHO and CSA specifications. The difference is particularly large for girders, and increases with the span.

   Regarding the slabs, the differences vary between 25% and 40%.

   For simple span beams, the difference concerning the moments varies from 32% to 110%, and concerning the reactions from 51% to 148%.

   For continuous two span girders the differences of positive moments vary from 20% to 93%, and of reactions on the middle support from 84% to 120%.

c) What conclusion should be drawn from this comparison? Are the vehicles used in Europe so much heavier than those used in North America? This is difficult to believe, because all these countries are highly industrialized, on both sides of the Atlantic Ocean, and the weight of the heavy vehicles which are using the highways cannot be very different.

In other respects, we have seen, in the first part of this paper, which are the load trains used in the specifications, and it is easy to be seen that the weights assumed are much larger in the West European Countries, even for the normal traffic.

It is evident that a Code cannot be provided for the actual loadings of the vehicles in circulation, which are very variable as well regarding the loads, as the spacing of the axles. It is necessary to adopt a conventional loading which must be on the safe side for any span and for any type of actual load.

It follows therefore that, if we admit that the actual loads cannot be very different, either the conventional european loadings are too large, or the American ones are too small. The fact that the results obtained by applying the British and the French loadings, are very near, though the load systems are quite different, cannot be a mere coincidence. That seems rather to demonstrate that the vehicles which served as base for the establishment of these loadings and their arrangement along the bridge, are very similar.

This leads to the conclusion that the comparison shows rather that the HS20 loading is too weak.

This weakness is due not so much to the weight of the HS20 truck itself, but rather to the density of the loads. For the truck loading a single vehicle is allowed on the whole length of the bridge, while the French code provides two heavy trucks closely spaced and the British Code 3 heavy trucks, plus lighter trucks. As for the lane loading, as mentioned before, it is equivalent to a train of light H trucks, only one of them being a H20 truck, and the spacing between the trucks very large.

For this reason, the lane loading has a very reduced value: only 640 lbs./ft., compared with 1,760 lbs./ft. given by the British Code for spans between 20 ft. and 75 ft. impact excluded. The lane loading being too small, it is the truck loading which governs for simple spans up to 140 ft. which are consequently designed for one single truck on a lane, though there is room enough for 3 consecutive HS20 trucks.

If we consider, on a 140 ft. span, 3 consecutive HS20 trucks spaced at 20 ft. intervals, we find that the bending moment is 4,950 kft. including the impact, instead of 2,677 kft. according to the AASHO Code. If we compare this value with those given by European Codes, we find that it is only

5% below the value given by the British Code. (Fig. 9).

It is therefore clear that the low results found by applying AASHO Code are mainly due to the fact that the lane loading is not equivalent to a train of HS20 trucks, but has a much smaller value and therefore the single HS20 truck governs for spans up to 140 ft.

It appears therefore to be very desirable that AASHO undertake an inquiry for establishing the value of the maximum actual loads of the vehicles presently in use in U.S.A., and derive from that a new type of conventional loading, which cover all these loads.

But, in establishing this new loading, there must be considered, not only the present loads, but also a prevision for the future increase of the loads.

It must not be forgotten that the bridges and particularly the concrete bridges, are structures made to last a long time. In the opinion of the author, design should provide for 100 years and make the previsions for probable load increases during that period.

This question is very important, particularly concerning concrete bridges. Steel bridges can easily enough be strengthened if they are no longer sufficient for the increased loads, but this operation is much more difficult if it concerns concrete bridges. The strengthening involves very difficult problems, which means that often it is preferrable to build a new bridge, instead of strengthening the old one.

After having established the weight of vehicles to be taken in account, it must be decided by an inquiry on site, at what intervals the consecutive trucks have to be placed on a traffic lane.

In conclusion, it appears from the comparison made on the values of the loadings, that those provided by the North American Codes seem to be unsufficient and that one has to verify and revise them so to be sure that they correspond to the present loads with a sufficient margin for their future increase.

2- Qualitative Comparison

If we now compare the qualitative structure of the loading systems used in the countries above mentioned, we find out the following:

In U.S.A. and Canada, for the live loads, two types of loadings are prescribed: the first is composed by concentrated loads of two sorts H loadings and HS loadings; the second consists of an uniform load and a concentrated load which is different for moments and for shears.

In France also, there are 2 types of loadings: one being an uniform loading, the other a train of trucks.

In Great Britain, it is normally one single loading type used, consisting of a uniform load, plus a concentrated load. The abnormal load is used only in special cases, and only for checking the bridge design.

Comparing the 3 loadings systems, it appears that the HA loading used in Great Britain is the easiest to apply.

First, there is only one load system, while in the other specifications there are at least two systems who have to be applied to determine the one producing the higher stresses. Secondly, the British loading is simpler, consisting of a uniform load and a single concentrated load, instead of a train of concentrated loads as provided by the AASHO truck loading and the system B loading of the French specifications. And, as everybody knows, it is much simpler and easier to work with uniform than with concentrated loads.

Therefore, it is desirable that, if a revision should be made in the loadings provided by AASHO and CSA code, this revision should refer not only to the values of the loads but also to the type of loading.

It would be desirable to find a variable uniform load which be equivalent to a conveniently spaced train of heavy trucks. To this should be added a concentrated load to compensate for the additional weight of an overloaded truck, located at the critical point.

This variable uniform load should satisfy more requirements:

a) It has to be conservative for all the possible types of present loads with sufficient previsions for the future.

b) It may be applied to all the members of the bridge: slabs, main girders, floorbeams, stringers, arches, etc., and for any material used.

c) It has to be applicable to any span, the variation of the load taking in account all the possible locations of the loads along the bridge.

d) It must include the impact factor.

Once the new loading established, it should be recommended that it be approved and enacted by the government, so to become an obligatory law in all the respective country.

TABLE 1. HIGHWAY LOADING. TYPE HA

Equivalent U.D.L. to be used in conjunction with the knife edge load.

Loaded length, ft	U.D.L. for beams per linear foot of lane	U.D.L. for longitudinal slabs per linear foot of lane	U.D.L. for transverse slabs and cross girders per linear foot of lane	Loaded length, ft	U.D.L. for beams per linear foot of lane	U.D.L. for longitudinal slabs per linear foot of lane	U.D.L. for transverse slabs and cross girders per linear foot of lane
3	24 200	24 200	22 700	12	4 870	3 250	2 600
4	17 000	17 000	11 800	13	4 540	2 950	2 400
5	12 250	12 250	7 700	14	4 210	2 700	2 300
6	9 660	8 850	5 800	15	3 880	2 500	2 200
7	8 280	6 550	4 600	16	3 550	2 400	2 200
8	7 250	5 200	3 900	17	3 220	2 300	2 200
9	6 440	4 520	3 400	18	2 880	2 250	2 200
10	5 800	4 000	3 100	19	2 540	2 200	2 200
11	5 200	3 600	2 800	20-75	2 200	2 200	2 200

Loaded length	Load	Loaded length	Load	Loaded length	Load	Loaded length	Load	Loaded length	Load
ft	lb/lin. ft	ft	lb/lin. ft	ft	lb/lin. ft	ft	lb/lin. ft	ft	lb/lin. ft
80	2 160	175	1 530	270	1 210	430	1 005	1 200	660
85	2 120	180	1 500	275	1 200	440	1 000	1 300	630
90	2 080	185	1 480	280	1 190	450	990	1 400	600
95	2 040	190	1 460	285	1 175	460	985	1 500	580
100	2 000	195	1 440	290	1 165	470	975	1 600	560
105	1 960	200	1 420	295	1 155	480	970	1 700	540
110	1 920	205	1 400	300	1 145	490	965	1 800	520
115	1 890	210	1 380	310	1 130	500	960.	1 900	510
120	1 860	215	1 360	320	1 115	550	935	2 000	490
125	1 830	220	1 350	330	1 105	600	910	2 100	480
130	1 800	225	1 335	340	1 090	650	880	2 200	470
135	1 770	230	1 320	350	1 080	700	860	2 300	460
140	1 740	235	1 305	360	1 070	750	835	2 400	450
145	1 710	240	1 290	370	1 060	800	810	2 500	440
150	1 680	245	1 280	380	1 050	850	790	2 600	430
155	1 650	250	1 265	390	1 040	900	770	2 700	420
160	1 620	255	1 250	400	1 030	950	750	2 800	410
165	1 590	260	1 240	410	1 020	1 000	730	2 900	410
170	1 560	265	1 225	420	1 015	1 100	690	3 000	400

TABLE 2 MOMENTS IN SIMPLE SPAN SLABS (IMPACT INCLUDED)

Span ft.	AASHO & CSA k.ft.	Great Britain k.ft.	France k.ft.
7-0	5.85	7.55	7.44
8-0	6.50	8.52	8.25
9-0	7.15	9.52	9.05
10-0	7.80	10.62	9.75
11-0	8.45	11.70	10.35
12-0	9.10	12.78	10.95

TABLE 3

MOMENTS, SIMPLE SPAN, ONE LANE (IMPACT INCLUDED)

Span ft.	AASHO & CSA k.ft.	Great Britain k.ft.	France k.ft.
50	808	1,025	1,070
60	1,024	1,395	1,490
70	1,240	1,821	1,972
80	1,450	2,268	2,480
90	1,660	2,714	3,020
100	1,865	3,175	3,570
110	2,066	3,647	4,110
120	2,270	4,158	4,640
130	2,470	4,680	5,140
140	2,677	5,208	5,620
150	2,926	5,738	6,100

TABLE 4

POSITIVE MOMENTS, ONE LANE, TWO EQUAL CONTINUOUS SPANS
(IMPACT INCLUDED)

Span ft.	AASHO & CSA k.ft.	Great Britain k.ft.	France k.ft.
40	465	561	535
50	645	805	817
60	820	1,092	1,142
70	995	1,421	1,510
80	1,165	1,770	1,900
90	1,340	2,115	2,305
100	1,510	2,473	2,725
110	1,680	2,838	3,150
120	1,845	3,234	3,560

TABLE 5

END REACTIONS, SIMPLE SPAN, ONE LANE (IMPACT INCLUDED)

Span ft.	AASHO & CSA k.	Great Britain k.	France k.
50	75.2	82.0	85.5
60	77.2	93.0	99.6
70	78.2	104.0	112.6
80	79.4	113.4	124.4
90	79.7	120.6	134.0
100	80.0	127.0	142.5
110	80.1	132.6	149.5
120	80.2	138.6	154.5
130	81.0	144.0	156.5
140	84.0	148.8	159.5
150	87.8	153.0	163.0

TABLE 6

MAXIMUM REACTION AT MIDDLE SUPPORT, ONE LANE, TWO EQUAL CONTINUOUS SPANS (IMPACT INCLUDED)

Span ft.	AASHO & CSA k.	Great Britain k.	France k.
40	84.5	137.0	155.5
50	87.2	164.5	178.0
60	89.0	192.0	193.5
70	97.5	219.5	199.5
80	106.0	243.0	206.0
90	114.5	261.0	209.0
100	122.0	277.0	210.5
110	130.5	291.0	212.0
120	139.0	306.0	213.0

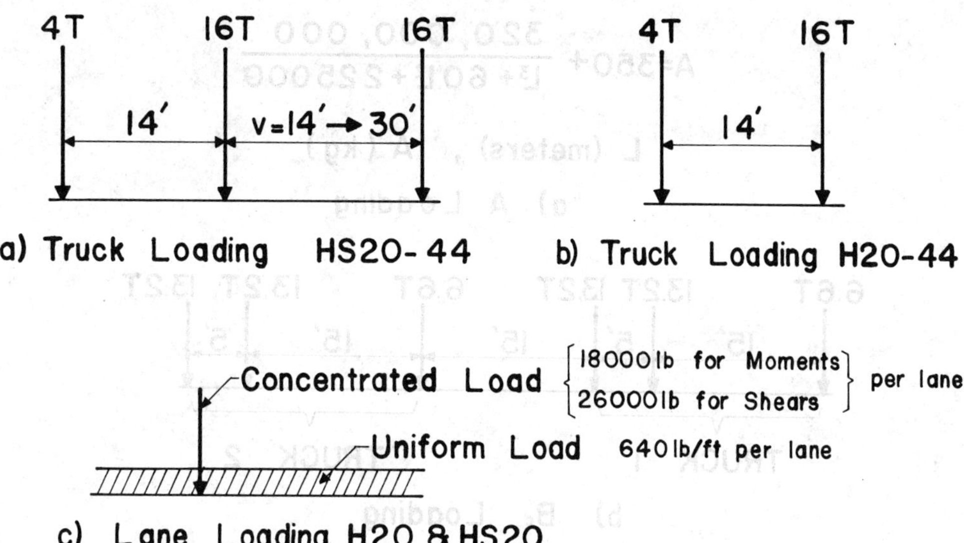

FIG. 1
AASHO & CSA LOADINGS

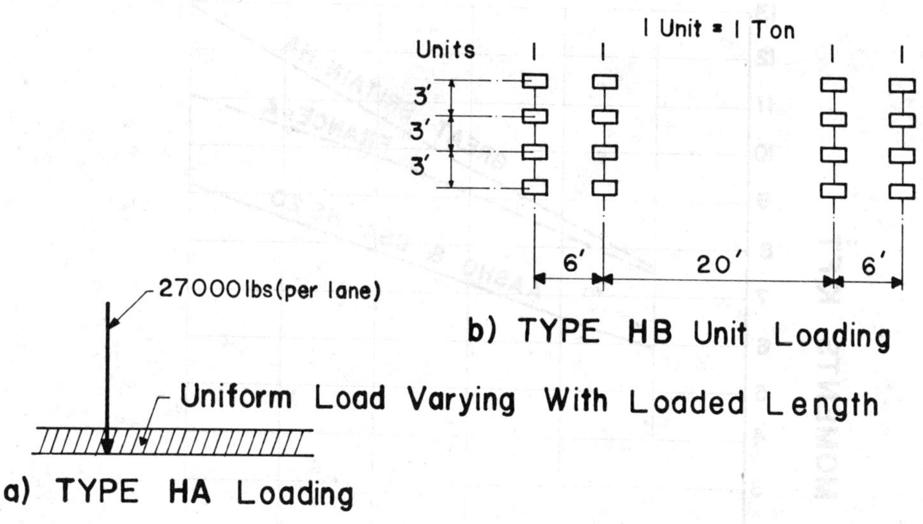

FIG. 2
BRITISH LOADINGS

$$A = 350 + \frac{320,000,000}{L^3 + 60L^2 + 225000}$$

L (meters) , A (kg)

a) A Loading

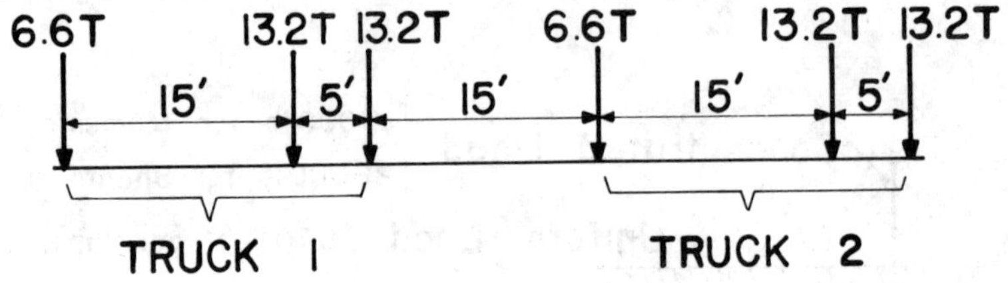

6.6T 13.2T 13.2T 6.6T 13.2T 13.2T

15′ 5′ 15′ 15′ 5′

TRUCK 1 TRUCK 2

b) B_c Loading

FIG. 3

FRENCH LOADINGS

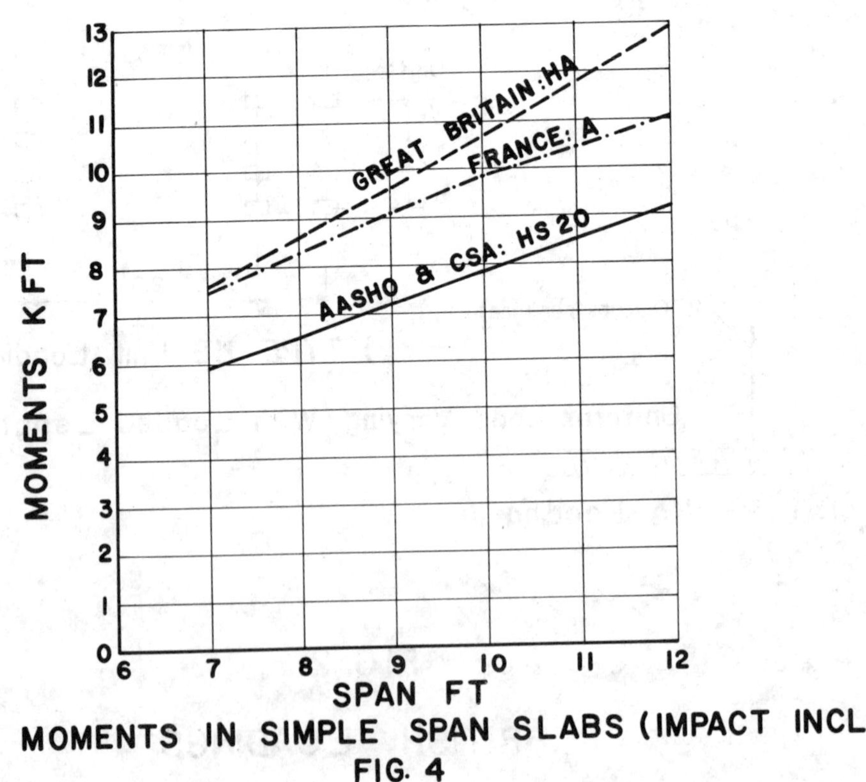

MOMENTS IN SIMPLE SPAN SLABS (IMPACT INCL.)

FIG. 4

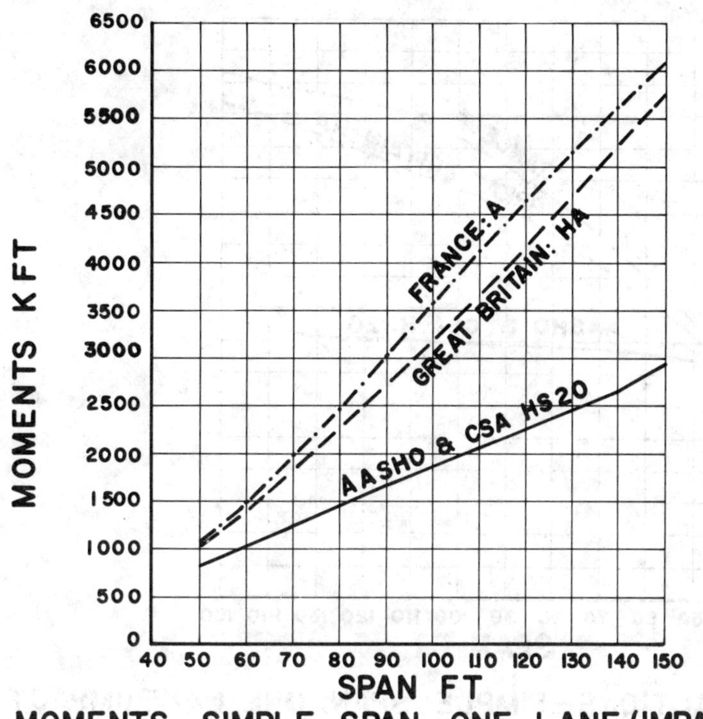

MOMENTS, SIMPLE SPAN, ONE LANE (IMPACT INCL.)

FIG. 5

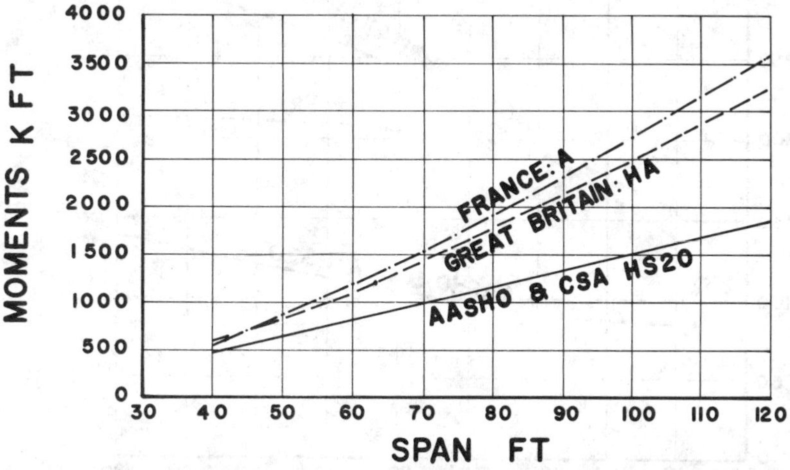

MAXIMUM POSITIVE MOMENTS, ONE LANE, TWO EQUAL CONTINUOUS SPANS (IMPACT INCL.)

FIG. 6

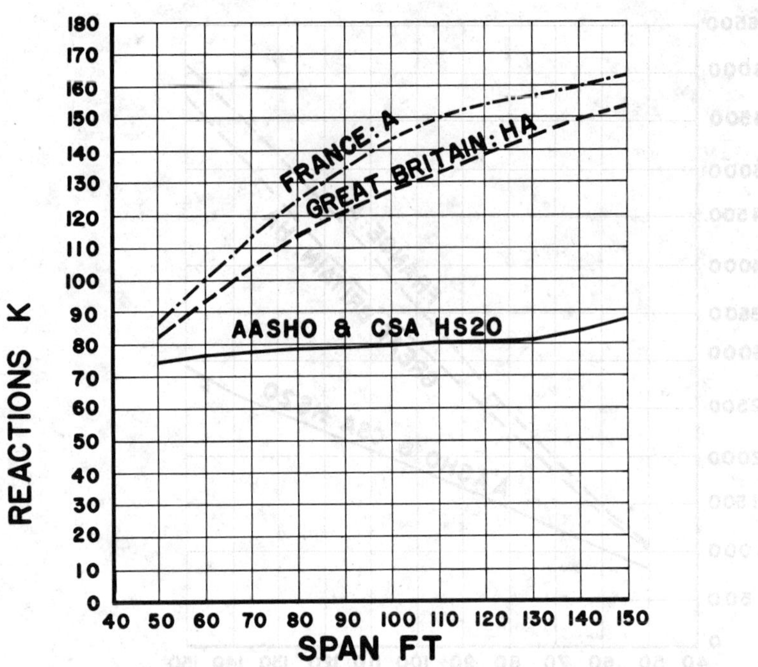

END REACTIONS - SIMPLE SPAN, ONE LANE (IMPACT INCL.)
FIG. 7

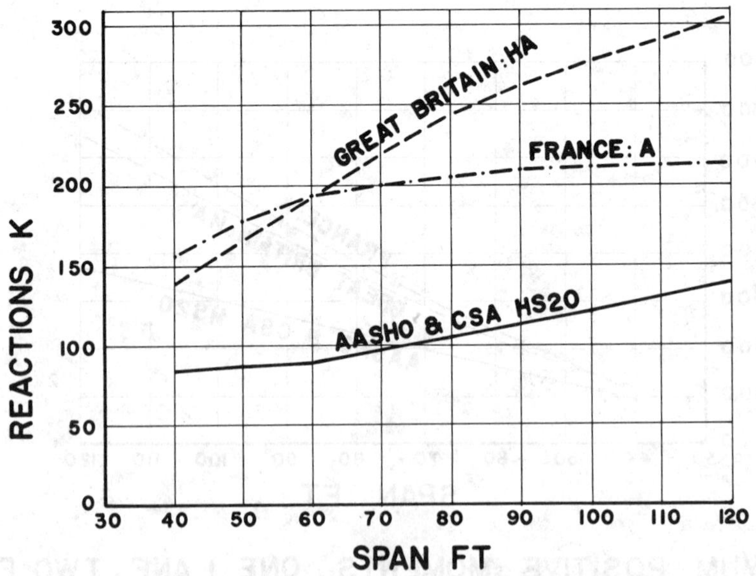

MAXIMUM REACTIONS AT MIDDLE SUPPORT, ONE LANE, TWO EQUAL CONTINUOUS SPANS (IMPACT INCLUDED)

FIG. 8

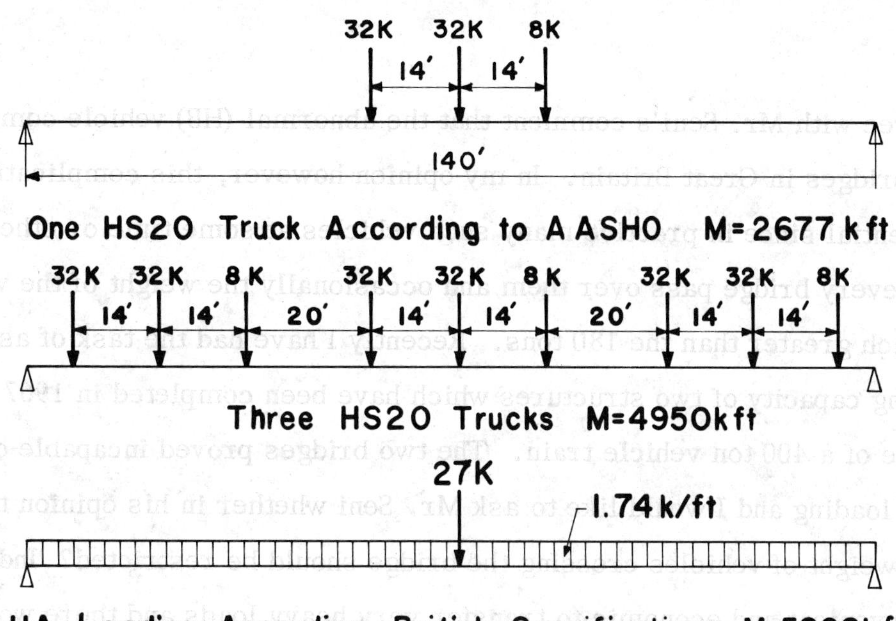
32K 32K 8K
14′ 14′
140′
One HS20 Truck According to AASHO M=2677 k ft
32K 32K 8K 32K 32K 8K 32K 32K 8K
14′ 14′ 20′ 14′ 14′ 20′ 14′ 14′
Three HS20 Trucks M=4950 k ft
27K
1.74 k/ft
HA Loading According British Specifications M=5208 k ft

FIG. 9

DISCUSSION

By F. SAWKO

Professor, Department of Civil Engineering, University of Liverpool

I agree with Mr. Seni's comment that the abnormal (HB) vehicle complicates design of bridges in Great Britain. In my opinion however, this complication is really essential since in practice many such vehicles at some time or other during the life of every bridge pass over them and occasionally the weight of the vehicle is very much greater than the 180 tons. Recently I have had the task of assessing the carrying capacity of two structures which have been completed in 1967 under the passage of a 400 ton vehicle train. The two bridges proved incapable of carrying this heavy loading and I would like to ask Mr. Seni whether in his opinion the maximum weight of vehicles crossing the bridge should be restricted? Industry finds it convenient and economic to transfer very heavy loads and there would probably be repercussions if any restriction were to be placed on the maximum load.

Referring again to the passage of very heavy abnormal vehicles over bridges, would it not be desirable in Mr. Seni's opinion to provide a set of influence surfaces which would form a permanent record of the structural action of the bridge during the design stage? Such a record would enable a rapid assessment of the carrying capacity of bridges without the necessity of a complete reanalysis of the structure.

By KARL G. TAMBERG

ACI Member, Bridge Research Engineer, Department of Highways of Ontario

In his paper Professor Seni discusses the important question of the heavy vehicle loading of highway bridges. The writer would like to make the following supplemental comments:

1) It would appear advantageous to have select governmental organizations specify live loads which should be used in the design of bridge structures, since roads and bridges together constitute a public highway facility, and the licensing of heavy vehicles which are permitted to travel on the facility should not be considered separately from the problem of specifying corresponding design loads. In other words, there is a need to synthesize practices followed in the licensing of heavy vehicles and bridge design. It seems logical that governmental organizations should be directly responsible for policies persued in regulating the operation of heavy vehicles by specifying corresponding design loads. The need for the overall planning of the highway transportation complex has become evident (1,2). On the other hand, it is believed that a substantial amount of research into such areas as heavy vehicle operations, the design and performance of pavements and bridges, political jurisdictions, and local economic conditions awaits completion before it will become feasible, in such countries as the United States and Canada, to consider the foundation of a central agency which is solely in charge of controlling the operation of heavy vehicles and the specification of corresponding live loads. A concrete step towards intelligently controlling heavy vehicle operations, which also provides some information for fixing design loads, has been taken recently in the United States by the specification of maximum desirable dimensions and weights of vehicles operated on the Federal-aid systems (1). In the Province of Ontario the Department of Highways provides the

co-ordinating force in bridge design, and virtually no bridges are being designed for less than an HS20-44 loading in an attempt to render them capable of supporting modern highway traffic.

2) Through a comparison of design loads employed in the United States, Canada, Great Britain and France, Professor Seni points out that design loads in Europe are substantially heavier than those generally used in North America, and states that it is difficult to believe that such large differences in loading are warrented. The writer would agree that bridge design loadings used and associated bridge design practices followed in North America are in need of thorough study, but would at the same time also like to point out that failures of bridges which have occurred can virtually never be attributed to their overloading. Could Professor Seni quote an example where a soundly designed and constructed HS20-44 bridge has collapsed or has been excessively damaged due to overloading? The writer is not aware of such a case in Canada. Furthermore, the operation of heavy vehicles can be controlled through legislation (3), and it is questionable whether the unrestricted operation of extremely heavy vehicles is economically justifiable. Preliminary estimates carried out in the Province of Ontario indicate that the costs of damage to the public may outweigh by a considerable margin the cost of benefits to be reaped from the unrestricted operation of heavy vehicles which would require the employment of a design loading much in excess of an HS20-44 loading. Pending further study results, the

writer cannot therefore agree at this time, on a universal basis, with the author that "the HS20 loading is too weak".

3) Nevertheless, it must be emphasized that the validity of employing an HS20-44 design load is in need of further verification. Research studies relating to the design and performance evaluation of pavements and bridges, characteristics and conditions of heavy vehicle operation, associated cost streams, and the economy of all modes of transport must be undertaken in order to accumulate information on the basis of which types and magnitudes of bridge design loadings should be determined. It is essential that a complete logical reference framework be developed, utilizing principles of systems engineering, which provides guidance for the rational derivation of design loads. But, the fact that some European countries use design loads which are heavier than those generally used in North America does not provide a convincing argument that North American design loads should be revised.

4) The writer agrees t at if a revision should be made in the loadings specified by the AASHO and CSA codes, this revision should not only refer to the values of the loads but also to the type of loading - provided that more realistic and/or simpler loading systems can be derived. A loading system similar to the British HA loading, if applicable, would indeed be the simplest to apply. Preliminary studies which have been carried out with respect to the derivation of transformed highway loads are reported upon in references (4) to (7), but further work must be undertaken

before it can be finally determined under what conditions and whether heavy vehicle loads are best synthesized in terms of representative concentrated loads (design trucks) and/or equivalent uniformly distributed loads to be used without or together with one or more concentrated loads. A point worth noting is that the representation of truck loads in terms of uniformly distributed loads (with or without a concentrated load) is difficult if used for the design of skewed slab-type structures. It is therefore questionable whether a design loading similar to the British HA loading is adequate for the design of such structures. Furthermore, it may be observed that the HA loading is used both for the calculation of moments and shears and has a constant U.D.L.-value for loaded lengths 20 to 75 ft., which all seems to result in an overly crude approximation of the load effects generated by heavy vehicles in different structures. It should also be kept in mind that the automated design of bridge structures, utilizing analytical and/or experimental means of analysis (8,9), has become a reality, and that in view of this, a spectrum of critical axle configurations (5,6) should perhaps be derived to constitute live loadings in preference or supplementary to other equivalent load systems.

Although the space here is limited, it is hoped that the comments made draw to the reader's attention some of the complexities involved in establishing live loads. Professor Seni's paper makes the reader aware that the designers must be bewildered by the differences encountered between loadings used in various countries. It is thus hoped that the need for further research to clarify this problem is universally recognized. It would not only be desirable that studies be made of bridge design loadings in North America, but there is undoubtedly also a need to carry out studies in Europe.

REFERENCES

1) Maximum Desirable Dimensions and Weights of Vehicles Operated on the Federal-Aid Systems
House Document No. 354, 88th Congress, 2d Session
U.S. Government Printing Office
Washington, D.C.

2) Policy On Maximum Dimensions and Weights Of Motor Vehicles To Be Operated Over The Highways of The United States
American Association of State Highways Officials, 1963

3) Restrictions on Motor Vehicle Sizes and Weights
Form No. CO-2 10M-63-1594 Reg. 12802
Ontario Department of Transport

4) Functional Relationships Between Actual Truck and AASHO Design Loadings for Simple Span Bridges
K.G. Tamberg and F.W. Jung
Report No. RR 129
Department of Highways of Ontario

5) The Overloading of Simple-Span Bridges
K.G. Tamberg and F.W. Jung
Report No. RR 117
Department of Highways of Ontario

6) Application of Transformed Highway Loads to Influence Lines of Any Shape
K.G. Tamberg, P.F. Csagoly and F.W. Jung
Report No. 131
Department of Highways of Ontario

7) A Method for Controlling Heavy Vehicle Operations
K.G. Tamberg
(To be published)

8) Electronic Design of Bridges on French Motorways
A. Thiebault
Travaux, April-May, 1966

9) Problems of Skew in Concrete Bridge Design
J.B. Kennedy and K.G. Tamberg
Report No. RR 144
Department of Highways of Ontario

AUTHOR'S CLOSURE

The author wishes to thank Professor Sawko and Mr. Tamberg for their discussion.

Professor Sawko asks if the maximum weight of vehicles crossing the bridges should be restricted. The author's opinion, expressed in the paper, is that the system of live loads should cover the loads of the vehicles presently in use, with some provision for a future increase.

It is obvious that the design cannot provide for occasionally extremely heavy vehicles, like the 400 ton vehicle train quoted by the discusser. For such cases, the bridge has to be checked assuming that no other live loads should be placed on the structure and allowing an overstress of the members. The use of ultimate strength design should be very suitable for such cases.

Referring to the influence surfaces proposed by Mr. Sawko, it is obvious that, if included in the design, it should facilitate a further check for such loads. But, as such exceptional loads seldom occur, the long calculations involved for this purpose, make this proposal unpractical. This is expecially the case in North America where the lateral distribution of the loads, for the design of the girders, is usually based on empirical coefficients provided by the specifications. Thus, for the influence surfaces, the design calculations should not be useful, a special analysis being necessary, by more exact methods, considering the structure as a grid.

Mr. K. Tamberg's discussion gives numerous references to reports of the Department of Highways of Ontario, which unfortunately were not brought to the public knowledge.

The author is pleased to note that, in spite of some objections, Mr. K. Tamberg expresses a general agreement with the main conclusions of the paper by pointing out that "the validity of employing on HS20-44 design load is in need of further verification" and that," if a revision should be made, this revision should not only refer to the values of the loads, but also to the type of loading".

Answering to the question asked by Mr. Tamberg, about any bridges having collapsed due to overloading, the author wants to point out the following:

The fact that one cannot quote collapses due to overloads, does not mean that the actual loads may not have largely exceeded the design live loads. The reason of this is that, on the one hand, for concrete bridges, the design stresses are 0.40 of the ultimate or yield strength of the materials, and on the other hand, the design stresses due to live loads are at most 50% of the total stresses. That means that, for reaching the collapse, the live load must be increased 4 times, i.e. an overload of 3 times the desigh live load. Thus, the fact that collapses or severe damages have not occurred does not mean that the actual live loads have not exceeded the design live loads, and no conclusion may be drawn of it, in favour of the present system of live loads.

The author's opinion is that the design loads must not be defined in terms of the behaviour of existing bridges, but by a thorough inquiry and study. This should be undertaken by the qualified organizations, taking in account the present loads with provisions for their future increase.

The increase of loads is an undeniable fact which worries many technical institutions and personalities (see the article "Bigger bridge loads coming - will we be ready?" by Arthur L. Elliot, Bridge Engineer, California Division of Highways, "Civil Engineering, Feb. 1969".)

COMPARISON OF LOADS AROUND THE WORLD FOR DESIGN OF HIGHWAY BRIDGES

By K. S. RAJAGOPALAN

SYNOPSIS

Design live loads for major bridges in eighteen countries are compared by studying their effects on simple spans of 30 to 140 ft. (9 to 42 meters nominal). A very wide diversity in the design load effects such as maximum bending moments and shear forces is noted--the heaviest effect being about two and one-half times that of the lightest. This wide diversity cannot be easily justified by the normal volumes of traffic loads in these countries. It is hoped a more uniform design load, if specified, will result in economy in some countries and perhaps greater safety in others.

Keywords: bending moments; bridges (structures); highway bridges; impact strength; live loads; loads (forces); moving loads; shear properties; spans; standards; structural design.

ACI member K. S. RAJAGOPALAN is a graduate student at the University of Texas at Austin. He graduated from the University of Madras, India, in civil engineering in 1960. After obtaining his MS degree from the Poona University, India, in 1963, he served as a lecturer in civil engineering in Sri Venkateswara University, Tirupati (A. P.), India. He joined the University of Texas at Austin in September, 1966. He is the author of several technical publications.

INTRODUCTION

A preliminary comparison[1] of the design loads for major highway bridges as per AASHO, German Code DIN 1072 and the Indian Road Congress revealed a very wide diversity in the resulting maximum live load bending moments and shear forces on simple spans of 30 to 140 ft. (9 to 42 meters nominal). It was then considered that it would be worthwhile to compare the effects of standard loads as obtained in other countries also.

INVESTIGATION

In 1965, Indian Road Congress published a digest of bridge design loads specified in various countries.[2] The loads used in this investigation have been taken out of the above reference and are summarized in Appendix A.

Some countries might have revised these standard loads since 1965; the author is not aware of any revisions and hence the following computations do not reflect revisions since 1965, if any. However, it is hoped that such revisions, if any, would be few and hence would not totally invalidate the observations in this paper.

In many countries there are different categories of specified loads for different types of bridges. Only the design loads for major bridges are compared in this paper. The general observations that follow are quite applicable to other categories of bridges as well.

Design loads as obtained in a total of thirteen countries are compared explicitly. In addition, Ontario (Canada), New South Wales (Australia) and the Phillipines follow generally the AASHO specifications; Malaysian and Rhodesian specifications are comparable to those of Great Britain.

In the comparisons that follow, the following have been assumed:

1. Effects of loads will be restricted to simple spans of 30 to 140 ft. (9 to 42 meters nominal).
2. Only two lanes of roadway with a total width of 24 ft. (7.2 meters nominal) will be considered.

Simple spans are chosen as samples and as indicative of what is likely to happen in other types of constructions. The above range of spans is selected since a majority of simple span bridges is likely to be covered by this range. Also two lane bridges are considered common and typical in most of the countries.

The maximum bending moments due to the standard loads have been computed. For easier plotting these values are divided by the respective spans. Figure 1 shows, for various countries, the variation of the maximum live load bending moment/span against the span.

The maximum shear forces imposed on simple spans due to the standard loads are represented against the spans in Fig. 2.

The effects of impact factors are not reflected in these figures; different impact factors are specified for steel and concrete bridges in many countries; also, in some cases, for the same type of bridge the impact factors differ from one category of load to another.

OBSERVATIONS

It is conceded, at the outset, that, in various countries, the standard loads for design of highway bridges may have been evolved on factors depending on, among others, the available data of vehicles, their loading capacities, the intensity and frequency of traffic, logistic considerations for general mobilization in case of national emergencies. Also the standard loads might depend on the allowable stresses in members. For instance, a smaller design load may be specified in case smaller permissible stresses are allowed. Hence a heavier design load does not per se lead to a heavier bridge superstructure under identical conditions of spans, road width and type of construction. But it is highly unlikely that the specified load factors will differ drastically from one country to another.

Hence the comparisons in Fig. 1 and 2 should be viewed as reflecting the general trend rather than strictly quantitative.

From Fig. 1 and 2 it can be seen that the variation of the intensities of live load effects differ considerably from one country to another, the ratio of the heaviest to the lightest being between 2 and 2-1/2. It is also seen that the order of countries arranged in the sequence of severity of the effect is different in the case of shear from that of moment; yet in both, design load of Great Britain is the heaviest, and that of AASHO is the lightest over a large range of spans (this is surprising especially because of the large volume of road traffic in USA both in sheer numbers and in terms of loads carried).

Even allowing for different load factors, differences in impact factors, traffic and load intensities that are actually likely to occur from country to country, it is not still easily justifiable why the loading severities should differ so drastically.

In concrete bridges, it may be that the effect of live load is not as significant as that of dead load. Even then a reduction or an increase of live load should similarly affect the dead load (except perhaps in cases of prestressed concrete bridges where the dead load is completely balanced by the prestressing force). Hence, if the standard loads are revised to result in less diversity, an overall economy could result in countries where the loading severity is very high. By a similar token, a greater safety may result in countries with the light intensity of loading effects.

SUMMARY

The loading effects due to standard loads for highway bridge design differ considerably between countries. A greater uniformity might result in a greater economy in some countries and a greater safety in others.

As design practices improve, and as better methods of analysis become available, it becomes necessary to critically reexamine the basic design loads. Also road traffic is increasing in volume and intensity day by day. A reevaluation of design loads may lead to greater economy and additional safety.

ACKNOWLEDGMENT

The author wishes to express his sincere thanks to Professor Phil M. Ferguson, Professor of Civil Engineering, The University of Texas at Austin, for his critical review.

REFERENCES

1. Chandrasekhar, C. S., and Rajagopalan, K. S., "Standard Loadings for Design of Highway Bridges--A Review." Eastern Engineer, India, Sept. 1966.

2. "Bridge Loadings Round the World," Transport-Communications Monthly Review, No. 208, published by Indian Road Congress, Dec. 1965.

TABLE A–Equivalent Distributed Load

(From Bridge Loadings—Italy)

Span	Bending load in t/ml					Span	Shear load in t/ml				
	Civil Loading		Military Loading				Civil Loading		Military Loading		
m	Type 1	Type 2	Type 4	Type 5	Type 6	m	Type 1	Type 2	Type 4	Type 5	Type 6
1	16.000	24.000	28.000	10.667	38.000	1	16.000	24.000	28.000	12.160	36.000
1.5	10.667	16.000	18.667	9.027	25.333	1.5	10.667	16.000	24.640	10.287	31.680
2	8.000	12.000	15.541	8.188	19.981	2	8.000	12.000	20.860	9.787	26.820
2.5	6.400	9.600	14.193	7.285	18.248	2.5	6.400	9.600	17.830	9.114	22.925
3	5.333	8.000	12.859	7.329	16.534	3	5.333	8.000	15.493	8.770	19.920
3.5	4.571	6.857	11.677	7.561	15.013	3.5	4.898	7.347	13.669	8.620	17.574
4	4.000	6.000	10.658	7.455	13.703	4	4 500	6.750	12.215	8.400	15.705
4.5	3.556	5.333	9.784	7.252	12.579	4.5	4.148	6.222	11.034	8.217	14.187
5	3.200	4.800	9.032	7.143	11.612	5	3.840	5.760	10.058	7.936	12.931
5.5	2.921	4.382	8.381	6.954	10.776	5.5	3.570	5.355	9.497	7.617	12.229
6	2.778	4.167	7.814	6.727	10 047	6	3.333	5.000	9.147	7.289	11.803
6.5	2.651	3.965	7.316	6.486	9.407	6.5	3.314	4.686	8.788	6.968	11.359
7	2.612	3.778	6.877	6.243	8.842	7	3.265	4.408	8.434	6.661	10.917
7.5	2.560	3.605	6.486	6.005	8.839	7.5	3.200	4.160	8.094	6.372	10.487
8	2.500	3.445	6.136	5.776	7.889	8	3.125	3.938	7.770	6.133	10.077
8.5	2.436	3.297	5.990	5.559	7.728	8.5	3.045	3.737	7.464	5.950	9.687
9	2.370	3.160	5.854	5.352	7.561	9	2.963	3.556	7.258	5.813	8.401
9.5	2.305	3.031	5.713	5.157	7.387	9.5	2.925	3.391	7.057	5.717	9.125
10	2.240	2.916	5.599	4.974	7.209	10	2.880	3.240	6.877	5.639	8.873
11	2.128	2.705	5.411	4 639	6 857	11	2.777	2.975	6.609	5.554	8.474
12	2.111	2.521	5.206	4.342	6.518	12	2.667	2.750	6.331	5.511	8.079
13	2.083	2.360	4.997	4.231	6.200	13	2.651	2.556	6.057	5.453	7.700
14	2.122	2.217	4.793	4.137	5.933	14	2.612	2.388	5.809	5.355	7.358
15	2.133	2.091	4.597	4.110	5.710	15	2.560	2.240	5.607	5.234	7.072
16	2.125	1.978	4.420	4.106	5.521	16	2 531	2.109	5.408	5.117	6.798
17	2.104	1.876	4.340	4.120	5.357	17	2.491	1.993	5.216	5.032	6.537
18	2.086	1.784	4.291	4.136	5.195	18	2.444	1.889	5.098	4.982	6.291
19	2.083	1.701	4.230	4.204	5.638	19	2.438	1.795	5.051	4.958	6.059
20	2.080	1.625	4.159	4.253	4.885	20	2.420	1.710	5.006	4.944	5.840
21	2.068	1.555	4.113	4.293	4.739	21	2.395	1.633	4.947	4.920	5.635
22	2.050	1.491	4.060	4.308	4.599	22	2.380	1.562	4.877	4.879	5.443
23	2.028	1.432	4.000	4.304	4.475	23	2.359	1.497	4.829	4.827	5.261
24	2.028	1.378	3.936	4.286	4.363	24	2.333	1.438	4.795	4.778	5.091
25	2.022	1.327	3.870	4.257	4.255	25	2.330	1.382	4.750	4.742	4.930
26	2.036	1.280	3.818	4.220	4.151	26	2.320	1.331	4.702	4.720	4.778
27	2.041	1.236	3.790	4.177	4.051	27	2 305	1.284	4.664	4.709	4.635
28	2.041	1.196	3.766	4.145	3.954	28	2.296	1.240	4.634	4.702	4.500
29	2.036	1.157	3.737	4.118	3.860	29	2.283	1.199	4.600	4.688	4.372
30	2.031	1.121	3.703	4.106	3.771	30	2.267	1.160	4.559	4.665	4.251
31	2.031	1.088	3.666	4.104	3.685	31	2.264	1.124	4.515	4.635	4.137
32	2.031	1.056	3.626	4.105	3.602	32	2.258	1.090	4.477	4.608	4.028
33	2.028	1.026	3.584	4.110	3.522	33	2.248	1.058	4.436	4.591	3.924
34	2.021	0.997	3.567	4.125	3.446	34	2.242	1.028	4.391	4.578	3.825
35	2.012	0.971	3.567	4.137	3.372	35	2.233	0.999	4.357	4.571	3.732
36	2.012	0.945	3.583	4.157	3.302	36	2.222	0.972	4.310	4.568	3.642
37	2.010	0.921	3.612	4.169	3.233	37	2.221	0.947	4.330	4.558	3.557
38	2.017	0.898	3.634	4.174	3.168	38	2.216	0.922	4.314	4.543	3.475
39	2.020	0.876	3.648	4.173	3.105	39	2.209	0.899	4.294	4.523	3.397
40	2.020	0.856	3.657	4.167	3.044	40	2 205	0.878	4.276	4.508	3.323
45	2.015	0.765	3.673	4.107	2.771	45	2.181	0.782	4.212	4.475	2.993
50	2.010	0.691	3.658	4.116	2.541	50	2.163	0.706	4.135	4.429	2.722
55	2.010	0.631	3.646	4.138	2.345	55	2.147	0.643	4.079	4.400	2.496
60	2.004	0.580	3.621	4.107	2.177	60	2.133	0.590	4.041	4.380	2.304
70	2.005	0.500	3.570	4.124	1.903	70	2.116	0.507	3.962	4.337	1.997
80	2.005	0.439	3.602	4.104	1.689	80	2.101	0.444	3.923	4.306	1.762
90	2.003	0.391	3.597	4.107	1.518	90	2.089	0.396	3 878	4.286	1.576
100	2.003	0.353	3.577	4.112	1.379	100	2.079	0.356	3.849	4.268	1.426
120	2.001	0.295	3.583	4.107	1.164	120	2.061	0.298	3.799	4.239	1.197
140	2.002	0.253	3.570	4.103	1.007	140	2.051	0.255	3.765	4.220	1.031
160	2.001	0.222	3.577	4.104	0.887	160	2.043	0.224	3 741	4.205	0.906
180	2.000	0.198	3.572	4.106	0.793	180	2.037	0.199	3.722	4.190	0.808
200	2.001	0.178	3.571	4.086	0.717	200	2.033	0.179	3.707	4.179	0.729

N.B. For any intermediate span, linear Interpolation is to be made.

This table is taken out of page 131 of reference 2 cited in References.

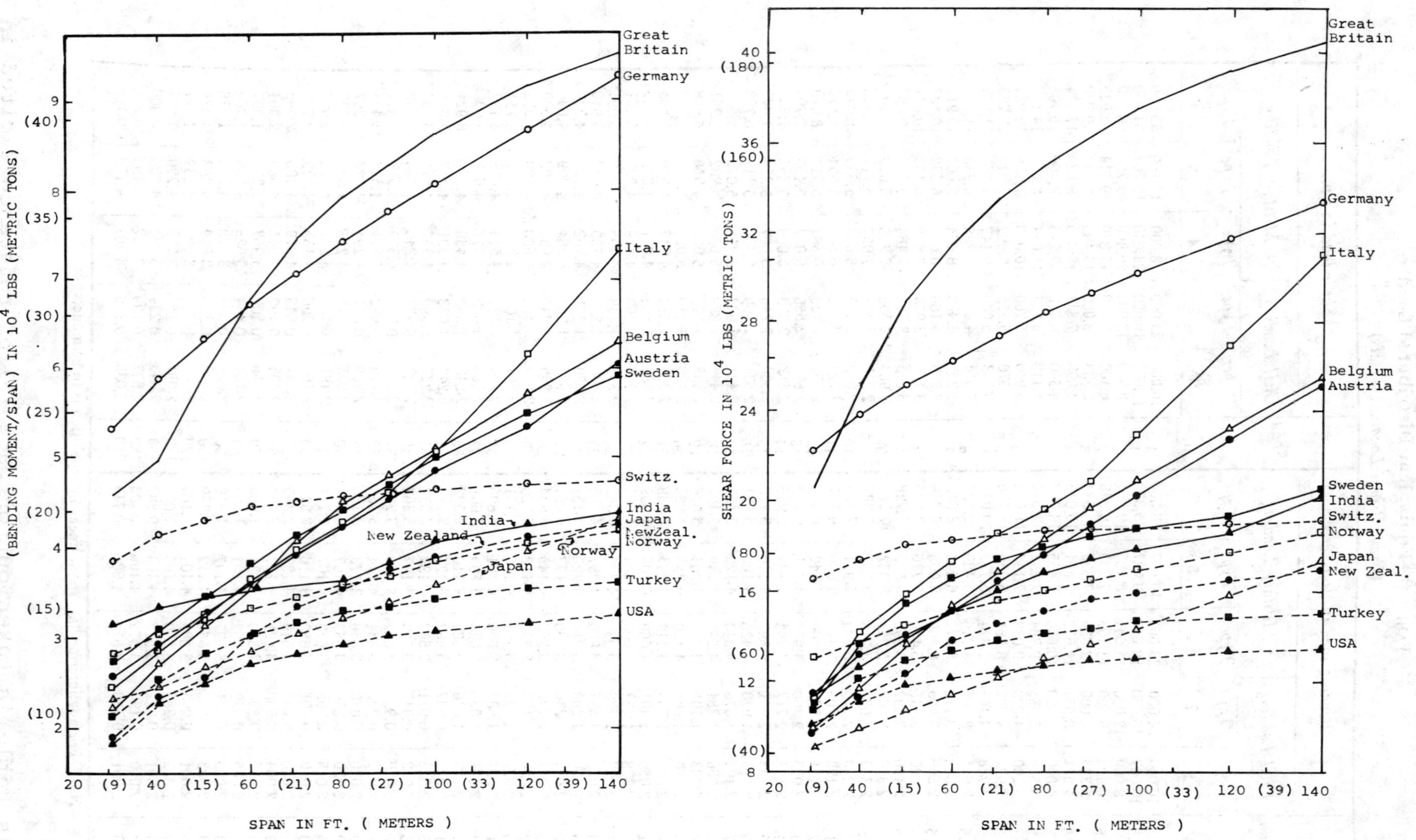

Fig.1. (Bending moment/span) versus span

Fig.2. Shear Force versus Span.

APPENDIX A

Details of loadings for two lane bridges.

AUSTRIA

TRUCK

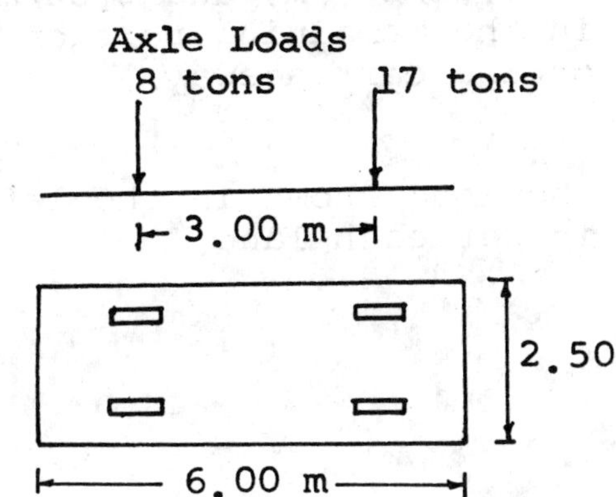

Bridge Class I

On two adjoining lanes, one truck of 25t each. The rest of the roadway and footpath to be covered with uniformly distributed load of 0.5t per meter^2.

CATERPILLAR

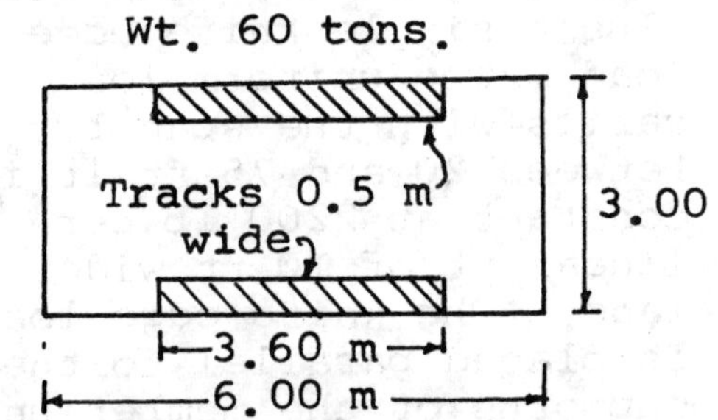

For a caterpillar, as the only load on the roadway, has a maximum of 0.5m on both sides from the longitudinal center line of the roadway.

All units metric.

BELGIUM

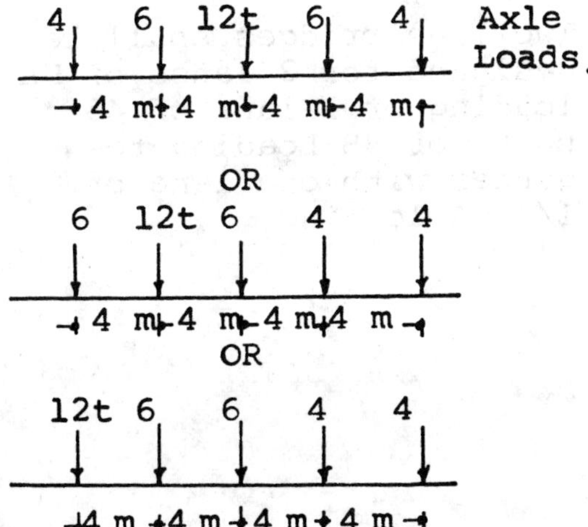

Simultaneously a load of 400 kg. per square meter uniformly distributed on the carriageways and footpath.

Over traffic lane 2.50 m. min. wide to 4.00 m. max. width.

All units metric.

GERMANY (FEDERAL REPUBLIC)

CLASS 60

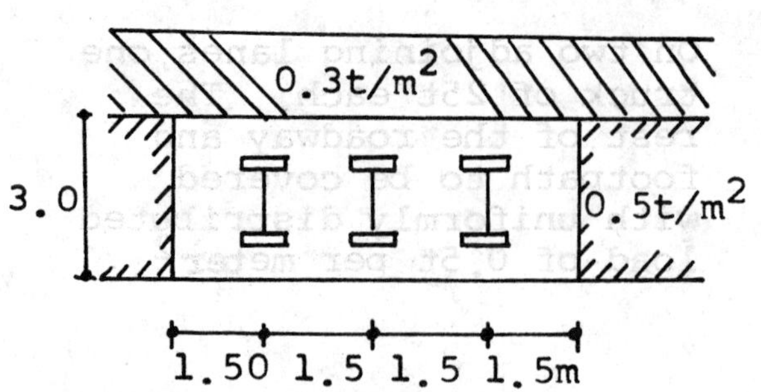

Outside the carriageway, uniformly distributed load of 0.3t/sq. m. and $0.5t/m^2$ in the remaining portion of the carriageway.

The load shown in the left is per each lane.

Wheel load each 10t.
All units metric.

GREAT BRITAIN

HB LOADING

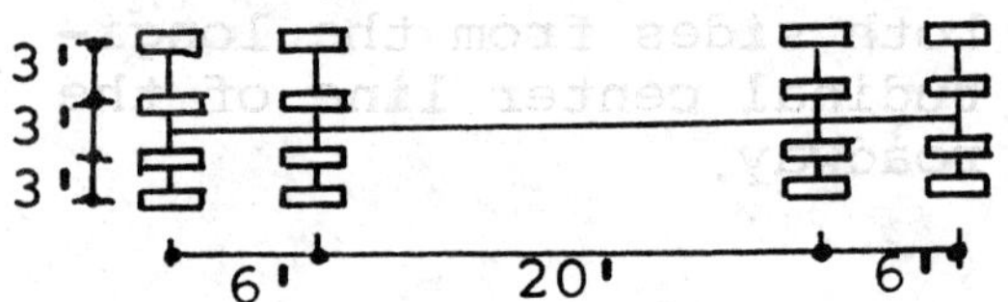

1 unit of HB Loading -
Axle load = 1 ton = 2240 lbs.
All British units.

HA Loading consists of a uniformly distributed load plus a single knife edge load. The uniform load varies with the span but between 20 and 75 ft it is constant at 2200 lb per linear ft of 10 ft wide lane. The knife edge load is placed parallel to the supports of the member under consideration and has a value of 27,000 lb for a 10 ft wide lane.

Two lane bridges shall be designed for 2 lanes of HA loading or 1 lane of 45 units of HB Loading together with one lane of 1/3 HA loading.

INDIA

CLASS AA

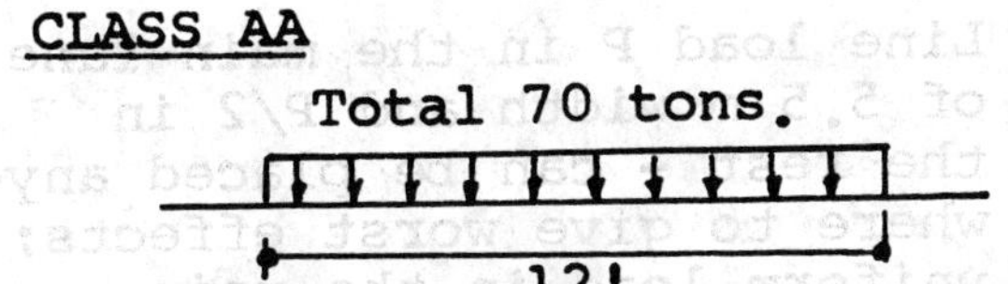

1 ton = 2240 lbs.

One train of class AA vehicle or two lanes of class A train of vehicles for two lane major bridges.

CLASS A

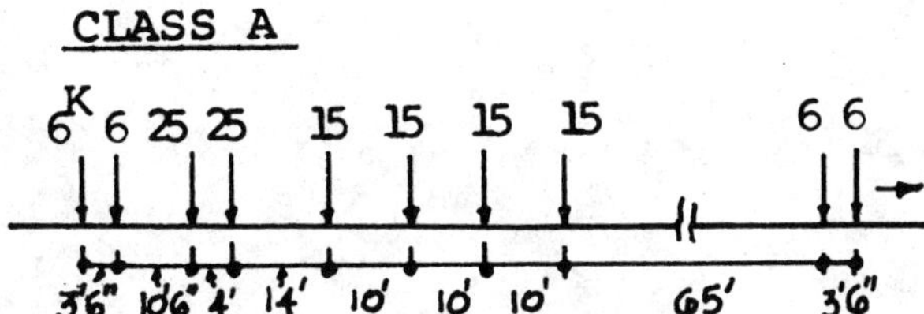

All axle loads in kips.

ITALY

Category I

Equivalent loads for various types of loadings as per table A.

For two lane bridges:

The heaviest of types 4,5 or 6 flanked by one or more trains of type 1 with crowd loading of 400 kg/m^2 (type 3) on the footpaths.

JAPAN

L-20

Line load P in the main lane of 5.5 m width and P/2 in the rest - can be placed anywhere to give worst effects; uniform load in the main lane width is p and on sides p/2.

P

uniform load p

p/2 P/2

P p 5.5m

p/2 P/2

P = 5000 kg/m.

p = 350 kg/m^2 for $\ell \leq$ 80 m.

All units metric.

NEW ZEALAND

H20-S16-T16 Truck

Two trucks in two lanes to produce worst effects.

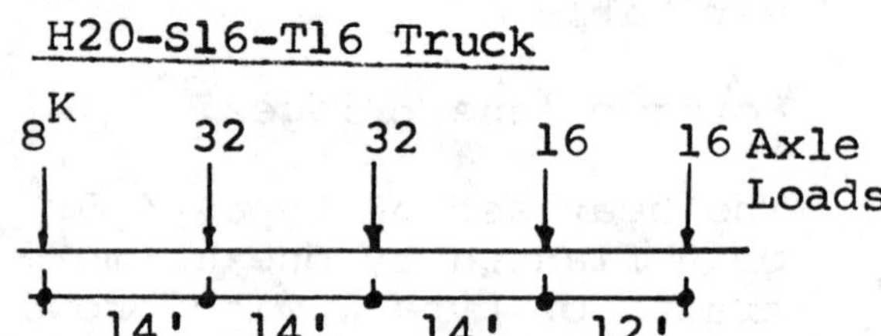

NORWAY

Equivalent loading per lane

The equivalent load in each lane.

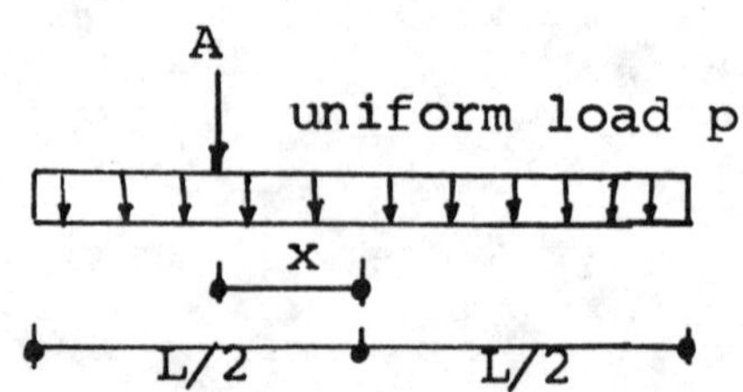

A = 12 + 8x/L tons.

p = 0.5 + 35/(L+5) tons per linear meter of lane.

All units metric.

SWEDEN

Two lane loading or single truck loading for two lane bridges.

Lane Loading.

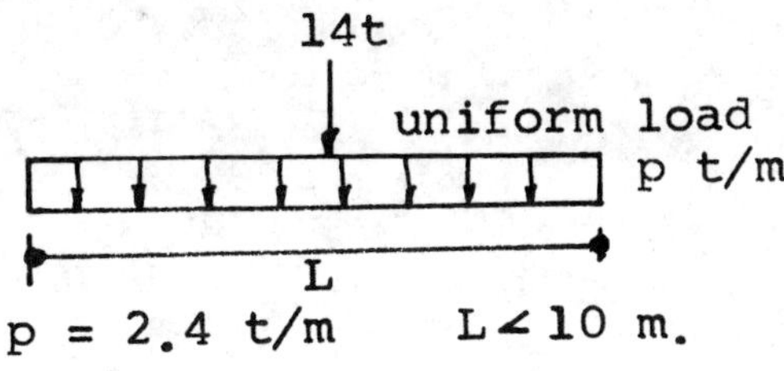

p = 2.4 t/m L < 10 m.

p = 2.4 - 13(L-10)/80

as 10 < L < 90m.

p = 1.1 t/m L > 90m.

Single Truck Loading.

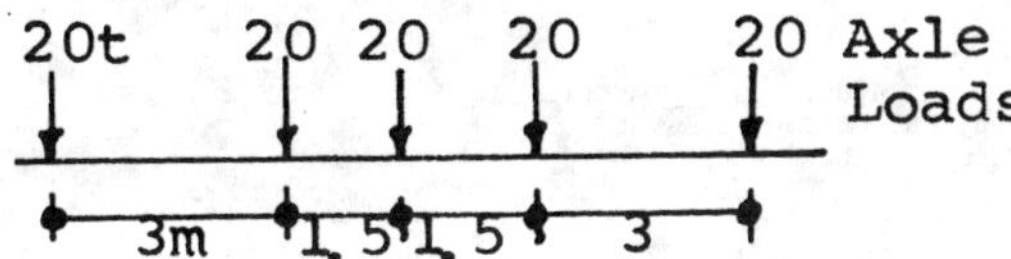

All units metric.

SWITZERLAND

A train in each lane or the lane loading as shown.

Lane Loading.

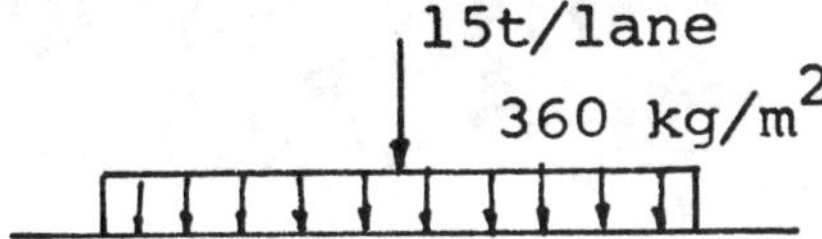

Train Load.

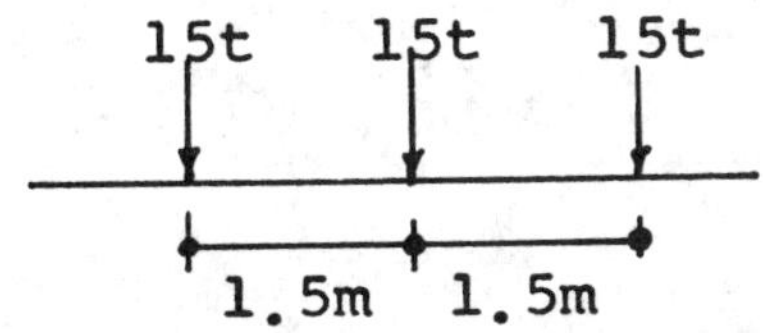

All units metric.

TURKEY

One truck for each lane.

H20-S16 Truck

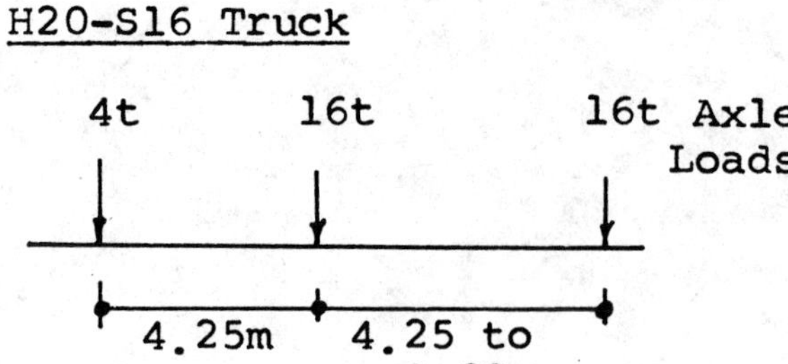

All units are metric.

U.S.A.

One truck per lane.

H20-S16 Truck

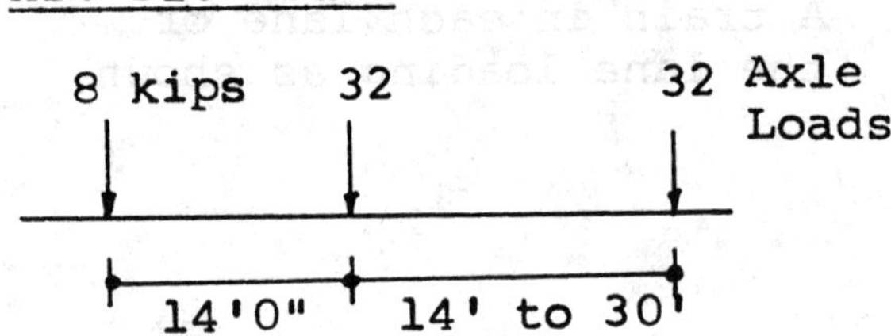

STATISTICAL EVALUATION OF LOAD FACTORS FOR CONCRETE BRIDGE DESIGN

By PRADYOT K. NIYOGI, HARESH C. SHAH, KISHORE D. DOSHI, and WILSON TANG

SYNOPSIS

This paper presents an important aspect of the structural design of concrete bridges under various combinations of loading. 'Load Factors', which are quantities used to define the pattern and magnitude of design loadings, are evaluated from a statistical point of view in such a manner as to assure a desired level of safety for the structure.

An approach is presented in this paper to formulate and develop a procedure for quantitative evaluation of the load factors under dead loads, live loads and earthquake loads, taking into consideration the pertinent factors including the random probabilistic character of loads, within the framework of information available about the loading conditions and the associated 'functional' failure patterns of the bridge structure. Central to the development of such a procedure are the following considerations:

i. The load factors as defined above, should provide a desired level of safety, i.e., system reliability under various combinations of dead loads, live loads and earthquake loads.

ii. The procedure should be formulated in such a way that any additional information about the loading environments can be systematically incorporated to obtain a better set of load factors, and the results and confidence should improve with an increase in available data and with increased usage of the method.

iii. The final results concerning the quantitive evaluation of load factors should be simple and easy to be used by design engineers.

The method developed in this paper for obtaining load factors under different loading configurations to obtain desired reliabilities, is applied to an example of a concrete bridge structure design.

Keywords: bridges (structures); dynamic loads; earthquakes; live loads; load factors; loads (forces); moving loads; probability theory; reinforced concrete; reliability; safety factor; static loads; statistical analysis; structural design.

PRADYOT K. NIYOGI is a post-doctoral fellow at the University of Pennsylvania.

ACI Member HARESH C. SHAH is an associate professor of structural engineering at Stanford University.

KISHORE D. DOSHI is the senior research engineer for the Whittaker Corp. in San Diego.

WILSON TANG is a graduate student at Stanford University.

1. Introduction

The present practice of taking statistical nature of loads and resistances into account while designing is to multiply the loads by certain given constant factors, known as "load factors." This method is somewhat indirect, and does not consider the variation of distributions of loads and resistances for specific cases. On the contrary, these factors are arrived at from certain predetermined assumptions about the reliability of the structures and can not be varied even if the designer may wish to do so.

The simplest way of incorporating the statistical nature of the load and resistance parameters of a bridge structure design will be to modify "load factors" in such a way that the designer can select them according to the desired level of reliability and the statistical distribution of structural parameters. An approach is presented in this paper to formulate and develop a procedure for quantitative evaluation of the load factors under dead loads, live loads and earthquake loads. The suggested approach takes into consideration the pertinent factors including the random probabilistic character of loads within the framework of information available about the loading conditions. Central to the development of such a procedure are the following considerations:

i. The load factors as defined above should provide a desired level of safety, i.e., system reliability under various combinations of dead loads, live loads and earthquake loads.

ii. The procedure should be formulated in such a way that any additional information about the loading environments can be systematically incorporated to obtain a better set of load factors, and the results and confidence should improve with an increase in available data and with increased usage of the method.

iii. The final results concerning the quantitive evaluation of load factors should be simple in form and easy to be used by design engineers.

The suggested method is particularly important for structures which will cause extensive life hazard and damage of properties on failure. Bridge structures come under such a category. Examples giving load factors for live loads and dead loads on bridge structures are given. Method is indicated when earthquake loads are present.

2. Statistical Considerations:

Random Loads, Deterministic Resistance

The simplest and idealized case is the one which the applied loads on a structure are random in nature, but the resistance of the structure is deterministic.

Let W_i be the i-th case of loading combination (vis. Dead Load and Live Load, Dead Load, Live Load and Earthquake, and so on). This is actually the combination of the component loads (Dead Load, Live Load, etc.) which have certain mean and variance.

We can write,

$$W_i = \alpha_{i1}\mu_1 + \alpha_{i2}\mu_2 + \ldots\ldots = \sum_{j=1}^{n} \alpha_{ij}\mu_j \qquad (1)$$

n = number of components of loads

where α_{ij} will be the load factors corresponding to the i-th combination of loading and j-th component of loads, μ_j, are the mean of the component loads.

Let σ_j^2 be the variances of the component loads, and k_i be the factors corresponding to the desired reliabilities and is defined in Fig. 1, assuming the loads have normal distribution.

For the components of loads W_i, we define,

$$\ell_{ij} = \mu_j + k_i\sigma_j \qquad (2)$$

which represents load ℓ_{ij} corresponding to μ_j and σ_j and a reliability corresponding to k_i.

From (2),

$$\ell_{ij} = \mu_j(1 + k_i v_j) \qquad (3)$$

where, $$v_j = \frac{\sigma_j}{\mu_j} = \text{coefficient of variation.}$$

Considering the combination of all the component loads that constitute W_i, the overall mean and variance may be expressed as

$$\mu_L = \sum_{j=1}^{n} \mu_j$$

$$\sigma_L^2 = \sum_{j=1}^{n} (\sigma_j)^2 .$$

Hence, the design load for the i-th loading, W_i can be written as

$$W_i = \sum_{j=1}^{n} \mu_j + k_i \left[\sum_{j=1}^{n} (\sigma_i)^2 \right]^{1/2} . \qquad (4)$$

This design load W_i has the reliability corresponding to k_i.

To obtain the expression for load factors, W_i should be expressed as in Eq. (1), i.e.,

$$W_i = \sum_{j=1}^{n} \alpha_{ij}\mu_j$$

so that the coefficients of μ_j are the load factors.

This can be done by some manipulation without much significance of the intermediate steps as follows:

We have

$$W_i = \sum_{j=1}^{n} \mu_j + k_i\left[\sum_{j=1}^{n} (\sigma_j)^2\right]^{1/2}$$

and

$$\ell_{ij} = \mu_j + k_i\sigma_j .$$

So,

dividing W_i by $\sum_{j=1}^{n} \ell_{ij}$, we get,

$$\frac{W_i}{\sum_{j=1}^{n} \ell_{ij}} = \frac{\sum_{j=1}^{n} \mu_j + k_i\left[\sum_{j=1}^{n} (\sigma_j)^2\right]^{1/2}}{\sum_{j=1}^{n} \mu_j + k_i \sum_{j=1}^{n} \sigma_j} . \tag{5}$$

Now, $$W_i \equiv \sum_{j=1}^{n} \cdot \alpha_{ij}\mu_j = \sum_{j=1}^{n} \frac{\ell_{ij}}{\mu_j} \cdot \frac{W_i}{\sum_j \ell_{ij}} \cdot \mu_j .$$

So, $$\sum_{j=1}^{n} \alpha_{ij}\mu_j = \sum_{j=1}^{n} \left(\frac{\ell_{ij}}{\mu_j}\right)\frac{W_i}{\sum_j \ell_{ij}} \cdot \mu_j$$

whence,
$$\alpha_{ij} = \left(\frac{\ell_{ij}}{\mu_j} \cdot \frac{W_i}{\sum_{j=1}^{n} \ell_{ij}} \right) \tag{6}$$

From (5) and (6), the load factors can be expressed as,

$$\alpha_{ij} = \left(1 + \frac{k_i \sigma_j}{\mu_j}\right) \left(\frac{\sum_{j=1}^{n} \mu_j + k_i \left[\sum_{j=1}^{n} (\sigma_j)^2 \right]^{1/2}}{\sum_{j=1}^{n} \mu_j + \sum_{j=1}^{n} k_i \sigma_j} \right) \tag{7}$$

$$\alpha_{ij} = [1 + k_i v_j] \frac{1 + \dfrac{k_i \left(\sum_{j=1}^{n} \sigma_j^2 \right)^{1/2}}{\sum_{j=1}^{n} \mu_j}}{1 + k_j \left(\sum_{j=1}^{n} \sigma_j / \sum_{j=1}^{n} \mu_j \right)} \tag{8}$$

where, v_j = coefficient of variation of component loads = $\dfrac{\sigma_j}{\mu_j}$.

Consider the following example:

In the design of the floor system of the bridge, properties of the loads are given:

Mean dead load = 60 psf. Std. Dev. of dead load = 5 psf.

Mean live load = 80 psf. Std. Dev. of live load = 20 psf.

Reliability desired = 99.99%, i.e., probability of failure desired is 10^{-4}.

Corresponding to 99.99% reliability, the value of k is 3.72 from Normal Probability tables. Using Eq. (8),

$$\alpha_{11} = \left[1 + \frac{3.72(5)}{60}\right] \left[\frac{1 + \dfrac{3.72(425)^{1/2}}{140}}{1 + 3.72(25/140)} \right] \tag{9}$$

whence, $\alpha_{11} \approx 1.22$.

Similarly, $\alpha_{12} \approx 1.79$.

The design load $W = 1.22\mu_{DL} + 1.79\mu_{LL} \approx 217$ psf.

As a check, $R = (60 + 80) + 3.72(425)^{1/2} = 217$ psf., R = required resistance of the structure.

Once α_{ij} are calculated, these can be used for similar structures, loading and material properties remaining the same.

3. Load and Resistance Both Random

Usually, the resistance, which depends on a large number of variables, has certain statistical distribution depending on the parameters of the structure.

If $\sigma_R = [\Sigma\,(\sigma$ of all variables contributing to resistance$)^2]^{1/2}$ then the required resistance of a structure for a level of reliability corresponding to a reliability factor k' as defined before, is

$$R = \mu_R + k'\sigma_R \tag{10}$$

where μ_R = mean resistance.

In this case, the overall reliability is equal to the probability that the resistance is greater than the loading. If a new random variable

$$W = R - L \tag{11}$$

is introduced, the overall reliability is then the probability that W is greater than zero. Since both the loading and the resistance are independent normal distribution, W is also normal with

$$\begin{aligned} \mu_W &= \mu_R - \mu_L \\ \sigma_W^2 &= \sigma_R^2 + \sigma_L^2 . \end{aligned} \tag{12}$$

Given that the loading and resistance are designed to the levels of reliability corresponding to k and k' respectively, it may be shown, Fig. 2, that

$$\mu_R = L^* + k'\sigma_R$$
$$= (\mu_L + k\sigma_L) + k'\sigma_R \; . \tag{13}$$

For simplicity, it can be assumed that the designer wants the same reliability for both the loading and the resistance, i.e.,

$$k = k' \; . \tag{14}$$

Then

$$\mu_R = \mu_L + k(\sigma_L + \sigma_R) \tag{15}$$

and

$$\mu_W = k(\sigma_L + \sigma_R) \tag{16}$$

$$\text{Overall Reliability} = \int_0^{\alpha} \frac{1}{\sqrt{2\pi}\sqrt{\sigma_R^2 + \sigma_L^2}} \exp\left[-\frac{\{W - k(\sigma_L + \sigma_R)\}^2}{\sigma_R^2 + \sigma_L^2}\right] dW \tag{17}$$

If we perform the change of variable,

$$V = W - k(\sigma_L + \sigma_R) \tag{18}$$

$$\text{Overall Reliability} = \int_{-k(\sigma_L+\sigma_R)}^{\alpha} \frac{1}{\sqrt{2\pi}\sqrt{\sigma_R^2 + \sigma_L^2}} \exp\left[-\frac{V^2}{\sigma_R^2 + \sigma_L^2}\right] dV$$
$$= 1 - F[\,-k(\sigma_L + \sigma_R)\,] \tag{19}$$

where F is the cumulative distribution for the normal distribution with mean zero and standard deviation $\sqrt{\sigma_R^2 + \sigma_L^2}$.

If k* denotes the level of the overall reliability, i.e.,

$$\text{Overall Reliability} = 1 - F\,[\,-k^*\sigma_V]$$
$$= 1 - F[\,-k^*\sqrt{\sigma_R^2 + \sigma_L^2}] \tag{20}$$

Equating Equations (19) and (20),

$$k = \frac{\sqrt{\sigma_R^2 + \sigma_L^2}}{\sigma_R + \sigma_L} k^* = \frac{\sqrt{(V_R\mu_R)^2 + \sigma_L^2}}{V_R\mu_R + \sigma_L} k^* \qquad (21)$$

Thus the value of k corresponding to the individual level of reliability for loading and resistance may be determined for any level of overall reliability.

As Fig. 2 indicates, the resistance R that is designed in this case is μ_R instead of L^* as is in the case with deterministic resistance.

$$\mu_R = \mu_L + k\sigma_L + k\sigma_R$$

$$= \mu_L + k\sigma_L + kV_R\,\mu_R$$

where, $V_R = \frac{\sigma_R}{\mu_R}$ = coefficient of variation of resistance.

Therefore,

$$\mu_R = (\mu_L + k\sigma_L)\frac{1}{1-kV_R}$$

$$= \frac{L^*}{1-kV_R}\,. \qquad (22)$$

The expression for α_{ij} can now be modified as

$$\alpha_{ij} = (1 + k_i\,V_j)\left[\frac{1 + \{k_i\left(\sum_{j=1}^{n}\sigma_j^2\right)^{1/2} / \sum_{j=1}^{n}\mu_j\}}{1 + \{k_i\sum_{j=1}^{n}\sigma_j / \sum_{j=1}^{n}\mu_j\}}\right]\frac{1}{(1-k_iV_R)}\,. \qquad (23)$$

For the previous example, if $V_R = 0.15$ and $k^* = 3.72$, i.e., an overall reliability of 99.99%, then from (21)

$$k = \frac{\sqrt{(V_R\mu_R)^2 + 425}}{V_R\mu_R + \sqrt{425}} k^* = \frac{\sqrt{(0.15\mu_R)^2 + 425}}{0.15\mu_R + 20.6} k^* . \tag{24}$$

From (22)

$$\mu_R = \frac{\mu_L + k\sigma_L}{1 - k\,V_R} = \frac{140 + 20.6k}{1 - 0.15k} . \tag{25}$$

Substituting (25) in (24) and by trial and error, $k = 2.87$. Then

$$\alpha_{11} = (1 + \frac{2.87 \times 5}{60})\left(\frac{1 + \frac{2.87(425)^{1/2}}{140}}{1 + 2.87 \times \frac{25}{140}}\right)\frac{1}{1 - 2.87 \times 0.15}$$

$$= 1.238 \times \frac{1.5}{1.6} \times \frac{1}{0.568} = 2.04$$

$$\alpha_{12} = 1 + \frac{2.87 \times 20}{80} \quad \frac{1 + \frac{2.87(425)^{1/2}}{140}}{1 + 2.87 \times \frac{25}{140}} \quad \frac{1}{1 - 2.65 \times .1}$$

$$= 1.718 \times \frac{1.5}{1.6} \times \frac{1}{0.568} = 2.83$$

4. Design Procedure

To use these load factors in actual design work, these expressions should be simplified. This can be done by defining some new terms as follows:

V_L = coefficient of variation of design load = $\frac{\sigma_L}{\mu_L}$

$V_{iL} = \sum_{j=1}^{n} \sigma_j \Big/ \mu_L$

$V_j = \sigma_j/\mu_j$ of individual loads,

$V_R = \sigma_R/\mu_R$ = coefficient of variation of resistance, as defined before.

From (23)

$$\alpha_{ij} = \frac{1 + k_i V_j}{1 - k_i V_R} \cdot \frac{\sum_{j=1}^{n} \mu_j + k_i \sigma_L}{\sum_{j=1}^{n} \mu_j + k_i \sum_{j=1}^{n} \sigma_j}$$

$$= \frac{1 + k_i V_j}{1 - k_i V_R} \cdot \frac{\mu_L + k_i \sigma_L}{\mu_L + k_i \sum_{j=1}^{n} \sigma_j}$$

$$= \frac{1 + k_i V_j}{1 - k_i V_R} \cdot \frac{1 + k_i V_L}{1 + k_i V_{iL}}$$

$$= \frac{1 + k_i V_L}{1 - k_i V_R} \cdot \frac{1 + k_i V_j}{1 + k_i V_{iL}}$$

$$= P_i \alpha'_{ij} \qquad (26)$$

where $$P_i = \frac{1 + k_i V_L}{1 - k_i V_R} \cdot \frac{1}{1 + k_i V_{iL}} \qquad (27)$$

and $$\alpha'_{ij} = 1 + k_i V_j \; . \qquad (28)$$

A step-by-step procedure is outlined below:

(1) From given σ_j and μ_j, obtain V_j.

(2) V_R = Coef. of variation of resistance. For reinforced concrete members,(2)

$$V_R^2 = V_M^2 + V_F^2 + V_E^2 \qquad (29)$$

where,

V_M = Coef. of variation of material strength

V_F = Coef. of variation for fabrication

V_E = Coef. of variation for engineering formula.

The usual ranges of these quantities are as follows:

$V_M^2 = 0.01$ to 0.02 depending on the degree of inspection

$V_F^2 = a - 0.01\ m_D$ where $a \approx 0.18$, m_D = mean depth in inches

$V_E^2 =$ (i) 0.0006 for very accurate formula,

(ii) 0.01 for standard approximation,

(iii) 0.04 for approximate or uncertain theory; some effects are not known.

(3) From given load data, obtain

$$V_L = \frac{\sigma_L}{\mu_L} = \frac{\left[\sum_{j=1}^{n} \sigma_j^2\right]^{1/2}}{\sum_{j=1}^{n} \mu_j}$$

(4) also obtain $V_{iL} = \dfrac{\sum_{j=1}^{n} \sigma_j}{\mu_L}$

(5) choose k_i^* from (Reliability vs. k*) curve corresponding to a desired level of reliability

(6) Using Equations (21) and (22) solve for k_i by trial and error method.

(7) Calculate $P_i = \dfrac{1 + k_i V_L}{(1 - k_i V_R)(1 + k_i V_{iL})}$

(8) Calculate $\alpha'_{ij} = 1 + k_i V_j$ for each j

(9) Calculate $\alpha_{ij} = P_i \alpha'_{ij}$.

A Design Example

Consider the previous problem of designing a bridge floor system. The given information is

Mean dead load = 60 psf. Std. Dev. of dead load = 5 psf.

Mean live load = 80 psf. Std. Dev. of live load = 20 psf.

Required Reliability = 99.99%, i.e., $P_F = 10^{-4}$.

Assume Normal distribution of loads and resistances.

Let us follow the steps as outlined in Section 4.

(1) $V_{DL} = 1/12; \quad V_{LL} = 1/4$

(2) $V_R^2 = 0.01 + .015$, say, $= 0.0225; \quad V_R = 0.15$

(note that $V_F = 0$)

(3) $V_L = \dfrac{(425)^{1/2}}{140} = 0.147$

(4) $V_{iL} = \dfrac{25}{140} = 0.1785$

(5) $k* = 3.72$

(6) Try $k = 3$, Eq. (22) gives $\mu_R = 367$ and substitute into Eq. (21) gives $k = 2.88$. Using this new value of k and iterate one more cycle, $k = 2.87$. It is close enough and 2.87 is used for the value of k.

(7) $P_i = \dfrac{1 + 2.87 \times 0.147}{(1 - 2.\ 7 \times 0.15)(1 + 2.87 \times 0.1785)}$

$= 1.65$

(8) $\alpha'_{11} = 1 + 2.87 \times \dfrac{1}{12} = 1.239$

$\alpha'_{12} = 1 + 2.87 \times \dfrac{1}{4} = 1.718$

(9) $\alpha_{11} = 1.65 \times 1.239 = 2.04$

$\alpha_{12} = 1.65 \times 1.718 = 2.83.$

Design Load for the above example is,

$W = 2.04\ (60) + 2.83\ (80) = 348.8$ psf.

5. Inclusion of Earthquake Loads

In addition to dead and live load, a structure may be subjected to earthquake load. This is especially important for structures with long service life and located around 'earthquake active' regions. When earthquake load is included in our design, the possible loading combinations are namely: (EL = Earthquake Load)

$$W_1 = DL + LL$$
$$W_2 = DL + EL \qquad (30)$$
$$W_3 = DL + LL + EL$$

and the corresponding design values are:

$$W_1^* = \alpha_{11} P_1^* + \alpha_{12} P_2^*$$
$$W_2^* = \alpha_{21} P_1^* \qquad + \alpha_{23} P_3^* \qquad (31)$$
$$W_3^* = \alpha_{31} P_1^* + \alpha_{32} P_2^* + \alpha_{33} P_3^*$$

where α_{ij} are load factors and P_j^* are nominal values of the respective loads.

If the mean values are taken to be μ_j of P_j^* (31) becomes

$$W_1^* = \alpha_{11} \mu_1 + \alpha_{12} \mu_2$$
$$W_2^* = \alpha_{21} \mu_1 \qquad + \alpha_{23} \mu_3 \qquad (32)$$
$$W_3^* = \alpha_{31} \mu_1 + \alpha_{32} \mu_2 + \alpha_{33} \mu_3$$

Let us first assume that the resistance is deterministic.

5.1 LL is time independent, i.e., LL is constant

Assume: (i) DL and LL are normal as before

(ii) the maximum earthquake load EL for a period of service life of T years is normal with μ_3 and σ_3^2 as parameters.

Then Equation (30) for this case becomes

$$W_1 = \mu_1 + \mu_2 + k_1\sqrt{\sigma_1^2 + \sigma_2^2}$$

$$W_2 = \mu_1 + \mu_3 + k_2\sqrt{\sigma_1^2 + \sigma_3^2} \qquad (33)$$

$$W_3 = \mu_1 + \mu_2 + \mu_3 + k_3\sqrt{\sigma_1^2 + \sigma_2^2 + \sigma_3^2}$$

where k_1, k_2, k_3 are determined by the level of reliability in each combination. If the same level of reliability $\bar{u}$ is desired,

$$k_1 = k_2 = k_3 = k(\bar{u}) \qquad (34)$$

where $k(\bar{u})$ represents a function of $\bar{u}$.

Then using the technique as discussed previously,

$$\alpha_{ij} = \frac{\ell_{ij}}{\mu_j} \cdot \frac{W_i}{\sum_j \ell_{ij}} \qquad (35)$$

where $\ell_{ij} = \mu_j + k_i\sigma_j$. (36)

Thus load factors for each load combination are obtained for any level of reliability $\bar{u}$ desired.

However, max EL for a period of T years is not necessarily normal. It is more likely to be the Type II, largest value distribution, whose density function is

$$f(EL) = \frac{k}{u}\left(\frac{u}{EL}\right)^{k+1} e^{-\left(\frac{u}{EL}\right)^k} \qquad (37)$$

$$\text{where} \quad \text{mean of EL} = u\Gamma(1 - \tfrac{1}{k})$$
$$\text{variance of EL} = u^2[\Gamma(1 - \tfrac{2}{k}) - \Gamma^2(1 - \tfrac{1}{k})] \quad (38)$$

This distribution has a slight skewness from the symmetrical normal distribution. If the magnitude of EL is small relative to LL and DL, the combined loading (DL + EL) or (DL + LL + EL) will be close to normal distribution, and the method proposed on previous pages is justified. However when EL is relatively large, a more sophisticated computation may be used. The distribution of (DL + EL) or (DL + LL + EL) is no longer normal but something else, say $f_2(x)$ and $f_3(y)$.

$$f_2(x) = \int_{-\infty}^{\infty} f_{DL}(DL) f_{EL}(x - DL) d(DL) \quad (39)$$

where x is the value of (DL + EL).

Similarly,

$$f_3(y) = \int_{-\infty}^{\infty} f_{DL+LL}(DL + LL) f_{EL}(y - (DL + LL)) d(DL + LL) \quad (40)$$

where y is the value of (DL + LL + EL).

Since f_{DL} and f_{DL+LL} are known normal distribution and also f_{EL} is given by equation (37), the corresponding $f_2(x)$ and $f_3(y)$ may be computed analytically or using numerical integration. Once $f_2(x)$ and $f_3(y)$ are computed, the values of X and Y such that

$$P\{x \le X\} = \bar{u} \quad \text{where } \bar{u} \text{ is the desired level of}$$
$$P\{y \le Y\} = \bar{u} \quad \text{reliability for each loading combination} \quad (41)$$

may be determined.

Thus, for this case, equation (33) becomes:

$$W_1 = \mu_1 + \mu_2 + k_1\sqrt{\sigma_1^2 + \sigma_2^2}$$

$$W_2 = X \qquad (42)$$

$$W_3 = Y$$

and $\ell_{i3} = Z$ where Z is such that

$$P\{EL \leq Z\} = \bar{u} \,. \qquad (43)$$

With these modifications, equation (35) may now be used to compute the corresponding load factors.

5.2 <u>LL is time dependent, i.e., LL varies with time</u>

Assume that we may determine the fraction of time at which certain LL occurs throughout its period of service life of T years. This represents the "<u>temporal</u> distribution of LL." Since EL is a rare event compared to LL and also its duration is very short, the probability of finding a certain magnitude of LL at the time when an earthquake occurs should obey the distribution defined by Fig. 5. Also, given an earthquake occurs, the distribution of the magnitude EL is known. Therefore, <u>at each occurrence</u> of earthquake, the combined (LL + EL) has a probability distribution. For simplicity, assume Fig. 5 and Fig. 6 are normal with parameters (μ_1', σ_1') and (μ_2', σ_2'). Then (LL + EL) will be normal with parameters

$$\mu_3' = \mu_1' + \mu_2'$$
$$\sigma_3'^2 = \sigma_1'^2 + \sigma_2'^2 \,. \qquad (44)$$

Let $P\{(LL + EL) \geq w_o \,/\,$given an earthquake occurs$\}$

$$= p_{w_o} = \int_{w_o}^{\infty} \frac{1}{\sqrt{2\pi}\sigma_3'} \exp - \frac{(w-\mu_3')^2}{\sigma_3'^2}\, dw \qquad (45)$$

and let n be the expected number of occurrences of earthquake during T years, and assume that each earthquake occurrence is an independent event.

Using the method of "Bernoulli Tries," for a period T years,

$$P\{(LL + EL)_{max} < w_o\} = [1 - p_{w_o}]^n . \tag{46}$$

Therefore, we may derive a distribution curve for $(LL + EL)_{max}$ for a period of T years.

Once this distribution $(EL + LL)_{max}$ is computed, we may proceed with the procedure outlined earlier.

Assume: (i) a normal curve (μ_1^*, σ_1^*) may be fitted through Fig. 7.

(ii) the $(EL)_{max}$ for a period of T years is normal with parameters (μ_2^*, σ_2^*).

Equation (33) becomes:

$$\begin{aligned} W_1 &= \mu_1 + \mu_2 + k\sqrt{\sigma_1^2 + \sigma_2^2} \\ W_2 &= \mu_1 + \mu_2^* + k\sqrt{\sigma_1^2 + \sigma_2^{*2}} \\ W_3 &= \mu_1 + \mu_1^* + k\sqrt{\sigma_1^2 + \sigma_1^{*2}} \end{aligned} \tag{47}$$

and

$$\begin{aligned} \ell_{11} &= \mu_1 + k\sigma_1 \\ \ell_{12} &= \mu_2 + k\sigma_2 \\ \ell_{21} &= \mu_1 + k\sigma_1 \\ \ell_{23} &= \mu_2^* + k\sigma_2^* \\ \ell_{31} &= \mu_1 + k\sigma_1 \\ \ell_{32} &= \mu_2^* + k\sigma_2^* \\ \ell_{33} &= \mu_2^* + k\sigma_2^* \end{aligned} \tag{48}$$

and use equation (35) to determine the corresponding load factors α_{ij}. If Figure 7 is not normal, more sophisticated method as outlined in equations 39 and 40 may be used.

6. Conclusion

The derivation given in section 5 is for deterministic resistance. If the resistance is assumed to be normal with coefficient of variation V_R, a modification factor in equation (35) is added. Thus,

$$\alpha_{ij} = \left(\frac{\ell_{ij}}{\mu_j} \quad \frac{W_i}{\sum_j \ell_{ij}} \right) \left(\frac{1}{1 - kV_R} \right) \tag{49}$$

and the overall reliability of the system is determined by k'.

$$k' = \frac{k(\sigma_L + \sigma_R)}{\sqrt{\sigma_L^2 + \sigma_R^2}} \tag{50}$$

which measures the number of standard deviations away from the mean of $(R - L)$ curve. The numerical calculations, when earthquake loads are considered, are being done at Stanford University and the results will be made available shortly.

Incorporation of new information can be made by using Beta Distributions for loads and resistances. Such a model is being considered at present. Such a model has the following properties.

(i) it represents the state of the knowledge,

(ii) it is possible to incorporate new information without much trouble.

This paper has given the techniques by which floor system and the girders of a bridge structure can be designed for constant reliability under varying load conditions. To make these methods simple to use for design engineers, further work is continuing at Stanford.

REFERENCES

(1) Benjamin, J. R., and Lind, N. C., "A Probabilistic Framework for the Safety Provisions of the ACI Code," Symposium on the Application of Probabilistic Concepts to Strength Design of Reinforced Concrete Members, ACI Fall Conference. Memphis 1968.

(2) Cornell, C. A., "A Reliability-based Code Format," a memorandum to members of ACI Committee 348, Subcommittee E, July 1967.

(3) Cornell, C. A., "A Reliability Based Code Format," Symposium on the Application of Probabilistic Concepts to Strength Design of Reinforced Concrete Members, ACI Fall Conference, Memphis 1968.

(4) Niyogi, P. K., "Application of Statistical Methods and Information Theory to Structural Reliability Estimates," Ph.D. dissertation, Department of Civil Engineering, University of Pennsylvania, Philadelphia, Pennsylvania, 1968.

(5) Sexsmith, R. G., and Nelson, M. F., "Difficulties in Application of Probabilistic Code Formats to Real Structures," Symposium on the Application of Probabilistic Concepts to Strength Design of Reinforced Concrete Members, ACI Fall Conference, Memphis 1968.

(6) Shah, H. C., "The Rational Probabilistic Code Format," Symposium on the Application of Probabilistic Concepts to Strength Design of Reinforced Concrete Members, ACI Fall Conference, Memphis 1968.

(7) Shah, H. C., and Benjamin, J. R., "Statistical and Probability Methods for Analysis and Design of Reinforced Concrete Structures," International Conference on Shear, Torsion and Bond in Reinforced and Prestressed Concrete. PSG College of Technology, Coinbatore, India, January 1969.

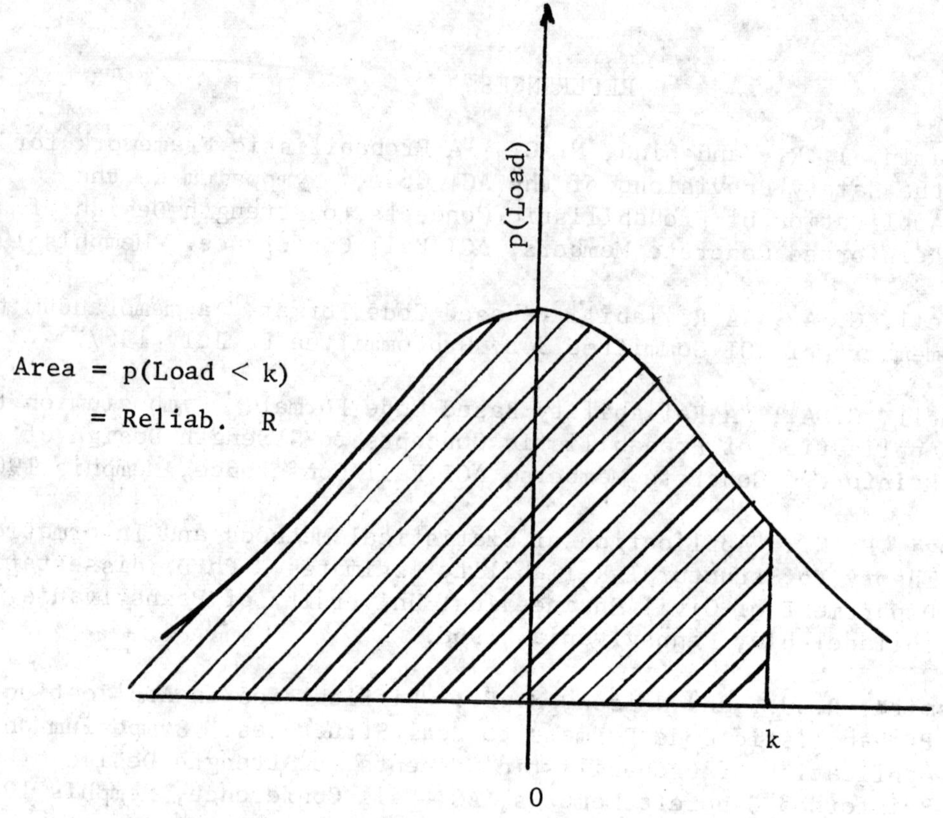

FIGURE 1. NORMALIZED GAUSSIAN PROB. DISTRIBUTION

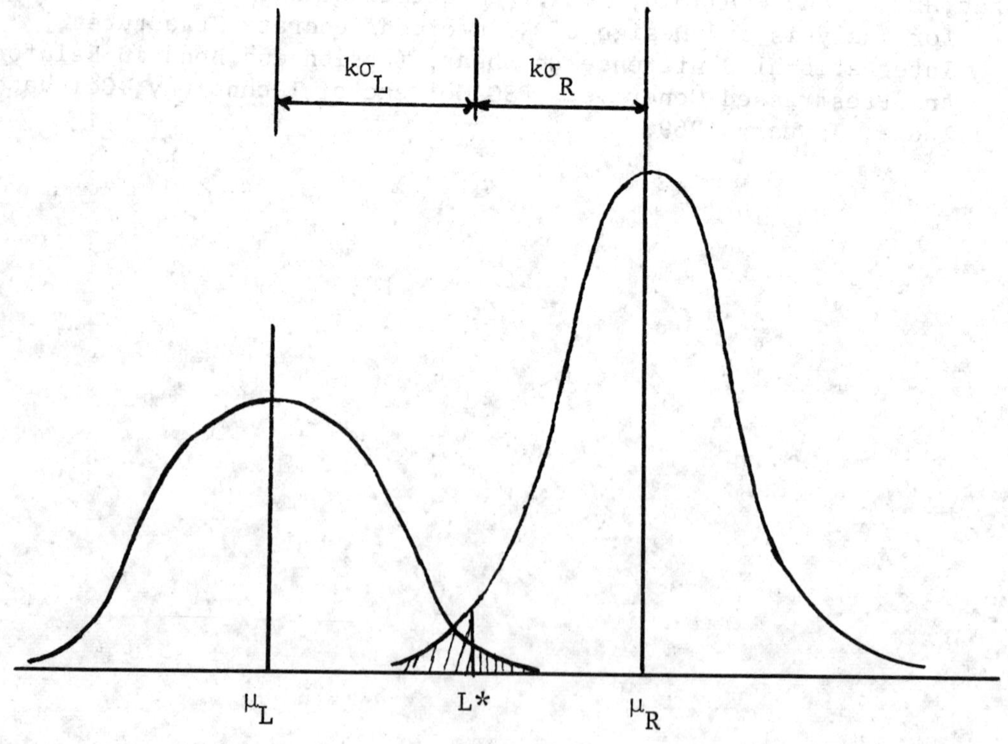

FIGURE 2. DISTRIBUTION OF LOADING AND RESISTANCE.

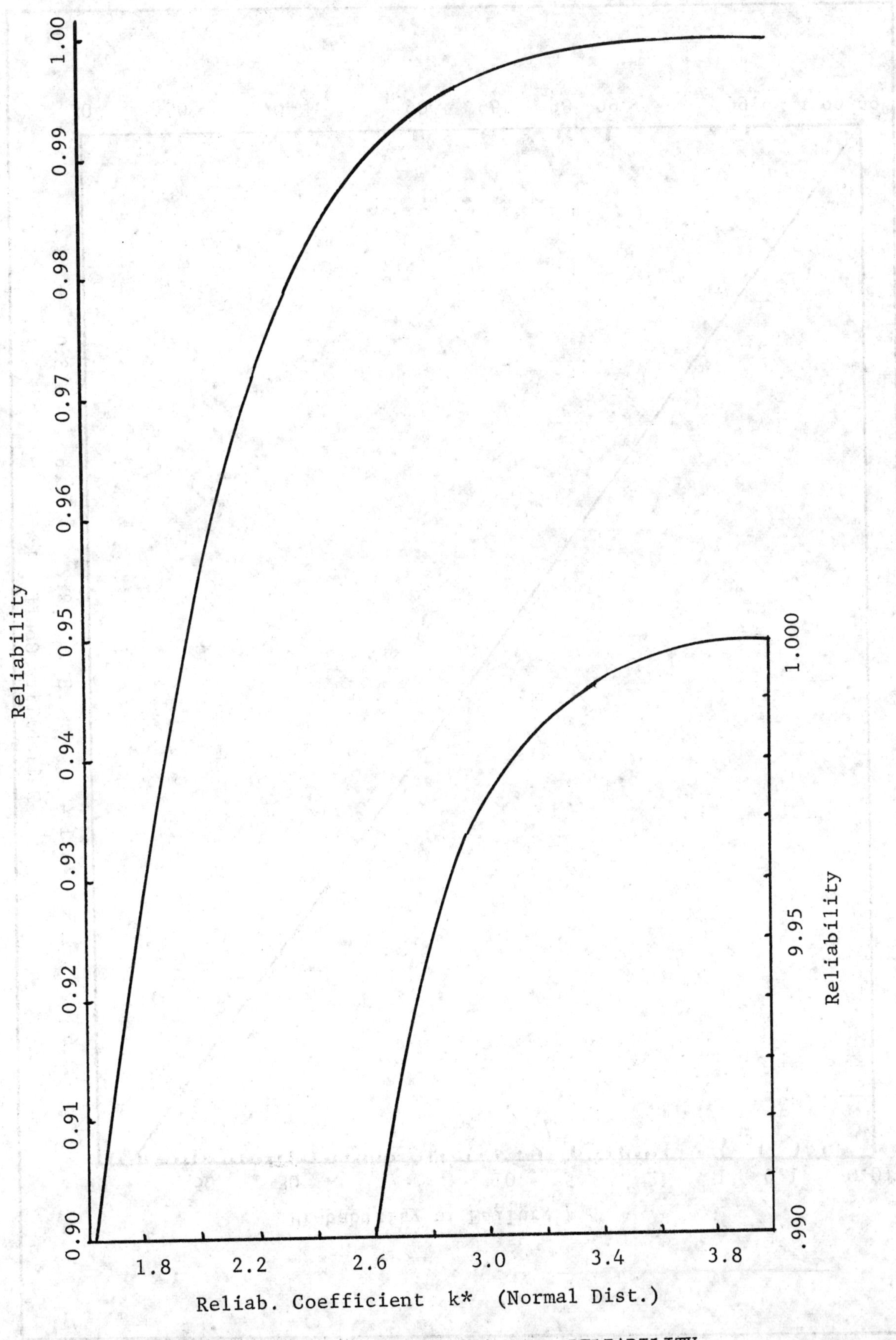

FIGURE 3. RELIAB. COEFF. k* VS. RELIABILITY

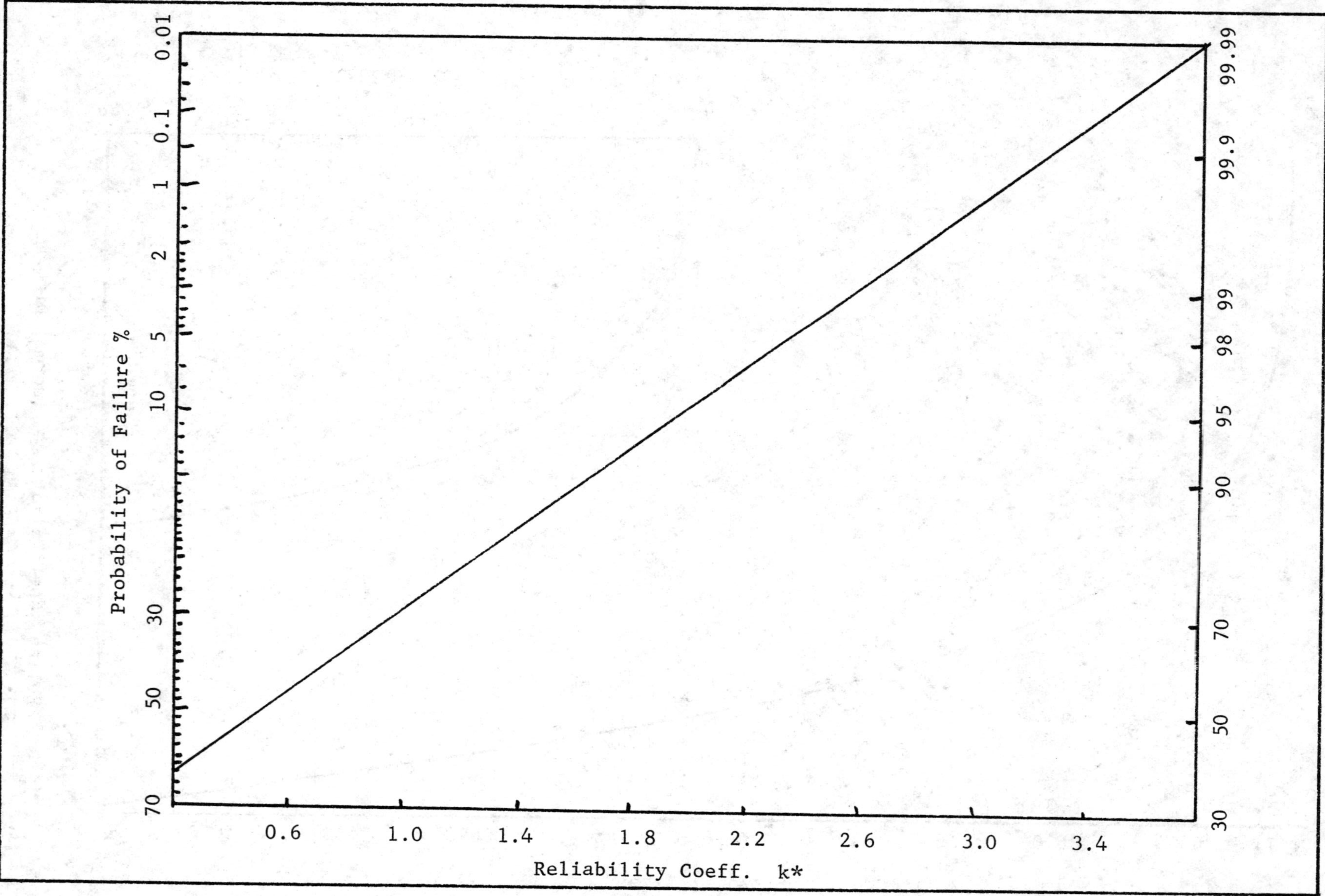

FIGURE 4. RELIABILITY COEFF. k* VS. RELIABILITY

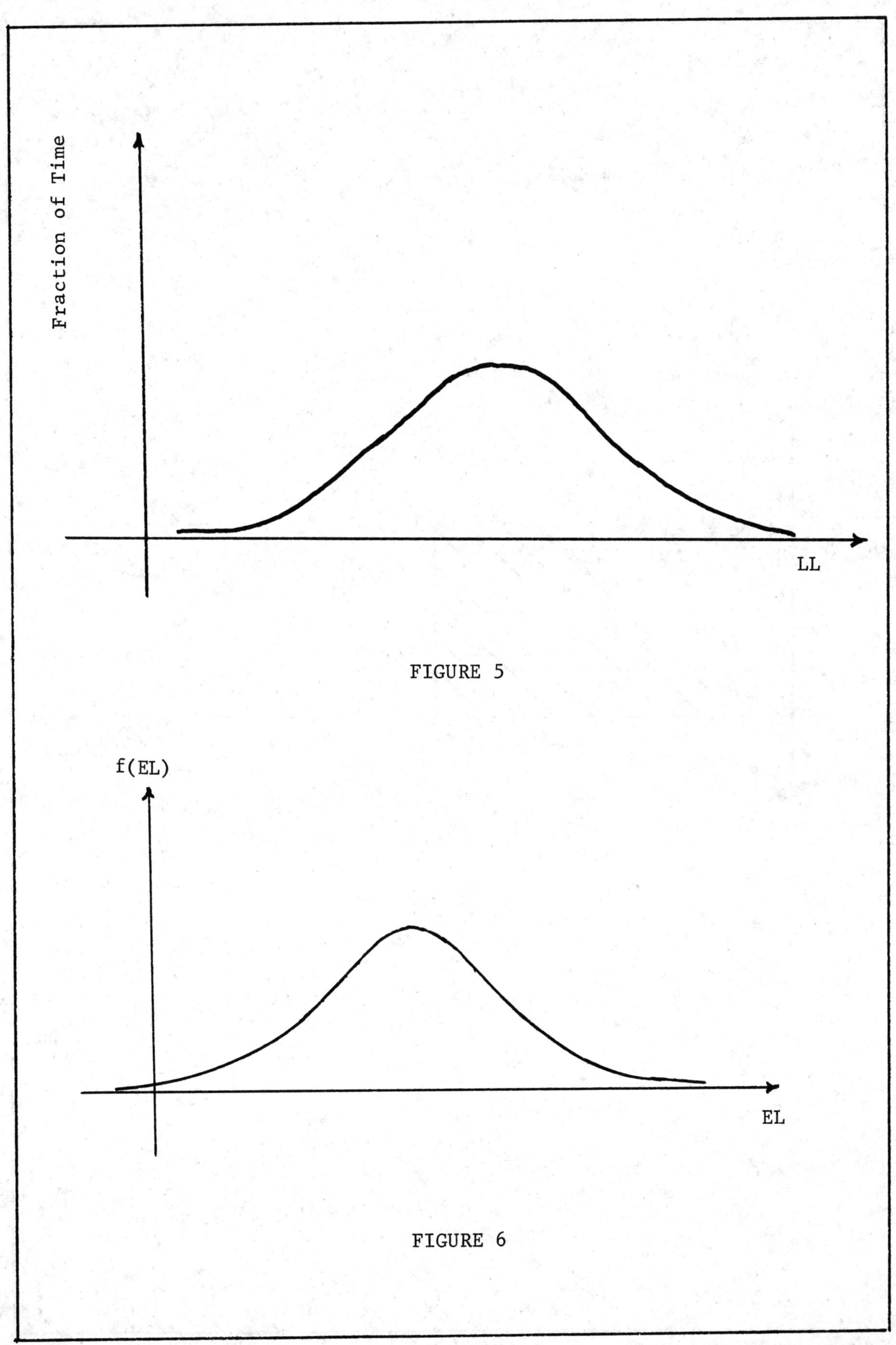

FIGURE 5

FIGURE 6

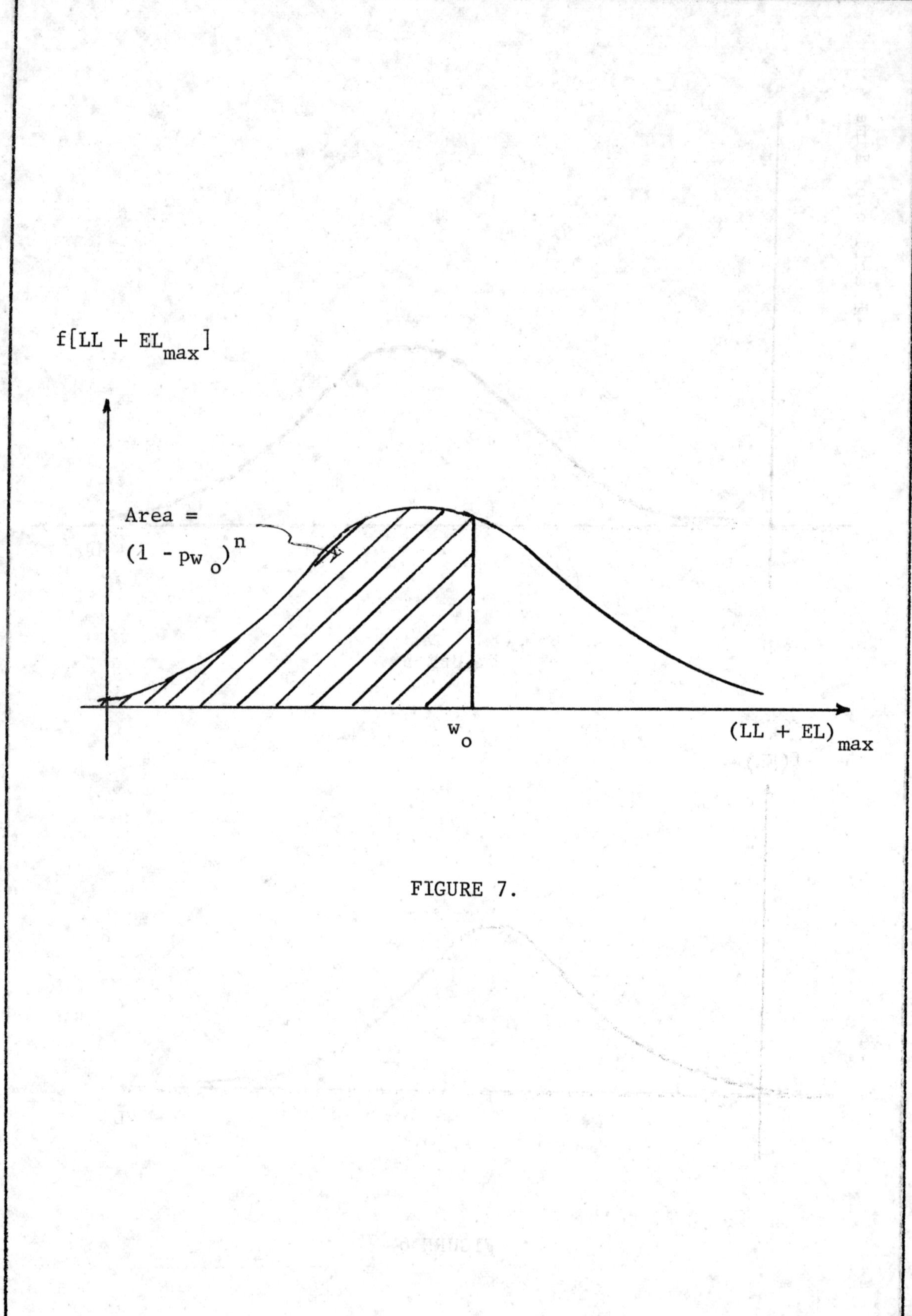

FIGURE 7.

PAPER SP 26-4

INFLUENCE CHARACTERISTICS FOR SLAB BRIDGES

By G. C. NAYAK and J. D. DAVIES

SYNOPSIS

The paper describes a numerical method for the direct determination of influence fields or surfaces for the generalised stress resultants in slab bridges. These stress resultants include bending moments, twisting moments, shears and reactions per unit length at a specified position in the deck slab. Slabs with isotropic and orthotropic elastic properties may be analysed using rectangular or skew co-ordinate systems.

The theoretical treatment is based on the "elastic pinch" procedure whereby a prescribed pattern of loads is applied adjacent to the observation point under consideration and the resulting deflected shape provides the influence surface. The appropriate patterns of loads are determined from the basic force-deformation relationships used in classical thin plate theory and include direct loads and couples. It is shown that the finite element technique provides a powerful and convenient method of calculating the deflected shapes and several examples are included to demonstrate the versatility of the method.

Keywords: bending moments; bridge decks; bridges (structures); concrete slabs; deformation; finite element method; reinforced concrete; shear properties; stresses; structural analysis; torsion.

ACI member G. C. NAYAK, is reader in civil engineering at the University of Roorkee, India and is currently a visiting Commonwealth research scholar at the University of Wales, Swansea. His main interests lie in the application of numerical methods to the analysis of bridge and other structural systems. He is the co-author of a comprehensive report on design procedures for concrete slab bridges in India and has written a number of papers on bridge analysis.

J. D. DAVIES is reader in civil engineering at the University of Wales, Swansea. His research interests are concerned with the behavior of plate and shell structures, the use of models and the tensile properties of concrete.

A frequent contributor to the proceedings of the ACI, Dr. Davies is the author of two test books, one on structural concrete and one on the use of models for concrete structures.

2. INTRODUCTION

Influence characteristic charts are widely used in modern bridge design where large numbers of load combinations have to be considered in the analysis. Influence surfaces for generalised displacements (deflections and rotations) are easily obtained by applying a generalised load (force or couple) to the observation point on the structure for which the influence values are required. By the reciprocal theorem, the deflected profile of the structure then serves as an influence field for the displacement of that point.

Influence surfaces for generalised forces or stress resultants (bending moments, twisting moments, shears and reactions) are more difficult to obtain. Although influence lines for forces in beams are easily obtained by using methods based on Müller-Breslau's principle, the determination of influence surfaces for forces in slabs is not so straightforward. The main difference arises because whereas in beams we need influence lines for total force actions at a specified section, in slabs we need influence characteristics for the stress resultants or forces per unit length at a specified point.

Basically, there are three methods of determining influence fields for the forces per unit length at a point in a laterally loaded plate with linear load-deflection properties :-

(i) experimental methods

(ii) analytical methods

(iii) numerical methods

The method described in this paper falls in the third category and is based on the finite element method of analysing slab structures. However, in common with other numerical processes in structural mechanics, the original concepts arise from methods (i) and (ii).

Previous Work

Before digital computers became available as aids in structural analysis, the large volume of tedious calculations required for the preparation of influence charts for bridge slabs was a daunting prospect. It took Pucher[(1)] more than two decades to provide data for 93 influence surfaces and these were based on a value of Poisson's ratio equal to zero.

In earlier works by Westergaard[(2)] and Baron[(3)], influence surfaces for forces were obtained for a few relatively simple cases based directly on the reciprocal theorem using singularity functions. Krug and Stein[(4)] extended Pucher's work on isotropic plates to orthotropic rectangular plates by transforming the side ratios in relation to the constants of orthotropy.

In the absence of suitable analytical procedures, Rüsch and Hergenröder[(5)] Kurata and Hatano[(6)], and Mehmel and Weise[(7)] obtained influence surfaces for simply supported, clamped and continuous point supported skew slabs respectively, based on measurements taken on model plates.

Morley[8] has used the singularity method to obtain computer solutions for rectangular and skew plates on discrete supports.

Newmark[9], Chen, Siess and Newmark[10] and Wooding and Siess[11] have adopted finite difference methods in conjunction with the singularity approach to obtain a large number of influence surfaces for plates. Narouka and Ohmura[12] have extended these techniques to the analysis of orthotropic parallelogram plates.

During the past decade, the finite element method has found wide application in plate analysis. A large number of papers have been published on the subject and a comprehensive treatment has been given by Zienkiewicz and Cheung[13].

3. BASIS OF ELASTIC PINCH OR SINGULARITY METHOD

The elastic pinch method of determining influence characteristics for elastic continua (for '2D' plates and shells or for '3D' solid structures) is an extension of Müller Breslau's principle used to determine influence lines for forces in '1D' skeletal structures. A relative displacement is caused by introducing some hinge or singularity mechanism to deform the structure to provide an influence surface for the force per unit length for an observation point in the structure. This singularity mechanism or elastic pinch is produced by applying a pattern of highly localised loads (forces and couples) adjacent to the observation point. Instead of physically "cutting" a section as in indirect model analysis, the discontinuity is simulated very closely by the application of the set of self-equilibrating concentrated forces. The resulting displacement field may be used as an influence surface directly except within the small zone of application of the loads causing the elastic pinch. It will be observed that this is the principle used in the moment deformeter technique to obtain influence lines for framed structures.

In this paper, the concept of the elastic pinch is used in conjunction with the finite element method so that it is possible to follow a unified approach to the determination of influence characteristics for all categories of structures with linear load-deformation characteristics. The particular advantage of finite element methods in plate and slab analysis is that they yield nodal rotations as well as deflections and it is possible to use nodal couples as well as transverse forces to create an elastic pinch. This reduces the zone over which the load patterns are applied and increases the accuracy of the solution.

4. DERIVATION OF LOADING PATTERNS FOR LINEAR SYSTEMS

General Theory

At a point 'a' in an elastic continuum we define displacement and load vectors, each of size n, by the expressions

$$\{\delta\}_a = \{\delta_1 \ \delta_2 \ ---- \ \delta_m \ ---- \ \delta_n\}$$
$$\{F\}_a = \{F_1, F_2, ---- \ F_m \ ---- \ F_n\} \qquad (1)$$

such that δ_m and F_m have the same translational and rotational directions.

Let the generalised stress resultant σ_{ki} at an observation point i be expressed as a function of the linear combinations of the displacements at i and at a group of points a, b, c ---- so that

$$\sigma_{ki} = A_k \ \delta_a^T + B_k \ \delta_b^T + C_k \ \delta_c^T + ---- + I_k \ \delta_i^T \qquad (2)$$

where the suffix k denotes the particular stress resultant under consideration and A_k, B_k, C_k ---- I_k are row vectors of order n such as

$$\{A_k\} = \{A_{k1}, \ A_{k2}, \ ---- \ A_{kn}\}$$

If a unit generalised force $P_j = 1$ is acting at point j, then let U_j be the corresponding displacement at j affecting the work done by P_j.

Expanding the first term on the right hand side of (2) we have

$$A_k \ \delta_a^{T \ P_j=1} = \left[A_{k1} \ \delta_1^{P_j=1} + A_{k2} \ \delta_2^{P_j=1} + --- + A_{kn} \ \delta_n^{P_j=1}\right]$$

and similarly for all the other right hand terms.

From the reciprocal theorem

$$A_{k1}\ \delta_1^{P_j=1} = U_j^{F_1=A_{k1}},\ \text{----}\ A_{kn}\ \delta_n^{P_j=1} = U_j^{F_n=A_{kn}}$$

or more briefly

$$A_k\ \delta_a^{P_j=1} = U_j^{F_a=A_k}$$

and we may re-write the stress resultant as

$$\sigma_{ki}^{P_j=1} = U_j^{F_a=A_k} + U_j^{F_b=B_k} + U_j^{F_c=C_k} + \text{----} + U_j^{F_i=I_k} \tag{3}$$

If R_k denotes the row matrix

$$\{A_k,\ B_k,\ C_k,\ \text{----}\ I_k\}$$

and δ denotes the column matrix

$$\{\delta_a,\ \delta_b,\ \delta_c,\ \text{----}\ \delta_i\}^T$$

then equation (2) becomes

$$\sigma_{ki} = \{R_k\}\ \{\delta\} \tag{4}$$

Equation (3) may be denoted by

$$\sigma_{ki}^{P_j=1} = U_j^{R_k} \tag{5}$$

Thus, when obtaining the influence surface for a particular stress resultant σ_{ki}, the load vector R_k remains fixed whereas the point j is arbitrarily chosen and may be considered at all points. Therefore, the fixed pattern of loads represented by R_k produces a displacement field which serves as an influence surface for σ_{ki}, that is, the load system R_k causes the elastic pinch or singularity at observation point i.

In equation (5) the unit load P_j can be a unit force or a unit couple and the corresponding displacement U_j will be either a deflection or a rotation. It is in this context that finite element methods show advantage over first order finite difference methods because in addition to the lateral load and lateral displacement at a node, the corresponding orthogonal couples and rotations about the axes at the node are included as part of the general solution process.

As mentioned previously, equation (4) represents the stress resultant at point i for a particular type of resultant defined by k. However, if σ_i denotes a set of stress resultants for k = 1 to m then a more complete form could be written as

$$\{\sigma\}_i = [R] \{\delta\} \tag{6}$$

where $$[R] = \begin{bmatrix} R_1 \\ R_2 \\ \cdot \\ \cdot \\ R_m \end{bmatrix}$$

and these may be used to represent bending moments, twisting moments, shears or reactions using different values for m.

For example, all the moments in plates at the point i could be represented by

$$\{\sigma\}_i = \begin{Bmatrix} M_x \\ M_y \\ M_{xy} \end{Bmatrix}_i$$

where M_x, M_y and M_{xy} are the moments per unit length corresponding to a set of co-ordinate axes x and y. Also, by pre-multiplying by a transformation matrix $[T]$ the stress resultants $\{\sigma\}_i$ can be easily transformed to another set of axes x^1 and y^1 where $[T]$ is composed of sine and cosine values of the angle between x and x^1. In short, if the stress resultants $\{\sigma\}_i$ are to be transformed, the loading pattern matrix is transformed as shown

$$[R^1] = [T] \quad [R] \tag{7}$$

It will be observed that this unified approach may be used to determine the influence fields for generalised stress resultants in any linear elastic structural system whether the geometric form is 1D, 2D, 3D or "mixed".

5. LOADING PATTERNS FOR AN ORTHOTROPIC PLATE

Suitable forms for the stress-displacement relationships for an observation point given by equation (6)

$$\{\sigma\}_i = [R] \{\delta\}$$

may be obtained in several ways. Many of these forms lead to satisfactory results over the general surface of the plate but may differ significantly within the zone of the elastic pinch caused by the pattern of applied loads. An obvious answer may appear to be to apply corrective solutions within this zone. However, for most engineering applications, this may not be necessary if the size of the zone is reduced and is not large compared with the thickness of the plates. Certain loading expressions show up to advantage when the observation point is located on or near a boundary.

Loading patterns for beams

To illustrate the relative accuracies of the various possible loading patterns, the influence lines for a prismatic beam will be considered in detail.

In Fig.1., the moment and shear influence lines with respect to the observation point 0 in the beam have been obtained in terms of the generalised displacements of neighbouring points 1 or 2 or both, situated at small distances h_1 and h_2 to the left and right of 0 respectively. For simplicity, let $h_1 = h_2 = h$. Loading expressions are obtained by assuming a variation

6. APPLICATIONS

The calculation of the right hand side of equation (5) to obtain the ordinates of the influence field for the particular generalised force at the observation point is now a routine matter and may be conveniently done by any finite element plate solution program. The loading pattern causing the elastic pinch may be input as data or calculated by a suitable subroutine. Also, the influence field thus obtained as a displacement surface can be utilised in further calculations for the effects of any specified applied loading on the plate.

However, a detailed investigation is necessary to assess the suitability of the loading expressions used to simulate the elastic pinch. To compare the accuracy of these procedures with existing solutions, three well known plate influence field problems have been analysed by the finite element technique and the loading patterns used are those given in Appendix 1(b). The influence fields for bending moments, twisting moments and shears at various observation points are plotted and compared with the results published by Pucher[(1)] and Krug and Stein[(4)].

(a) Isotropic square plate simply supported on all sides (Poisson's ratio = 0)

Using a 20 x 20 mesh, Fig.4 shows the variation of the influence field coefficients for M_x at A along the two centre lines and compared with Pucher's results.

Again, Fig.2(d) and Fig.2(e) show that the influence lines for shear vary only in the zone of the elastic pinch. Table 1 shows the corrections that should be applied within the pinch zone.

The simple loading patterns shown in Fig.1(d), using the "averaging" of the expressions to the left and right of the observation point, may now be extended to plate problems.

Loading patterns for plates

Again, for simplicity of presentation, rectangular elements are considered as shown in Fig.3. In appendix 1(a) results are presented for the loading patterns for the three moments at 0 (two orthogonal bending moments and the twisting moment) in terms of the twelve nodal displacements (the vertical displacement ω and the two orthogonal slopes) for each of the four elements. When the four elements are of the same type, it is possible to take the arithmetic mean and the results are shown in Appendix 1(b) for M_x, M_y, M_{xy} and Q_x at interior points and boundary points.

Similar expressions can be obtained for parallelogram elements required for skew plate problems by using an oblique co-ordinate system. In the case of complex elements, the stress matrix given by equation (8) may be used to obtain the loading expressions by substituting the ordinates of the observation point in to the displacement functions for the elements. The loading vectors can then be separated and a suitable form of averaging between the elements, may be considered. Therefore, this needs only simple modifications in existing programs, viz ..

$$\{\sigma\}^e = [S] \{\delta\}^e \qquad (8)$$

of deflection in the pinch zone. Fig.1(a) shows a parabolic variation along 1-0-2 and the resulting moment-deflection relationships are shown. However, because the third derivative of a parabola is zero such a shape cannot be used for shear force influence lines.

If the vertical deflection ω and the slope θ are taken as the displacements at 1, 0 and 2, a 5th degree curve can be assumed and the results are shown in Fig.1(b). When the observation point 0 lies on a boundary, Fig.1(c) shows the results for two cases by assuming a cubic variation of the deflection.

In situations where the material properties are different to the left and right of 0, some form of averaging may yield more accurate loading expressions. When the properties are the same, it is simpler to take an arithmetic mean and obtain the loading expressions shown in Fig.1(d).

To test the accuracy of these expressions, five moment and shear influence lines for simply supported and clamped beams are plotted in Fig.2. for $h = \frac{\text{span}}{10}$. For Fig.2(a) and Fig.2(b), the moment influence lines for the mid-point vary only within the zone of the elastic pinch. For Fig.2(c), the influence line for moment at the clamped end, based on the cubic variation, coincides with the exact solution outside the pinch zone. However, the values obtain from the first order finite difference expressions suggested in reference (11) will be seen to underestimate the correct curve at all points. The finite difference expressions give

$$M_o = \frac{EI}{h^2} (2\omega_o - 2\omega_2)$$

and violate statics, as will be apparent if a uniformly distributed load is applied over the span.

(b) Isotropic square plate clamped on all sides (Poisson's ratio = 0)

Two observation points, A at the centre and B at the middle of an edge were considered. Figs. 5 to 7 show the variation of the influence field coefficients for M_x, M_{xy} and Q_x at A and Figs. 8 and 9 the coefficients for M_x and Q_x at B. Again these are compared with Pucher's results.

(c) Orthotropic rectangular plate, simply supported on two opposite edges and free along the other two.

Referring to Figs.10 and 11 the following data was used with a 24 x 12 mesh :-

$$\frac{a}{b} = 2.0 \quad \frac{Dx}{Dy} = 16 \quad \frac{Dx}{Dxy} = 20 \quad D_1 = 0$$

The influence field coefficients for M_x and M_y at the centre point A are compared with those given by Krug and Stein. There is a statical check within one half per cent when uniformly distributed line loads are considered acting along BA and CD.

Discussion

It will be seen from the plots shown in Figs. 4 to 11 that the bending moment, twisting moment and shear influence field coefficients for the three plates are accurately determined outside the region of the elastic pinch. Within the elastic pinch zone it would be desirable to make singularity corrections when analysing the effects of concentrated applied loads but the effects of distributed loads can be adequately determined. In all cases, the accuracy can be improved by reducing the size of the elastic pinch zone.

Because the finite element solution for the influence field will produce nodal slopes as well as deflections, these first derivative values may be used to determine the effects of applied couples as well as direct loads. The slope chosen will be that corresponding to the work done by the applied couple in accordance with Betti's Law.

7. OUTLINE OF FURTHER APPLICATIONS

The determination of the total stress resultants at an observation point i due to a set of applied point loads and distributed loads is obviously the next step in bridge deck analysis. The total stress T_{ki} due to these loads is given by

$$T_{ki} = \sum_{j=1}^{m} P_j \; U_j^{R_k} + \iint_A P\,(x, y)\, U^{R_k}\,(x, y)\, dxdy) \qquad (9)$$

in which P_j is the point load at location x_j, y_j: $P_{(x, y)}$ is the intensity of the distributed load acting over the area A and U^{R_k} are the influence field values calculated as a deflection function. Thus, the loading information on the right hand side of equation (9) could be input as data for a number of trial positions, based on the designer's judgement, to determine the maximum values for all the stress resultants represented by T_{ki}. Therefore, it would not be necessary to reproduce a whole series of influence charts for a particular bridge deck as the whole operation could be incorporated in the same solution program.

The simple problems considered in section (6) was included for demonstration purposes only. A number of other complex bridge deck problems such as skew plates, continuous plates, voided slabs, slabs on elastic point supports and slab/beam combinations may be analysed by the methods outlined in this paper.

In principle, there is no difficulty in extending these methods to three dimensional elasticity problems, for example, in the determination of influence fields for internal stresses in anchor zones or in massive structures.

8. CONCLUSIONS

Influence fields for any linear elastic continuum may be conveniently obtained by finite element programs and generally required less storage and computation time than conventional analyses because only nodal displacements have to be calculated.

The loading expressions proposed for simulating the elastic pinch to obtain influence fields for bending moment, twisting moment and shear are accurate for positions of the observation point outside the elastic pinch zone.

The particular advantages of the finite element basis of the solution may be summarised as follows :-

(i) By incorporating couples as well as direct forces in the loading patterns, the size of the elastic pinch may be reduced and the accuracy improved. The nodal rotations facilitate the interpolation of influence fields for loads applied between nodal positions.

(ii) It presents a unified approach for any type of continuum and influence fields may be obtained directly based on existing finite element programs.

(iii) The effects of moving loads on the bending moment, twisting moment and shear (at the observation point) in any specified direction, are easily obtained by use of a simple transformation in the program solution routine.

(iv) The effects of applied couples (or rotational reactions at column heads) are obtained by using the nodal rotations from the influence surface output data.

(v) The problem of determining maximum total stresses due to various combinations of moving loads could be handled in the same program, obviating the need for extensive influence field charts.

9. REFERENCES

1. PUCHER,A. "Influence surfaces of elastic plates" Springer-Verlag (3rd Ed.) New York, 1964.

2. WESTERGAARD, H.M. "Computations of stresses in bridge slabs due to wheel loads" Public Roads, Vol.11, No.1, March 1930, pp. 1-23

3. BARON, F.M. "Influence surfaces for stresses in slabs" J. Appl. Mechs, Vol.8 , No.2 March 1941, pp. A3 - A13.

4. KRUG, S. and STEIN, P. "Moment influence surfaces of orthotropic plates" Springer-Verlag, Berlin, 1961.

5. RUSCH, H. and HERGENRODER, A. "Influence surfaces for moments in skew slabs" C. and C.A. Library Translation, 1965.

6. KURATA, M. and HATANO, S. "Influence for indeterminate clamping moments of slab bridge type skew plates". Int. Assoc. of Br. and Struct.Eng. Vol. 24, 1964, pp. 101-112.

7. MEHMEL, A. and WEISE, H. "Model investigation on skew slabs on elastically yielding point supports" C. and C.A. Library Translation No. 125, 1963.

8. MORLEY, L.S.D. "The analysis of column supported plates with special application to bridges" Int. Assoc. of Br. and Struct. Eng. Vol. 28, 1968, pp. 95-138.

9. NEWMARK, N.M. "Note on calculation of influence surfaces in plates by use of difference equations" J. Appl. Mechs, Vol.8, No.2, June 1941, pp. A92.

10. CHEN,T.Y., SIESS,C.P. and NEWMARK, N.M.
"Studies of slab and beam highway bridges,"Part IV.
University of Illinois Res. Stn. Bull. 439, 1957.

11. WOODRING, R.E. and SIESS, C.P. "Influence surfaces for continuous plates".
Proc. ASCE, Struct. Div, ST1, Jan. 1968, pp. 211-226.

12. NAROUKA, M. and OHMURA, H.
"On the analysis of skew girder bridge by the theory of orthotropic parallelogram plates"
Int. Assoc. of Br. and Struct. Eng. Vol. 19, 1959, pp. 231-256.

13. ZIENKIEWICZ, O.C. and CHEUNG, Y.K.
"The finite element method in structural and continuum mechanics"
McGraw-Hill, London, 1966.

APPENDIX 1

LOADING PATTERNS FOR AN ORTHOTROPIC PLATE.

(a) Tables 2, 3 and 4 show the nodal loading patterns to be applied to the four rectangular elements surrounding the central observation point 0 indicated in Figure 3. The nodal listing indicates the magnitudes of the three generalised loads - one direct force and two orthogonal couples - corresponding to the three generalised displacements ω, θ_x and θ_y. The stress resultant - deformation relationships for the seven stress resultants required, with respect to x, y axes, at a point in an orthotropic plate are shown in Table 4.

(b) Tables 5, 6, 7 and 8 show the nodal loading patterns that may be used to produce influence fields for M_x, M_y, M_{xy} and Q_x, for interior and exterior points, when the elements around the observation point have the same constants of orthotropy. The lengths of the elements are 'a' in the x direction and 'b' in the y direction.

APPENDIX 2 : NOTATION

$\{\delta\}_a$	:	displacement row vector at point a
$\{F\}_a$	:	force " " " " "
σ_{ki}	:	stress resultant at an observation point i k indicates the type of stress resultant.
$\{A_k\}$, $\{B_k\}$ etc.	:	row vector of order n corresponding to points a, b etc.
P_j	:	generalised force acting at point j
U_j	:	generalised displacement corresponding to P_j
i, j, o	:	nodal points in the system
k	:	indicates particular type of stress resultant
n	:	number of displacement or force unknowns at a point
m	:	number of stress resultants to be considered at the observation point
h	:	length of sub-division in a beam
a, b	:	lengths of element in a plate in x and y direction
L	:	span of plate
ω	:	vertical deflection in beam or plate
θ	:	slope in a beam
θ_x, θ_y	:	rotations in a plate about x and y axes
$[S]$	:	stress matrix
M_x, M_y	:	bending moments per unit length

M_{xy} : twisting moments per unit length

Q_x, Q_y : shear per unit length

V_x, V_y : reactions per unit length

D_x, D_y, D_{xy}, D_1 : constants of orthotropy for plate

$H = D_1 + 2\,D_{xy}$

T_{ki} : total stress resultant at i due to specified applied loads

$[R]_k$: loading pattern matrix to produce influence field for stress resultant σ_{ki}

	LOAD EXPRESSION	MOMENT CORRECTION	SHEAR CORRECTION	
			TO LEFT OF 'O'	TO RIGHT OF 'O'
(a)	1 0 2	$\left(\frac{r^3}{6}\right)h$	—	—
(b)	1 0 2	$\left(\frac{r^3}{3}-\frac{r^2}{4}\right)h$	$0{\cdot}75r^2-1{\cdot}25r^3$	$1{\cdot}25r^3-0{\cdot}75r^2$
(c)	0 2	$(r^3-r^2)h$	—	$3r^2-2r^3$
(d)	1 0	$(r^3-r^2)h$	$2r^3-3r^2$	—
(e)	1 0 2	$\left(\frac{r^3}{2}-\frac{r^2}{2}\right)h$	$r^3-1{\cdot}5r^2$	$1{\cdot}5r^2-r^3$

$r = 1-|\xi|$ where $\xi = \frac{x}{h}$

TABLE 1

CORRECTIONS TO BE APPLIED TO MOMENT AND SHEAR INFLUENCE VALUES WITHIN THE PINCH ZONE FOR A PRISMATIC BEAM

Nodal loading patterns to cause influence field for bending moment at O

$M_x \begin{Bmatrix} \omega \\ \theta_x \\ \theta_y \end{Bmatrix}$

TABLE 2

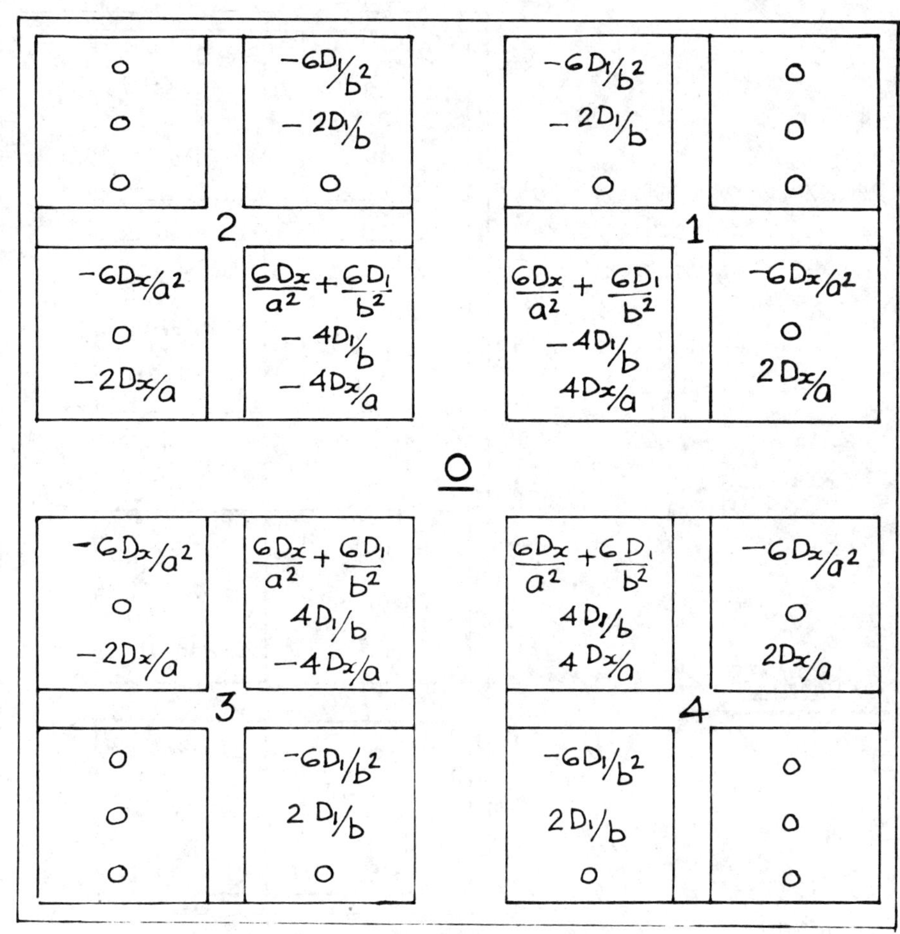

Nodal loading patterns to cause influence field for bending moment at O

$M_y \begin{Bmatrix} \omega \\ \theta_x \\ \theta_y \end{Bmatrix}$

TABLE 3

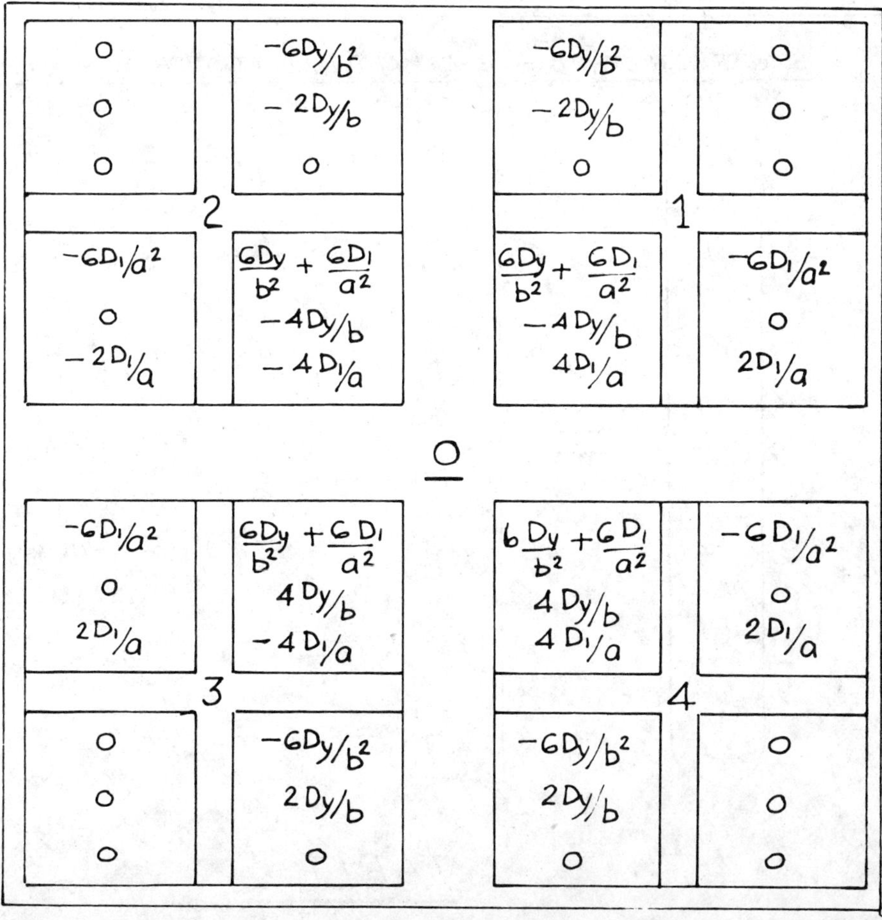

Nodal loading patterns to cause influence field for twisting moment at O

$$M_{xy} \begin{Bmatrix} \omega \\ \theta_x \\ \theta_y \end{Bmatrix}$$

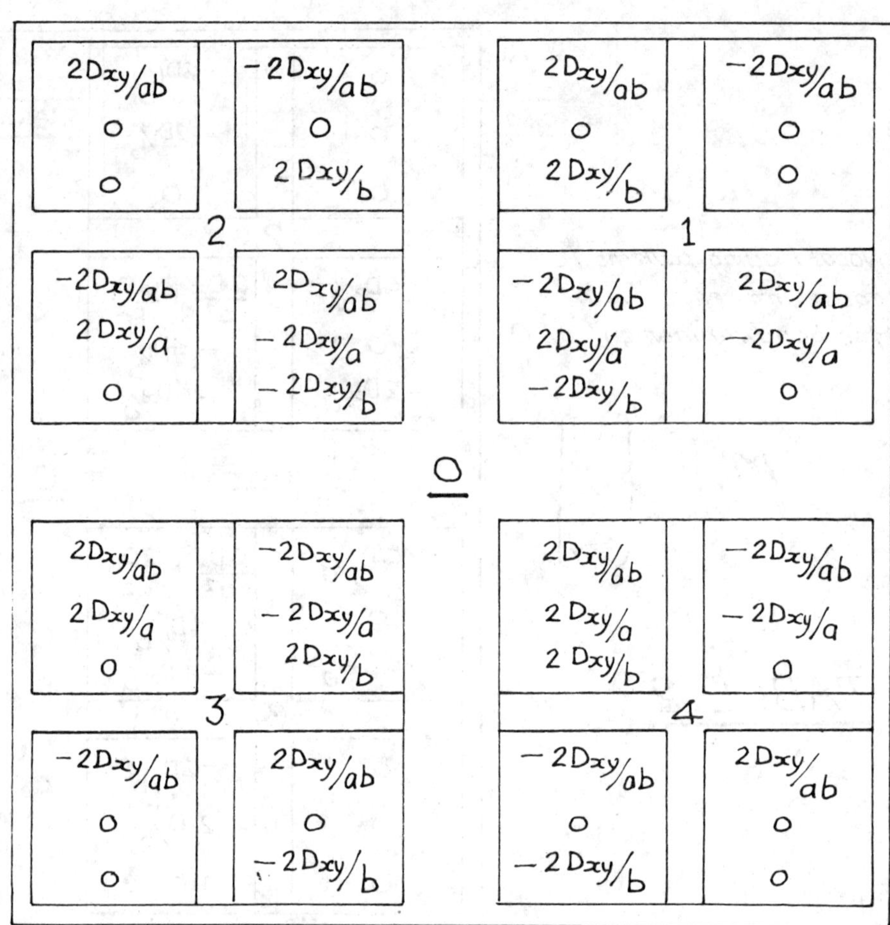

TABLE 4

STRESS RESULTANT — DEFORMATION RELATIONSHIPS FOR ORTHOTROPIC PLATES

$$\begin{Bmatrix} M_x \\ M_y \\ M_{xy} \\ Q_x \\ V_x \\ Q_y \\ V_y \end{Bmatrix} = \begin{bmatrix} D_x & D_1 & - & - & - & - & - \\ D_1 & D_y & - & - & - & - & - \\ - & - & D_{xy} & - & - & - & - \\ - & - & - & D_x & (D_1+2D_{xy}) & - & - \\ - & - & - & D_x & (D_1+4D_{xy}) & - & - \\ - & - & - & - & - & D_y & (D_1+2D_{xy}) \\ - & - & - & - & - & D_y & (D_1+4D_{xy}) \end{bmatrix} \begin{Bmatrix} -\frac{\partial^2 \omega}{\partial x^2} \\ -\frac{\partial^2 \omega}{\partial y^2} \\ \frac{2\partial^2 \omega}{\partial x \partial y} \\ -\frac{\partial^3 \omega}{\partial x^3} \\ -\frac{\partial^3 \omega}{\partial x \partial y^2} \\ -\frac{\partial^3 \omega}{\partial y^3} \\ -\frac{\partial^3 \omega}{\partial y \partial x^2} \end{Bmatrix}$$

TABLE 5

STRESS RESULTANT	INTERIOR POINT (grid spacing a, a in x; b, b in y)			EXTERIOR POINT (grid spacing a, a in x; b in y)		
M_x $\begin{Bmatrix}\omega\\ \theta_x\\ \theta_y\end{Bmatrix}$	0 0 0	$-3D_1/b^2$ $-D_1/b$ 0	0 0 0	$-3D_x/a^2$ 0 $-D_x/a$	$6D_x/a^2+6D_1/b^2$ $4D_1/b$ 0	$-3D_x/a^2$ 0 D_x/a
	$-3D_x/a^2$ 0 $-D_x/a$	$6D_x$ [illegible] b^2 [illegible] 0	$-3D_x/a^2$ 0 D_x/a	0 0 0	$-6D_1/b^2$ $2D_1/b$ 0	0 0 0
	0 0 0	$-3D_1/b^2$ D_1/b 0	0 0 0	—	—	—
M_y $\begin{Bmatrix}\omega\\ \theta_x\\ \theta_y\end{Bmatrix}$	0 0 0	$-3D_y/b^2$ $-D_y/b$ 0	0 0 0	$-3D_1/a^2$ 0 $-D_1/a$	$6D_y/b^2+6D_1/a^2$ $4D_y/b$ 0	$-3D_1/a^2$ 0 D_1/a
	$-3D_1/a^2$ 0 $-D_1/a$	$6D_y/b^2+6D_1/a^2$ 0 0	$-3D_1/a^2$ 0 D_1/a	0 0 0	$-6D_y/b^2$ $2D_y/b$ 0	0 0 0
	0 0 0	$-3D_y/b^2$ D_y/b 0	0 0 0	—	—	—

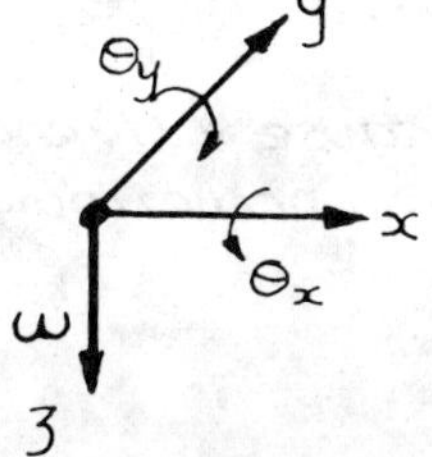

Loading patterns to cause influence fields for M_x and M_y in orthotropic plates

TABLE 6

STRESS RESULTANT — Interior point (grid spacing a, a in x; b, b in y) and Exterior point (grid spacing a, a in x; b in y). Each box gives $\{\omega, \theta_x, \theta_y\}$.

M_{xy} $\begin{Bmatrix}\omega\\ \theta_x\\ \theta_y\end{Bmatrix}$

Interior point:

$D_{xy}/2ab$ 0 0	0 0 D_{xy}/b	$-D_{xy}/2ab$ 0 0
0 D_{xy}/a 0	0 0 0	0 $-D_{xy}/a$ 0
$-D_{xy}/2ab$ 0 0	0 0 $-D_{xy}/b$	$D_{xy}/2ab$ 0 0

Exterior point:

D_{xy}/ab D_{xy}/a 0	0 0 $2D_{xy}/b$	$-D_{xy}/ab$ $-D_{xy}/a$ 0
$-D_{xy}/ab$ 0 0	0 0 $-2D_{xy}/b$	D_{xy}/ab 0 0
—	—	—

Q_x $\begin{Bmatrix}\omega\\ \theta_x\\ \theta_y\end{Bmatrix}$

$H = D_1 + 2D_{xy}$

Interior point:

$1{\cdot}5H/ab^2$ $0{\cdot}5H/ab$ 0	0 0 0	$-1{\cdot}5H/ab^2$ $0{\cdot}5H/ab$ 0
$-\frac{6D_x}{a^3}-\frac{3H}{ab^2}$ 0 $-3D_x/a^2$	0 0 $-6D_x/a^2$	$\frac{6D_x}{a^3}+\frac{3H}{ab^2}$ 0 $-\frac{3D_x}{a^2}$
$1{\cdot}5H/ab^2$ $0{\cdot}5H/ab$ 0	0 0 0	$-1{\cdot}5H/ab^2$ $0{\cdot}5H/ab$ 0

Exterior point:

$-\frac{6D_x}{a^3}-\frac{3H}{ab^2}$ $-2H/ab$ $-3D_x/a^2$	0 0 $-6D_x/a^2$	$\frac{6D_x}{a^3}+\frac{3H}{ab^2}$ $2H/ab$ $-3D_x/a^2$
$3H/ab^2$ H/ab 0	0 0 0	$-3H/ab^2$ H/ab 0
—	—	—

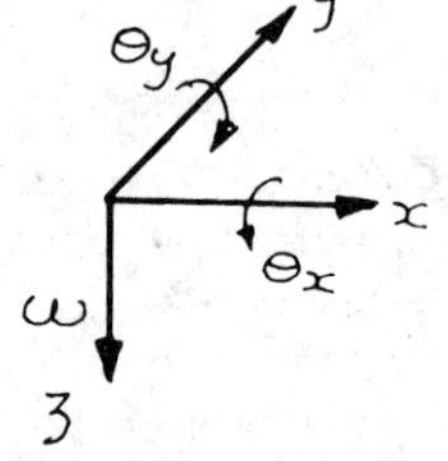

Loading patterns to cause influence fields for M_{xy} and Q_x in orthotropic plates

TABLE 7

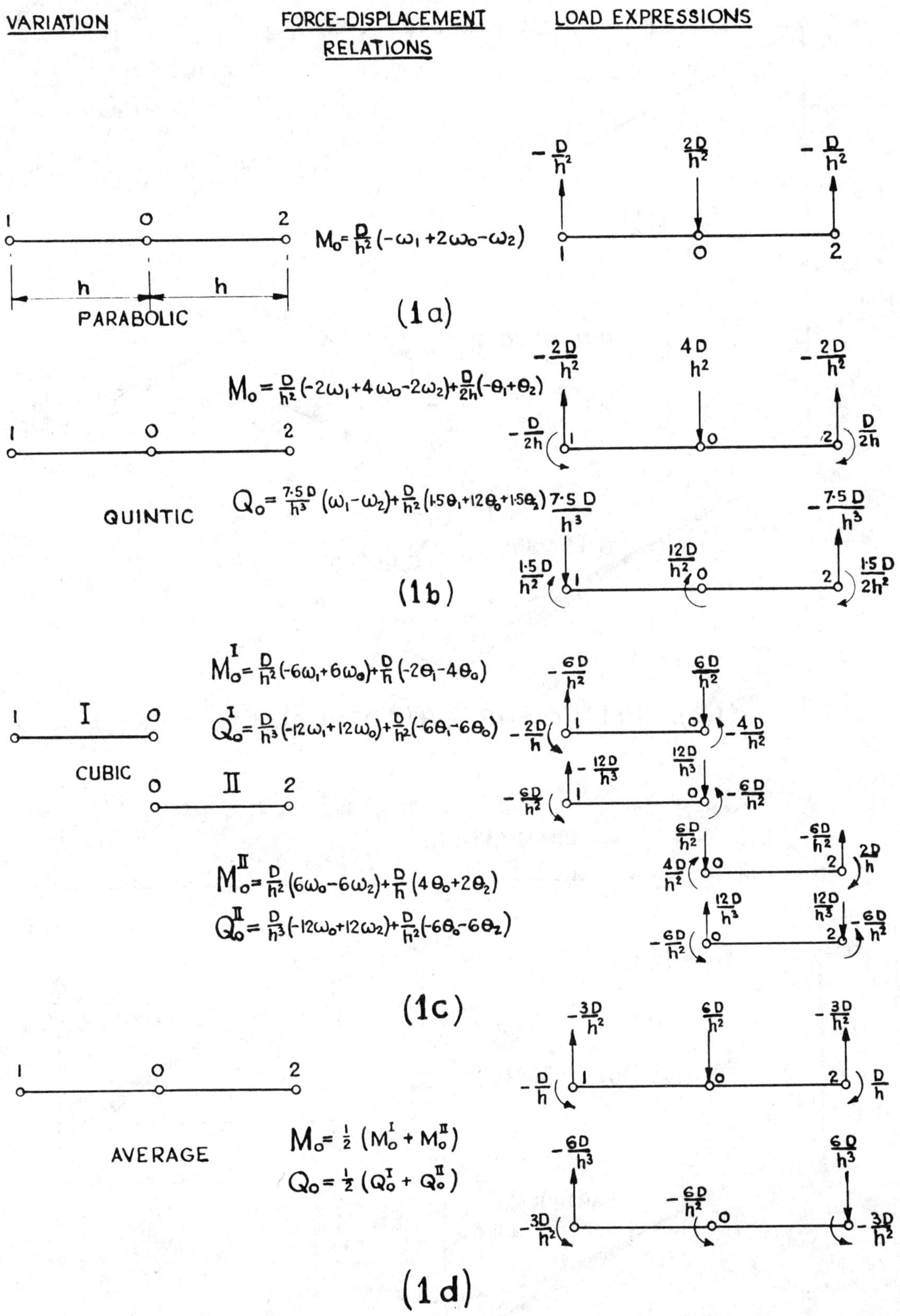

FIG. 1. LOADING PATTERNS FOR MOMENT AND SHEAR INFLUENCE LINES IN PRISMATIC BEAMS.

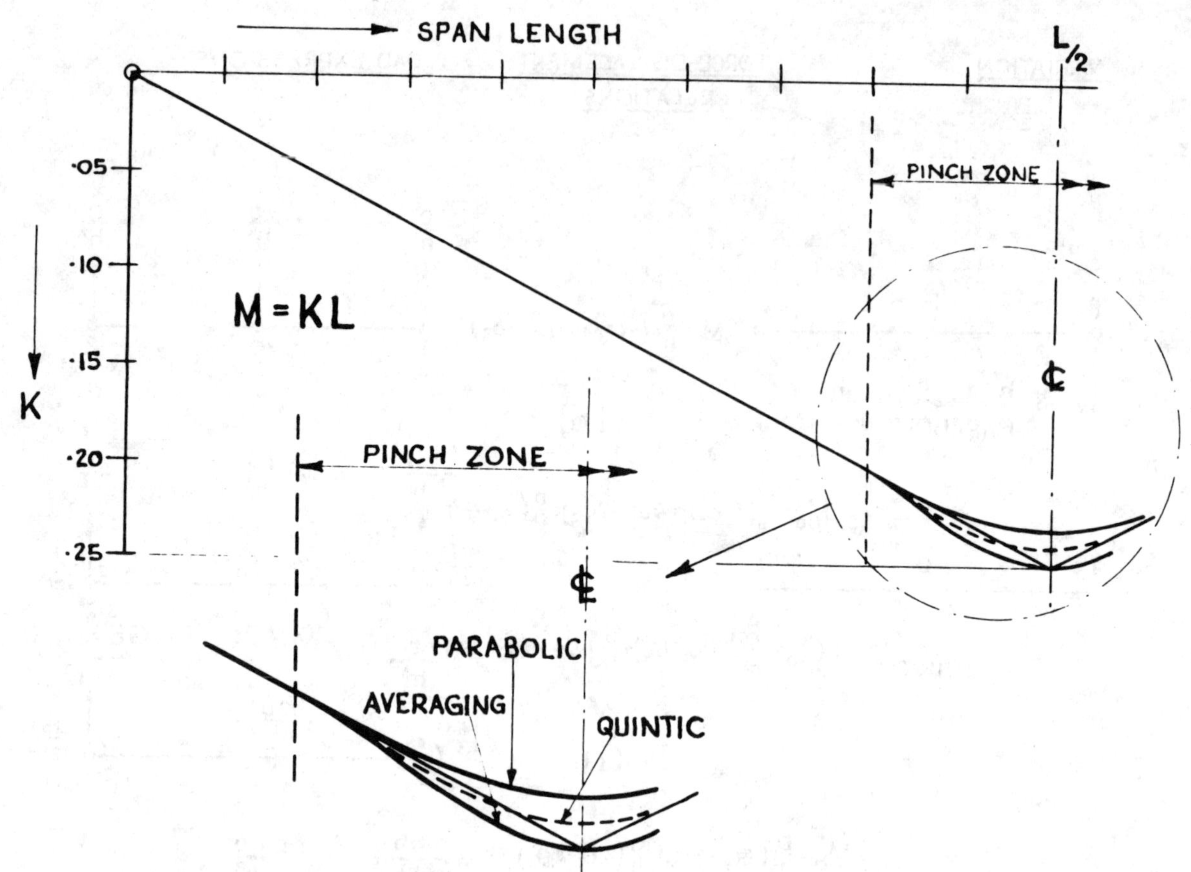

2(a). SIMPLY SUPPORTED BEAM: MOMENT AT MID-SPAN.

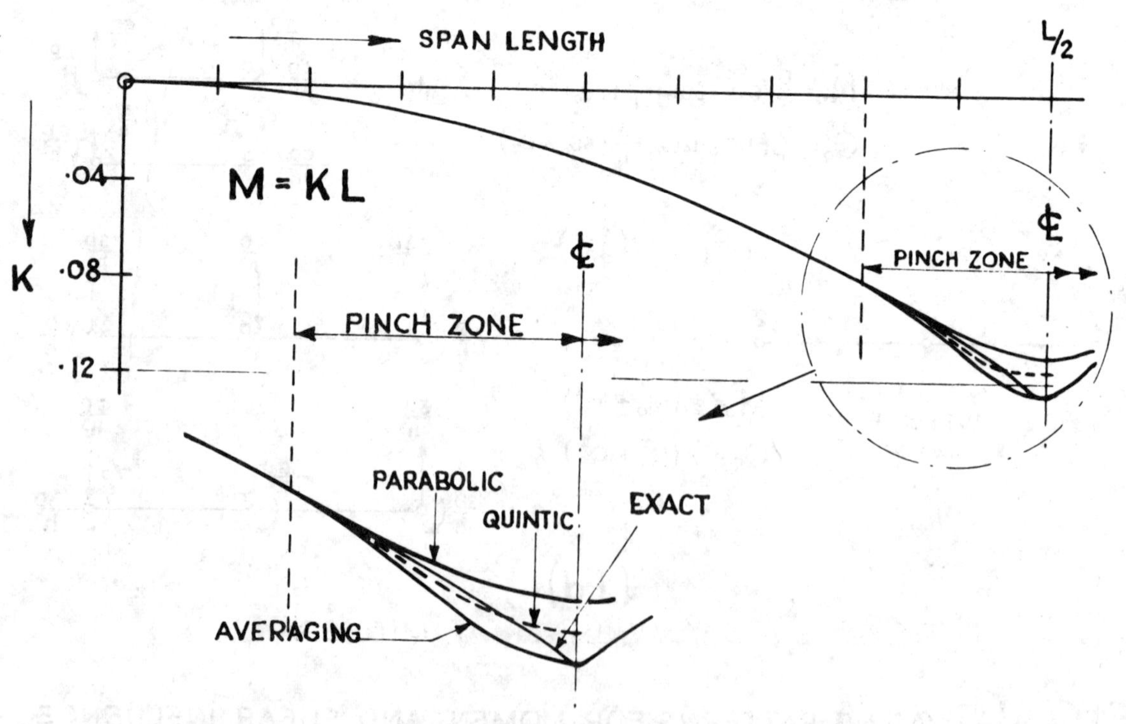

2 (b). CLAMPED BEAM: MOMENT AT MID-SPAN.

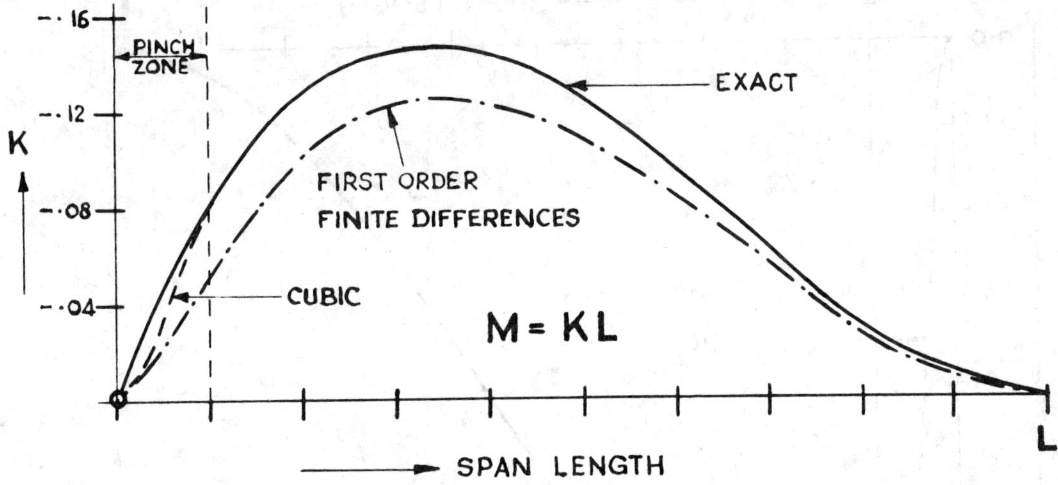

2 (c). CLAMPED BEAM: MOMENT AT CLAMPED EDGE.

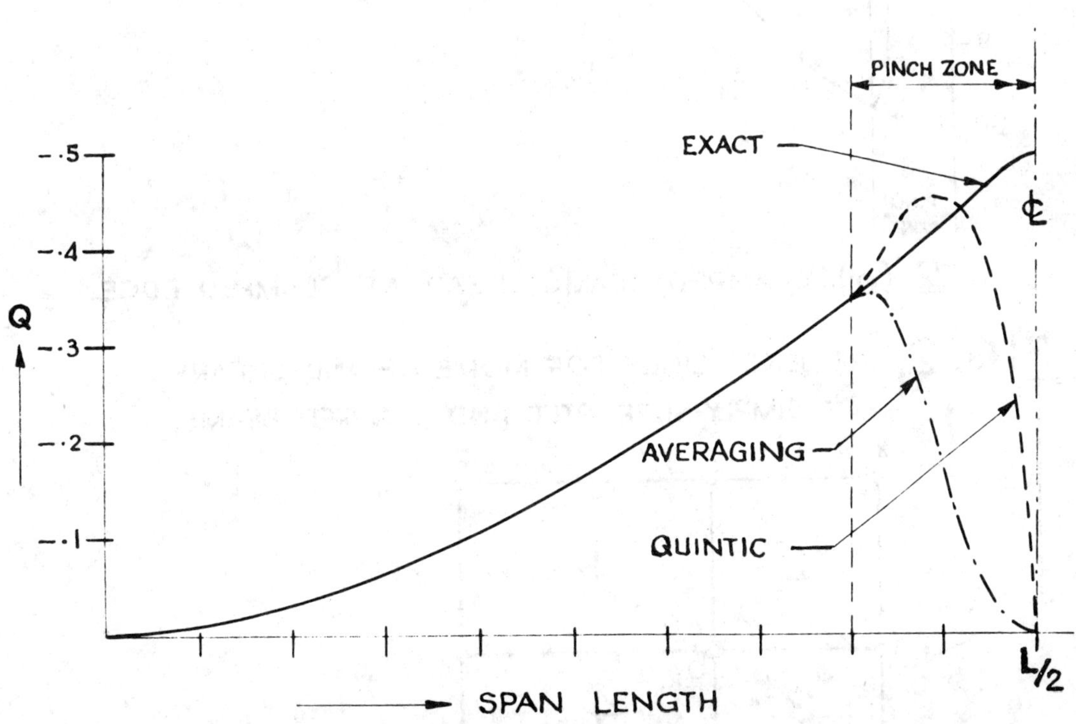

2 (d). CLAMPED BEAM: SHEAR AT MID-SPAN.

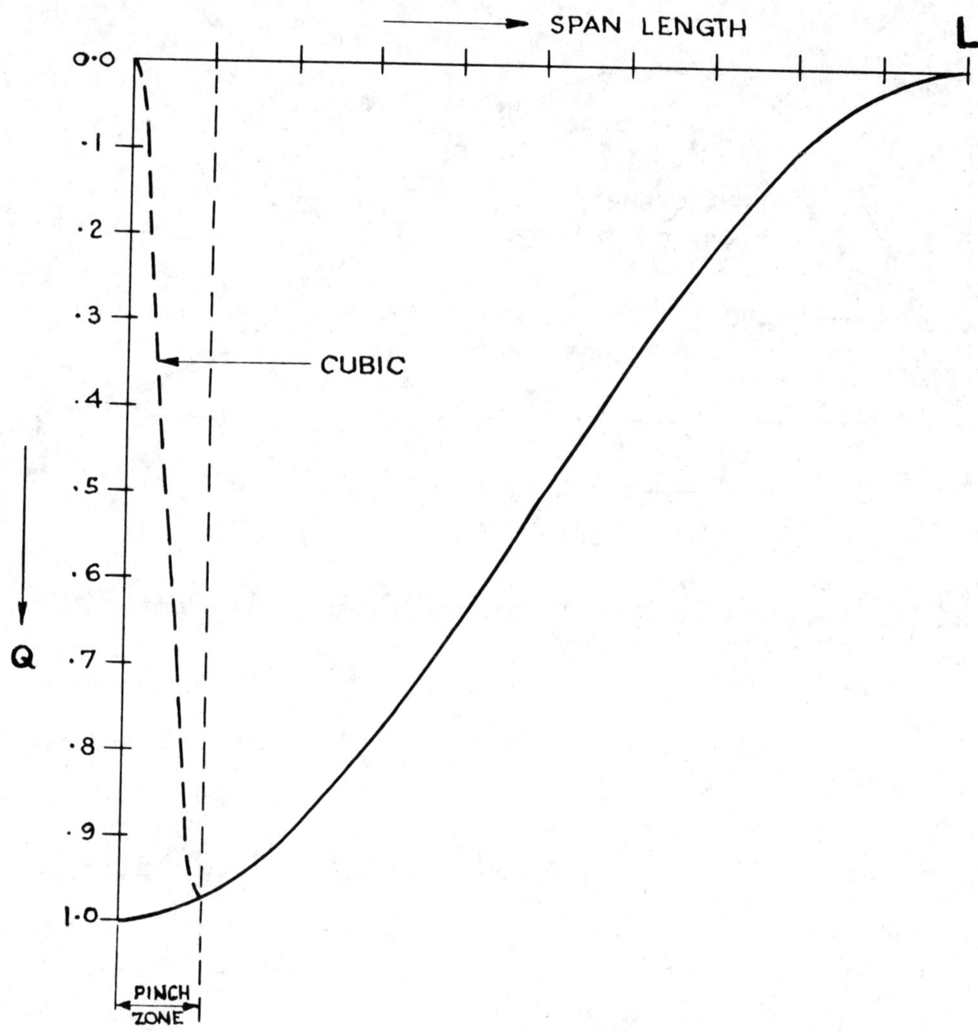

2 (e). CLAMPED BEAM: SHEAR AT CLAMPED EDGE.

FIG. 2. INFLUENCE LINES FOR MOMENTS AND SHEARS FOR SIMPLY SUPPORTED AND CLAMPED BEAMS.

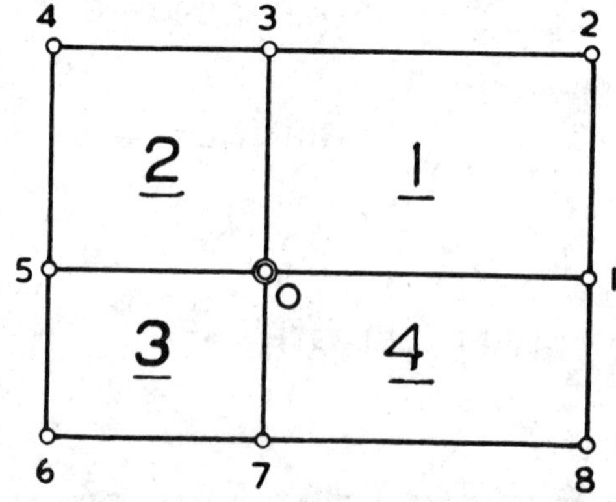

FIG. 3. FOUR RECTANGULAR FINITE ELEMENTS CONSIDERED AROUND OBSERVATION POINT 'O'.

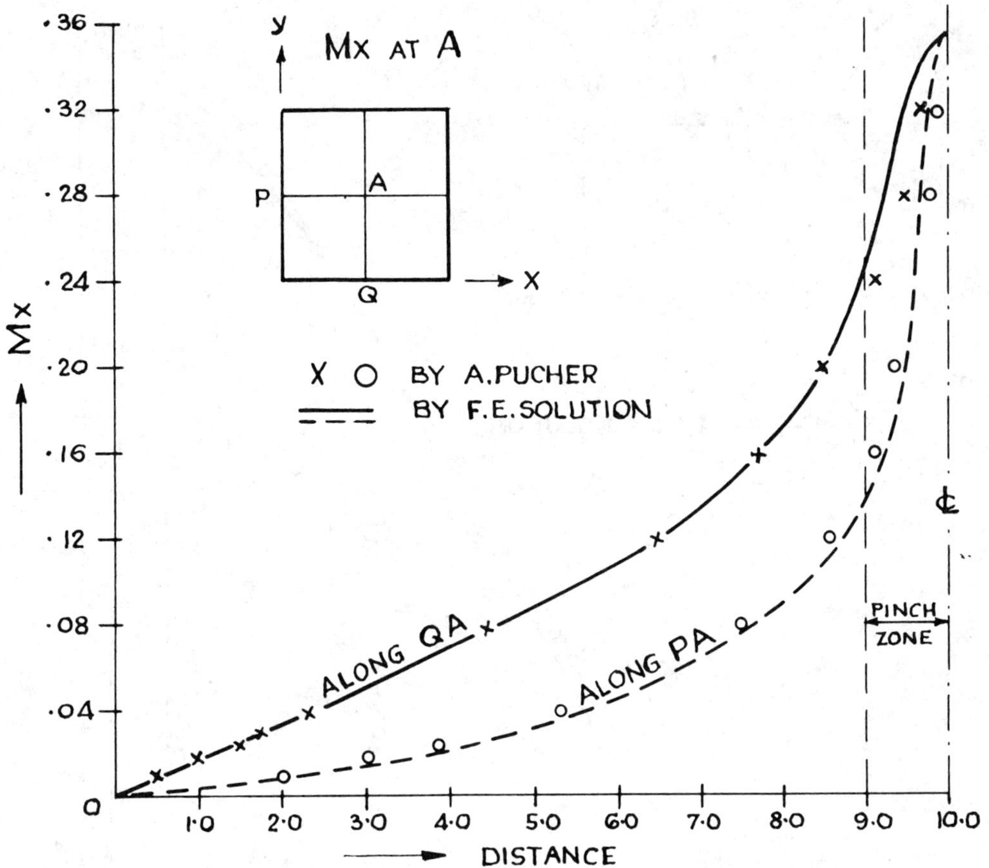

FIG.4. ISOTROPIC SIMPLY SUPPORTED SQUARE PLATE: Mx AT CENTRE.

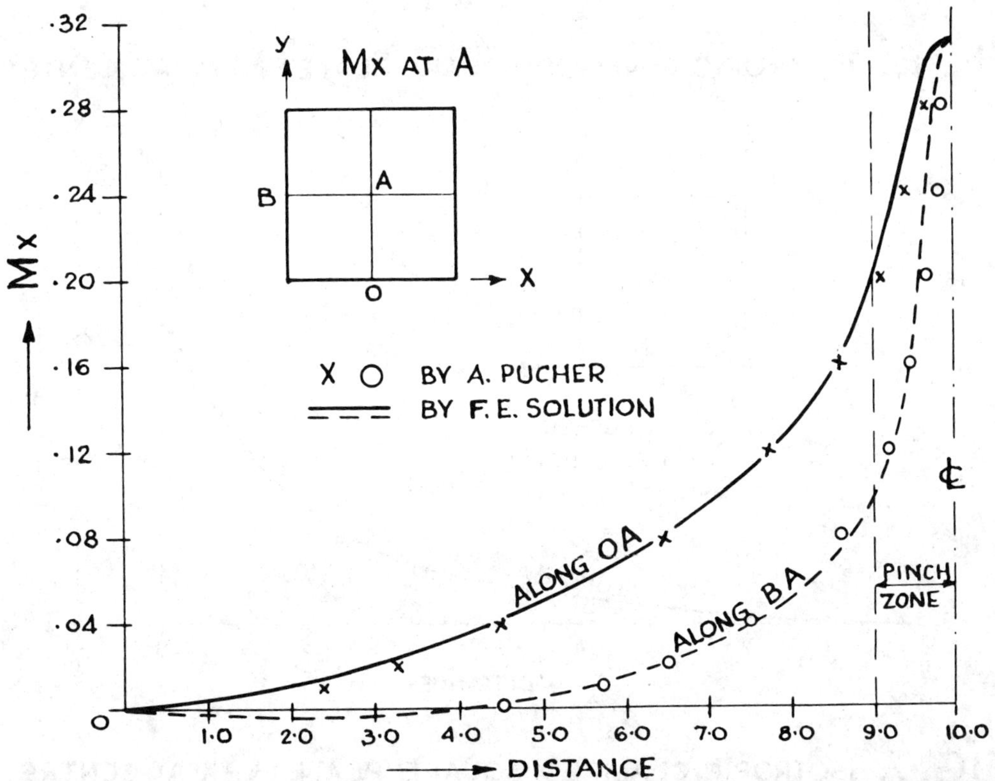

FIG. 5. ISOTROPIC CLAMPED SQUARE PLATE: Mx AT CENTRE.

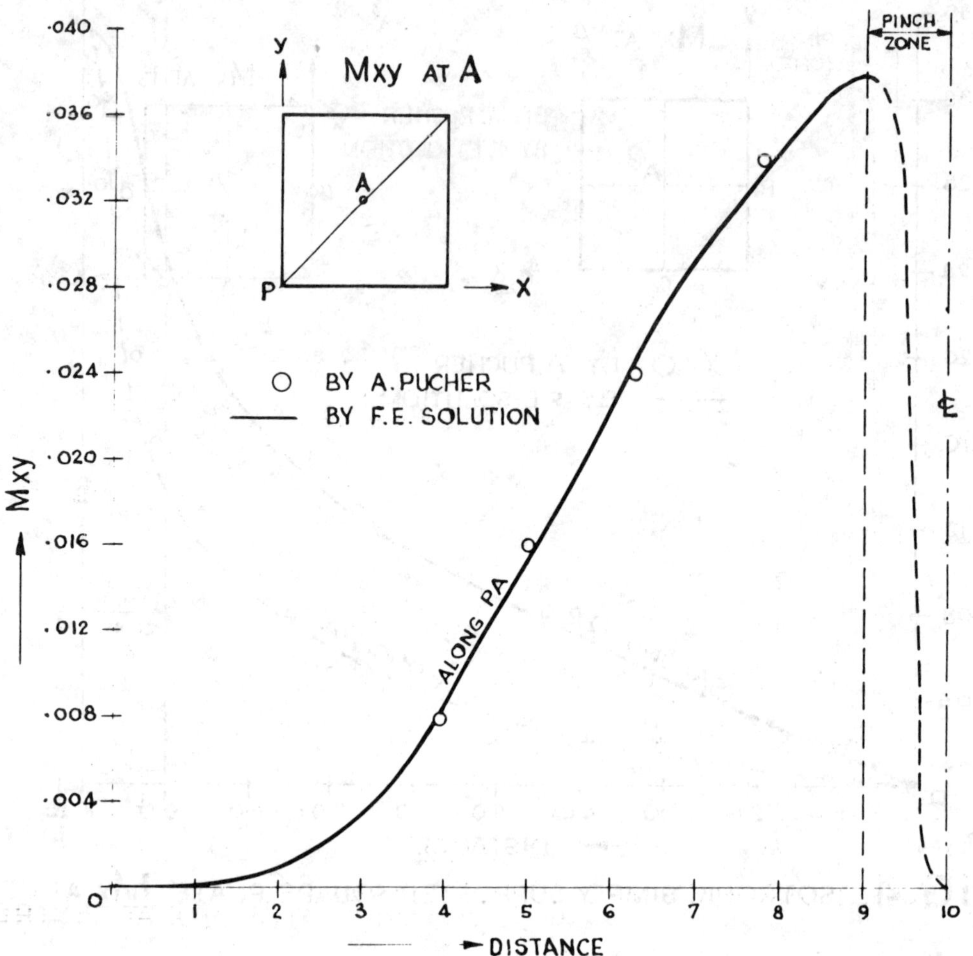

FIG. 6. ISOTROPIC CLAMPED SQUARE PLATE : Mxy AT CENTRE.

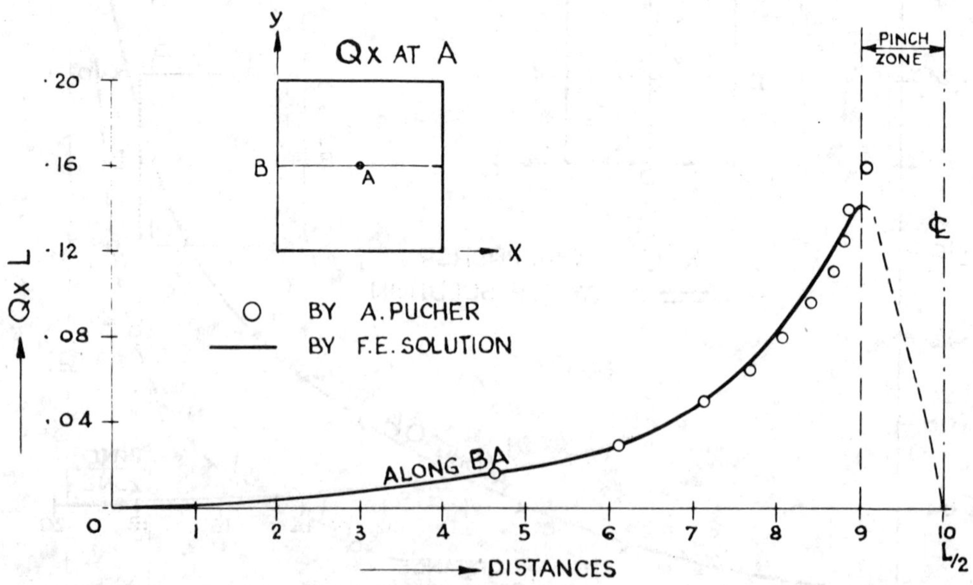

FIG. 7. ISOTROPIC CLAMPED SQUARE PLATE : Qx AT CENTRE.

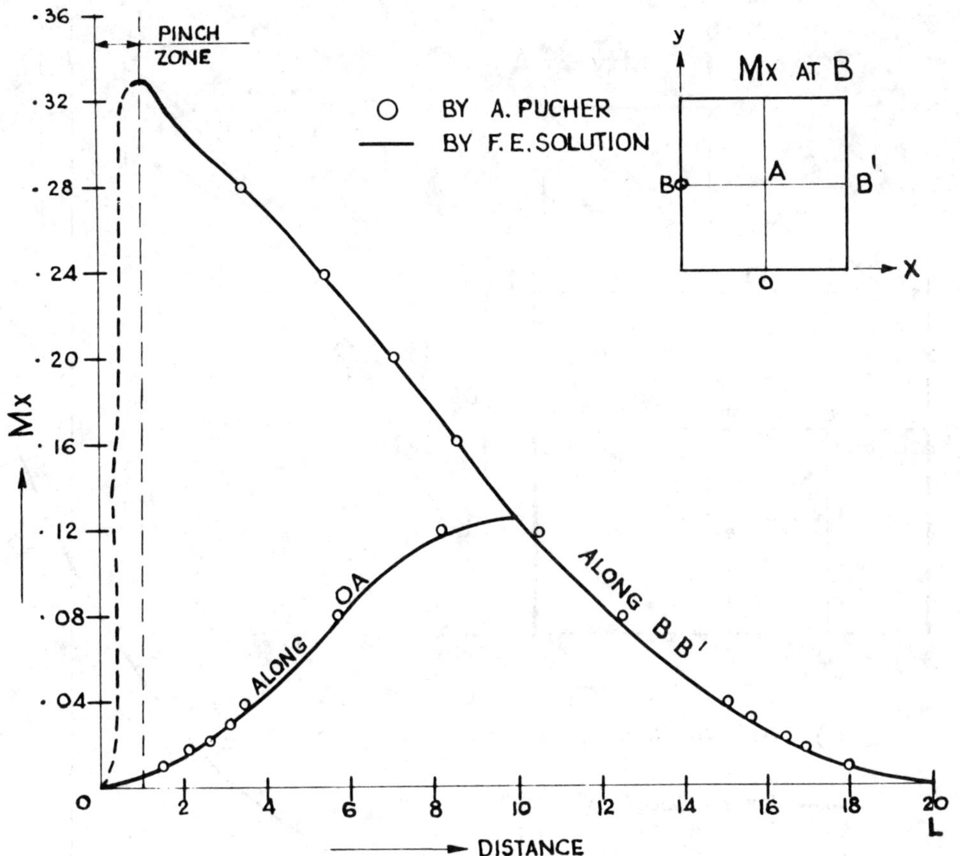

FIG. 8. ISOTROPIC CLAMPED SQUARE PLATE: Mx AT CENTRE OF EDGE.

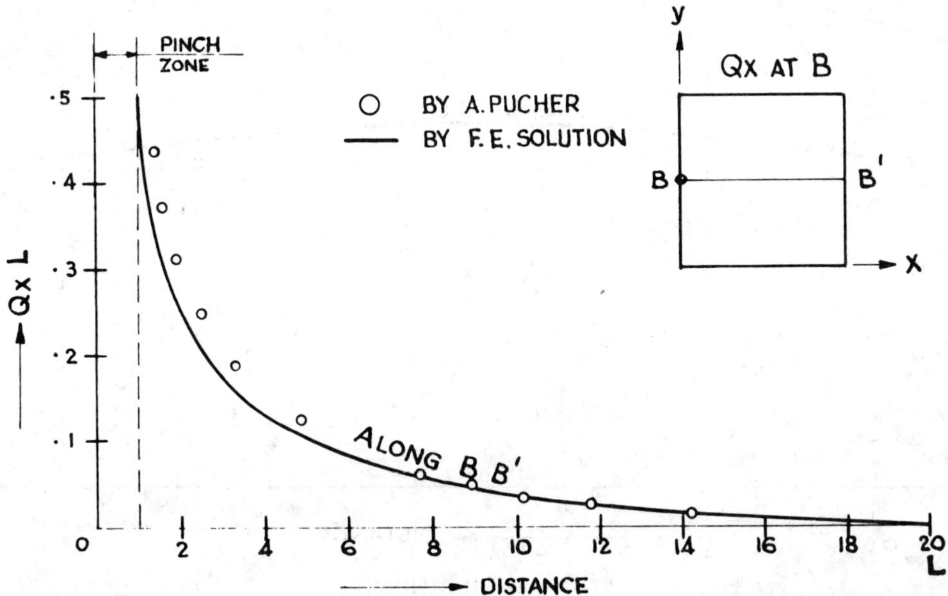

FIG. 9. ISOTROPIC CLAMPED SQUARE PLATE Qx AT CENTRE OF EDGE.

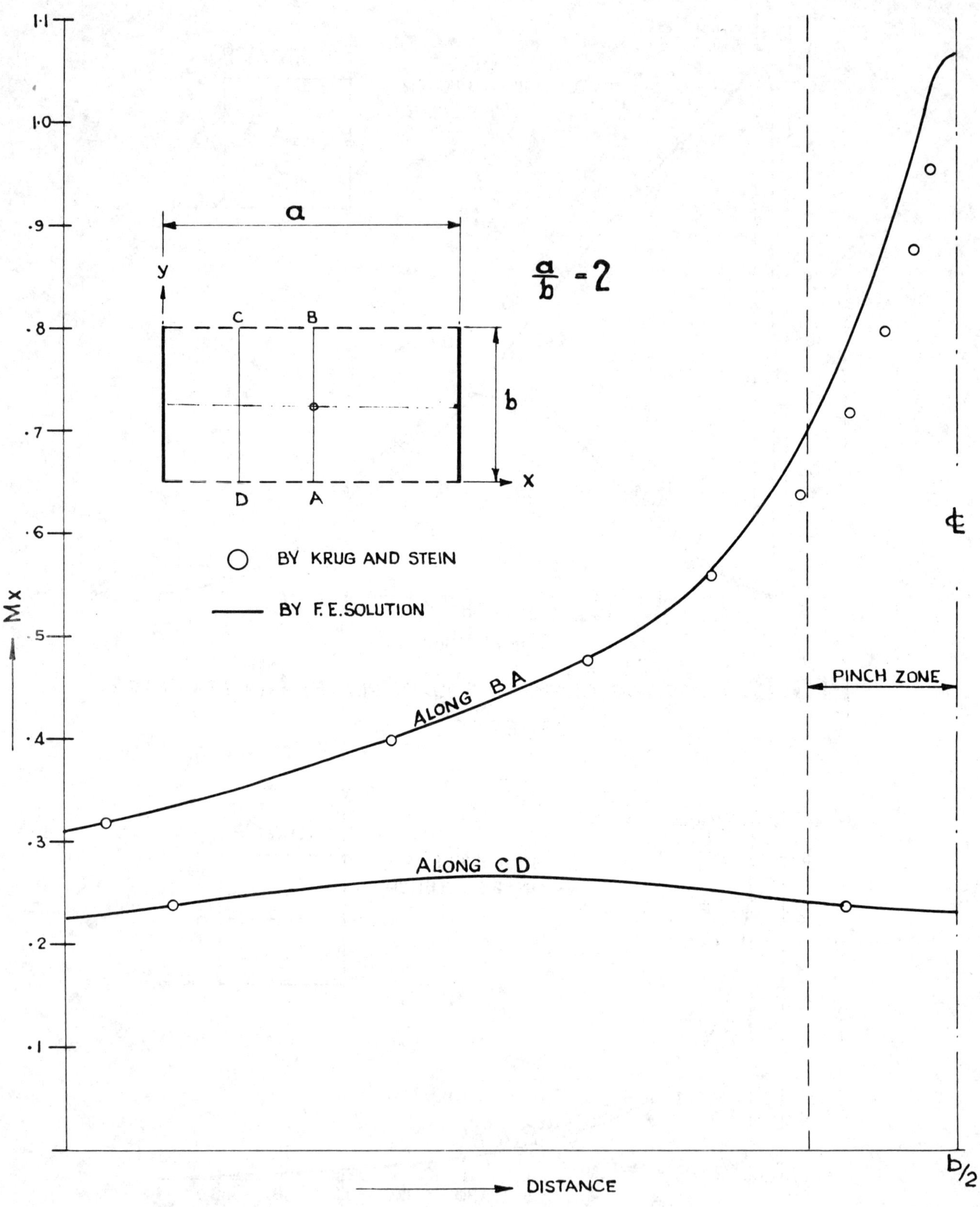

FIG. 10. ORTHOTROPIC RECTANGULAR PLATE: Mx AT CENTRE.

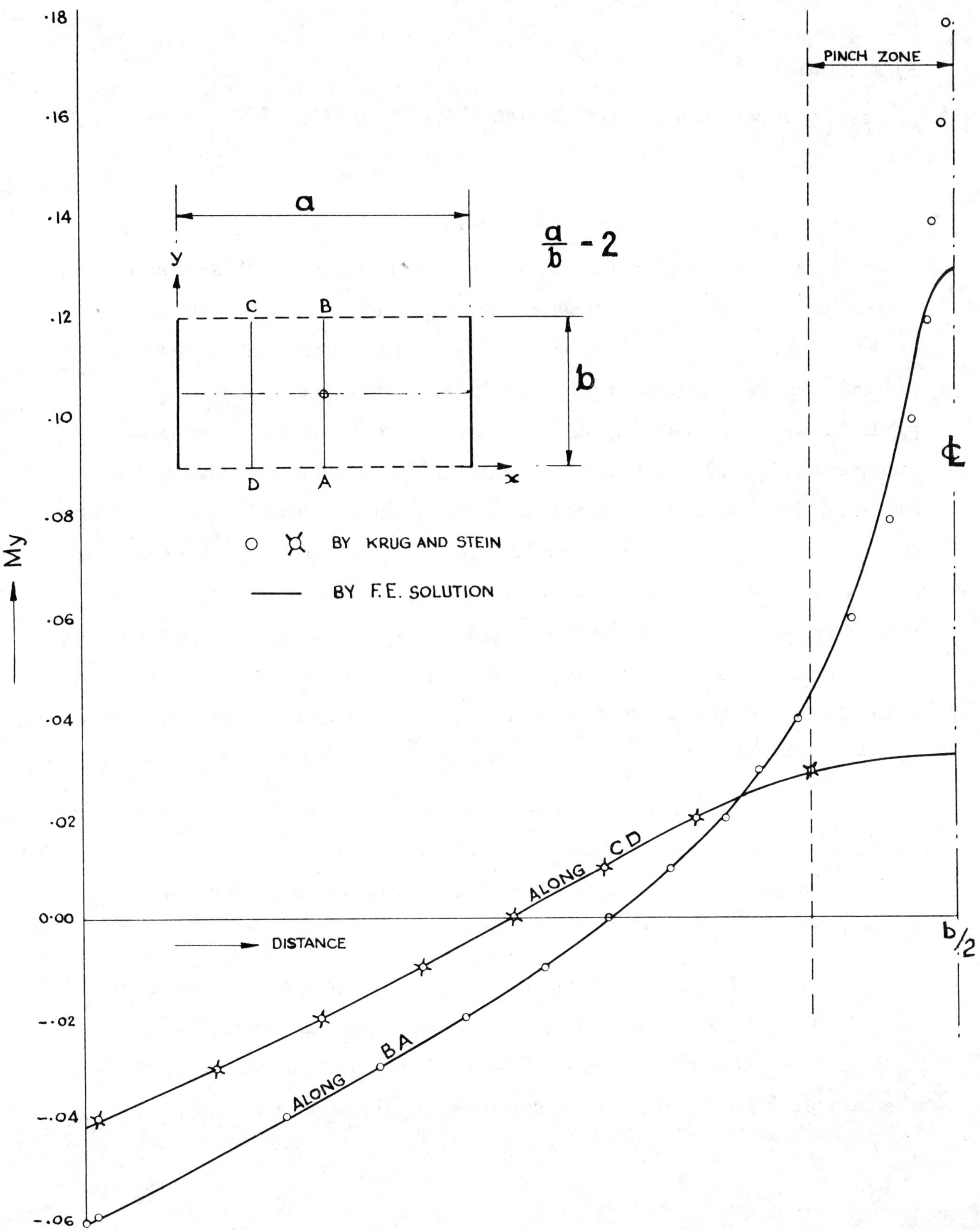

FIG. 11. ORTHOTROPIC RECTANGULAR PLATE: MY AT CENTRE.

DISCUSSION

By F. SAWKO

Professor, Department of Civil Engineering, University of Liverpool

I would like to appeal to the organisers of this Conference to publish its proceedings as soon as possible. With an increasing number of these conferences, it is quite impossible to attend them all, especially for those of us working in the academic life. There is an ever increasing danger that important developments presented as papers in conferences where proceedings are not subsequently published can be overlooked by other research workers, and this paper is an example in point. The method for obtaining influence surfaces for slab bridges outlined by Drs. Nayah and Davies is identical to that developed by my co-worker, Dr. Cope, and myself four years ago and presented at an International Conference on the Use of Computers in Structural Engineering, at Newcastle, England, in September 1966. Figures 1 and 2 are reproduced diagrams from the original paper. I must say immediately that this does not detract anything from the value of the present paper, but rather reinforces the old saying that "great minds think alike".

The next three figures show influence surfaces for skew plates obtained using the same method. These surfaces derived using the program developed by Dr. Cope and myself, are compared with experimental results of Rusch and Hergenroder.

The origin of all these developments can in fact be traced to my paper entitled "Determination of Influence Lines and Surfaces by Electronic Computer" published in The Structural Engineer in August 1964, when I demonstrated that it is possible to develop an influence surface of a grillage by determining its deformation under a set of concentrated nodal loads. The elevation of the deformed grillage above datum gave the required influence surface. An extension of the basic method to finite elements was an extension of this concept to two dimensional elements.

I would finally like to ask Drs. Nayah and Davies how much use have practising engineers made of the finite element influence surfaces program for bridge design? In my experience, influence lines are frequently used for design of portal type bridges but designers prefer to use direct methods of analysis rather than influence surfaces in design to two dimensional structures. In my opinion, one advantage of influence surfaces is that they form a permanent record of the behaviour of the bridge and subsequent loading cases can be examined very rapidly without having to reanalyse the complete structure. This is important in cases of very heavy abnormal loading and I have recently had the task of investigating the carrying capacity of existing bridge under a 400 ton vehicle train. If influence surfaces were available, this task would have reduced to simple arithmetic.

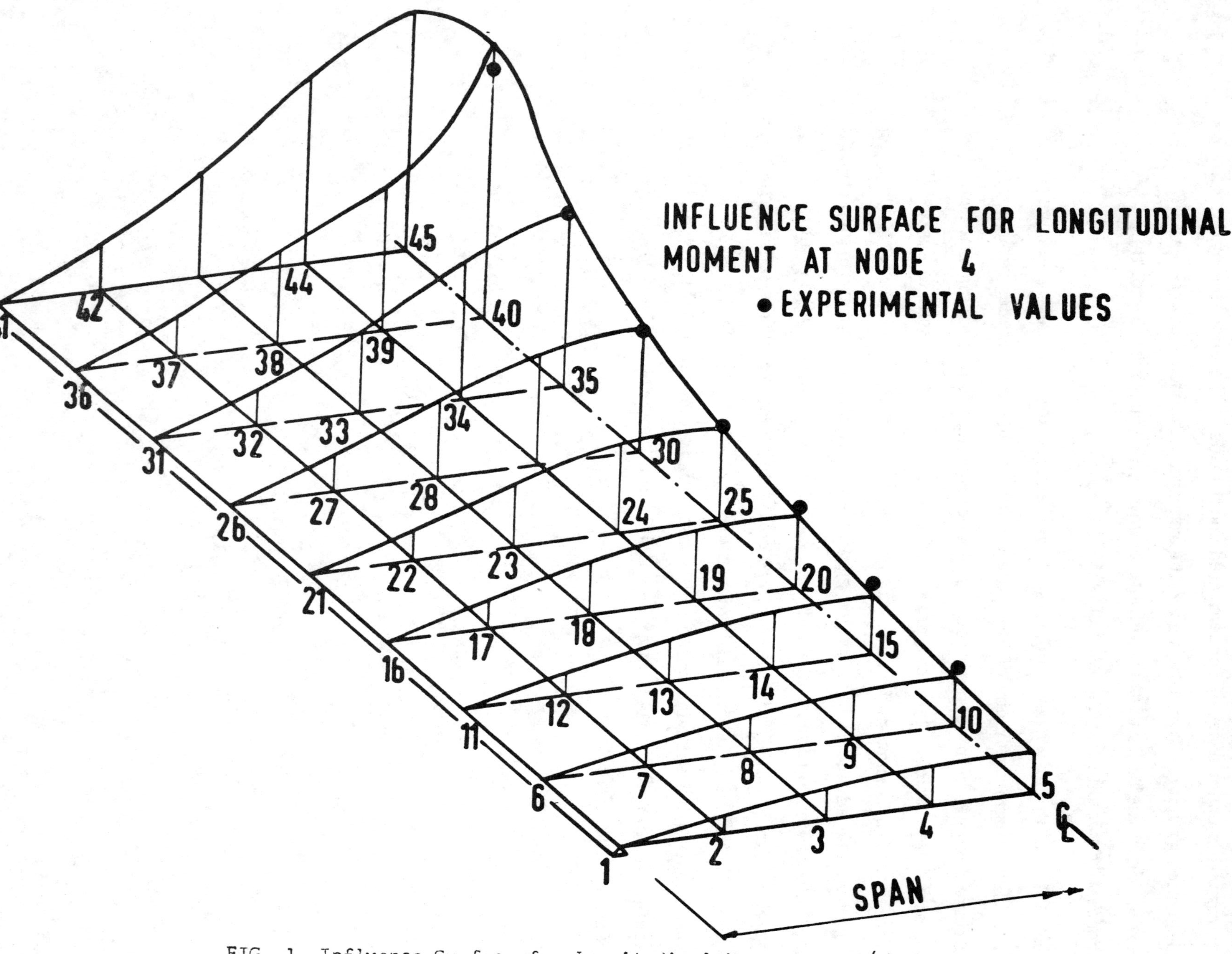

FIG 1 Influence Surface for Longitudinal Moments at 3/4b for the Square Bridge

INFLUENCE SURFACE FOR TRANSVERSE MOMENT
AT NODE 25
• EXPERIMENTAL VALUES

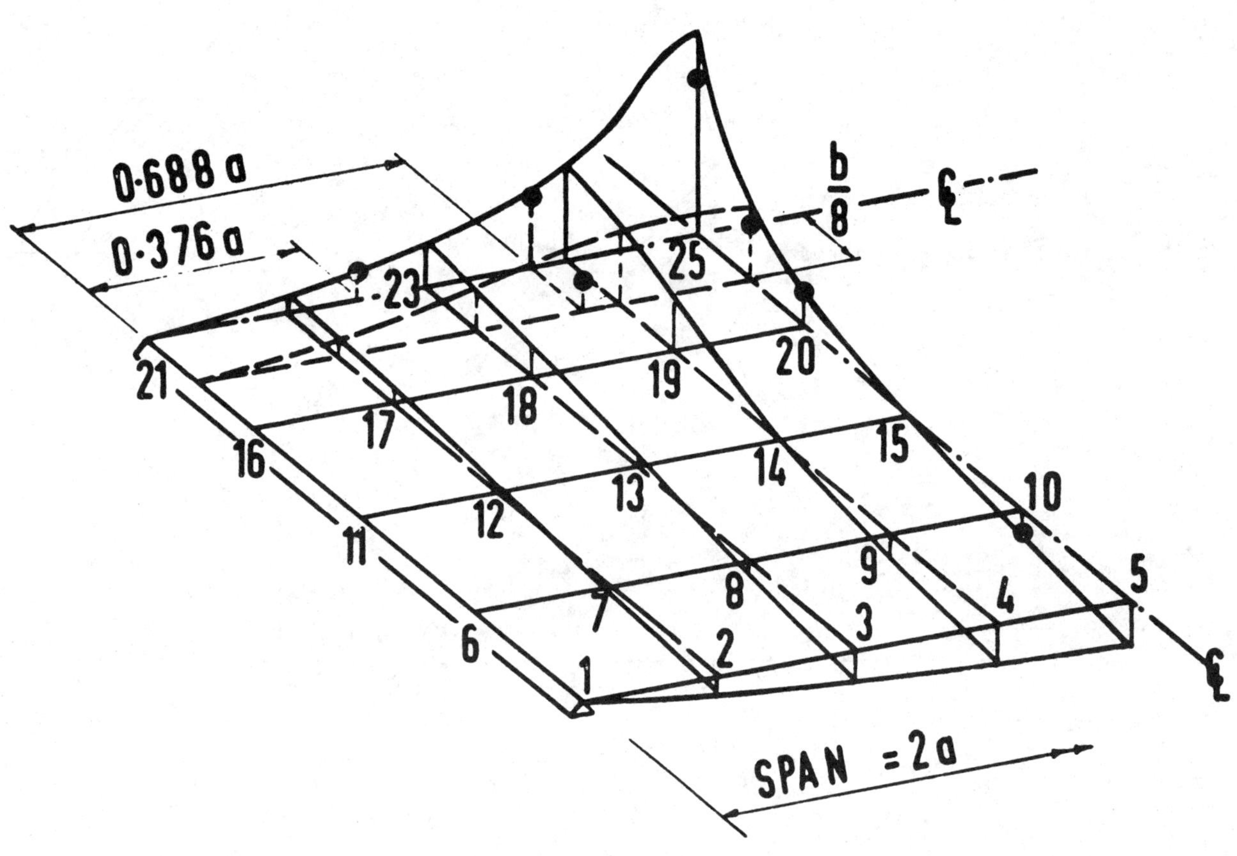

FIG 2

Influence Surface for Transverse Moments at the Centre of the Square Bridge Deck

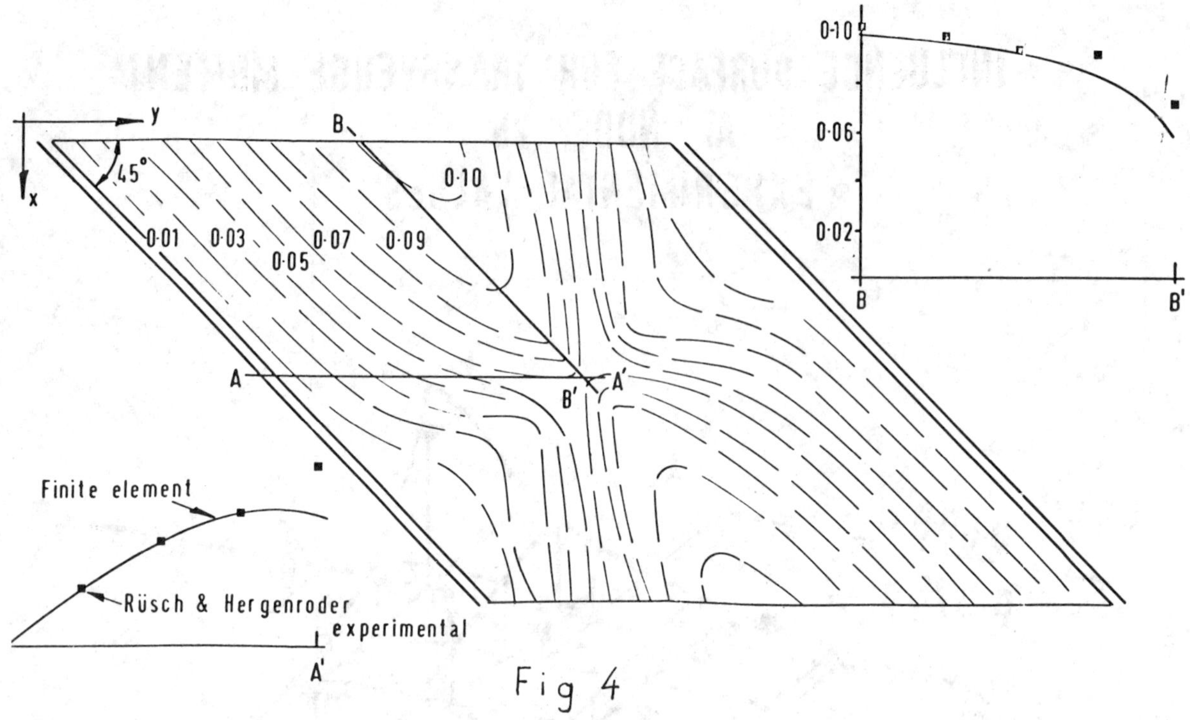
y
x
45°
B
0·10
0·01
0·03
0·05
0·07
0·09
A
A'
B'
Finite element
Rüsch & Hergenroder
experimental
A'
0·10
0·06
0·02
B
B'

Fig 4

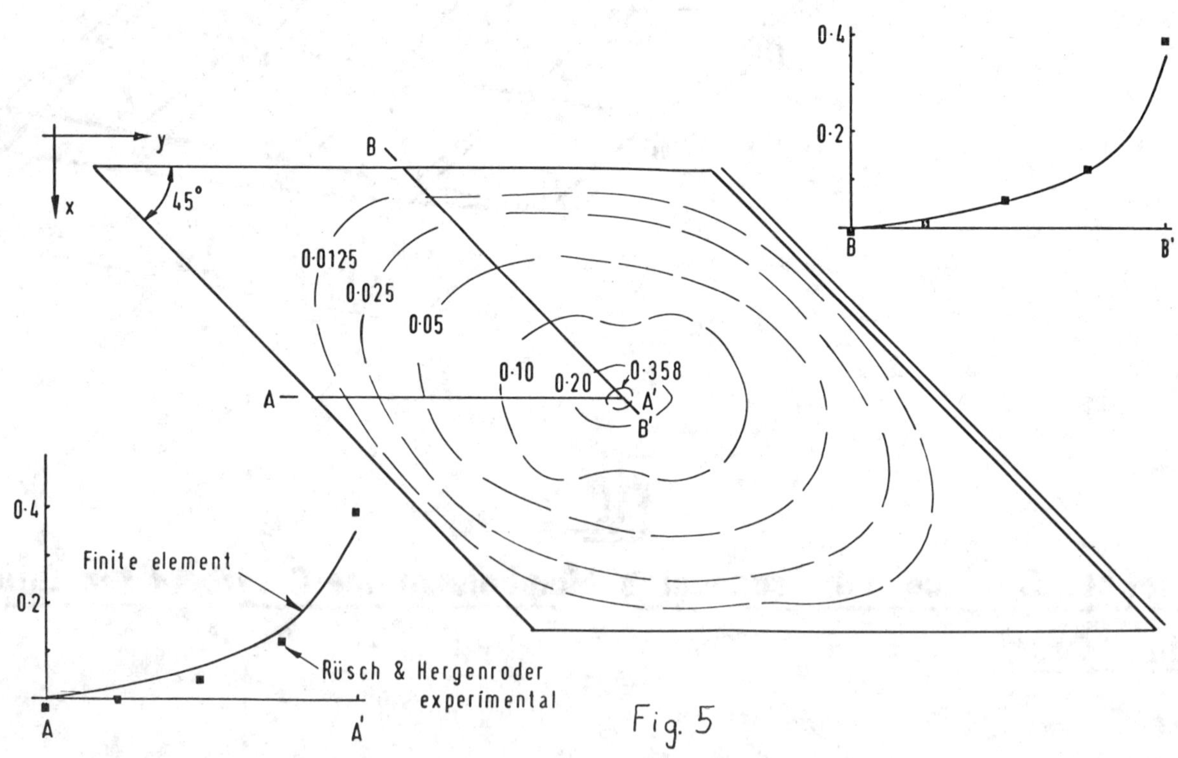
y
x
45°
B
0·0125
0·025
0·05
0·10
0·20
0·358
A
A'
B'
0·4
0·2
B
B'
0·4
0·2
Finite element
Rüsch & Hergenroder
experimental
A
A'

Fig. 5

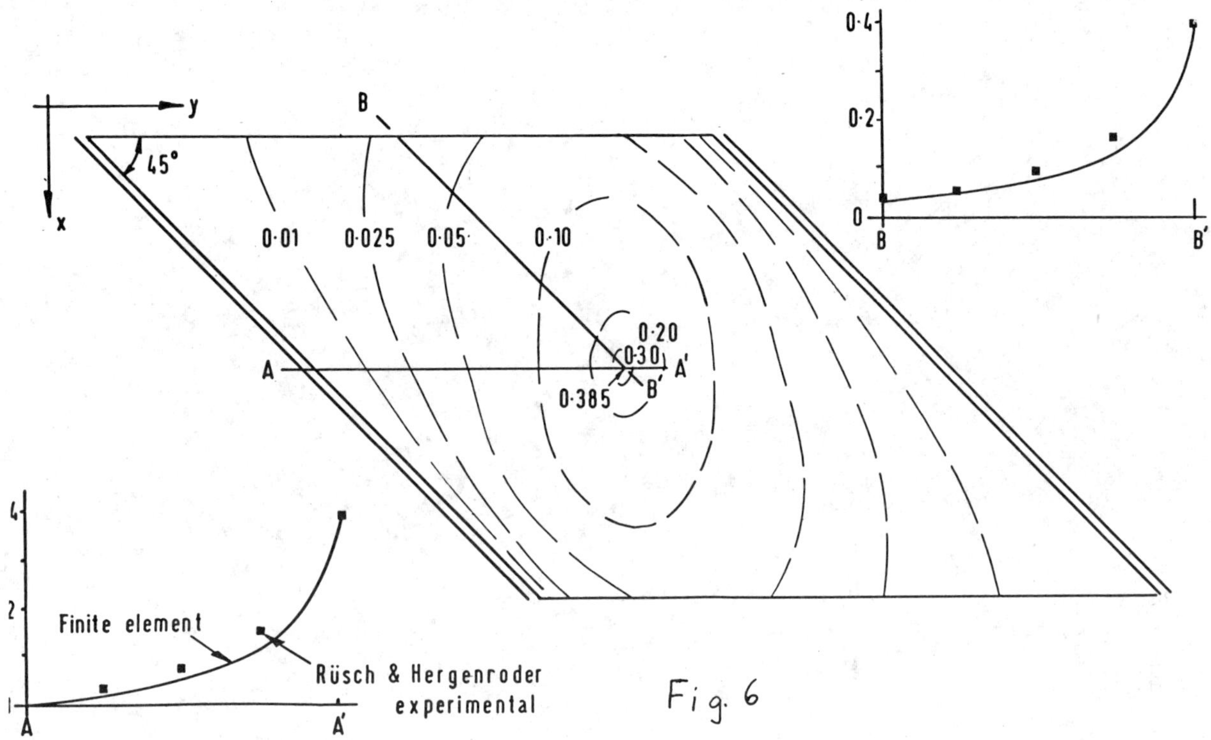
y
x
45°
B
0·01
0·025
0·05
0·10
0·20
0·30
0·385
A
A'
B'
0·4
0·2
0
B
B'
4
2
1
Finite element
Rüsch & Hergenroder experimental
A
A'

Fig. 6

FINITE ELEMENT PROGRAMS FOR SLAB BRIDGE DESIGN

By MALCOLM R. DOUGLAS, CHANDRAKANT J. PAREKH, and OLGIERD C. ZIENKIEWICZ

SYNOPSIS

A successful computer program for the solution of plate problems - such as one based on the finite element idealization - can provide a basis for the design of slab bridge decks. Much additional work must be done before a fully streamlined program suitable for design work is practicable.

First, the approximations involved in the solution or in its basic assumptions must be reconciled with practical demands. The interpretation of concentrated loads and stresses near columnar heads falls in this category.

Second, input to the program must be organized in the simplest possible manner to expedite its use.

Third, quick and efficient means must be developed for processing the output so that design changes may be readily executed.

The paper deals with the three aspects of the problem.

Keywords: bending moments; bridge decks; bridges (structures); computer programs; concrete slabs; finite element method; matrix methods; reinforced concrete; stresses; structural analysis.

M. R. DOUGLAS is the senior engineer of R. Travers Morgan and Partners, a consulting engineering firm in London.

C. J. PAREKH is research assistant in civil engineering at the University of Wales, Swansea. He has made a special study of the development of complete solution systems based on the finite element technique. These embrace plane stress/strain, plate and shell problems and much of the data preparation and processing can now be handled automatically by special input/output programs. Mr. Parekh has also studied general transient phenomena.

O. C. ZIENKIEWICZ is professor of civil engineering at the University of Wales, Swansea. He has made a special study of the applications of numerical methods in engineering science and is the author of the standard textbook describing the finite element method of analysis. He holds the D.Sc. degree of London University and is the author of some 80 scientific papers. Prior to his appointment to Head of Department at Swansea, Professor Zienkiewicz taught at Northwestern University, United States, and Edinburgh University, Scotland.

1. INTRODUCTION

The finite element method provides today the most powerful tool for the computer solution of complex structural problems. (1) Plate problems may be solved, more or less efficiently, with many of the finite element formulations available. Some of these are discussed in reference 1 and a variety of papers dealing with alternate elements is given in the Proceedings of the 1st and 2nd Conference on Matrix Methods at Wright Patterson Air Force Base (2)(3). Some very elaborate and accurate elements have been presented recently (4)(5).

None of these solutions are however any more accurate than the basic assumptions on which they are founded. All presume elastic thin plate behaviour and are therefore subject to the limitation of this theory as applied to real bridge situations, where the term 'flat plate' refers to concrete decks of uniform thickness and voided slabs or sandwich construction.

In this paper therefore a simple element is used in the basic program as it has been verified that sufficiently accurate solutions are obtainable with the element subdivision required for adequate geometrical description of the problem. This element introduced in ref.(1) and (2) is 'tested' with respect to its accuracy in representing ideal bridge slab situations in reference (6); nevertheless some special problems encountered in bridge engineering require more attention. Two such problems are the interpretation of concentrated load actions and the treatment of thick columns.

As the program is based on thin plate theory which inevitably under a concentrated load produces infinite stresses in the exact solution (and large ones in finite element approximations) it is necessary to provide suitable means of interpretation for practical engineering purposes. Near thick columns, again, the basic assumptions of plate theory fail. The situation is three dimensional and it is necessary to devise 'artifices' to deal with the restraint imposed by the column. Some conclusions of an exhaustive investigation of these two aspects are discussed in Part II of this paper.

Turning now our attention to the 'mechanics' of finite element computer usage further points arise. General finite element programs have an extremely wide field of applicability and if written in a computer 'system' provide a variety of elements subject to very general input and output specification. The plate subsystem must be capable of dealing with slab/beam combinations of elements covering all possible geometric forms and producing all possible variants of output.

The inevitable penalty of such generalities is (a) the need to specify fully the element geometry loading, and boundary condition, involving a large volume of input data and (b) a voluminous output of information. Both these aspects make it difficult for an engineer to apply such programs to mundane, everyday, situations. Thus attention has to be given to the production of:

1. input processing subprograms which are specific to typical bridge work and therefore allow minimum data specification; and

2. output processing subprograms which 'digest' the information produced and take the engineer as close as possible to the design decision.

Parts III and IV of this paper deal specifically with these two aspects in some detail. The basic, middle part of the program is part of a general finite element system developed at the Centre of Numerical Methods of the Civil Engineering Department, Swansea, this system being known as FESS (Finite Element Solution System).

The input and output stages as well as an intensive investigation of use of such programs in the context of bridge analysis are presented in a report to the Ministry of Transport (U.K.) who sponsored part of the research.(7)

II. CONCENTRATED LOADS AND COLUMN SUPPORTS

2.1 Concentrated Loads

Whenever a 'point' load acts on a slab then, according to plate theory, infinite bending moments will be produced while deflexions still remain finite (8). Clearly no numerical discrete approximation will be capable of dealing with such a singularity. The finite element method itself is unable to give this 'exact' solution for moments under the 'point' load but it enables the support and load conditions to be simulated more realistically than was hitherto possible.

In practice the concept of the 'point' load must be interpreted in terms of the finite area of contact of the load. In bridge design the most concentrated load used is a wheel load although a theoretical point load is of use in drawing influence surfaces. The British Standard Specification (9) of a wheel load has a contact area 15in. × 3in. which carries a load of 11 1/4 tons. The load is dispersed through the asphalt surfacing and the actual contact area at the surface of structural concrete will be larger (approximately 24in. × 12in.).

Westergaard (10) investigated the problem of contact area under concentrated loads and has shown by a three dimensional analysis that the ordinary flexural theory of slabs applies with satisfactory accuracy except for the purpose of expressing the stresses produced by a concentrated load in its immediate vicinity and that the maximum tensile stress at the bottom of the slab directly under a concentrated load may be found using the normal theory of thin plates if an equivalent contact area is used. The values of the bending moments computed have to be interpreted as equivalent moments for the calculation of tensile stresses in the face of the slab remote from the load. Kist and Bouma (11) carried out extensive tests on model slabs subjected to concentrated loads and have verified these conclusions.

If the moment values under 'point' loads obtained from the finite element analysis compare with the experimental and Westergaard's theoretical results, then these values will be sufficiently accurate for normal bridge design purposes.

The first comparative example chosen here is the Niester Bridge. A glass model of the structure was tested by Krebs, Mehmel and Bretthauer (12) who also analysed it by an iterative mathematical solution. Fig.1 shows the geometrical details and the finite element subdivisions used. The results of the model tests and the mathematical solutions were presented in the form of five influence surfaces. The agreement between these two sets of results and the finite element analysis is generally good (7) except when the load is placed over the position at which the moments are being measured. In these cases the moment values at the node fall well below the model results.

At this stage a comment on the evaluation of moments in the finite element analysis becomes necessary. The triangular plate bending element used in the basic finite element program is one of the 'lowest' members of element order possible. As such it endeavours to represent the average moment values over its area rather than to follow these by a linear variation. For this reason, the moment values are computed for the centroid of each triangular element and subsequently processed to compute the moment values of nodes by averaging the centroidal values of adjacent elements. This process will however have one considerable disadvantage. For a point singularity the nodal average will underestimate the values due its inability to 'extrapolate'. In order to obtain reliable moment values under the 'point' load (applied at a node) two techniques are proposed:

1. If the moment values at the centroids of the triangular elements adjacent to a line which passes through the loaded point are plotted, the moment value under the 'point' load can be extrapolated. Fig.2 (b) and (c) shows a plot of moment values at the centroids along line AA. Moment

values at the centroids of opposite triangles averaged on the base line BB are plotted in Fig.2 (e) and (f). In either case the extrapolated moment values are within 8% of the model results.

2. If the deflections at the node points are known, a numerical finite difference expression may be used to evaluate the moment values under the loaded point.

A rectangular finite difference mesh is shown superimposed on pact of the finite element mesh in Fig.2 (d). The finite difference expressions for moment values at node 72 are given by:

$$M_{x72} = D\left[\frac{(W_{85} - 2W_{72} + W_{59})}{\Delta x^2} + \mu\frac{(W_M - 2W_{72} + W_N)}{\Delta y^2}\right] \qquad (1)$$

and

$$M_{y72} = D\left[\frac{(W_M - 2W_{72} + W_N)}{\Delta y^2} + \mu\frac{(W_{85} - 2W_{72} + W_{59})}{\Delta x^2}\right] \qquad (2)$$

The moment values at node 72 evaluated using these expressions are within 3% to 9% of the model results.

The second test example investigated was an 'infinitely' wide simply supported slab. For comparison, now, the structure was also analysed using Westergaard's solutions for different wheel contact areas. Fig.3 shows the geometrical details and the finite element subdivisions used. The slab was analysed for nodal point loads at the centre and at positions 4ft. and 12ft. from the centre as shown in Fig.3.

In Fig.4 a comparison of the two solutions is given. The agreement between the two results is generally good up to about 4ft. from the point load.

Within this local region, Westergaard's solution for a contact area equal to 4 times the corresponding finite element mesh area, gives the same peak moment value under the load as the finite element nodal average moment value using a point load.

As before, the moment value averaged at the node fails to predict the true peak moment for a concentrated load at the loaded node. To get a better estimate of this value the two techniques outlined earlier need be applied. Both of these techniques give results which are equivalent to Westergaard's solution for a contact area approximately equal to the corresponding finite element mesh area.

The variation in position of the point load across the span does not effect these differences between the finite element and Westergaard's solutions, as can be seen in Fig.4.

A bridge designer working to British Standard 153 (9) is involved with the effects of a number of wheel loads on a slab. To examine the likely error in using the finite element moment values averaged at the nodes for combined wheel loads, a 120ft. wide and 40ft. span slab was analysed. An 11 1/4ton wheel load being placed as a nodal point load in twelve different positions. Fig.4 shows the finite element subdivisions and the load positions used. The structure was also analysed using Westergaard's solution for a contact area approximately equal to the corresponding finite element mesh area.

Fig.5 shows the precentage difference between the two solutions for the moments under different wheels calculated for different combinations of the wheel loads. When only one wheel is considered the moment value under the wheel obtained from the finite element nodal averages is 20% to 35%

below the Westergaard's solution, but this error decreases as the number of wheels increases and for more than 6 wheels it is less than 10%. It is thus concluded that when analysing a slab carrying the abnormal 16 wheeled vehicle (9) the moment values averaged at the nodes will be accurate for normal design purposes, presuming the size of the finite element mesh to be roughly comparable to the Westergaard distribution area.

2.2. Column Supports

The dimensions of column supports are frequently of the same order as the slab thickness. In idealising such a case the engineers is apt to assume a 'point' support to a slab. However, as it was seen in the previous section, difficulties arise immediately: The clasical plate theory gives infinite bending moments under the 'point' singularity although the deformations remain finite. The obvious solution is to assume that the column reaction is distributed over a finite area and to include this area in the calculation. The local problem of a column head is three-dimensional;

Footnote

The "Westergaard Equivalent Area" is given by:

$$C_1 = 2\left(\sqrt{0.4c^2 + h^2} - 0.675h\right) \quad \text{if } c \leqslant 3.45h$$

or $$C_1 = c \quad \text{if } c > 3.45h$$

where h is the thickness of slab and c is the diameter of the actual contact area.

however the techniques now suggested have been satisfactorily used to idealise the situation in the two-dimensional analysis.

A large column may be represented by a set of boundary conditions imposed on the slab and the column dimensions are an important factor in deciding these conditions. The freedom of the slab to deflect over the region of the column head (where it is in fact supported) may be modified by either of the following methods:

1. The column head is simulated by thickening the slab elements immediately over the column with the support stiffness concentrated at the centre of the column. The choice of thickness for the elements over the column head is quite arbitrary and a factor of four times the deck thickness is suggested by tests; or

2. The support stiffness is distributed between the corner and centre nodes of the column head. The distribution is such that the overall force/ deflection relationship for the column is satisfied. The vertical stiffness is distributed to each of the corner nodes whereas the rotational stiffnesses are associated with the centre node. The elastic coupling effect must also be included because a rotation at the centre causes a vertical deflection at the corner nodes. A detailed derivation of these values is given in reference 7.

The first illustrative example of a region around a column analysed using these techniques is shown in Fig.6. Both methods give valid results for the moment values throughout the slab. For the thickened elements very large moments are calculated over the column head. These values are however meaningless and should be neglected. The distribution of support stiffness gives a lower peak value over the column but the once again these values are of no signifinance. At the column/slab interface both methods give comparable deflections and moments.

The comparison of the full suite of programs was completed by reference to a 22 span curved high level flyover supported on columns to be built at Queens Drive Roundabout, Nottingham. A, 1:44, scale model of part of the structure, representing four spans of the bridge, was constructed out of a unplasticized P.V.C. Darvic sheet and tested at the City University, London (7). Fig.7 shows the geometrical details, model gauge positions and finite element mesh used. The deck is of constant thickness with tapered sections on the edges. In the finite element analysis the column heads were simulated by thickening the elements and concentrating the support stiffness at the centre. Comparison of results for several loading conditions are given in reference 7 of which only two cases are shown on Fig.8. In general the agreement between the finite element moment values and the model results around the column head is good.

The actual stress distribution over the column head presents a complex, three dimensional problem and is being currently investigated in detail. It is anticipated however that the detailed reinforcement for moments at the nodes around the column head will be sufficient to deal with the stresses in the head area. Attention must however be given to some shear reinforcement - and this can be assessed from the column reactions computed.

111. INPUT SUBPROGRAM

The plate system has an extremely wide field of application covering any beam/slab combination and, because of the triangular element, any geometric shape. To cope with this generality, the input to the main analysis program has to be very basic i.e. the coordinates of each node, node connection numbers for each triangular and beam element, material properties, boundary conditions, and load data which must be in terms of point loads applied at the nodes. Thus the amount of data to be prepared and checked becomes excessive for any practical problem.

To expedite the use of the basic program as a design tool the input must be specified in a simple manner. A subprogram IPUT has been developed which will accept the minimum amount of data needed to define the problem. The program is restricted to slab bridges, or slab and beam grillages, with parallel edges which must be straight, on a circular curve, or on a spiral transition curve.

The curved high level flyover, Fig.7, serves to illustrate the main points connected with the program.

The mesh consists of two sets of lines, one parallel to the sides of the bridge and the other parallel to the abutments of the bridge if straight, or radial if the bridge is curved. These lines completely specify the geometry of the problem and should be made to coincide with carriageways, charges of section, support points etc.

The divisions across the width of the structure are defined in the input and are constant throughout the full length. The lengthwise divisions are specified separately or in regions and can vary to suit the problem. The program accepts this data and calculates the coordinates of the nodes (the intersections of the two sets of lines) and forms the triangular elements by drawing the shorter diagonal across the quadrilaterals formed by the mesh lines.

Any node point on the structure is located by specifying the two mesh lines that intersect at that point. The material properties of the slab, defined by the flexural rigidity constants, are specified by patches in which the material properties remain constant. Each material patch is thus an area of the plate, and is defined by the nodes at the ends of the forward diagonal of the patch. Similarly a load patch is used to specify an area over which a uniformly distributed load is to be applied. For example, load patch 1 in Fig.7 is defined by its starting node (i=2,g=18) and its end node (i=5, g=32). The mesh lines are referred to as i and g lines for convenience. A patch type of specification is very convenient for lane loadings. These load patches can overlap which often enables a simpler specification of the problem.

Any node can also be loaded with a point load which can, if required, be combined with patch loadings to form one load case to be analysed by the main program. Thus load cases may consist of (a) uniformly distributed load applied on load patches, (b) point loads applied at nodes, and (c) combinations of (a) and (b).

IV. OUTPUT SUBPROGRAM

The volume of results of deformations, moments and shear forces calculated in the program are almost unmanageable manually and a special output sub-program has been written to process these results and to present an envelope of maximum "design reinforcement moments" which may be used directly for detailing the reinforcement by areas.

At any point in a slab under any loading the component moments are Mx, My and Mxy. The values of these moments together with the displacements are calculated at every element centroid in the finite element analysis. For the convenience of the designer the average values at the nodes are also calculated, together with the principal moments and their directions. These are all given in the printed output from the finite element analysis program.

Once the values of Mx, My and Mxy are known at either the centroids of triangles or at the nodes, the designer must choose a suitable reinforcement pattern so that the slab resisting moments are always greater than or equal to the calculated applied moments. A number of methods have been proposed for this: we have used Wood's (13) extension of Hillerbergs (14) method to calculate the area of reinforcement required. If the reinforcement is placed parallel to the x axis and parallel to an axis at an angle α to the x axis then the basic equations are:

$$Mx^* = Mx - k\,Mxy - \cot\alpha(My.k - Mxy) \tag{3}$$

$$M_\alpha^* = \frac{1}{\sin^2\alpha}\,\frac{(Myk - Mxy)}{\cot\alpha + k} \tag{4}$$

where k is an arbitary constant which satisifies the equation:

$$\frac{(Mxy + My\cot\alpha)}{\cot\alpha + k} \leq 0 \text{ for bottom reinforcement.} \tag{5}$$

and

$$\frac{(Mxy + My\cot\alpha)}{\cot\alpha + k} \geq 0 \text{ for top reinforcement} \tag{6}$$

In a continuous structure either hogging or sagging moments may occur at a particular section depending on the loading combination.

If only tensile reinforcement is considered, then the value of k to give minimum reinforcement is given by:

$$\frac{d}{dk}\left(M_x^* + M_\alpha^*\right) = 0 \tag{7}$$

this gives a value of k

$$k = -\cot\alpha \pm \frac{1}{\sin\alpha} \tag{8}$$

A output processing sub-program has been written based on equations (3) to (8), the input to the program being the magnetic tape of nodal or centroidal forces calculated by the Finite Element Program. This output program will also combine any of the loadings, or proportion of the loading, used in the analysis. Thus it is possible to examine the effect of combining loads in different lanes on different spans, with say temperature or wind loads. The only limit on the number of different combinations being computer time.

The output program if given details of the direction in which reinforcement is to be placed in different regions of the slab will then calculate the <u>reinforcement design moments</u> for each of the specified combinations. The output program then makes a search amongst all these top and bottom steel. These results being printed out against the equivalent loading combination. This output is the envelope of maximum design moments and may be used directly to detail the reinforcement.

Footnote:

Acknowledgement is made to the Ministry of Transport, London, for permission to write this paper. Any request for program listings should be directed to the Deputy Chief Engineer (Bridges).

References:

1. O.C. Zienkiewicz and Y.K. Cheung,
"The Finite Element Method in Structural and Continuum Mechanics."
Mc Graw - Hill, London - New York 1967.

2. Proçeedings of 1st Conference on Matrix Methods in Structural Mechanics.
Wright - Patterson, Air Force Base, Ohio 1965.

3. Proceedings of 2nd Conference on Matrix Methods in Structural Mechanics.
Wright - Patterson, Air Force Base, Ohio 1968.

4. B.M. Irons
A conforming quartic triangular element for plate bending.
J. Num. Methods in Engineering Vol.1 1969.

5. K. Bell
A refined triangular plate bending finite element.
J. Num. Methods in Engineering Vol.1 1969.

6. Y.K. Cheung, I.P. King and O.C. Zienkiewicz
Slab bridges with arbitrary shape and support conditions - a general method of analysis based on finite elements.
Proc. I.C.E. Vol.40. p 9-36, London. 1968.

7. Ministry of Transport, London,
R. Travers Morgan & Partners Consulting Engineers.
Report on Slab Bridge Analysis by Computer
London, 1968.

8. S.P. Timoshenko and S. Woinowsky-Krieger
Theory of Plates and Shells, 2nd Ed.
McGraw-Hill, 1959.

9. British Standards Institution
British Standards No.153, Part 3A. Loads
London, 1954.

10. H.M. Westergaard
Computation of stresses in bridge slabs due to wheel loads.
Public Roads, Vol.11, No.1, 1930.

11. Kist and Bouma
An experimental investigation of slabs subjected to concentrated loads.
I.A.B.S.E. Vol.14, 1954.

12. A. Krebs, A. Mehmel and G. Bretthauer
Calculation of influence zones on straight and skew slab bridges.
Beton und Stahlbetonbau, Vol.59, No.11, PP 246-50, 1964.

13. R.H. Wood,
The rienforcement of slabs in accordance with a predetermined field of moments.
Concrete 1968 Vol.2(2) Feb. pp 69-76.

14. A. Hillerborg,
A plastic theory for the design of reinforced concrete slabs.
Publication of the Sixth Congress I.A.B.S.E.
Stockholm 1960.

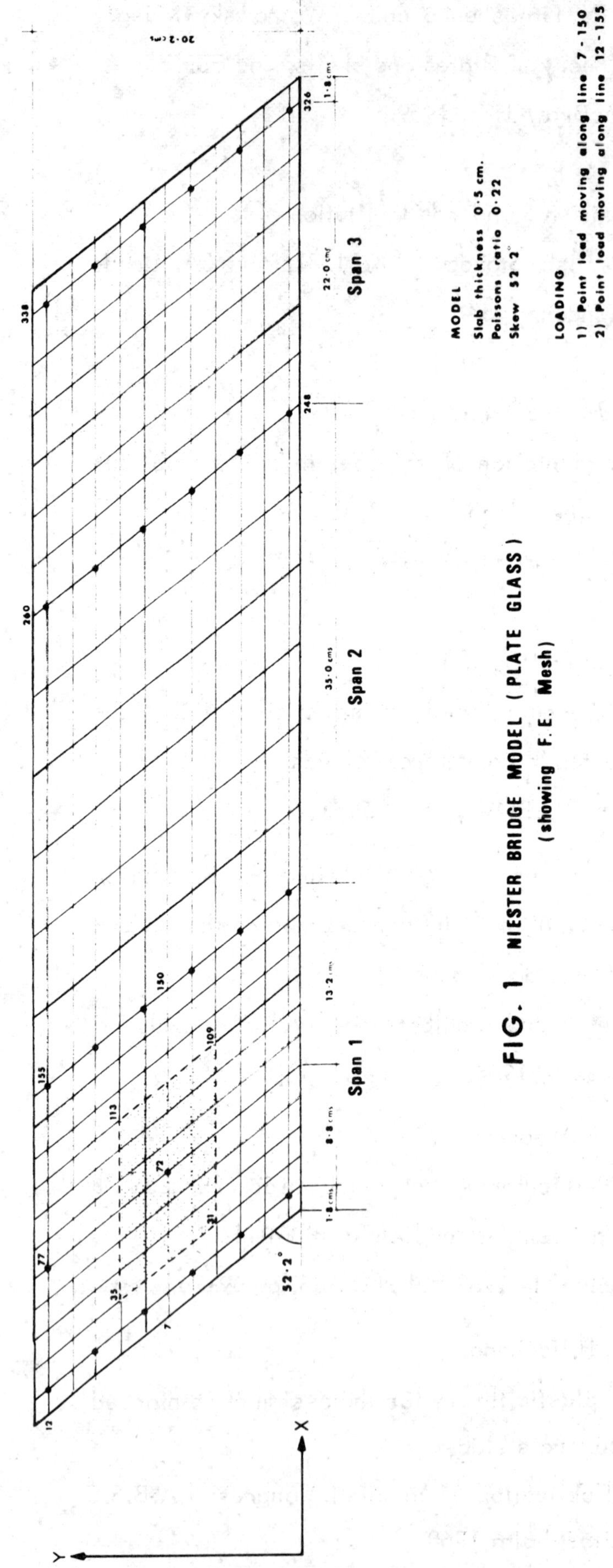

FIG. 1 NIESTER BRIDGE MODEL (PLATE GLASS)
(showing F. E. Mesh)

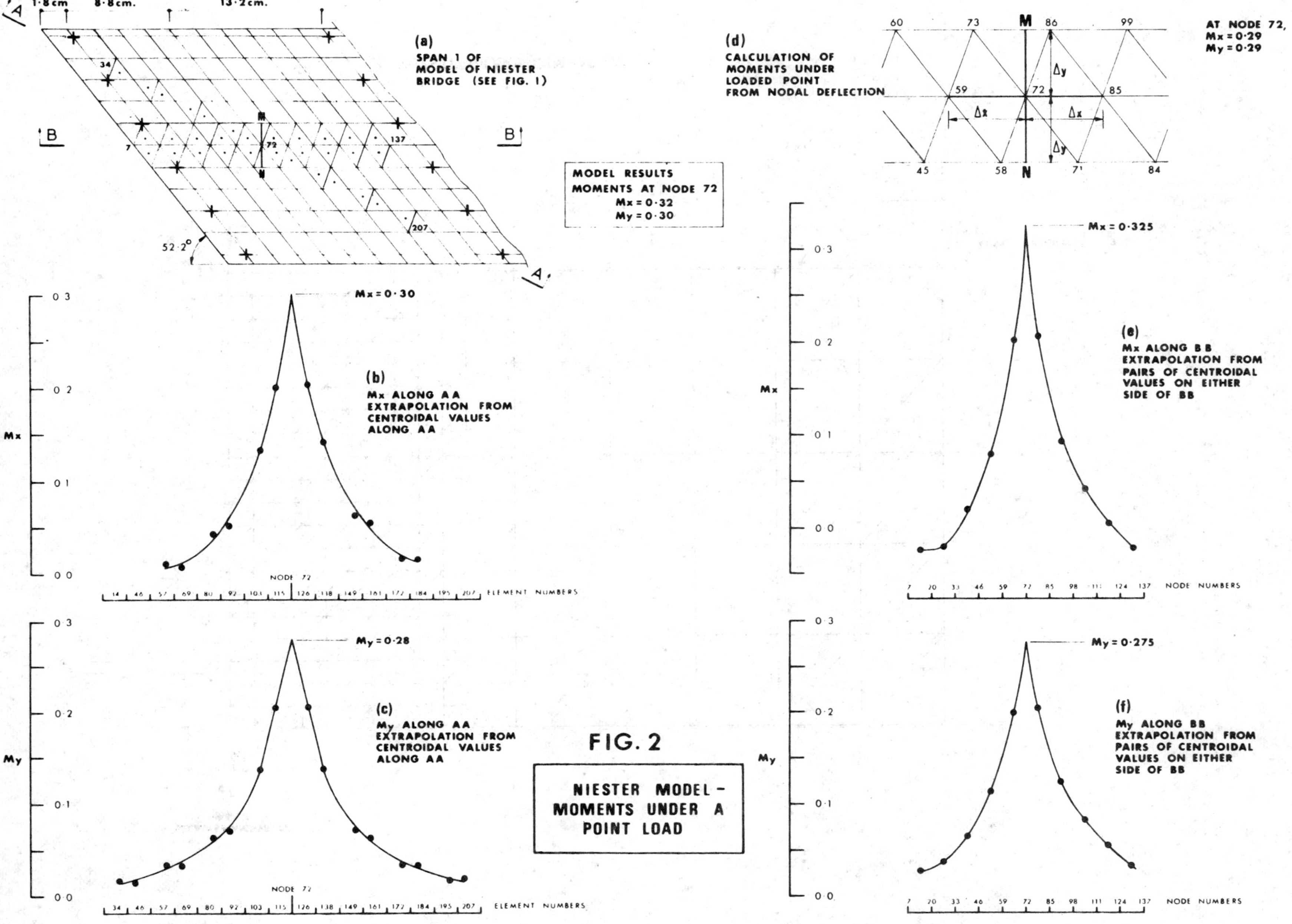
1·8 cm
8·8 cm.
13·2 cm.
(a)
SPAN 1 OF
MODEL OF NIESTER
BRIDGE (SEE FIG. 1)
52·2°
MODEL RESULTS
MOMENTS AT NODE 72
Mx = 0·32
My = 0·30
(d)
CALCULATION OF
MOMENTS UNDER
LOADED POINT
FROM NODAL DEFLECTION
AT NODE 72,
Mx = 0·29
My = 0·29
Mx = 0·30
(b)
Mx ALONG AA
EXTRAPOLATION FROM
CENTROIDAL VALUES
ALONG AA
ELEMENT NUMBERS
Mx = 0·325
(e)
Mx ALONG BB
EXTRAPOLATION FROM
PAIRS OF CENTROIDAL
VALUES ON EITHER
SIDE OF BB
NODE NUMBERS
My = 0·28
(c)
My ALONG AA
EXTRAPOLATION FROM
CENTROIDAL VALUES
ALONG AA
My = 0·275
(f)
My ALONG BB
EXTRAPOLATION FROM
PAIRS OF CENTROIDAL
VALUES ON EITHER
SIDE OF BB
NIESTER MODEL -
MOMENTS UNDER A
POINT LOAD

FIG. 2

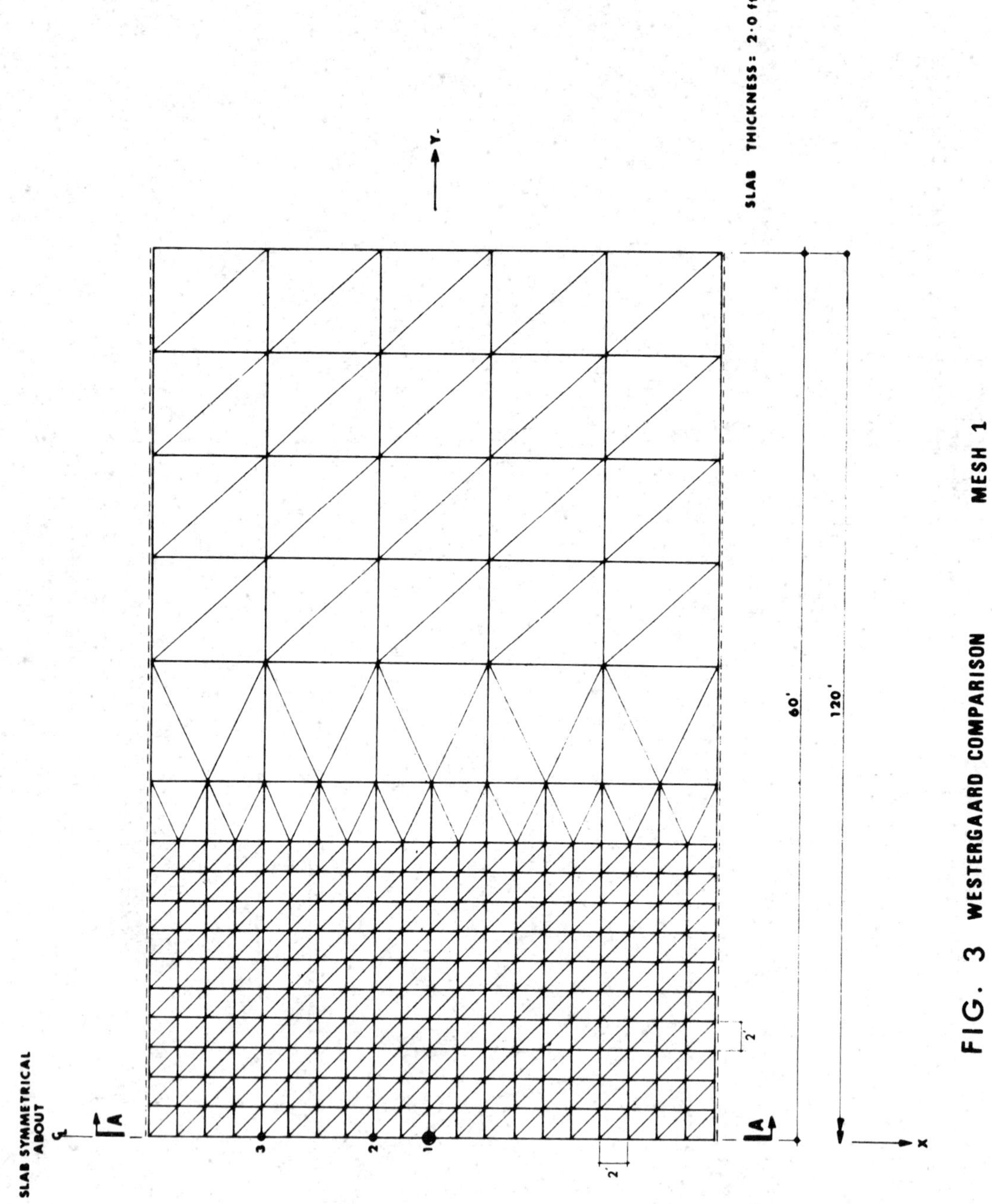

FIG. 3 WESTERGAARD COMPARISON MESH 1

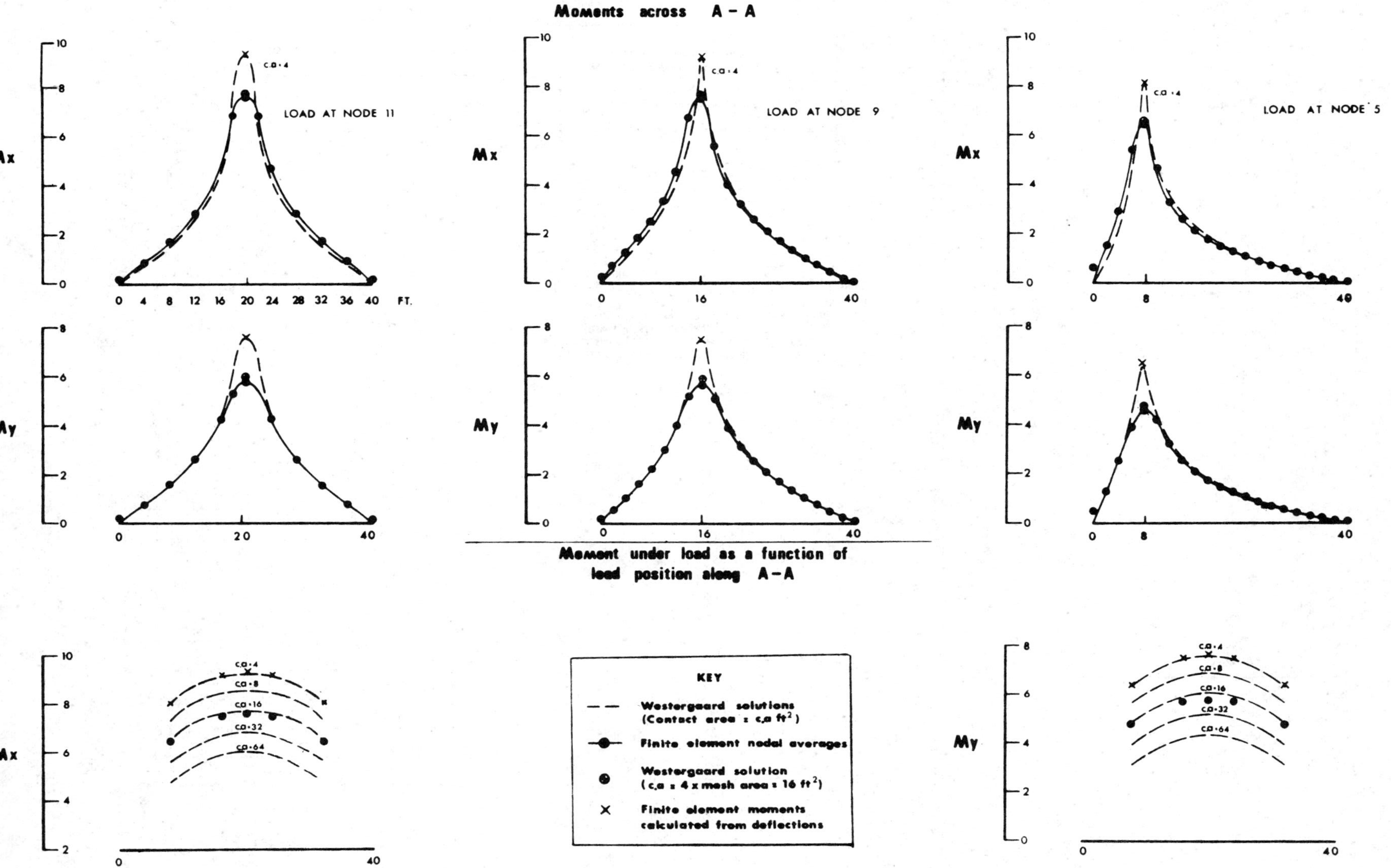

FIG. 4 WESTERGAARD COMPARISON MESH 1 BENDING MOMENTS

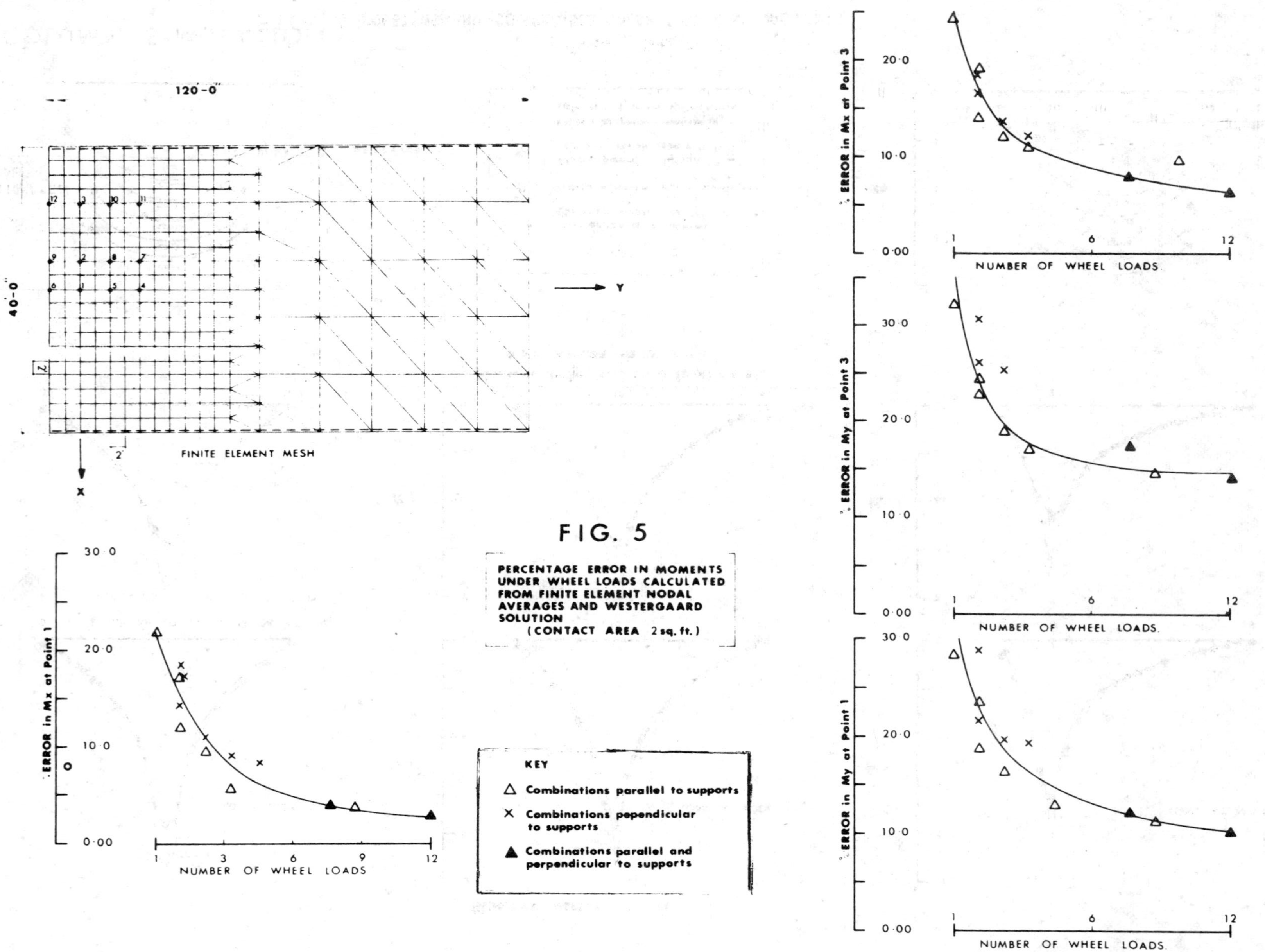

FIG. 5

PERCENTAGE ERROR IN MOMENTS UNDER WHEEL LOADS CALCULATED FROM FINITE ELEMENT NODAL AVERAGES AND WESTERGAARD SOLUTION (CONTACT AREA 2 sq. ft.)

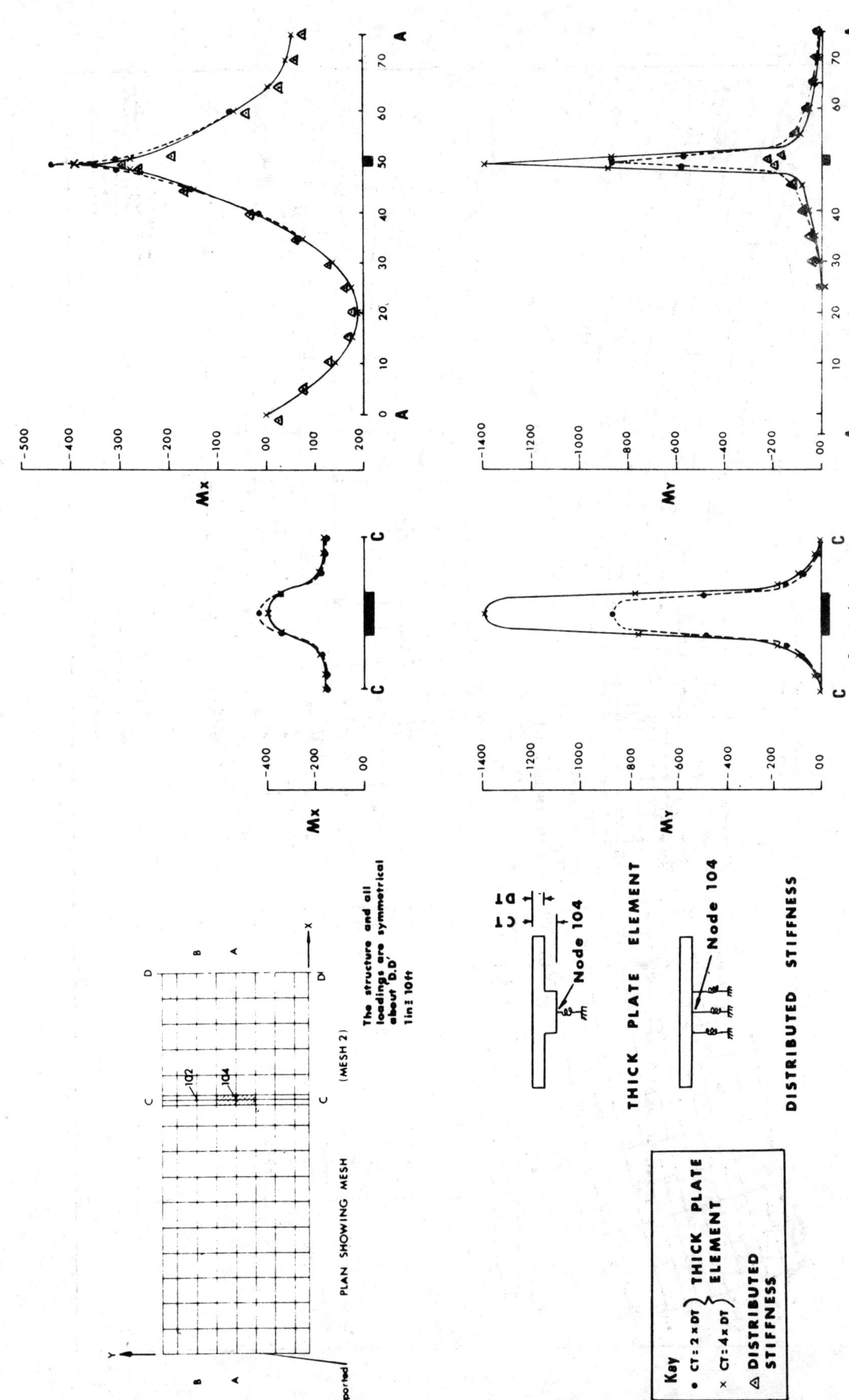

FIG. 6 COLUMN SIMULATION

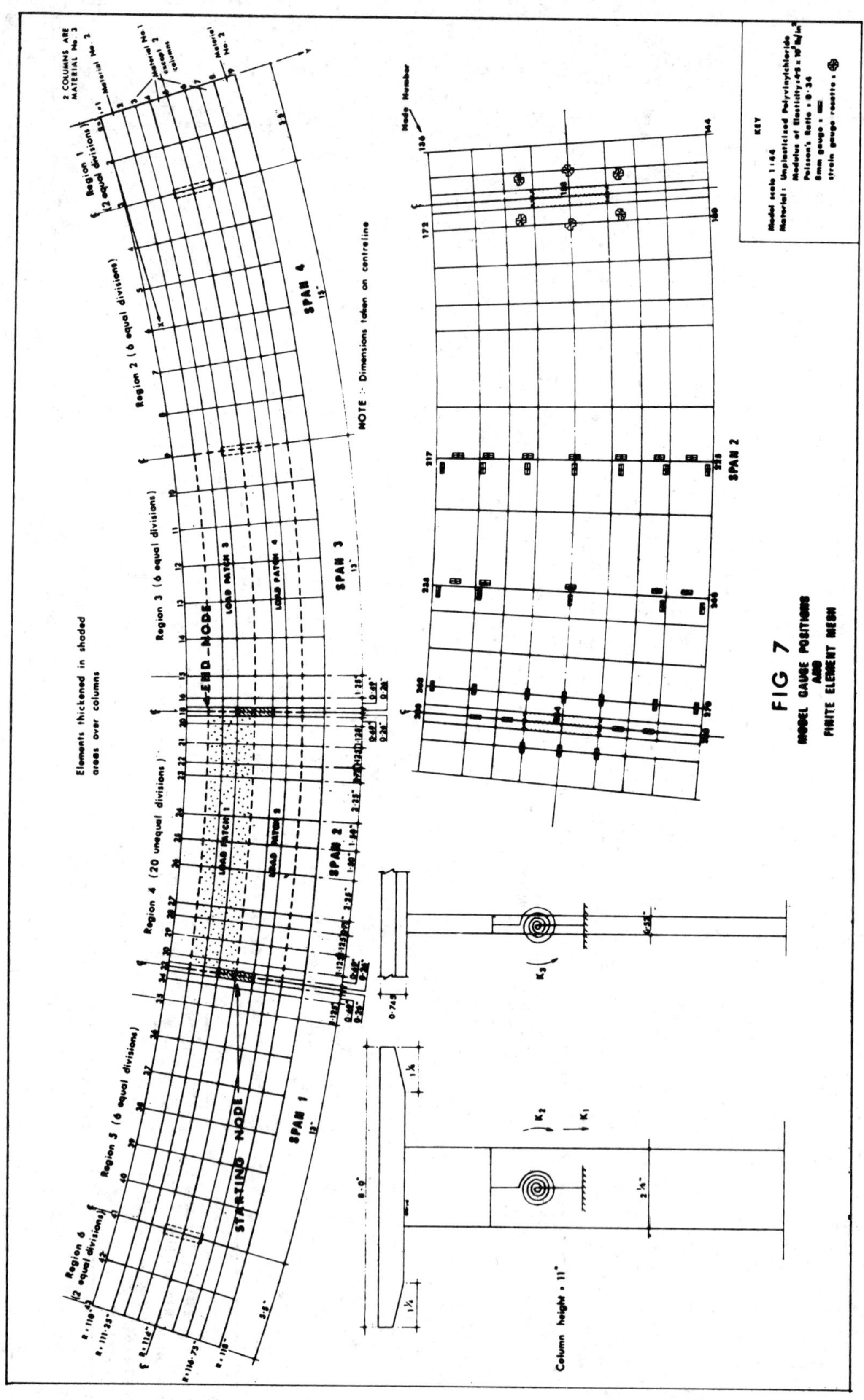

FIG 7
MODEL GAUGE POSITIONS AND FINITE ELEMENT MESH

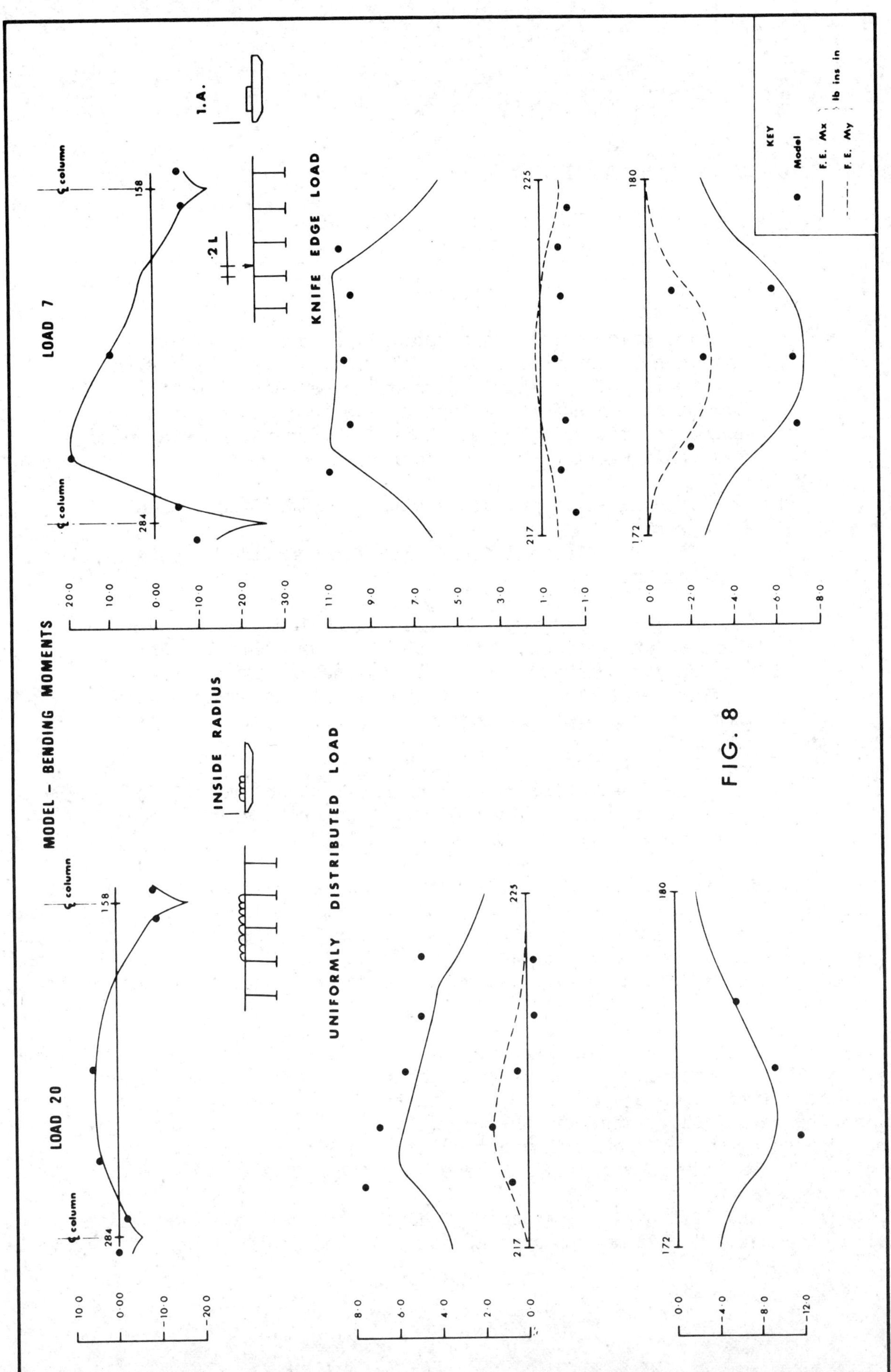
MODEL – BENDING MOMENTS
LOAD 20
LOAD 7
INSIDE RADIUS
I.A.
2L
UNIFORMLY DISTRIBUTED LOAD
KNIFE EDGE LOAD
℄ column
284
158
217
225
172
180
10·0
0·00
-10·0
-20·0
8·0
6·0
4·0
2·0
0·0
-4·0
-8·0
-12·0
20·0
-30·0
11·0
9·0
7·0
5·0
3·0
1·0
-1·0
-2·0
-6·0
KEY
Model
F.E. Mx
F.E. My
lb ins in

FIG. 8

ANALYSIS OF SLABS WITH EDGE BEAMS

By J. D. DAVIES, C. J. PAREKH, and O. C. ZIENKIEWICZ

SYNOPSIS

The paper describes an analytical and experimental investigation of the elastic behavior of flat slabs with edge beams. The analytical study is based on the finite element method and the solutions are compared with measurements on model perspex plates. Two types of slab/edge beam configurations are considered:

Type 1: slab and beams with coincident centroidal axes
Type 2: slab and beams with non-coincident centroidal axes

For the first type, simple triangular plate bending elements and beam elements each with three degrees of freedom per node are used. For the second type, triangular shell elements and variously simulated edge beam elements each with six degrees of freedom per node are adopted.

Keywords: bridge decks; bridges (structures); edge beams; finite element method; flat concrete slabs; models; reinforced concrete; structural analysis.

J. D. DAVIES is reader in civil engineering at the University of Wales, Swansea. His research interests are concerned with the behavior of plate and shell structures, the use of models, and the tensile properties of concrete. A frequent contributor to the proceedings of the ACI, Dr. Davies is the author of two text books, one on structural concrete and one on the use of models for concrete structures.

C. J. PAREKH is a research assistant in civil engineering at the University of Wales, Swansea. He has made a special study of the development of complete solution systems based on the finite element technique. These embrace plane stress-strain, plate, and shell problems and much of the data preparation and processing can now be handled automatically by special input-output programs. Mr. Parekh has also studied general transient phenomena.

O. C. ZIENKIEWICZ is a professor of civil engineering at the University of Wales, Swansea. He has made a special study of the applications of numerical methods in engineering science and is the author of the standard textbook describing the finite element method of analysis. He holds the D.Sc. degree of London University and is the author of some 80 scientific papers. Prior to his appointment to head of department at Swansea, Professor Zienkiewicz taught at Northwestern University, United States, and Edinburgh University, Scotland.

2. INTRODUCTION

Many analytical procedures are available for the design of simple slab bridge decks. When edge beams are incorporated, the structural behaviour is modified and the analysis is complicated due to the slab/beam interaction. To obtain maximum benefit from the edge stiffening, it is desirable to achieve a complete monolithic connection between the slab and the beams.

It is convenient to consider two types of slab/edge beam configuration. Fig.1(a) shows the cross-section of a slab with coincident edge-beams in which the centroidal axes of the slab and the edge beams lie in the same horizontal plane. This will be referred to as Type 1 and it is assumed that the applied loads are carried by plate action in the slab and flexural/torsion action in the edge beams. Fig.1(b) shows the type 2 configuration in which the centroidal plane of the slab does not coincide with the centroidal axes of the edge beams. Under loading, the edge beams are not free to bend and rotate about the beam axes and, as a consequence, in-plane axial forces will be developed at the slab/beam connection due to the composite action. It will be apparent that type 2 will provide a considerably stiffer structure than type 1 with regard to overall behaviour.

Several analytical procedures have been proposed for the type 1 sections. Massonnet(1) has described a method of solution for edge beams with negligible torsional stiffness and Hendry and Jaeger(2) have developed methods for full bending/shear/torsion interaction. An extension of the load distribution method developed at the Cement and Concrete Association Laboratories, England, has been given by Morice, Little and Rowe[(3) (4) (5)].

An infinite series solution allowing for tee-beam action in slabs with non-coincident beams has been described by Allen and Severn[(6)].

In this paper the finite element method has been adopted for both types of configuration and the results for some simple problems are compared with measurements taken on model slabs with edge beams. Only brief descriptions of the finite element techniques are given but a comprehensive treatment of the general method is given in reference (7).

3. THE FINITE ELEMENT METHOD OF ANALYSIS

The finite element method is essentially a generalisation of the standard stiffness formulation of structural problems using matrix notation. Any continuous system may be replaced by a finite number of elements interconnected at a finite number of nodes. These elements can be of any shape with specified elastic properties. The idealisation of continuous structures as a set of interconnected sub-structures leads to a unified approach in structural analysis which is convenient for solution by digital computers.

The individual elements may be simple or complex. The simple types may be beam elements with two nodes, and triangular elements with three nodes. Complex elements may have additional nodes along the sides or internal nodes or even extra nodes over the depth of the element.

Only simple beam and triangular elements have been used in the examples considered in this paper.

For type 1 bridge sections the principal structural action is flexural in character and the in-plane or membrane forces may be neglected. In this case it is sufficient to consider only three degrees of freedom per node : the lateral deflection ω and the orthogonal rotations θ_x and θ_y. These are treated as the unknowns of the problem and the solutions are obtained from the equations of equilibrium for each node. From the element stress matrices it is then possible to determine the bending stress resultants M_x, M_y and M_{xy} for the triangular plate elements and the bending moment M and torsion moment T for the beam element. Fig.2(a) shows the sign conventions used. For both elements, the displacement function is of third degree and yields linearly varying curvature states.

For type 2 bridge sections, the loads are carried partly by flexural action and partly by membrane action depending on the relative rigidities of the slab and edge beams and the degree of eccentricity of their centroids. This then becomes a "flat" shell or folded plate type problem and in addition to the three "bending" degrees of freedom, it is necessary to consider the three "membrane" degrees of freedom θ_z, u and v. It is assumed that the bending and membrane effects may be separated. From these extra nodal displacements it is possible to determine the membrane stress resultants N_x, N_y and N_{xy} for the triangular shell elements and the axial force F for the beam element. Fig.3 shows the sign conventions used for the bending and membrane effects. The components of the displacement function for membrane action are of second degree and yield constant strain states. Thus, whereas the bending stress resultants vary linearly the membrane stress resultants are uniform within an element.

4. TYPE 1 SECTIONS : SLAB AND BEAM SYSTEMS WITH COINCIDENT CENTROIDAL AXES

To test the accuracy of the finite element solution three examples have been investigated.

Example 1. Corner supported square slab with non-monolithic edge beams - Fig. 4.

In this problem it is assumed that there is no torsional interaction between the slab and the edge beams. This arrangement has been solved by Timoshenko[8], using a series solution, for a number of values of the dimensionless ratio $T = \frac{EI}{Da}$ relating the flexural rigidity EI of the edge beams to the total flexural rigidity Da of the slab of side a. The torsional rigidity of the beams GJ is not required.

A value of T = 10 was selected and a Poisson's ratio $\mu = 0.25$ was adopted for comparative purposes.

Table 1 shows typical values of deflections and bending moments in the slab for two positions, one at the centre of the slab and one at the centre of an edge beam. The series solution values are also included and the correlation is excellent.

Example 2. Corner supported square slab with monolithic edge beams - Fig. 5.

In order to check the finite element solution with the measurements taken on a perspex model, values of T = 9.14 and $\mu = 0.375$ were chosen. Three loading patterns were investigated :

(A) uniformly distributed load of intensity q,

(B) central concentrated load of magnitude P,

(C) two concentrated loads P/2 applied at the centres of two opposite edge beams.

Details of the model are shown in Fig.6. Table 2 shows deflection, rotation and curvature values for the centre of the slab and the centre of the long sides. The finite element values and the model values are given, and correlation is good except for curvatures near the centre concentrated load.

<u>Example 3. Rectangular slab with monolithic edge beams along long sides, simply supported on short sides. Fig. 7.</u>

A rectangular slab with aspect ratio b/a = 2 was investigated for values of T = 2.70 and 9.14 and μ = 0.375. The three loading patterns (A), (B) and (C) were again considered and the finite element solutions were checked against measurements taken on the perspex model shown in Fig.8. Table 3 summarises the results for the centre of the slab and the centre of the long edges. Again, except for the curvature values adjacent to the concentrated loads, the correlation between the theoretical and experimental quantities is good.

5. TYPE 2 SECTIONS : SLAB AND BEAM SYSTEMS WITH NON-COINCIDENT CENTROIDAL AXES

In this section, triangular shell elements have been used to represent the slab and various methods have been considered to represent the edge beams. These include triangular shell elements within the plane of the edge beam and conventional beam elements with modified flexural rigidities to allow for the eccentricity between the slab and edge beam centroids.

Example 4 : Corner supported square slab with monolithic upstand edge beams. Fig. 9.

One major problem in the solution of large systems of linear equations is the restriction on the size of the "half-band width" as dictated by the size of computer used for the inversion process. With the particular machine available this meant that for any element the nodal numbers must not differ by more than sixteen.

Fig.9(b) shows the mesh adopted for a typical quarter part of the slab. This shows the edge beams "flattened" into the plane of the slab. It will be appreciated that the simulation of the edge beam by two triangular shell elements over its depth is very restrictive because the in-plane or membrance forces are constant over each element. That is, it is very difficult to simulate a "plane-sections remain plane" distribution with only two constant stress elements.

A second device was to allow no common nodal connection between the ends of the edge beams meeting at a corner but to introduce extra boundary conditions at the nodes to prevent movements in the x and y directions. This permits a finer mesh and the pattern is shown in Fig.9(c).

A third approach entailed the use of ordinary beam elements to represent the edge beams. The procedure followed was to determine the position of the common centroidal axis for the complete section. Of course, this will be located somewhere between the centroidal axes of the individual slab and individual edge beams, assuming no interaction. The second moment of area of the edge beam is then calculated with respect to this common centroidal axis and the modified EI is used as the appropriate flexural rigidity for the beam elements.

In presenting the results the three methods will be referred to as "coarse", "fine and "beam" representations.

The perspex model used for the experimental investigation is shown in Fig.10. Table 4 gives deflection, slope and curvature values for the three loading conditions, (A), (B) and (C). The three analytical solutions and the model values are shown for the centre of the slab and the centre of an edge. In general, the modified edge beam solution provides the best correlation with the model values. As is to be expected, the simulation of the edge beams by two constant stress triangles over the depth for the "coarse" and "fine" cases leads to an overestimate of the general stiffness of the structure.

<u>Example 5 : Corner supported rectangular slab with monolithic upstand beams along long sides. Fig. 11.</u>

Fig.11 shows the mesh adopted for a typical quarter of the slab. This shows the edge beams on the long side "flattened" into the plane of the slab. Again only two triangular elements over the depth have been used to simulate the edge beam. This is referred to as the "shell" solution in the results given in Table 5.

The perxpex model used for the experimental investigation is shown in Fig.12 and typical values for the centre of the slab and the centre of an edge are listed in the "model" columns. As before, the results are given for the three loading cases (A), (B) and (C).

The best correlation with the model results is generally given by the modified edge beam stiffness solution but the "shell" solution also gives reasonable agreement particularly with regard to curvatures.

6. CONCLUSIONS

The preliminary studies outlined in this paper show that the finite element method provides a convenient procedure for the analysis of beam/slab systems.

The degree of accuracy of the solutions will depend on the size of sub-division and on the nature of the structural idealization.

In general, beam elements will be the most accurate representations for edge members unless it is possible to include a number of shell triangular elements over the depth of the edge beam.

For type 1 sections, standard plate and beam elements with three degrees of freedom per node give acceptable results compared with elastic model studies.

For Type 2 sections, the use of shell elements with six degrees of freedom per node give reasonable results compared with elastic model studies, especially when the edge beams are simulated with beam elements with modified flexural rigidities based on the centroidal axis of the complete section. Simulation of the edge beams with the triangular shell elements over the depth tends to over-estimate the general stiffness of the structure. Work is in hand to establish modified stiffness characteristics for eccentric edge beams to be included in a general solution program with simplified input data.

Further details of the examples briefly referred to in this paper are given by Davey[9] and Heathcock[10].

7. REFERENCES

1. MASSONNET, C. Complements a la method de calcul des ponts a poutras multiples
   Annales des Travaux Publics de Belgique, October, 1954

2. HENDRY, A.W. and JAEGER, L.G. The analysis of grid frameworks and related structures.
   Chatto and Windus, London, 1958.

3. MORICE, P.B., LITTLE, G. and ROWE, R.E.
   Design curves for the effects of concentrated loads on concrete bridge decks. Db. ila. Cement and Concrete Association, England, July 1956, p. 24.

4. LITTLE, G. and ROWE, R.E. The effect of edge stiffening beams on bridges. Technical Report, TRA.221. Cement and Concrete Association, England, February 1956.

5. LITTLE, G. and ROWE, R.E. The effect of edge stiffening and eccentric transverse prestress in bridges. Technical Report, TRA.279 Cement and Concrete Association, England, November 1957.

6. ALLEN, D.N.G. and SEVERN, R.T. Composite action between beams and slabs under transverse load

PART I	The Structural Engineer	Vol.39 No.5, May 1961, pp. 149-162
" II	" " "	Vol.39 No.7, Jul.1961, pp. 235-239
" III	" " "	Vol.40 No.6, Jun.1962, pp. 191-195
" IV	" " "	Vol.142 No.12 Dec. 1964, pp. 429-432

7. ZIENKIEWICZ, O.C. and CHEUNG, Y.K. The finite element method in structural and continuum mechanics. McGraw-Hill, London, 1966.

8. TIMOSHENKO, S. and WOINOWSKY-KREIGER, S. Theory of Plates and Shells McGraw-Hill, 1959, p.220.

9. DAVEY, J.F. The use of shell elements in the analysis of plate systems. M.Sc. Thesis, University of Wales, 1968.

10. HEATHCOCK, C.R. The analysis of slabs on discrete supports. M.Sc. Thesis, University of Wales, 1968.

Position	ω		M_x		M_y	
	F.E.	Series	F.E.	Series	F.E.	Series
Centre of slab	·00464	·00464	·0474	·0477	·0474	·0477
Centre of edge	·00047	·00044	·0052	—	·0080	—
Multiplying factor	$\frac{qa^4}{D}$		qa^2		qa^2	

TABLE 1

Deflection and moment values for Example 1. Corner supported square slab with non-monolithic edge beams. Uniformly distributed load q. $T = 10$

(A) Uniformly distributed load q

Position	ω		θ		$1/R$	
	F.E.	Model	F.E.	Model	F.E.	Model
Centre of slab	·00349	·00372	—	—	·0290	·0270
Centre of edge	·00057	·00062	·0077	·0084	·0054	·0052
Multiplying factor	$\frac{qa^4}{D}$		$\frac{qa^3}{D}$		$\frac{qa^2}{D}$	

(B) Central concentrated load P

Position	ω		θ		$1/R$	
	F.E.	Model	F.E.	Model	F.E.	Model
Centre of slab	·00980	·00965	—	—	·2030	·1710
Centre of edge	·00079	·00083	·0160	·0162	·0076	·0068
Multiplying factor	$\frac{Pa^2}{D}$		$\frac{Pa}{D}$		$\frac{P}{D}$	

(C) Two concentrated loads $P/2$ at centres of opposite edges

Position	ω		θ		$1/R$	
	F.E.	Model	F.E.	Model	F.E.	Model
Centre of slab	·00079	·00120	—	—	·0076	·0063
Centre of edge	·00110	·00116	·0028	·0028	·0132	·0141
Multiplying factor	$\frac{Pa^2}{D}$		$\frac{Pa}{D}$		$\frac{P}{D}$	

TABLE 2

Deflection, rotation and curvature values for Example 2.
Corner supported square slab with monolithic edge beams
$T = 9{\cdot}14$

(A) Uniformly distributed load q

Position	T	ω		θ		$1/R$	
		F.E.	Model	F.E.	Model	F.E.	Model
Centre of slab	2·70	·00166	·00180	—	—	·0147	·0159
	9·14	·00110	·00120	—	—	·0184	·0216
Centre of edge	2·70	·00195	·00197	·0018	·0021	·0188	·0130
	9·14	·00064	·00060	·0026	·0030	·0062	·0058
Multiplying factor		$\frac{qb^4}{D}$		$\frac{qb^3}{D}$		$\frac{qb^2}{D}$	

(B) Central concentrated load P

Position	T	ω		θ		$1/R$	
		F.E.	Model	F.E.	Model	F.E.	Model
Centre of slab	2·70	·00272	·00298	—	—	·0908	·1170
	9·14	·00267	·00296	—	—	·0960	·1160
Centre of edge	2·70	·00208	·00210	·0066	·0068	·0311	·0199
	9·14	·00098	·00092	·0075	·0080	·0102	·0099
Multiplying factor		$\frac{Pb^2}{D}$		$\frac{Pb}{D}$		$\frac{P}{D}$	

(C) Two concentrated loads $P/2$ at centres of long edges

Position	T	ω		θ		$1/R$	
		F.E.	Model	F.E.	Model	F.E.	Model
Centre of slab	2·70	·00208	·00216	—	—	·0107	·0140
	9·14	·00098	·00092	—	—	·0038	·0040
Centre of edge	2·70	·00335	·00355	·0029	·0030	·0406	·0261
	9·14	·00109	·00107	·0008	·0008	·0132	·0127
Multiplying factor		$\frac{Pb^2}{D}$		$\frac{Pb}{D}$		$\frac{P}{D}$	

TABLE 3

Deflection, rotation and curvature values for Example 3. Rectangular slab with monolithic edge beams along long sides, simply supported on short sides. $b = 2a$.

Position	Load	Deflection				Multiplying factor
		coarse	fine	beam	model	
Centre of slab	A	·0027	·0025	·0030	·0031	$\frac{qa^4}{D}$
Centre of edge	A	·0001	·0001	·0003	·0003	
Centre of slab	B	·0090	·0082	·0090	·0090	$\frac{Pa^2}{D}$
Centre of edge	B	·0002	·0002	·0004	·0004	
Centre of slab	C	·0002	·0002	·0004	·0004	$\frac{Pa^2}{D}$
Centre of edge	C	·0002	·0004	·0005	·0007	

Position	Load	Rotation				Multiplying factor
		coarse	fine	beam	model	
Centre of edge	A	·0062	·0059	·0069	·0077	$\frac{qa^3}{D}$
	B	·0143	·0132	·0149	·0145	$\frac{Pa}{D}$
	C	·0005	·0004	·0013	·0016	$\frac{Pa}{D}$

Position	Load	Curvature				Multiplying factor
		Coarse	fine	beam	model	
Centre of slab	A	·0235	·0236	·0262	·0263	$\frac{qa^2}{D}$
Centre of edge	A	—	—	·5050	·5330	
Centre of slab	B	·1270	·1930	·1970	·1750	$\frac{P}{D}$
Centre of edge	B	—	—	·7150	·7700	
Centre of slab	C	·0007	·0009	·0013	·0014	$\frac{P}{D}$
Centre of edge	C	—	—	·1230	·1960	

TABLE 4

Deflection, rotation and curvature values for Example 4.
Corner supported square slab with monolithic upstand edge beams.

Position	Load	Deflection			Multiplying factor
		shell	beam	model	
Centre of slab	A	·025	·028	·023	$\frac{qa^4}{D}$
Centre of edge	A	·002	·004	·004	
Centre of slab	B	·014	·015	·014	$\frac{Pa^2}{D}$
Centre of edge	B	·002	·004	·004	
Centre of slab	C	·002	·004	·004	$\frac{Pa^2}{D}$
Centre of edge	C	·003	·007	·007	

Position	Load	Rotation			Multiplying factor
		shell	beam	model	
Centre of edge	A	·041	·040	·036	$\frac{qa^3}{D}$
	B	·082	·080	·064	$\frac{Pa}{D}$
	C	·002	·003	·006	$\frac{Pa}{D}$

Position Centre of slab	Load	Curvature			Multiplying factor
		shell	beam	model	
$1/R_x$	A	·112	·110	·111	$\frac{qa^2}{D}$
$1/R_y$	A	·002	·004	·011	
$1/R_x$	B	·450	·447	·460	$\frac{P}{D}$
$1/R_y$	B	·284	·292	·304	
$1/R_x$	C	−·004	−·008	−·009	$\frac{P}{D}$
$1/R_y$	C	·010	·019	·022	

TABLE 5

Deflection, rotation and curvature values for Example 5. Corner supported rectangular slab with monolithic upstand beams along long sides.

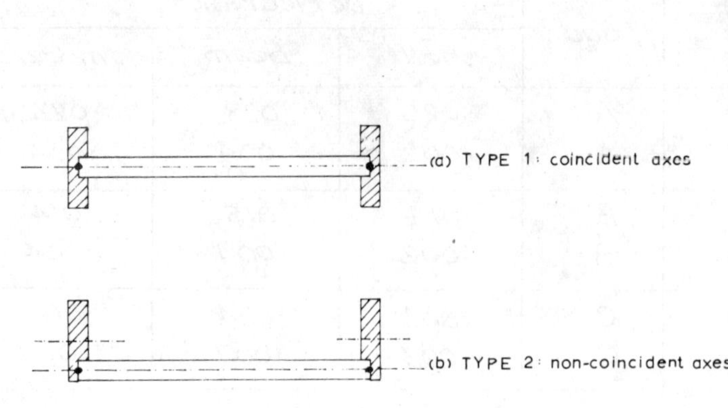

Fig. 1. Cross sections of bridge showing two types of slab/beam systems

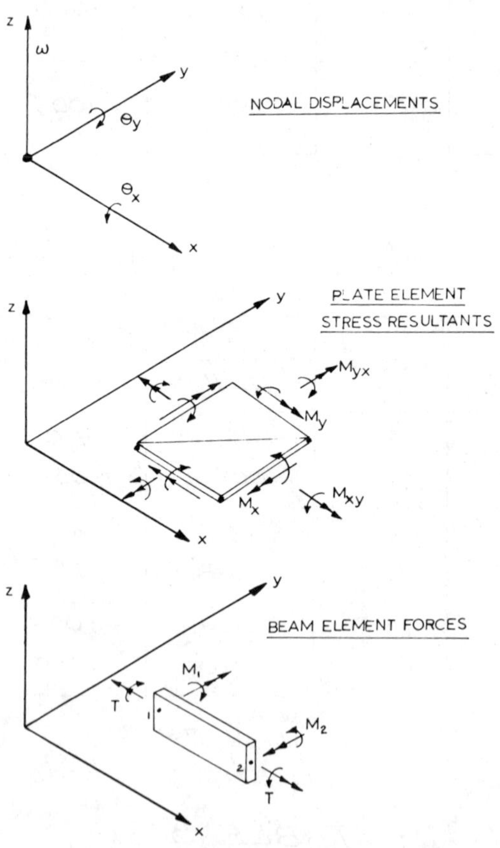

FIG. 2. Definitions and sign conventions for plate and beam elements used for Type 1 bridge sections

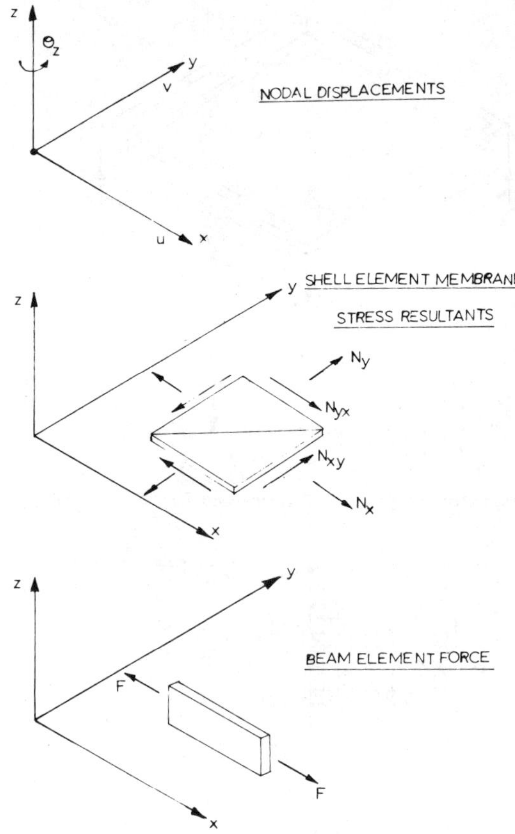

FIG. 3. Additional nodal displacements and membrane forces for shell and beam elements used for Type 2 bridge sections

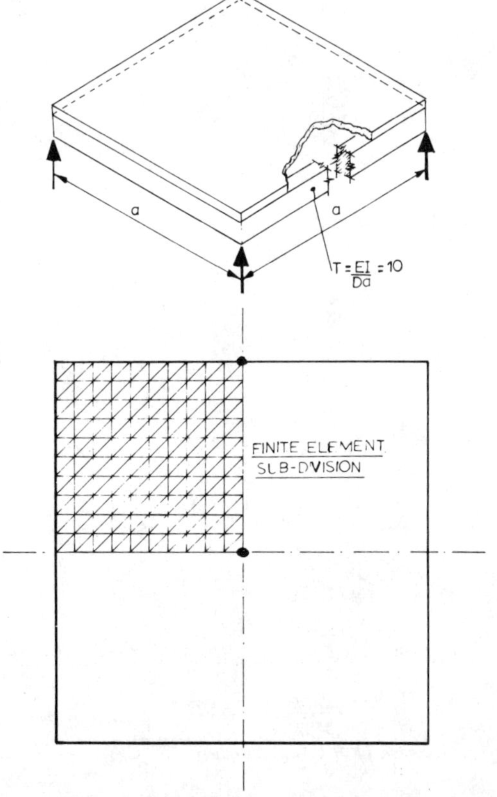

FIG. 4 Example 1: Corner supported square slab with non-monolithic edge beams

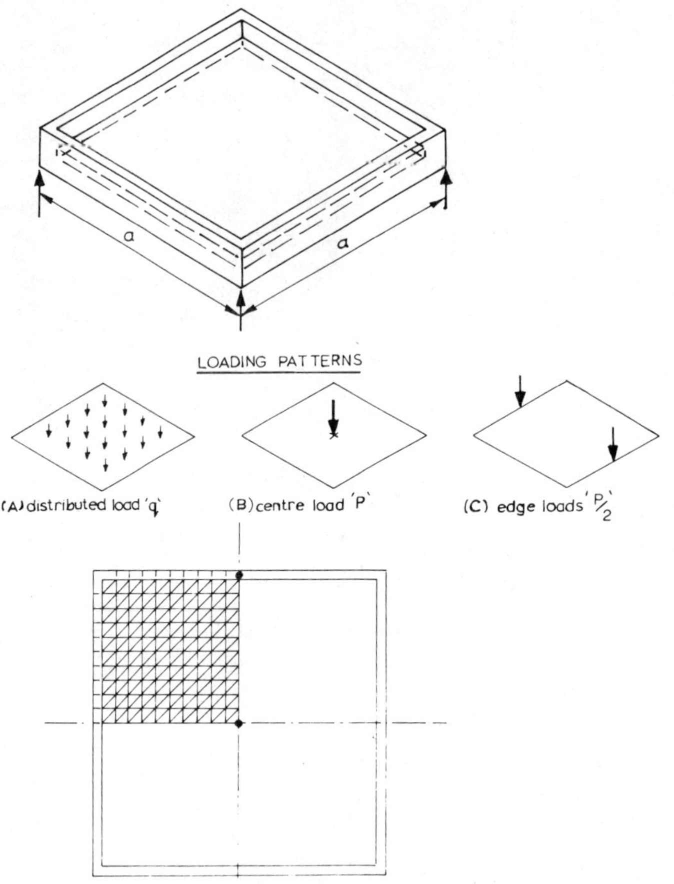

FIG 5 Example 2 : Corner supported square with monolithic edge beams

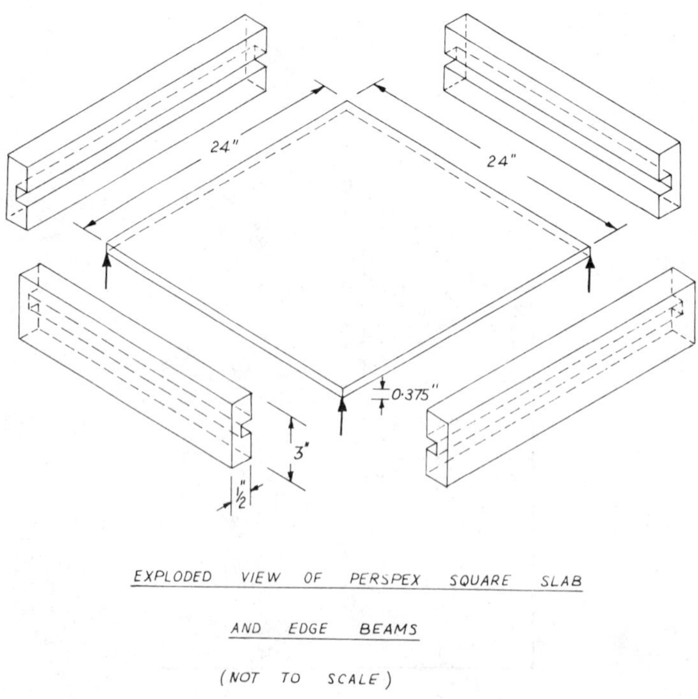

FIG. 6 Model used for Example 2

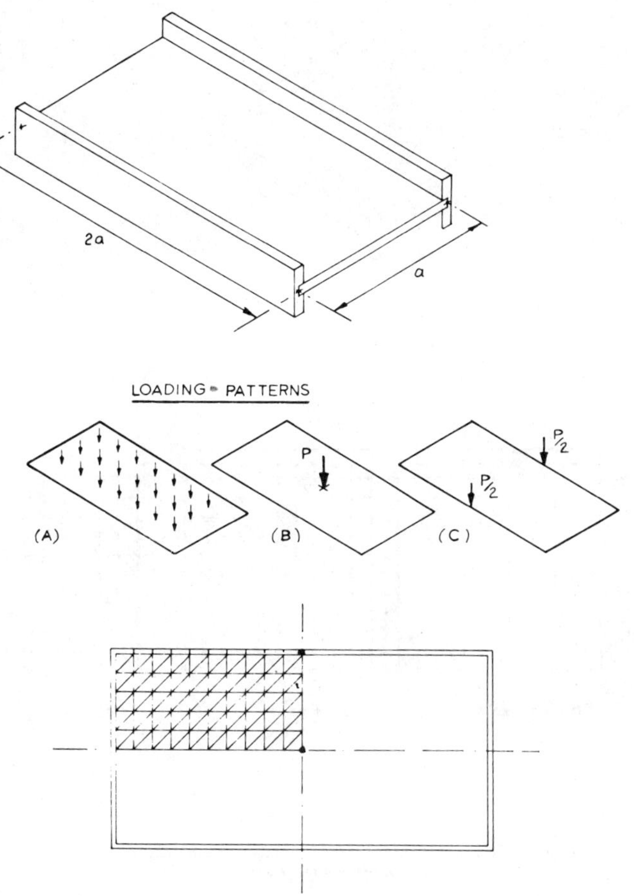

FIG. 7 Example 3 : rectangular slab with monolithic edge beams along long sides, simply supported on short sides.

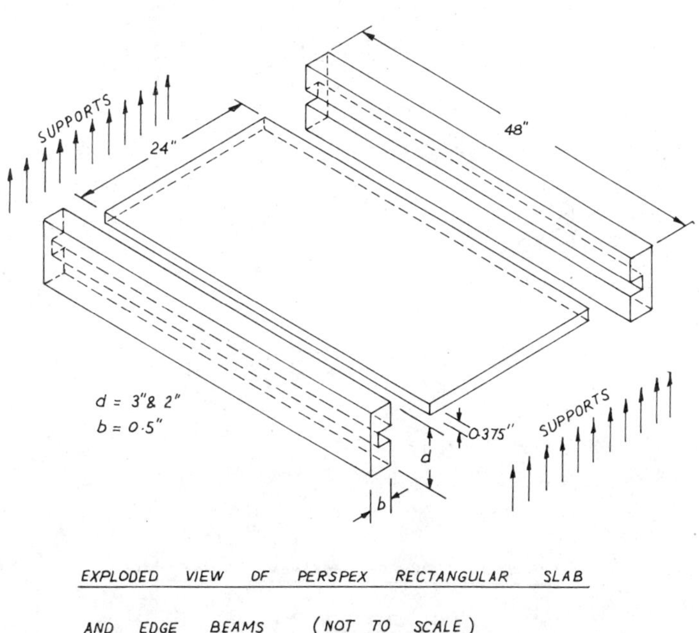

FIG. 8 Model used for Example 3

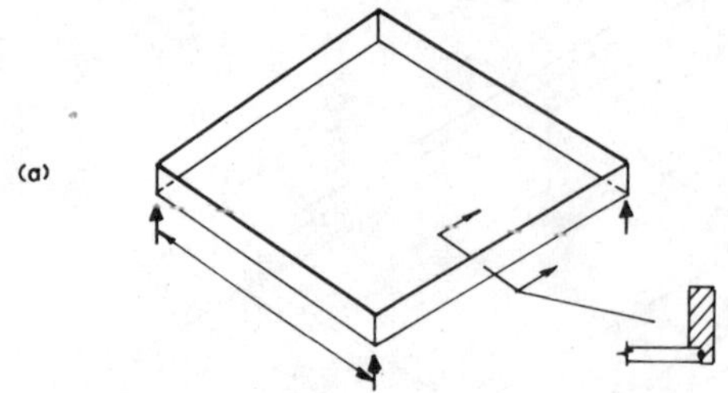

edge beam representations

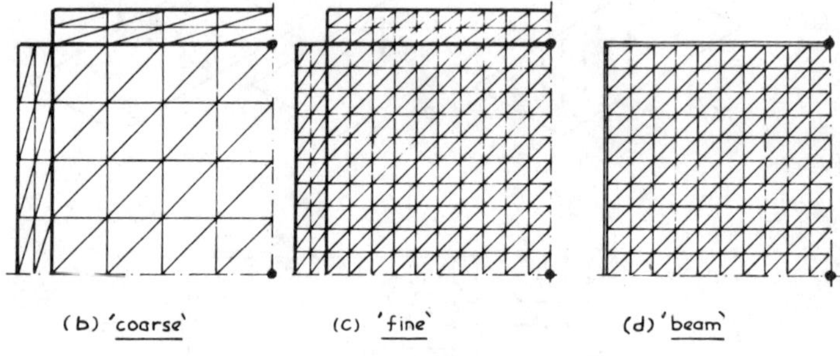

Fig. 9 Example 4 : corner supported square slab with monolithic upstand edge beams

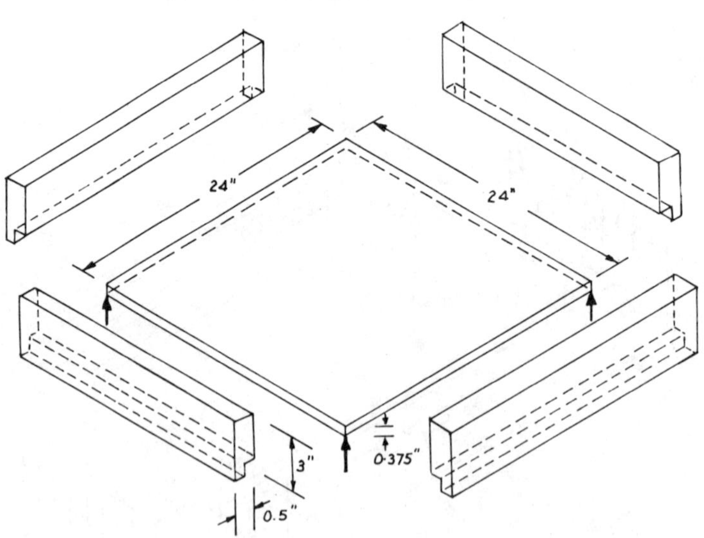

EXPLODED VIEW OF PERSPEX SQUARE SLAB AND EDGE BEAMS

(NOT TO SCALE)

FIG. 10 Model used for Example 4

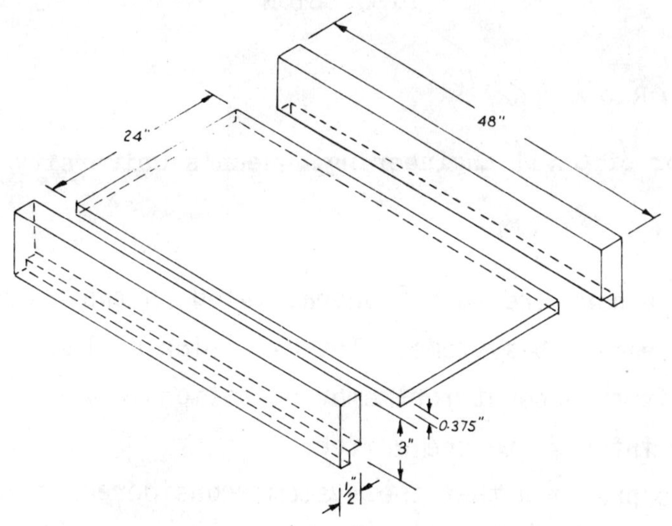

FIG. 12 Model used for Example 5

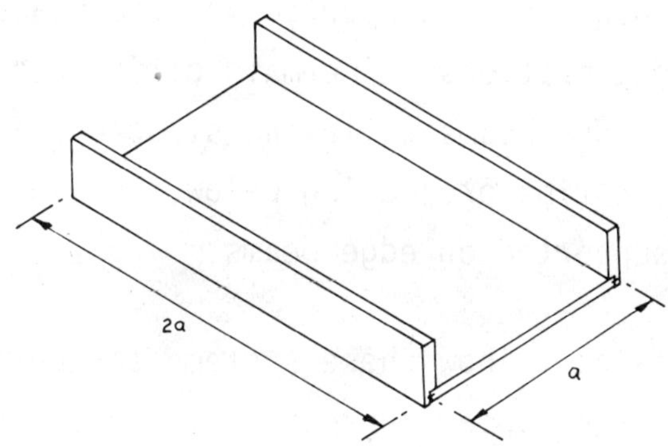

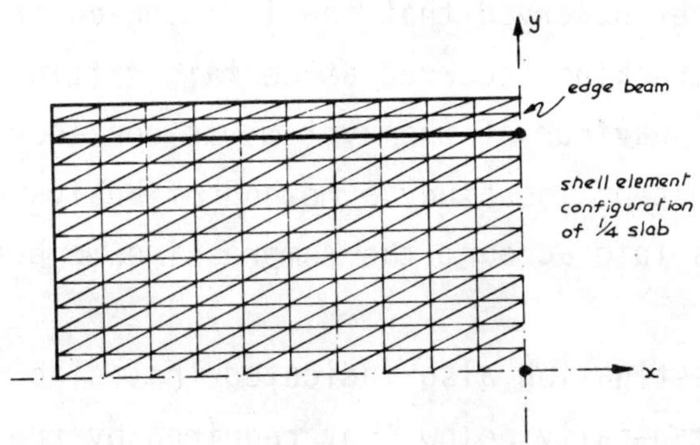

FIG. 11 Example 5 : corner supported rectangular slab with monolithic upstand beams along long sides

DISCUSSION

By B. DEV. BATCHELOR

Associate Professor of Civil Engineering, Queen's University at Kingston

The authors are to be congratulated on their contribution to the analysis of beam-slab systems. The extension of the finite element method of analysis to account for membrane action in Type 2 Sections (Fig.5) is of particular interest to the writer.

It is presumed that the systems considered are of reinforced concrete, and one wonders whether a limit analysis approach is not more appropriate in this case. This has been demonstrated in a study recently conducted at Queen's University at Kingston. [1]. The investigation was aimed mainly at studying the behaviour, under concentrated loads, of continuous two-way bridge slab systems supported by reinforced concrete beams. The study included a single panel slab supported on edge beams which resulted in a system similar to Type 2 sections. The main difference is that the authors' structure had upstanding edge beams while the structure investigated by the writer had edge beams with ribs projecting below the slab. All slabs in this series were integrally supported on edge beams.

Some comments as to how these systems can be expected to behave in the ultimate stage appear appropriate. Under centrally applied concentrated loads it was apparent that compressive membrane action was present both in the slabs failing in flexure and those failing in punching shear. It was further observed that the limiting compressive membrane action was developed when cracking occurred at certain critical positions of the edge beams. Subsequent behaviour of the system was considerably influenced by this cracking. As a result of the study a method of analysis and design has been proposed which takes into account the compressive membrane contribution to the system.

The investigation also indicated that slab reinforcement can be safely reduced substantially below that required by the elastic methods of analysis laid down by the AASHO Standard Specification for Highway Bridges.[2]

This reduction in slab reinforcement can be achieved without a large reduction in factor of safety. (A factor of safety of 6.5 was obtained for a model bridge tested under AASHO Type Loadings).

Finally, the writer is convinced that in beam-slab systems subjected to concentrated loads, the application of limit analysis methods is likely to yield better results and economy than refinement of existing elastic methods if the membrane contribution is to be taken into account.

Reference

1) Tong P.Y. " An Investigation of The Ultimate Shear Strength Of Two-Way Continuous Slabs Subjected to Concentrated Loads" Ph.D. Thesis - Queen's University At Kingston, Ontario

2) "Standard Specifications for Highway Bridges" American Association of State Highway Officials, 1961.

BRIDGE GRIDS WITH INTEGRAL SLABS--A NEW ANALYTICAL APPROACH

By P. S. DRAVID and C. L. MEHTA

SYNOPSIS

The rigorous analysis of bridge decks consisting of longitudinal girders, cross beams and deck slab is highly complex, since the cross beams and the slab contribute to a desirable load distribution over the entire system. The slab forms a continuous plate rigidly connected to elastic supports, namely the grid of cross beams and longitudinal girders.

The available methods of analysis make certain simplifying assumptions. One set of methods (Slope Deflection Method, Method of Moment & Torque Distribution, Lazaride's Method, etc.) replaces the structure by equivalent grid of discrete members. On the other hand, another set of methods (Methods of Pippard & DeWaele, Hendry & Jaeger, Guyon, Massonet, etc.) replaces the structure by a continuous elastic medium, either wholly or partially.

This paper:

(a) explains a new method of analysis developed to take into account the action of the slab and the grid in their actual physical set-up, so as to conform to the true load distribution among the different components of the structure,

(b) compares the results of the proposed method with those of the usual existing methods, and

(c) describes the experimental investigation carried out on a reinforced concrete model to verify the validity of the method.

The paper also serves as a new approach to load distribution studies in normal group cases of bridge structures.

Keywords: beams (supports); bending moments; bridge decks; bridges (structures); concrete slabs; continuity (structural); loads (forces); models; reinforced concrete; research; structural analysis.

DR. P. S. DRAVID, and ACI member, earned his Dr.-Ing. degree from Technische Hoschschule Dresden, Germany, in 1960 for his work in creep effect on rigid--frame columns. After teaching and conducting research in structural engineering and concrete technology for 8 years at Indian Institute of Technology, Bombay, he joined Dr. Shr-tien Li's concrete technology research team at South Dakota School of Mines and Technology, Rapid City, since July, 1968, as a post-doctoral research fellow and associate director of concrete technology research. Dr. Dravid has published one book and five papers. He serves as a member on ACI committee 211-Recommended Practice for Proportioning Concrete Mixes.

C. L. METHA is a design engineer for the Bombay firm, Engineering Consultants.

The rigorous analysis of bridge decks consisting of longitudinal girders, cross beams and deck slab is highly complex, since the cross beams and the slab contribute to a desirable load distribution over the entire system. The slab forms a continuous plate rigidly connected to elastic supports, namely the grid of cross beams and longitudinal girders.

The available methods of analysis make certain simplifying assumptions. One set of methods (Slope Deflection Method, Method of Moment and Torque Distribution) replaces the structure by equivalent grid of discrete members. On the other hand, another set of methods (Methods of Pippard and DeWaele[1], Hendry and Jaeger[2], Morice and Little[3]) replaces the structure by a continuous elastic medium, either wholly or partially.

A new method of analysis is developed by the authors, to take into account the action of the slab and the grid in their actual physical set-up. The treatment is limited to cases in which the slab can be considered to act one way only, and does not cover the case of two-girder bridges, wherein the slab has a two-way action. A point load applied to the system is considered in two steps. Firstly, the action of the slab is equated to that of an "equivalent beam" on "elastic supports", wherein the rigidities of the "beam" and the "supports" are evaluated on the basis of the flexural properties of the entire slab and of the longitudinal beams respectively. In this calculation, the rigidity of joints between the slab and the longitudinal beams is taken into account. In the second step, the open grid is analysed for the loads transferred by the slab (calculated in the first step).

LOAD DISTRIBUTION DUE TO DECK SLAB

The width of the slab panel (i.e. the spacing of the longitudinal beams) is usually small in comparison with its length (i.e. the spacing of the cross beams). For this reason, the deck will be treated as a one-way slab and will be analysed as an "equivalent beam" on "elastic supports" provided by the longitudinal beams. The entire slab distributes a point load over the longitudinal beams. The stiffness of the equivalent beam will be evaluated on this basis.

The length of the slab may be divided transversely into a number of small strips, each strip having width dx and taking its part in the process of load distribution, according to its position on the span of the longitudinal beam, relative to that of the strip undergoing maximum deflection. Fig. 1 shows a typical deflection diagram of a longitudinal beam with the connected slab. If the strips 1, 2, ... n, ... are imagined to undergo deflections y1, y2, ... yn, ... at their joint with the longitudinal beam, the relative distribution capacity of any strip 'n' is yn.dx. If ym is the maximum deflection of the beam, the relative distribution capacity of strip n is yn/ym.

Let EIe = Flexural rigidity of the equivalent beam representing the entire slab, and

EI = Flexural rigidity of one strip

Then, $$\frac{EIe}{EI} = \frac{y1\ dx + y2\ dx + \cdots + yn\ dx + \cdots}{ym dx} = \frac{A1}{A2}\frac{L}{dx}$$

where L = span of the longitudinal beam,

A1 = area bounded by the elastic curve of the beam for a given position of the load,

A2 = area of the rectangle enclosing the elastic curve

Let EIs = Flexural rigidity of the slab per unit width

Then, $$Ie = \frac{Is\ L\ A1}{A2} \qquad (1)$$

Considering various positions of a unit load on a beam of span L, it is seen that the ratio A1/A2 remains within limits of 0.620 and 0.655. An average constant value of 0.637 can be chosen to cover all load positions, without materially affecting accuracy.

Thus, $EIe = 0.637 EIs\ L$ . . . . (2)

is the flexural rigidity of the equivalent beam.

Flexibility coefficients of elastic supports are obtained from similar considerations. Under a point load on a beam, as shown in Fig. 2,

$$\text{maximum deflection} = \frac{Wb\,(a^2 + 2ab)^{3/2}}{9\sqrt{3}\,EIb.L}$$

for $a \geqslant L/2$

where Ib = the relevant moment of inertia of the longitudinal beam, or deflection per unit load, $K = \frac{L^3}{C.EIb}$ . . . .(3)

$$\text{where } C = \frac{9\sqrt{3}\,L^4}{b\,(a^2 + 2ab)^{3/2}}$$

The values of C for various values of a are as follows:

a:	L/2	3L/5	5L/8	3L/4	4L/5	7L/8
C:	48.0	50.6	52.2	68.6	82.9	127.5

The values of C are naturally symmetrical about the midspan section.

Knowning the flexural rigidity of the equivalent beam (equation 2), and the flexibility coefficient of the elastic support (equation 3), the analysis is carried out.

As an example, the three-girder case represented in figure 3, analysed by this approach, gives :

$$RA = \frac{1}{1 + 9m}\left[\frac{3}{2}m\,(5-3A) + \frac{1}{4}\,(4-5A + A^3)\right]$$

$$RB = (2-A-2RA)$$

$$RC = 1-(RA + RB)$$

where $m = \frac{EIeK}{h^3}$

This solution, programmed for a wide range of practical values of parameters m and A, gives useful results, which are represented on semilog graph sheets (Fig. 4). For any position of a unit load on a three-girder symmetrical bridge, Fig. 4 gives the reactions at two of the three supports as functions of parameter m. The torsional rigidity of longitudinal beam can be taken into account by solving a problem for two extreme cases: (1) zero torsional rigidity (equivalent beam pinned to the elastic supports), and (2) infinite torsional rigidity (equivalent beam clamped at elastic supports). The actual solution to the problem will be fixed between these two extreme solutions as follows:

$$RF = Ro + (R_\infty - Ro).\ F \quad \ldots\ldots\ldots\ldots (4)$$

where,

F = the percentage of fixity calculated as usual by the orthotropic plate theory

R_F = Reaction at given fixity (intermediate case),

R_o = Reaction for zero torsion case

R_∞ = Reaction for infinite torsion case

J_L = Torsional inertia of the longitudinal beam

I_L = Moment of inertia of the longitudinal beam

N = Number of longitudinal beams

B = Width of the bridge

L = Length of the bridge

J_T = Torsional inertia of the transverse system $= nJ_c + L\ J_s$

I_T = Moment of inertia of the transverse system $= nI_c + L\ I_s$

J_c = Torsional inertia of a **cross girder**

I_c = Moment of inertia of a cross girder

J_s = Torsional inertia of slab per unit width

I_s = Moment of Inertia of slab per unit width, and

N = Number of cross girders

LOAD DISTRIBUTION DUE TO GRID ACTION

Reactions to the deck slab, calculated as load distribution due to deck slab, represent the loads on longitudinal beams. These are distributed over the system by grid action. Grid analysis can be considerably simplified, and general solutions easily obtained, if one assumes that the torsional stiffness of rectangular beams is very small, and therefore negligible, in comparison with their flexural stiffness. With the usual proportions of beams in reinforced concrete bridge structures, this assumption leads to very small errors (about 3%). Loads on longitudinal beams can, therefore, be transferred to the grid joints, by treating the longitudinal beams as ordinary continuous beams rigidly supported at their joints with the cross beams, and evaluating the reactions at these imaginary rigid supports. A torsionless grid with a point load at a joint is more amenable to a general solution, if the principle of symmetry and antisymmetry is employed. For example, the grid shown in Fig. 5 when loaded at the joint 1, is analysed, and the joint moments shown as functions of V and T, in Fig. 6. Here, $V = h/a$, and $T = I_c/I_L$,

I_c = moment of inertia of the cross girder

I_L = moment of inertia of the longitudinal beam

Fig. 6 also shows transverse moments at joints 2 and 5 (TM2 and TM5).

APPLICATION OF THE PROPOSED METHOD

1. The load acting anywhere on the bridge is first distributed to various longitudinal beams through the slab action, treating the slab as an equivalent beam on elastic supports. The rigidity of connection between the slab and the longitudinal beam is taken into consideration through an interpolation function.

2. The distributed load on the longitudinal beams is transferred to the grid joints, by analysing each longitudinal beam as a continuous beam on rigid

supports, and evaluating the reactions at these imaginary supports.

3. The grid is analysed for these joint loads in very general terms, and the joint moments expressed as functions of dimensionless parameters representing the configuration and stiffness ratios of the grid.

The net bending moment at any cross section of a beam is obtained by the algebraical addition of the corresponding bending moments from steps 2 and 3. This procedure completely defines the treatment of a point load acting anywhere on the bridge. The bending moments for any given position of a train of live loads can be obtained by super-position.

COMPARISON OF RESULTS WITH THOSE OF OTHER METHODS

For a simply supported bridge having the girder configuration shown in Fig. 5, the following values were chosen for solving an example:

$L = 66'\text{-}0''$, $h = 8'\text{-}3''$, $I_L = 9.035 \times 10^5$ in^4, $I_C = 0.758 \times 10^5$ in^4,

thickness of slab = 7", $J_L = 0.4071 \times 10^5$ in^4,

$J_C = 0.1288 \times 10^5$ in^4, $I_S = 343$ in^4/ft. width,

$J_S = 1372$ in^4/ft. width

Table 1 shows the results obtained by the proposed method in comparison with those of three usual methods.

The difference between the results by orthotropic plate theory[4] and by the proposed method is within 8 per cent in the case of bending moments at loaded joints.

Pippard and DeWaele's method gives fairly close results when the inner girder is loaded, presumably because its assumption of zero twist for longitudinal girders is realistic in such a case, due to symmetry. Its results appear to be approximate in this example, when the outer girder is loaded.

Agreement between Hendry & Jaeger's method and the proposed method is reasonably satisfactory when the outer girder is loaded (difference is about 8 per cent), but not so good when the inner girder is loaded (difference is about 32 per cent).

EXPERIMENTAL INVESTIGATION

In order to study the effect of the simplifying assumptions of the proposed method in a typical case, it was considered necessary to compare the result of the proposed method with experimental results. A reinforced concrete model, having the girder configuration shown in Fig. 5, was therefore prepared. The model was designed with the following values:

$L = 64''$, $h = 8''$, $I_L = 59.88\ in^4$, $I_C = 8.00\ in^4$,

thickness of the slab = 0.75", $J_L = 5.626\ in^4$,

$J_C = 3.43\ in^4$, $I_S = 0.035\ in^4/in.$ width

$J_S = 0.140\ in^4/in.$ width. Longitudinal beams were 1.5" x 6" in cross section, reinforced with 2 steel bars 3/16" dia. and 2 steel bars 1/16" dia. at bottom, and with 2 steel bars 1/8" dia. at top. Cross beams were 1.5" x 4" in cross section, and reinforced with 2 steel bars 1/8" dia. at top and at bottom. Deflections were measured by dial indicators.

The deflections in a reinforced concrete structure are considerably affected by the degree of reinforcement, extent of crack formation, and stress-strain relation of concrete. The purpose of this investigation was to confirm the validity of moment distribution obtained by the proposed method. No attempt was, therefore, made to calculate and compare the absolute values of deflections. Regarding the deflection at the loaded joint as 100 per cent, relative deflections at other joints were calculated from the bending moments obtained by the proposed method, and these were compared with the relative deflections obtained experimentally. Table 2 shows the comparison. It is seen that the experimental and the calculated values of relative deflections are in good agreement with each other. The difference in three cases is upto 15 per cent of the deflection at the loaded joint (deflections at joints 3 and 4 due to load at joint 1, deflection at joint 6 due to load at joint 4). The difference in all other cases is within 7 per cent of the deflection at the loaded joint. From the pattern of relative deflections experimentally obtained, it appears that the proposed method gives a realistic moment distribution.

CONCLUDING REMARKS

The proposed method takes into account the action of the slab and the grid in their actual forms. Its results, compared with those of other usual methods and with experimental results, show a reasonable degree of reliability. Its results can be easily expressed in general terms as functions of dimensionless parameters, as in figures 4 and 6, so as to serve as a new approach to load distribution studies in normal group cases of bridge structures. Except that it is not applicable to two way slabs, it is a general method. Diagrams similar to those in figures 4 and 6 can be easily constructed for other usual beam configurations. Bending moment coefficients for standard live load trains can then be evaluated and graphically represented in normal group cases.

ACKNOWLEDGEMENTS

This work was carried out at the Indian Institute of Technology, Bombay. Authors are grateful to Prof. S. K. Bose, Director of the Institute, for the opportunity to do this investigation. Thanks are also due to Dr. C. K. Ramesh, Professor of Civil Engineering at the same Institute, for his very valuable suggestions during the investigation.

REFERENCES

1. Pippard, A. J. S., and DeWaele J. P. A., "Studies in Elastic Structures," Arnold, London, 1952.

2. Hendry, A. W., and Jaeger, L. G., "The Analysis of Grid Frameworks and Related Structures," Chatto and Windus, London, 1958.

3. Morice, P. B., and Little, G. "The Analysis of Right Bridge Decks Subjected to Abnormal Loading," Cement and Concrete Association, London, 1956.

4. Rowe, R. E., "Concrete Bridge Design," John Wiley and Sons, 1962.

TABLE 1 - COMPARISON OF BENDING MOMENTS OBTAINED BY DIFFERENT METHODS

Moments are expressed as percentage of free bending moment.
Sagging bending moments are considered **positive.**

Loaded Joint	Bending Moment at Joint	Pippard & DeWaele's Method	Orthotropic Plate Theory	Hendry & Jaeger's Method	Proposed Method
1	1	53.90	70.26	75.90	76.60
	2	25.90	30.94	32.20	29.60
	3	20.20	- 1.20	- 8.10	- 6.20
	4	29.20	70.26	71.80	74.60
	5	35.60	30.94	35.20	34.50
	6	35.20	- 1.20	- 7.00	- 9.10
2	1	26.00	30.50	31.60	29.65
	2	48.00	39.00	36.80	40.70
	3	26.00	30.50	31.60	29.65
	4	35.60	30.50	35.20	34.60
	5	28.80	39.00	29.60	30.80
	6	35.60	30.50	35.20	34.60
4	1	29.20	70.26	71.80	73.50
	2	35.60	30.94	35.20	34.60
	3	35.20	- 1.20	- 7.00	- 8.10
	4	46.70	70.26	80.00	74.00
	5	28.10	30.94	25.40	31.00
	6	25.20	- 1.20	- 5.40	- 5.00
5	1	35.60	30.50	35.20	34.25
	2	28.80	39.00	29.60	31.50
	3	35.60	30.50	35.20	34.25
	4	28.00	30.50	25.40	31.50
	5	44.00	39.00	49.20	37.00
	6	28.00	30.50	25.40	31.50

TABLE 2 - COMPARISON BETWEEN EXPERIMENTAL AND CALCULATED RELATIVE DEFLECTIONS

Downward deflections are considered positive.

Relative Deflection at Joint	Loaded Joint: 1		Loaded Joint: 2		Loaded Joint: 4		Loaded Joint: 5	
	Experimental	Calculated	Experimental	Calculated	Experimental	Calculated	Experimental	Calculated
1	100.00	100.00	95.00	92.50	74.50	68.70	68.00	65.50
2	41.00	45.20	100.00	100.00	37.60	32.50	68.00	68.00
3	- 15.00	- 5.85	95.00	92.50	- 5.68	- 3.19	68.00	65.50
4	106.00	121.80	110.90	113.20	100.00	100.00	93.40	95.80
5	51.00	56.20	107.00	118.00	54.40	47.20	100.00	100.00
6	- 4.00	- 7.48	110.90	113.20	0.00	- 4.46	93.40	95.80
7	72.00	77.10	68.00	74.00	74.50	68.70	68.00	65.50
8	38.00	36.30	75.80	74.00	37.60	32.50	68.00	68.00
9	- 10.00	- 4.95	68.00	74.00	- 5.68	- 3.19	68.00	65.50

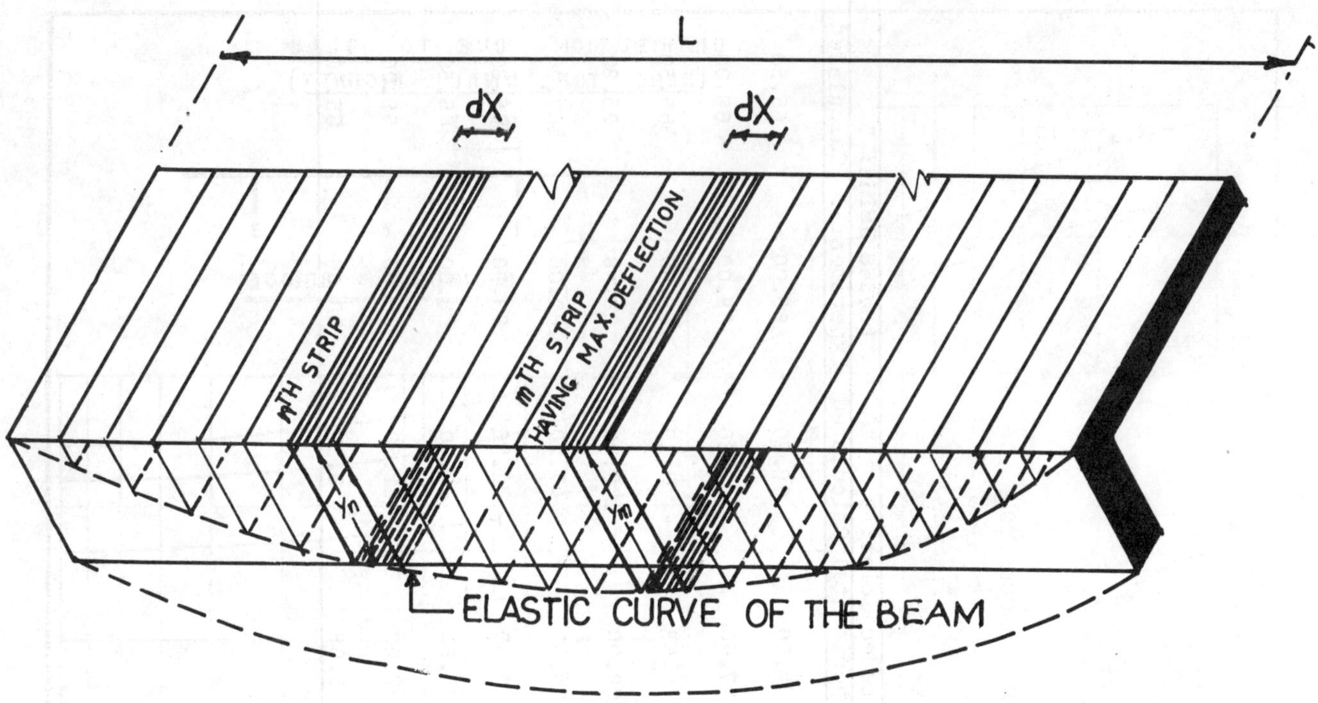

Fig. 1 Elastic Curve of Longitudinal Beam with Integral Slab

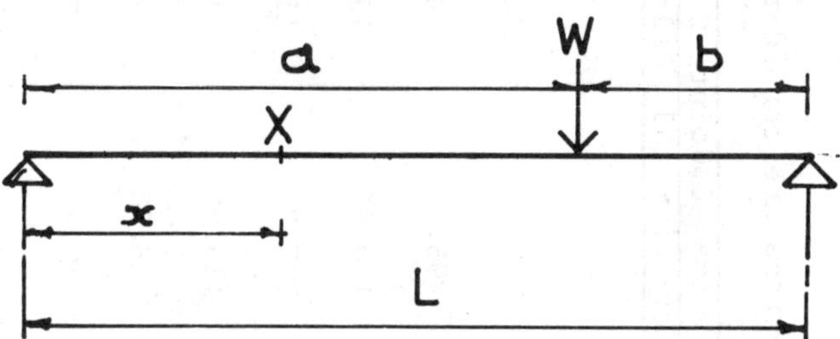

Fig. 2 Point Load on a Simply Supported Beam

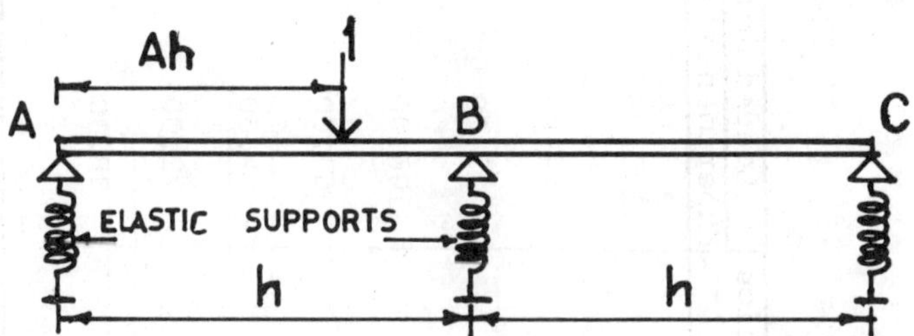

Fig. 3 Point Load on a Continuous Beam with Elastic Supports

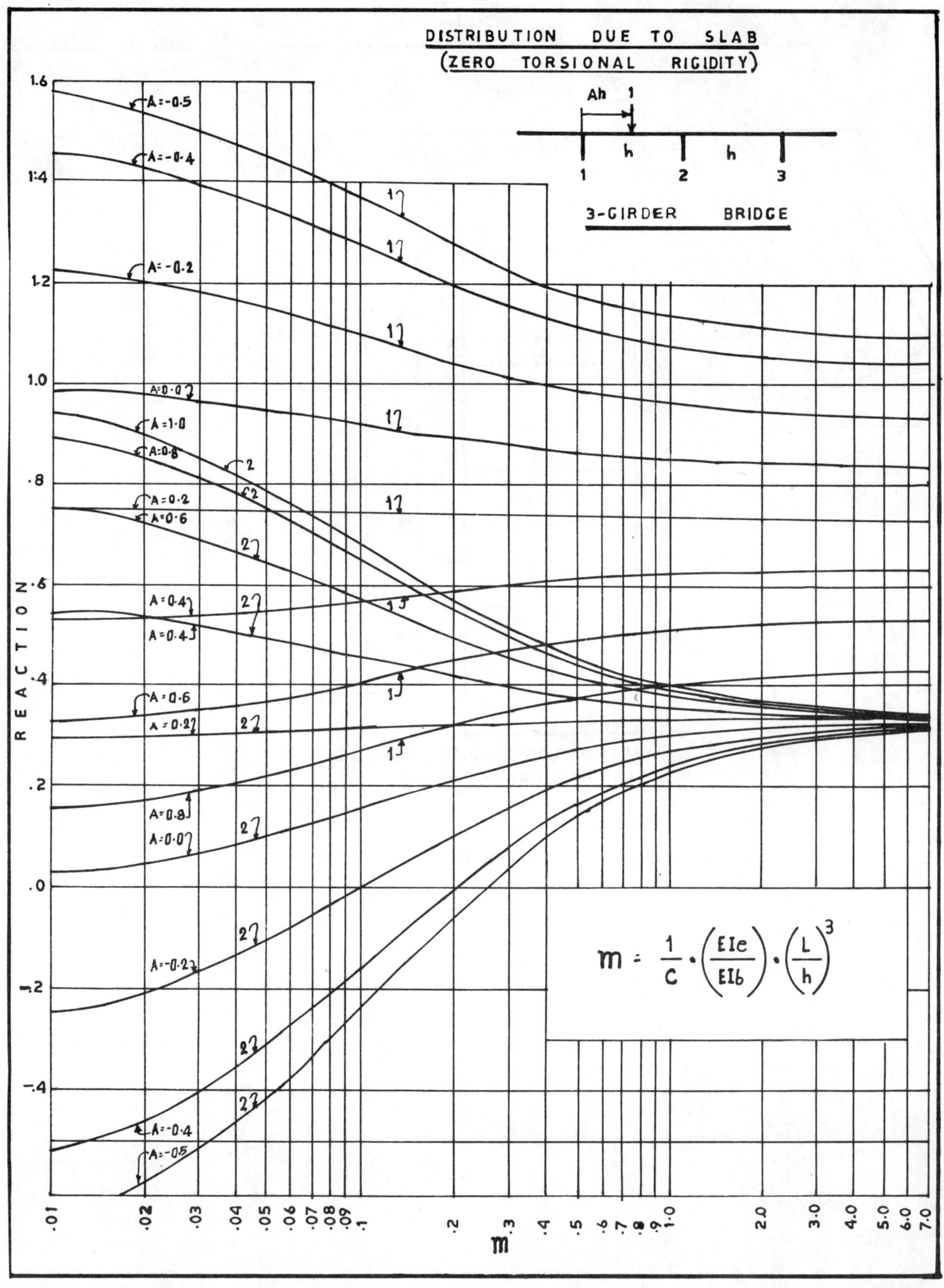

Fig. 4 Reactions of Longitudinal Beams to the Slab

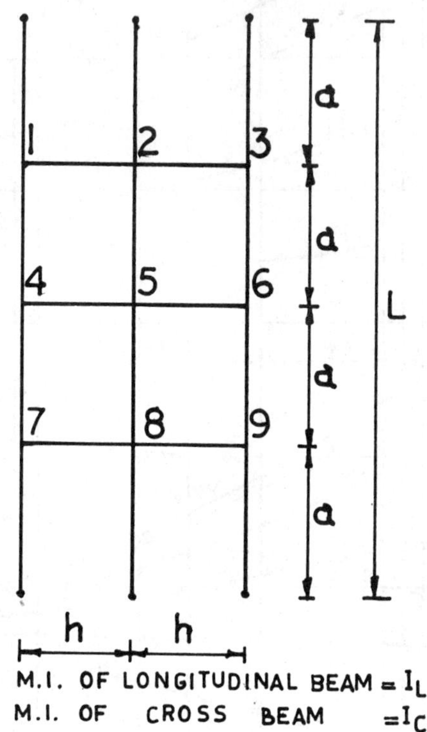

Fig. 5 Configuration of Beams in Three-girder Bridge

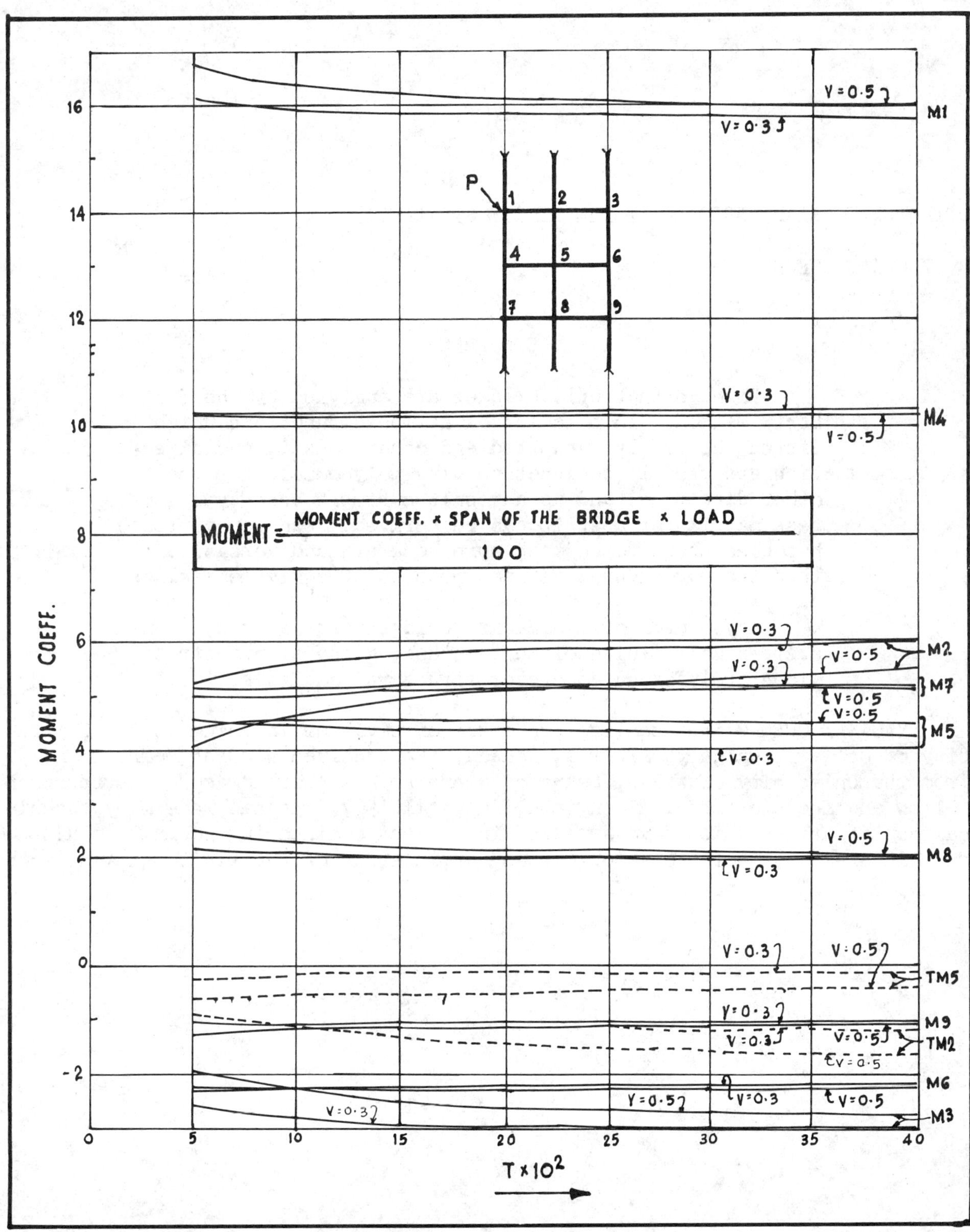

Fig. 6 Bending Moments in a Three-girder Bridge

ORTHOTROPIC RIGHT BRIDGES BY THE FINITE STRIP METHOD

By YAU-KAI CHEUNG

SYNOPSIS

Right orthotropic bridges are analyzed by the Finite Strip Method. In this method harmonic functions which fitted the simply supported end conditions in one direction are used in conjunction with polynomials for the other direction, and as a result a simple beam-type stiffness matrix for a strip can be derived. Such an approach has been shown to be much more accurate and versatile than the Guyon and Massonnet methods of equivalent slabs.

Keywords: bridge decks; bridges (structures); concrete slabs; finite element method; girders; orthotropic slabs; reinforced concrete; structural analysis.

YAU-KAI CHEUNG is associate professor of civil engineering at the University of Calgary, Calgary, Alberta, Canada. He received his PhD degrees in 1964 from the University of Wales, Swansea, where he also worked as senior research fellow and lecturer in civil engineering until 1967. He has made many technical contributions which have appeared in various engineering journals. His main interest is in the development and application of the finite element method.

INTRODUCTION

It is well known that bridges composed of a slab and girder system can be treated as orthotropic plates, and the various cases (of slab and beam arrangements) in which the orthotropic plate theory is applicable has been given by Chu and Krishnamoorthy[1]. Such complex bridge deck problems can be solved by the Finite Element Method using rectangular and triangular elements [2],[3]. However, for the case of right bridge decks which can be regarded as an isotropic or orthotropic plate with two of the opposite edges free or elastically restrained, and the other two opposite edges simply-supported, an alternative approach is available[4]. In this Finite Strip Method, the bridge is divided into longitudinal strips instead of into elements in both directions. The displacement function chosen for an elemental strip has the form $\psi(x)\ \psi(y)$, in which $\psi(y)$ satisfied the boundary conditions at the end supports automatically, while $\psi(x)$ is a simple polynomial with undetermined coefficients. With such a treatment it is possible to reduce a two dimensional problem to that of a one-dimensional problem, and as a consequence, the band width of the resulting matrix can be reduced dramatically. It should also be mentioned that the computer program for such an approach is comparatively short and that very little input data is required for its execution (all the examples given require less than 20 data cards each). The method is ideally suitable for programming on small computers,and the present program can be run both on the IBM-1130 or the multi-programming IBM 360-50.

The Finite Strip Method has considerable advantage over the methods developed by other writers[5], [6] in that although the method is quite simple and straightforward, problems involving variable transverse properties, longitudinal interior or edge beams, etc., can be dealt with without complication or difficulty.

The Finite Strip Process

An outline of the process has been given in reference (4), but shall also be recapitulated for completeness.

It is now assumed that the simply-supported bridge is subdivided into a number of strips. A typical strip is shown in Fig. 1 where the sides are numbered i and j. The properties of a strip are regarded as constant in its own, but can differ from adjacent strips so as to approximate transversely variable property problems. A suitable displacement function is

$$w = \sum_{m=1,2..r} \left[\left(1 - \frac{3x^2}{b^2} + \frac{2x^3}{b^3}\right) w_{im} + \left(x - \frac{2x^2}{b} + \frac{x^3}{b^2}\right) \theta_{im} + \left(\frac{3x^2}{b^2} - \frac{2x^3}{b^3}\right) w_{jm} + \left(\frac{x^3}{b^2} - \frac{x^2}{b}\right) \theta_{jm} \right] \sin \frac{m\pi y}{a} \qquad (1)$$

where w_{im}, θ_{im} etc. are the generalised displacements of the mth term at the side of the strip.

In matrix form equation (1) can be written as

$$w = C^e W^e = \left[C_1, C_2 \ldots\ldots\ldots\ldots C_r \right] \begin{Bmatrix} W_1^e \\ W_2^e \\ \vdots \\ W_r^e \end{Bmatrix} \qquad (2)$$

$$= \Sigma C_m W_m^e$$

in which $m = 1, \ldots\ldots\ldots\ldots r$

$$C_m = \left[1 - \frac{3x^2}{b^2} + \frac{2x^3}{b^3},\ x - \frac{2x^2}{b} + \frac{x^3}{b^2},\ \frac{3x^2}{b^2} - \frac{2x^3}{b^3},\ \frac{x^3}{b^2} - \frac{x^2}{b} \right] \sin \frac{m\pi y}{a}$$

and $W_m^e = \left\{ W_{im}\ \theta_{im}\ W_{jm}\ \theta_{jm} \right\}^T$

It can be seen that with such a function the displacements and its first derivatives along the boundary of two adjacent strips are determined uniquely by the generalised displacement parameters of that particular boundary only, and therefore compatibility is assured. A convergent solution(7) can therefore be expected since the deformed surface will have continuous first derivatives for all points in the domain.

The curvature matrix of the plate strip can be obtained by differentiating equation (1) with respect to x and y.

$$\chi^e = \begin{Bmatrix} -\dfrac{\partial^2 w}{\partial x^2} \\ -\dfrac{\partial^2 w}{\partial y^2} \\ 2\dfrac{\partial^2 w}{\partial x \partial y} \end{Bmatrix} = BW^e = [B_1 B_2 \ldots\ldots B_r] \begin{Bmatrix} W_1^e \\ W_2^e \\ \vdots \\ W_r^e \end{Bmatrix} = \Sigma\, B_m W_m^e \qquad (3)$$

and the moment matrix for orthotropic plates are given by(8)

$$M = \begin{matrix} M_x \\ M_y \\ M_{xy} \end{matrix} = \begin{bmatrix} D_x & D_1 & 0 \\ D_1 & D_y & 0 \\ 0 & 0 & D_{xy} \end{bmatrix} \begin{Bmatrix} -\dfrac{\partial^2 w}{\partial w^2} \\ -\dfrac{\partial^2 w}{\partial y^2} \\ 2\dfrac{\partial^2 w}{\partial x \partial y} \end{Bmatrix} = D\chi^e = DBW^e \qquad (4)$$

where $D_x = D_y = D$, $D_1 = \nu D$ and $D_{xy} = \frac{1-\nu}{2} D$ for isotropic plates.

The expression for the total potential energy of each strip are also given in Timoshenko[8], and we have

$$U^e = 1/2\int_0^a \int_0^b \left(-M_x \frac{\partial^2 w}{\partial x^2} - M_y \frac{\partial^2 w}{\partial y^2} + 2M_{xy} \frac{\partial^2 w}{\partial x \partial y}\right) dxdy$$

$$- \int_0^a \int_0^b w^T q dxdy \qquad (5)$$

in which the first integral denotes the strain energy of the strip and the second integral the work done by external loads.

Substituting (3) and (4) into (5),

$$U^e = 1/2\int_0^a \int_0^b M^T \chi^e dxdy - \int_0^a \int_0^b w^T q dxdy$$

$$= 1/2\int_0^a \int_0^b ({W^e}^T B^T D B W^e)\, dxdy - \int_0^a \int_0^b ({W^e}^T {C^e}^T q) dxdy$$

$$= \sum_{\substack{m=1,\dots r \\ n=1,\dots r}}\sum 1/2\, {W^e_m}^T \left(\int_0^a \int_0^b B_m^T D B_n\, dxdy \right) {W^e_m}^T$$

$$- \sum_{m=1,\dots r} {W^e_m}^T \int_0^a \int_0^b (C_m^T q) dxdy \qquad (6)$$

If the load q is also resolved into a sine series in the y direction similar to the deflexion function, then

$$q = q_1 \sin \frac{\pi y}{a} + q_2 \sin \frac{2\pi y}{a} + q_3 \sin \frac{3\pi y}{a} + \dots + q_r \sin \frac{r\pi y}{a}$$

$$= \sum_{n=1,\dots r} q_n \sin \frac{n\pi y}{a} \qquad (7)$$

where

$$q_n = \frac{\int_c^d q \sin\frac{n\pi y}{a}\, dy}{\int_0^a \sin^2(\frac{n\pi y}{a})\, dy} \qquad \text{for distributed loads from } y = c \text{ to } y = d$$

and

$$q_n = \frac{P \sin\frac{n\pi c}{a}}{\int_0^a \sin^2(\frac{n\pi y}{a})dy} \qquad \text{for a concentrated load } P \text{ at } y = c$$

Equation (6) can now be rewritten as

$$U^e = \sum_{\substack{m=1,\ldots r \\ n=1,\ldots r}}\sum \Bigg[W_m^{e^T} \Big(\int_0^a \int_0^b B_m^T D B_n dxdy \Big) W_m^e - W_m^{e^T} \int_0^a \int_0^b (C_m^T q_n \sin\frac{n\pi y}{a})\, dxdy \Bigg] \tag{7}$$

Only four types of integrals are required in equation (7), and they are all orthogonal and extremely simple. We have

$$\int_0^a \sin\frac{m\pi y}{a} \sin\frac{n\pi y}{a}\, dy = 0 \quad \text{for } m \neq n \qquad\qquad = \frac{a}{2} \quad \text{for } m = n \tag{8a}$$

$$\int_0^a (\sin\frac{m\pi y}{a})''(\sin\frac{n\pi y}{a})''\, dy = \int_0^a (\frac{-m\pi}{a})^2 \sin\frac{m\pi y}{a}(\frac{-n\pi}{a})^2 \sin\frac{n\pi y}{a}\, dy$$

$$= \frac{m^2 n^2 \pi^4}{a^4} \int_0^a \sin\frac{m\pi y}{a} \sin\frac{n\pi y}{a}\, dy$$

$$= 0 \qquad \text{for } m \neq n$$

$$= \frac{m^4\pi^4}{2a^3} \qquad \text{for } m = n \tag{8b}$$

$$\int_0^a \left(\sin\frac{m\pi y}{a}\right)'\left(\sin\frac{n\pi y}{a}\right)' dy = \frac{mn\pi^2}{a^2}\int_0^a \cos\frac{m\pi y}{a}\cos\frac{n\pi y}{a}\,dy$$

$$= 0 \qquad \text{for } m \neq n$$

$$= \frac{m^2\pi^2}{2a} \qquad \text{for } m = n \tag{8c}$$

$$\int_0^a \sin\frac{m\pi y}{a}\left(\sin\frac{n\pi y}{a}\right)'' dy = \frac{-n^2\pi^2}{a^2}\int_0^a \sin\frac{m\pi y}{a}\sin\frac{n\pi y}{a}\,dy$$

$$= 0 \text{ for } m \neq n$$

$$= \frac{-m^2\pi^2}{2a} \quad \text{for } m = n \tag{8d}$$

It can now be seen that the integration work required is trivial and that each term of the sine series can be solved individually and then summed to give the final answers. Therefore, instead of solving one set of r x s equations, the solution of r sets of s equations are required, and as a consequence, both the core storage required and solution time can be very much reduced. In the text which follows, the subscripts n and one of the Σ sign will be duly dropped.

Differentiating equation 7 with respect to the generalized displacements one after the other and equating each of the differentials to zero will yield a set of 4 simultaneous equations.

$$\frac{\partial U^e}{\partial W^e_m} = \left\{\frac{\partial U^e}{\partial W_{im}} \quad \frac{\partial U^e}{\partial \theta_{im}} \quad \frac{\partial U^e}{\partial W_{jm}} \quad \frac{\partial U^e}{\partial \theta_{jm}}\right\}^T$$

$$= \int_0^a \int_0^b B_m^T DB_m \, dxdy \; W_m^e - \int_0^a \int_0^b C_m^T q_m \sin \frac{m\pi y}{a} \, dxdy$$

$$= [S_m] \left\{ W_m^e \right\} - \left\{ F_m^e \right\} = 0 \qquad (9)$$

$[S_m]$ is a square symmetric matrix similar in form to a stiffness matrix and F_m^e to a load matrix in structural analysis. They have been worked out explicitly and are given in Appendix 1.

The stiffness matrix of a generalized finite element is always singular and cannot be inverted, while the present $[S_m]$ is no longer singular due to pre-set boundary conditions. Therefore it is not essential here to insert any other prescribed displacement conditions for the solution of the structure.

The final equations for minimizing the total potential energy of the whole bridge can be obtained by summing up the contributions from the individual strips. This procedure is identical to the assemblage of stiffness matrices of beam elements.

The final stiffness is always of a compact tridiagonalized submatrix form and has a very narrow half-band width (Fig. 2). The solution subroutine can be written either for minimum storage, in which only three 2x2 submatrices are required but at the same time data transfer from disk or tape to memory will be needed, or for minimum solution time, in which the whole matrix is stored in core as a rectangular array of n x 4(n=40 is good enough for most problems) and solved directly by band matrix solution techniques.

Strip with Higher Order Polynomials

It is also possible to use a higher order polynomial which includes up to the fifth power of x in the transverse direction so that the generalised displacements at the two sides will now have w, $\frac{\partial w}{\partial x}$, $\frac{\partial^2 w}{\partial x^2}$ terms. If such a strip is used, all the moments will be continuous throughout the whole domain after deformation. Experience has shown[9] that such higher order elements usually give better accuracy for a problem with the same number of unknowns when compared with lower order elements, although they do possess the disadvantage of not being able to deal with abrupt change of properties.(At sections where there are abrupt changes in properties, the moments are continuous but the curvatures must necessarily be discontinuous).

The Problem of Free Edges and Longitudinal Beams

For free edges, no special treatment is required since it is only necessary to put the appropriate load terms equal to zero. Obviously the boundary conditions at the free edges (transverse moment and Kirchoff shear force equal to zero at every point) are not satisfied exactly, but rather the integral of such forces are made equal to zero. From the subsequent examples it can be seen that the transverse moments at the centre of the free edges are so small that they can usually be neglected. This follows from the fact that both $\frac{\partial^2 w}{\partial x^2}$ and $\frac{\partial^2 w}{\partial y^2}$ vary as a sine series, and if the integral of the first sine term (which is the dominant one and is always positive) is made equal to zero the amplitude of the first sine term must also be zero.

For bridges which are made up of slabs and heavy longitudinal beams that are spaced fairly widely apart, it is more appropriate to analyse the structure as a composite beam-slab system rather than as an orthotropic plate. Such a modification is quite straightforward, since it is fairly easy to derive a beam bending stiffness using a sine series, and a beam torsion stiffness matrix using a cosine series.

If the centre line of the beam is now chosen as one of the imaginary boundary lines for the strips, the coupling of the beam and the slab will simply mean the addition of the two types of stiffness for the particular nodal line.

Examples

1. Isotropic bridge under uniform load. Due to symmetry, only five strips are used for the square bridge and three strips for the rectangular bridge. From Table I it can be seen that two terms of the series will produce results of adequate accuracy.

2. Isotropic square bridge under a concentrated load placed at five different locations along the transverse centre line ($\nu = 0.15$)

The bridge is divided into sixteen strips and eight terms of the series are used. The moments along the transverse central section (Fig. 3 to Fig. 9) are compared with the results obtained from a 8x8 finite element analysis given by Sawko and Cope[10] and from the Method of Distribution Coefficients[11]. It can be seen that the Method of Distribution Coefficients always underestimate the maximum value of moments, while the agreement between the Finite Element Method and the Finite Strip Method is quite remarkable.

The moments for the concentrated load converge slower than that for the distributed load. However, this is a rather severe test, as in practice the working loads consist of distributed dead loads and a number of truck wheel loads which are spaced some distances apart.

3. Isotropic square bridge with abrupt change of section (Fig. 10) and with a concentrated load at the centre ($\nu = 0.15$). Half of the bridge is divided into eight strips and eight terms of the series are used. As expected, the stiffening of the bridge on the two sides reduces the

central maximum moments significantly.

4. Orthotropic Square Bridge Under Uniform Loading

The flexural and torsional rigidities of slabs with two way reinforcements and slab stiffened by ribs can be obtained from Timoshenko[8]. For the present example, the rigidities are taken as D_x, D_y, $D_1 = \nu \sqrt{D_x D_y}$ and $D_{xy} = \frac{1-\nu}{2} \sqrt{D_x D_y}$, in which ν is Poisson's ratio for concrete, assumed to have a value of 0.15.

In order to show the effect of orthotropy, the bridge in example 1 has been reanalysed using two more stiffness ratio (D_y/D_x) of 4 and 9. The results are summarised in Table 2. A fairly good agreement is obtained when they are compared with an approximate solution due to Coull[11].

CONCLUSIONS

The finite strip method has been shown to be ideally suitable for the analyses of orthotropic right bridges. It is simple, easy to program, requires minimal input data, fairly small storage and little time to run. The bridge in example 1, which used 16 strips and 8 terms of the sine series, was completely solved in less than one minute (execution time) on the multiprogramming IBM 360-50 computer. In this case the whole stiffness matrix is stored in core as a rectangular array of 34x4, and then solved by a narrow band matrix solution technique.

ACKNOWLEDGEMENT

The author wishes to thank the National Research Council of Canada for partial financial support of the project, and Mr. M. S. Cheung who helped to compile the contents of Appendix I.

References

(1) Chu, K.H. and Krishnamoorthy, G., "Use of Orthotropic Theory in Bridge Design", Journal of Struct. Div., Proc. A.S.C.E., June 1962, pp. 35-77.

(2) Zienkiewicz, O.C. and Cheung, Y.K., "Finite Element Method in Structural and Continuum Mechanics", McGraw-Hill Book Co., 1967.

(3) Cheung, Y.K., King, I.P. and Zienkiewicz, O.C., "Slab Bridges with Arbitrary Shape and Support Conditions", Proc. Inst. of Civil Engrs., May 1968, pp. 9-36.

(4) Cheung, Y.K., "The Finite Strip Method in the Analysis of Elastic Plates with Two Opposite Simply Supported Ends", Proc. Inst. of Civil Engrs., May 1968, pp. 1-7.

(5) Massonet, C., "Method of Calculation for Bridges with Several Longitudinal Beams taking into Account their Torsional Resistance", I.A.B.S.E., 1950, pp. 147-182 (In French).

(6) Cornelius, W., "Die Berechnung der ebener Flachentragwerke mit Hilfe der Theone der Orthogonal-anisotropen Platte", Der Stahlbau, 1952, Vol. 1, pp. 21-26; Vol. 3, pp. 43-48; Vol. 4, pp. 60-64.

(7) Tong, P. and Pian, T.H.H., "The Convergence of Finite Element Method in Solving Linear Elastic Problems", Int. J. Solids Structure, 1967, Vol. 3, pp. 865-879.

(8) Timoshenko, S. and Woinowsky-Krieger, S., "Theory of Plates and Shells", 2nd. Edition, McGraw-Hill Book Co., New York, 1959.

(9) Bogner, F.K., Fox, R.L. and Schmidt, L.A., "The Generation of Inter-

element, Compatible Stiffness and Mass Matrices by the Use of Interpolation Formulae", Proc. Conf. on Matrix Methods in Struct. Mech., Air Force Inst. of Technology, Wright-Patterson Air Force Base, October 1965.

(10) Sawko, F. and Cope, R.J., "The Use of Finite Elements for the Analysis of Right Bridge Decks", Int. Sym. on the Use of Electonic Digital Computers in Structural Engineering, paper No. 16, University of Newcastle upon Tyne, July 1966.

(11) Coull, A., "Direct Stress Analysis of Orthotropic Bridge Decks", Journal of Struct. Div., Proc. A.S.C.E., April 1964, pp. 1-12.

Table 1 ($\nu = 0.3$)

Aspect ratio	Method of Analysis	1			2	
		w_1	M_{x1}	M_{y1}	w_2	M_{y2}
$\lambda = 1$	Finite Strip 2 terms	0.01309	0.02697	0.12175	0.01500	0.13029
	Finite Strip 4 terms	0.01309	0.02717	0.12224	0.01500	0.13141
	Reference (8)	0.01309	0.0271	0.1225	0.01509	0.1318
$\lambda = 2$	Finite Strip 2 terms	0.01368	0.01216	0.12266	0.01461	0.12673
	Finite Strip 4 terms	0.01368	0.01236	0.12331	0.01461	0.12743
	Reference (8)	0.01377	0.0102	0.1235	0.01443	0.1259
Multiplier		$\frac{qa^4}{D}$	qa^2		$\frac{qa^4}{D}$	qa^2

point 1 at centre of bridge

point 2 at centre of side

Table 2 Orthotropic square bridge

	w_1			M_{x1}			M_{y1}			w_2			M_{y2}		
D_y/D_x	1	4	9	1	4	9	1	4	9	1	4	9	1	4	9
2 terms	0.01290	0.00323	0.00154	0.01424	0.00855	0.00601	0.12232	0.12277	0.12302	0.01371	0.00345	0.00143	0.12790	0.12889	0.12914
4 terms	0.01290	0.00323	0.00154	0.01434	0.00858	0.00604	0.12307	0.12342	0.12367	0.01371	0.00345	0.00143	0.12859	0.12958	0.12982
Coull (11)				0.01438	0.00912	0.00701							0.12775		0.12925
Multiplier	$\frac{qa^4}{D_x}$			qa^2						$\frac{qa^4}{D_x}$			qa^2		

point 1 at centre of bridge
point 2 at centre of side

APPENDIX 1 - STIFFNESS AND LOAD MATRICES

$$
[S_m] = \begin{bmatrix}
\frac{13ab}{70} k^2 D_y + \frac{12a}{5b} k D_{xy} + \frac{12a}{10b} k D_1 + \frac{6a}{b^3} D_x &
\frac{3a}{5} k D_1 + \frac{a}{5} k D_{xy} + \frac{3a}{b^2} D_x + \frac{11ab^2}{420} k^2 D_y &
\frac{9ab}{140} k^2 D_x - \frac{12a}{5b} k D_{xy} - \frac{6a}{5b} k D_1 - \frac{6a}{b^3} D_x &
-\frac{13ab^2}{840} k^2 D_y + \frac{a}{5} k D_{xy} + \frac{a}{10} k D_1 + \frac{3a}{b^2} D_x \\
\frac{3a}{5} k D_1 + \frac{a}{5} k D_{xy} + \frac{3a}{b^3} D_x + \frac{11ab^2}{420} k^2 D_y &
\frac{ab^3}{210} k^2 D_y + \frac{4ab}{15} k D_{xy} + \frac{2ab}{15} k D_1 + \frac{2a}{b} D_x &
\frac{13ab^2}{840} k^2 D_y - \frac{a}{5} k D_{xy} - \frac{a}{10} k D_1 - \frac{3a}{b^2} D_x &
-\frac{3ab^3}{840} k^2 D_y - \frac{ab}{15} k D_{xy} - \frac{ab}{30} k D_1 + \frac{a}{b} D_x \\
\frac{9ab}{140} k^2 D_y - \frac{12a}{5b} k D_{xy} - \frac{6a}{5b} k D_1 - \frac{6a}{b^3} D_x &
\frac{13ab^2}{840} k^2 D_y - \frac{a}{5} k D_{xy} - \frac{a}{10} k D_1 - \frac{3a}{b^2} D_x &
\frac{13ab}{70} k^2 D_y + \frac{12a}{5b} k D_{xy} + \frac{6a}{5b} k D_1 + \frac{6a}{b^3} D_x &
-\frac{11ab^2}{420} k^2 D_y - \frac{a}{5} k D_{xy} - \frac{3a}{5} k D_1 - \frac{3a}{b^2} D_x \\
-\frac{13ab^2}{840} k^2 D_y + \frac{a}{5} k D_{xy} + \frac{a}{10} k D_1 + \frac{3a}{b^2} D_x &
-\frac{3ab^3}{840} k^2 D_y - \frac{ab}{15} k D_{xy} - \frac{ab}{30} k D_1 + \frac{a}{b} D_x &
-\frac{11ab^2}{420} k^2 D_y - \frac{a}{5} k D_{xy} - \frac{3a}{5} k D_1 - \frac{3a}{b^2} D_x &
\frac{ab^3}{210} k^2 D_y + \frac{4ab}{15} k D_{xy} + \frac{2ab}{15} k D_1 + \frac{2a}{b} D_x
\end{bmatrix}
$$

$$
(k = \frac{m^2 \pi^2}{a^2})
$$

$$
\{F_m\} = \frac{q_m a^2}{2} \begin{Bmatrix} b/2 \\ b^2/12 \\ b/2 \\ -b^2/12 \end{Bmatrix}
$$

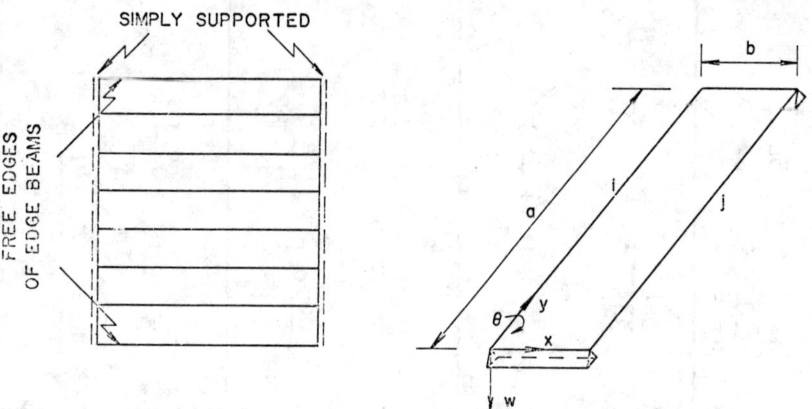

Fig. 1 A typical strip and an arbitrary bridge.

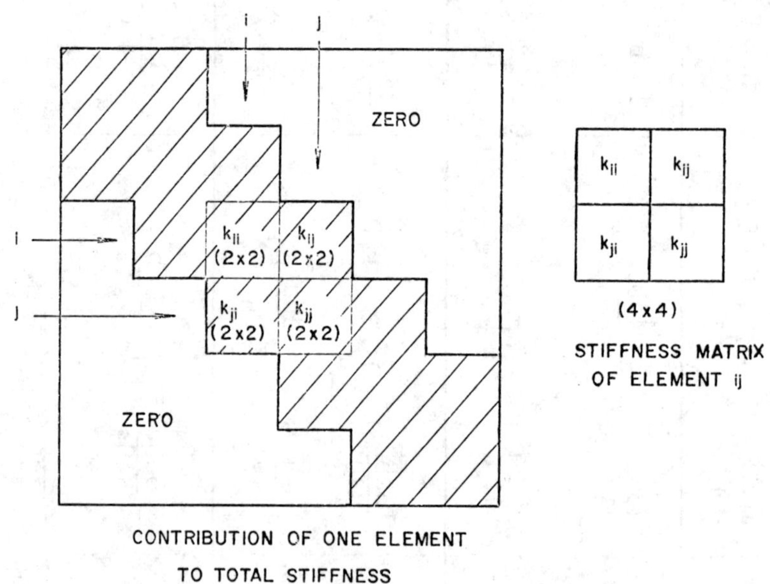

Fig. 2 Individual and overall stiffness matrices.

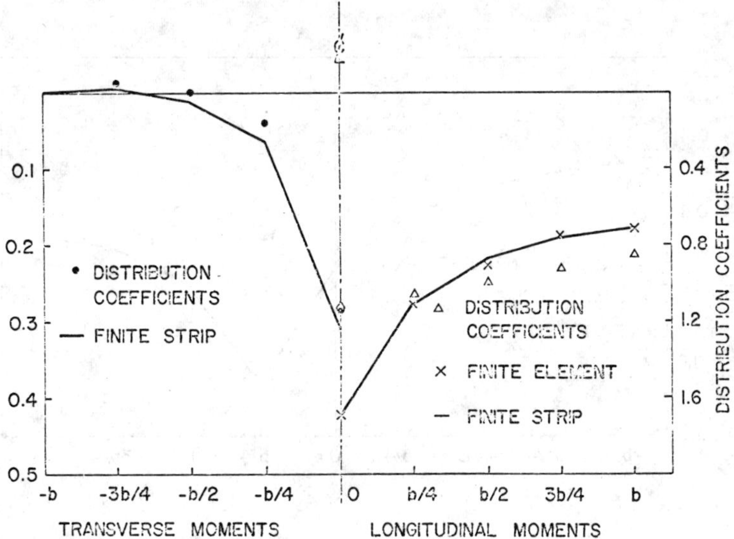

Fig. 3 Distribution of moments for a unit point load at 0.

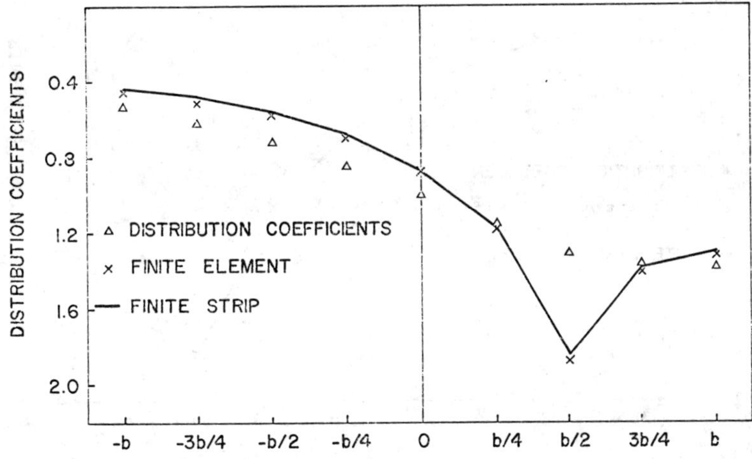

Fig. 4 Distribution coefficients for longitudinal moments for a unit point load at b/4.

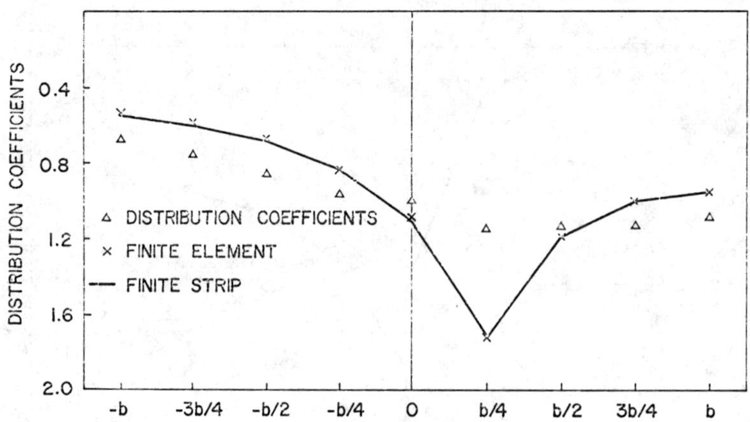

Fig. 5 Distribution coefficients for longitudinal moments for a unit point load at b/2.

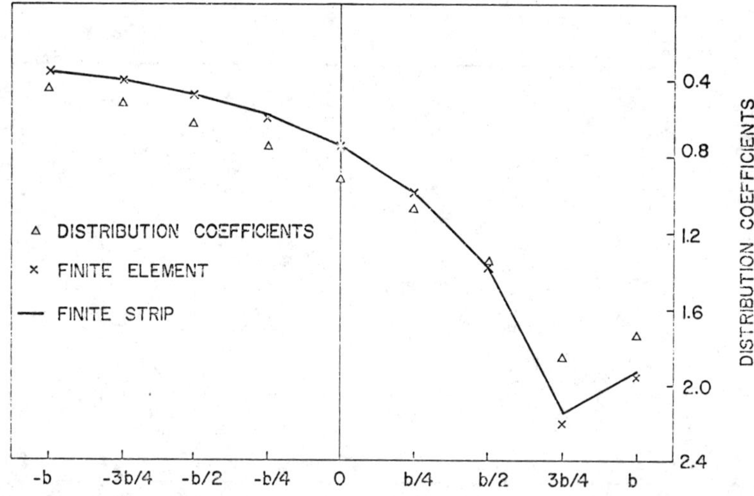

Fig. 6 Distribution coefficients for longitudinal moments for a unit point load at 3b/4.

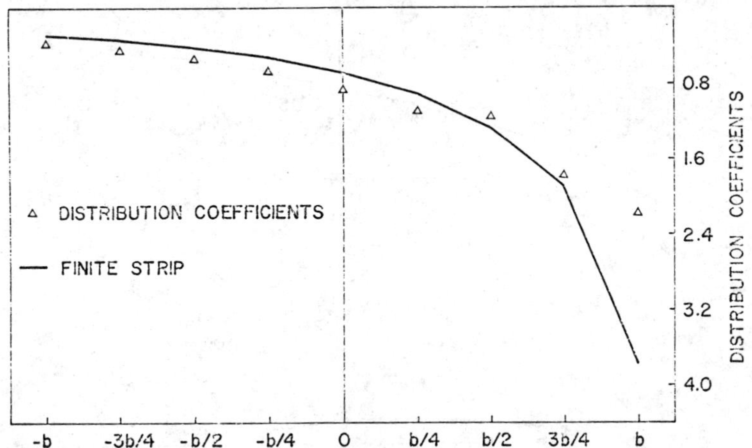

Fig. 7 Distribution coefficients for longitudinal moments for a unit point load at b.

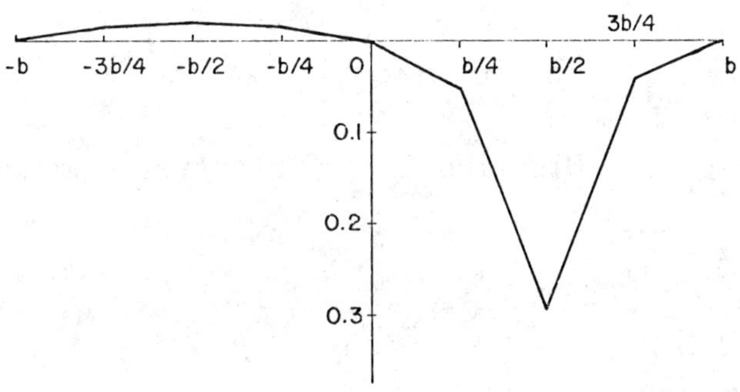

A. POINT LOAD AT b/2

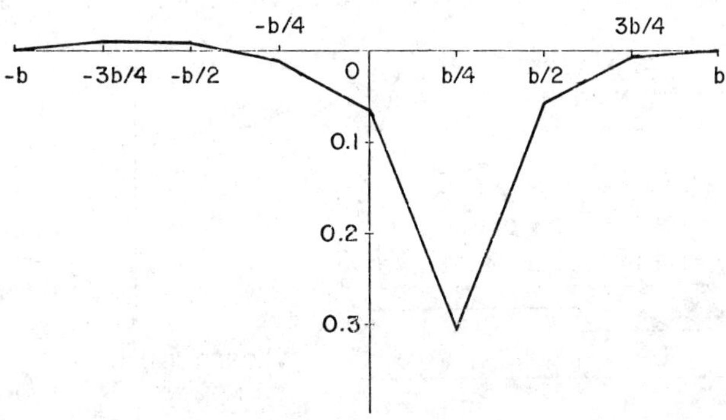

B. POINT LOAD AT b/4

Fig. 8 Distribution of transverse moments.

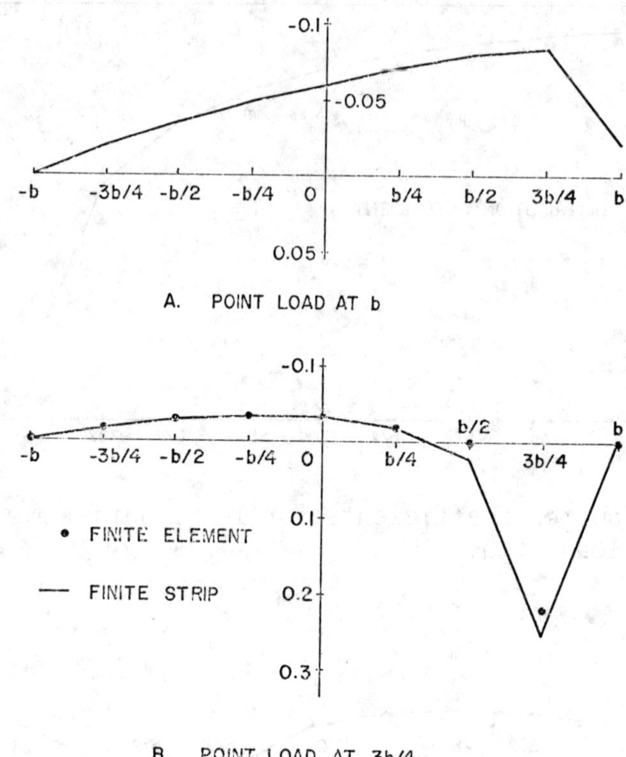

Fig. 9 Distribution of transverse moments

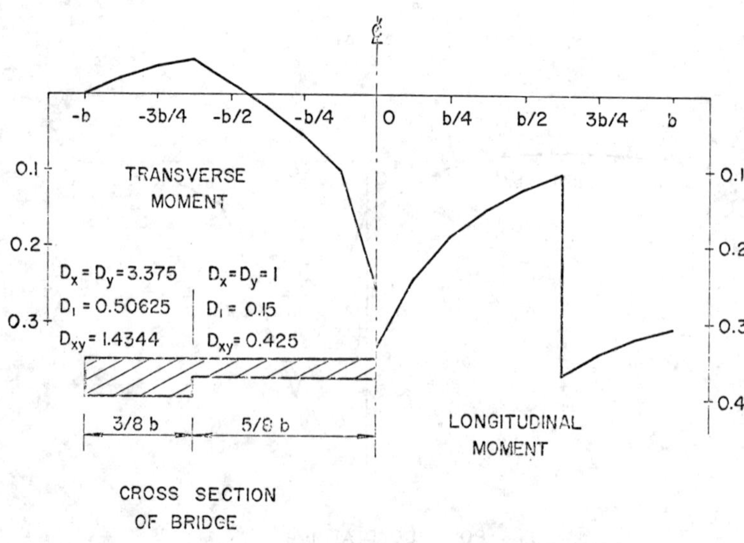

Fig. 10 Bridge and variable cross-section distribution of moments for a point load at 0.

DISCUSSION

By A. R. CUSENS

Head, Civil Engineering Department, University of Dundee

In his paper Dr. Cheung has compared the finite strip method with a finite element analysis and with the Method of Distribution Coefficients. He concludes that the Method of Distribution Coefficients always underestimates the maximum value of moments.

The distribution coefficient method is based on a series solution of the orthotropic plate equation. The theory was originally developed[12,5,13] before electronic digital computers were available and employs only the first term of the series. Thus the comparison is between two series methods. In Figs. 3 to 9 Dr. Cheung is taking eight terms for his finite strip method and comparing them with the first term of the orthotropic plate solution. Had he taken similar numbers of terms for both methods he would have found identical results. A recent paper[14] demonstrates the effects of the number of terms on the distribution coefficient method (better described as the orthotropic plate method) when a right bridge deck is loaded with concentrated loads.

The results of Table 2 were checked by orthotropic plate theory developed for patch loads and good correspondence was found with the author's values. However it appears that in the paper for $D_y/D_x = 9$, the values for w_1 and w_2 have been transposed.

The finite strip method appears to hold distinct promise for certain types of structure and Dr. Cheung is to be congratulated on its development. For orthotropic right bridges it appears to hold no advantage over orthotropic plate theory in terms of accuracy, and to be less efficient in terms of computing time.

REFERENCES

12. Guyon, Y., " Calcul des Ponts larges à Poutres Multiples Solidarisées par des Entretoises" , Annales des Ponts et Chaussees, Paris, No. 24, September-October, 1946, pp. 553-612.

13. Rowe, R.E. Concrete Bridge Design John Wiley, New York

14. Cusens, A.R. and Pama, R.P., " The Distribution of Concentrated Loads on Orthotropic Bridge Decks" , The Structural Engineer (to be published).

Table 2 (Amended) Orthotropic square bridge

	w_1			M_{x1}			M_{y1}			w_2			M_{y2}		
D_y/D_x	1	4	9	1	4	9	1	4	9	1	4	9	1	4	9
2 terms	0.01290	0.00323	0.00154	0.01424	0.00855	0.00601	0.12232	0.12277	0.12302	0.01371	0.00345	0.00143	0.12790	0.12889	0.12914
4 terms	0.01290	0.00323	0.00154	0.01434	0.00858	0.00604	0.12307	0.12342	0.12367	0.01371	0.00345	0.00143	0.12859	0.12958	0.12982
Coull (11)				0.01438	0.00912	0.00701							0.12775		0.12925
Plate theory (5 terms)	0.01293	0.00322	0.00143	0.01430	0.00857	0.00604	0.1237	0.1236	0.1241	0.01374	0.00344	0.00154	0.1292	0.1299	0.1301
Multiplier	$\frac{qa^4}{D_x}$			qa^2						$\frac{qa^4}{D_x}$			qa^2		

point 1 at centre of bridge

point 2 at centre of side

DESIGN OF SIMPLY-SUPPORTED SKEW CONCRETE GIRDER BRIDGES

By AMIN GHALI

SYNOPSIS

In a paper presented at the First International Symposium on Concrete Bridge Design, Toronto, April, 1967(1), a numerical method was used for the analysis of skew bridges composed of a deck slab monolithic with two main girders and the method was verified by model testing. In the present paper design tables prepared by this method are presented, giving the values of the bending and twisting moments and the reactions in the girders due to uniform load and the influence coefficients for these stress resultants in simply-supported skew bridges. These tables can be used with various angles of skew and a fairly wide range of variation of width to span ratio and bending and torsional rigidities. Skew bridges of box type can be analysed by these tables. The assumptions involved in the preparation of the tables and the method of their use are briefly described.

Keywords: bending moments; box beams; bridges (structures); finite difference theory; girders; numerical analysis; reinforced concrete; skew bridges; structural design; torsion.

ACI member AMIN GHALI is associate professor of civil engineering, University of Calgary, Alberta, Canada. In 1957, he received a PhD degree from Leeds University, England. Prior to his present appointment he worked with a consulting firm in Cairo, Egypt and later he was assistant professor at Cairo University. In Switzerland, he spent a year at the Statics Laboratory of Lausanne University and was designer for two years with the engineering firm Conrad Zschokke Ltd., Geneva. He has served extensively as a designer and consultant on structural engineering problems for industrial firms in Egypt, Switzerland and Canada. He designed several concrete bridges in Switzerland and in Ontario, Canada. Dr. Ghali is a member of ACI Committee 344, Circular Prestressed Structures. He is the author and co-author of many papers in the field of structural analysis.

INTRODUCTION

The tables presented in this paper can be used for the analysis of simply-supported skew bridges of uniform cross section of the types shown in Fig. 1. The bridge deck is considered to be equivalent to two main girders (Fig. 2), having both flexural and torsional rigidity, rigidly connected in the transverse direction by the slab and/or by equally spaced cross girders.

The tables give the bending moment, twisting moment and the reactions due to uniform or a concentrated vertical load acting directly on the girders. A vertical load between the girders or on the overhang is to be approximated by statical equivalent concentrated vertical load and twisting couples acting on the girders. The computer program used for the analysis gives influence coefficients corresponding to a unit vertical load or a unit twisting couple on the girders. However, the influence coefficients due to external applied twisting couples are not presented here for space limitation. The analysis by the use of the tables is concerned with the stress resultants in the girders not the slab. This, of course, will have to be supplemented by a separate analysis to design the slab for the local effect of a load acting away from the girders.

The statical behaviour of the bridge depends upon the width to span ratio, $\frac{b}{\ell}$, the skew angle (Fig. 2), the ratio ζ of the flexural rigidity in the transverse direction for the whole span to the flexural rigidity of one main girder, $(EI_s^{'}\ell/EI)$ and the ratio ϕ of the torsional and bending rigidities of one main girder. The tables presented are for $\frac{b}{\ell}$ = 0.10, 0.20 and 0.40 with four different skew angles as indicated in Table 1.

TABLE I

Skew Angles Corresponding to the Values of (b/ℓ) Included in the Analysis

Value of $\frac{b}{\ell}$	0.10	0.20	0.40
Tangent of the angle of skew	0	0	0
	2/3	0.10	1/6
	4/3	2/3	1/3
	2.0	1.0	1/2

With each of the cases listed in Table I the values of ϕ and ζ are taken: ϕ = 0.10, 0.30, 0.5, 2.00 and 3.00 and ζ = 0.10, 0.20, 0.40 and 2.00. This is believed to cover a wide range of practical cases. If the bridge is continuous the tables can still be used with some judgement for preliminary design.

BASIC ASSUMPTIONS AND METHOD OF ANALYSIS

The deck slab is assumed to have two effects: to increase the bending and torsional rigidity of the girders forming T or box-sections, and to transmit the external loads to the main girders acting as strips having only flexural rigidity in the transverse direction. The effect of symmetrical haunches at the two slab edges at their intersection with the webs is included in the analysis by appropriate evaluation of S and r, which are the end rotational stiffness and carry-over moment of a transverse slab strip of unit width. These are the same factors used in the usual moment-distribution procedure and are available in several references[2]. The flexural rigidity of equally-spaced cross girders is to be assumed distributed over the length of the bridge and added to the rigidity of the slab.

When the tables are used for the analysis of a bridge composed of one box (Fig. 1c), the cross section is to be replaced by two girders along the centre line of the webs, the bending and torsional rigidity of each is equal to half that of the box including the overhangs, and the flexural rigidity in the transverse direction is equal to the sum of the flexural rigidity of the two slabs.

For the preparation of the tables presented, the finite differences method is used to obtain influence coefficients of displacements, reactions and stress resultants. All the influence coefficients are calculated from an "equivalent stiffness matrix"[1] of the structure (ESM). The elements of the ESM are the coefficients of the finite difference equations relating the displacements to the external applied loads. Each main girder is divided into five equal intervals, $\lambda = 0.2\ell$, see Fig. (1d).

DESIGN TABLES

For the use of the tables, the dimensionless values ζ and ϕ are first determined from the geometrical properties of the bridge.

$$\zeta = EI_s' \ell/EI \qquad (1)$$

EI is the flexural rigidity of one main girder and EI_s' is an effective flexural rigidity of the slab including the effect of haunches

$$I_s' = b(S+r)/6E \qquad (2)$$

when the slab is of constant thickness $S = (4EI_s/b)$, $r = (2EI_s/b)$ and $I_s' = I_s$, where I_s is the moment of inertia of a strip of unit width of the slab. When equally spaced cross girders are provided, their moment of inertia per unit length of the span should be included in I_s' in Eq.(1).

The ratio of the torsional to the bending rigidity of one main girder

$$\phi = \frac{GJ}{EI} \qquad (3)$$

Methods of calculating the torsion constant J for non-circular cross sections are treated in literature, see for example, reference (3).

For any values of $\frac{b}{\ell}$, skew angle, ϕ or ζ within the range covered in the tables, interpolation can be used for the required coefficient.

Tables 1 - 12 give influence coefficients of bending moment and twisting moment in main girders due to a unit vertical load applied at any of the points 2 to 11. Tables 13-16 give bending moment and twisting moment variation in the main girders due to a uniform line load of unit intensity on each of the two girders. The influence coefficients of the reactions at the supports due to a unit vertical load are given in Tables 17-20. The coefficients for the bending moments are given for the section at the nodes indicated in Fig. 2, while the coefficients of twisting moments are for points midway beteen the nodes.

The positive directions of the bending moment and twisting moments are indicated in Fig. 3 by vectors drawn in the top view of an element of length (dx) of a main girder. The reaction is positive when upwards.

CONCLUSION

The analysis of bridges composed of a slab monolithic with two main girders which have torsional and flexural rigidity can be simplified by the use of the tables presented. The same tables may also be used for bridges composed of one box section.

ACKNOWLEDGMENT

This project was supported by a grant from the National Research Council of Canada which is gratefully acknowledged. The computer facilities offered by the Data Centre of the University of Calgary made it possible to prepare presented tables.

REFERENCES

(1) Ghali, A., "Analysis of Continuous Skew Concrete Girder Bridges" International Symposium on Concrete Bridge Design, Toronto, April 5, 1967, ACI Publication.

(2) Handbook of Frame Constants, Portland Cement Association, Chicago, 1958, 34 pp.

(3) Kollbrunner, C.F. and K. Basler, Torsion, Springer-Verlag New York, 1966 (in German).

NOTATION

b distance from centre to centre of main girders.

EI flexural rigidity of one main girder. When the bridge is composed of one box section, EI is half the total flexural rigidity of the cross section.

GJ torsional rigidity of one main girder. When the bridge is composed of one box section, GJ equals half the total torsional rigidity of the section.

I_s moment of inertia of a strip of unit width of slab.

I'_s equivalent moment of inertia per unit width for a slab with symmetrical haunches, defined by Eq. (2).

ℓ span length.

S,r end rotational stiffness and carry-over moment of a transverse slab strip of unit width.

ϕ ratio of the torsional rigidity GJ to the flexural rigidity EI.

ζ ratio of the total flexural rigidity in the transverse direction in the whole length of the bridge to the flexural rigidity of one main girder.

TABLE 1 - SIMPLY-SUPPORTED SKEW GIRDER BRIDGE

INFLUENCE COEFICIENT OF BENDING MOMENT IN MAIN GIRDER

BENDING MOMENT = COEF.x ℓ

$(b/\ell) = 0.10$ ANGLE OF SKEW=ARCTAN(0.0)

UNIT VERTICAL LOAD APPLIED AT POINT:

BENDING MOMENT AT POINT 2

ϕ	ζ	2	3	4	5	8	9	10	11
0.10	0.10	0.1235	0.0781	0.0486	0.0240	0.0365	0.0419	0.0314	0.0160
	0.20	0.1185	0.0744	0.0462	0.0227	0.0415	0.0456	0.0338	0.0173
	0.40	0.1150	0.0720	0.0447	0.0218	0.0450	0.0480	0.0353	0.0182
	2.00	0.1114	0.0698	0.0432	0.0210	0.0486	0.0502	0.0368	0.0190
0.30	0.10	0.1168	0.0729	0.0469	0.0244	0.0432	0.0471	0.0331	0.0156
	0.20	0.1097	0.0685	0.0444	0.0228	0.0503	0.0515	0.0356	0.0172
	0.40	0.1040	0.0657	0.0428	0.0216	0.0560	0.0543	0.0372	0.0184
	2.00	0.0973	0.0630	0.0409	0.0204	0.0627	0.0570	0.0391	0.0196
0.50	0.10	0.1149	0.0715	0.0469	0.0249	0.0451	0.0485	0.0331	0.0151
	0.20	0.1071	0.0670	0.0444	0.0233	0.0529	0.0530	0.0356	0.0167
	0.40	0.1008	0.0643	0.0427	0.0219	0.0592	0.0557	0.0373	0.0181
	2.00	0.0929	0.0617	0.0408	0.0204	0.0671	0.0583	0.0392	0.0196
1.00	0.10	0.1130	0.0703	0.0470	0.0257	0.0470	0.0497	0.0330	0.0143
	0.20	0.1046	0.0658	0.0446	0.0240	0.0554	0.0542	0.0354	0.0160
	0.40	0.0978	0.0632	0.0429	0.0224	0.0622	0.0568	0.0371	0.0176
	2.00	0.0889	0.0609	0.0408	0.0205	0.0711	0.0591	0.0392	0.0195
1.50	0.10	0.1122	0.0698	0.0471	0.0260	0.0478	0.0502	0.0329	0.0140
	0.20	0.1036	0.0653	0.0448	0.0244	0.0564	0.0547	0.0352	0.0156
	0.40	0.0966	0.0627	0.0431	0.0227	0.0634	0.0573	0.0369	0.0173
	2.00	0.0874	0.0606	0.0408	0.0206	0.0726	0.0594	0.0392	0.0194

BENDING MOMENT AT POINT 3

ϕ	ζ	2	3	4	5	8	9	10	11
0.10	0.10	0.0741	0.1639	0.0949	0.0449	0.0459	0.0761	0.0651	0.0351
	0.20	0.0715	0.1590	0.0921	0.0437	0.0485	0.0810	0.0679	0.0363
	0.40	0.0703	0.1562	0.0909	0.0432	0.0497	0.0838	0.0691	0.0368
	2.00	0.0694	0.1537	0.0901	0.0428	0.0506	0.0863	0.0699	0.0372
0.30	0.10	0.0670	0.1520	0.0865	0.0415	0.0530	0.0880	0.0735	0.0385
	0.20	0.0639	0.1450	0.0833	0.0405	0.0561	0.0950	0.0767	0.0395
	0.40	0.0626	0.1407	0.0823	0.0402	0.0574	0.0993	0.0777	0.0398
	2.00	0.0622	0.1366	0.0822	0.0403	0.0578	0.1034	0.0778	0.0397
0.50	0.10	0.0651	0.1490	0.0845	0.0409	0.0549	0.0910	0.0755	0.0391
	0.20	0.0620	0.1413	0.0813	0.0399	0.0580	0.0987	0.0787	0.0401
	0.40	0.0608	0.1365	0.0804	0.0398	0.0592	0.1035	0.0796	0.0402
	2.00	0.0607	0.1317	0.0807	0.0400	0.0593	0.1083	0.0793	0.0400
1.00	0.10	0.0636	0.1465	0.0831	0.0406	0.0564	0.0935	0.0769	0.0394
	0.20	0.0603	0.1383	0.0798	0.0396	0.0597	0.1017	0.0802	0.0404
	0.40	0.0593	0.1330	0.0790	0.0396	0.0607	0.1070	0.0810	0.0404
	2.00	0.0598	0.1274	0.0797	0.0399	0.0602	0.1126	0.0803	0.0401
1.50	0.10	0.0630	0.1457	0.0826	0.0405	0.0570	0.0943	0.0774	0.0395
	0.20	0.0597	0.1373	0.0793	0.0396	0.0603	0.1027	0.0807	0.0404
	0.40	0.0588	0.1318	0.0785	0.0396	0.0612	0.1082	0.0815	0.0404
	2.00	0.0595	0.1258	0.0794	0.0399	0.0605	0.1142	0.0806	0.0401

BENDING MOMENT AT POINT 4

ϕ	ζ	2	3	4	5	8	9	10	11
0.10	0.10	0.0449	0.0949	0.1639	0.0741	0.0351	0.0651	0.0761	0.0459
	0.20	0.0437	0.0921	0.1590	0.0715	0.0363	0.0679	0.0810	0.0485
	0.40	0.0432	0.0909	0.1562	0.0703	0.0368	0.0691	0.0838	0.0497
	2.00	0.0428	0.0901	0.1537	0.0694	0.0372	0.0699	0.0863	0.0506
0.30	0.10	0.0415	0.0865	0.1520	0.0670	0.0385	0.0735	0.0880	0.0530
	0.20	0.0405	0.0833	0.1450	0.0639	0.0395	0.0767	0.0950	0.0561
	0.40	0.0402	0.0823	0.1407	0.0626	0.0398	0.0777	0.0993	0.0574
	2.00	0.0403	0.0822	0.1366	0.0622	0.0397	0.0778	0.1034	0.0578
0.50	0.10	0.0409	0.0845	0.1490	0.0651	0.0391	0.0755	0.0910	0.0549
	0.20	0.0399	0.0813	0.1413	0.0620	0.0401	0.0787	0.0987	0.0580
	0.40	0.0398	0.0804	0.1365	0.0608	0.0402	0.0796	0.1035	0.0592
	2.00	0.0400	0.0807	0.1317	0.0607	0.0400	0.0793	0.1083	0.0593
1.00	0.10	0.0406	0.0831	0.1465	0.0636	0.0394	0.0769	0.0935	0.0564
	0.20	0.0396	0.0798	0.1383	0.0603	0.0404	0.0802	0.1017	0.0597
	0.40	0.0396	0.0790	0.1330	0.0593	0.0404	0.0810	0.1070	0.0607
	2.00	0.0399	0.0797	0.1274	0.0598	0.0401	0.0803	0.1126	0.0602
1.50	0.10	0.0405	0.0826	0.1457	0.0630	0.0395	0.0774	0.0943	0.0570
	0.20	0.0396	0.0793	0.1373	0.0597	0.0404	0.0807	0.1027	0.0603
	0.40	0.0396	0.0785	0.1318	0.0588	0.0404	0.0815	0.1082	0.0612
	2.00	0.0399	0.0794	0.1258	0.0595	0.0401	0.0806	0.1142	0.0605

BENDING MOMENT AT POINT 5

ϕ	ζ	2	3	4	5	8	9	10	11
0.10	0.10	0.0240	0.0486	0.0781	0.1235	0.0160	0.0314	0.0419	0.0365
	0.20	0.0227	0.0462	0.0744	0.1185	0.0173	0.0338	0.0456	0.0415
	0.40	0.0218	0.0447	0.0720	0.1150	0.0182	0.0353	0.0480	0.0450
	2.00	0.0210	0.0432	0.0698	0.1114	0.0190	0.0368	0.0502	0.0486
0.30	0.10	0.0244	0.0469	0.0729	0.1168	0.0156	0.0331	0.0471	0.0432
	0.20	0.0228	0.0444	0.0685	0.1097	0.0172	0.0356	0.0515	0.0503
	0.40	0.0216	0.0428	0.0657	0.1040	0.0184	0.0372	0.0543	0.0560
	2.00	0.0204	0.0409	0.0630	0.0973	0.0196	0.0391	0.0570	0.0627
0.50	0.10	0.0249	0.0469	0.0715	0.1149	0.0151	0.0331	0.0485	0.0451
	0.20	0.0233	0.0444	0.0670	0.1071	0.0167	0.0356	0.0530	0.0529
	0.40	0.0219	0.0427	0.0643	0.1008	0.0181	0.0373	0.0557	0.0592
	2.00	0.0204	0.0408	0.0617	0.0929	0.0196	0.0392	0.0583	0.0671
1.00	0.10	0.0257	0.0470	0.0703	0.1130	0.0143	0.0330	0.0497	0.0470
	0.20	0.0240	0.0446	0.0658	0.1046	0.0160	0.0354	0.0542	0.0554
	0.40	0.0224	0.0429	0.0632	0.0978	0.0176	0.0371	0.0568	0.0622
	2.00	0.0205	0.0408	0.0609	0.0889	0.0195	0.0392	0.0591	0.0711
1.50	0.10	0.0260	0.0471	0.0698	0.1122	0.0140	0.0329	0.0502	0.0478
	0.20	0.0244	0.0448	0.0653	0.1036	0.0156	0.0352	0.0547	0.0564
	0.40	0.0227	0.0431	0.0627	0.0966	0.0173	0.0369	0.0573	0.0634
	2.00	0.0206	0.0408	0.0606	0.0874	0.0194	0.0392	0.0594	0.0726

$(b/\ell) = 0.10$ ANGLE OF SKEW=ARCTAN(0.67)

UNIT VERTICAL LOAD APPLIED AT POINT:

BENDING MOMENT AT POINT 2

ϕ	ζ	2	3	4	5	8	9	10	11
0.10	0.10	0.1339	0.0859	0.0522	0.0253	0.0021	-.0036	-.0093	-.0094
	0.20	0.1291	0.0817	0.0491	0.0232	0.0038	-.0019	-.0076	-.0083
	0.40	0.1228	0.0771	0.0459	0.0213	0.0062	0.0008	-.0047	-.0061
	2.00	0.0991	0.0622	0.0366	0.0167	0.0119	0.0098	0.0047	0.0009
0.30	0.10	0.1206	0.0686	0.0385	0.0185	-.0032	-.0154	-.0247	-.0216
	0.20	0.1137	0.0619	0.0331	0.0148	-.0031	-.0165	-.0255	-.0223
	0.40	0.1063	0.0567	0.0292	0.0119	-.0018	-.0155	-.0236	-.0208
	2.00	0.0819	0.0452	0.0232	0.0087	0.0056	-.0042	-.0102	-.0098
0.50	0.10	0.1150	0.0613	0.0327	0.0156	-.0058	-.0208	-.0316	-.0269
	0.20	0.1066	0.0528	0.0256	0.0108	-.0068	-.0238	-.0343	-.0292
	0.40	0.0983	0.0465	0.0206	0.0069	-.0065	-.0242	-.0335	-.0285
	2.00	0.0737	0.0362	0.0154	0.0037	0.0007	-.0130	-.0193	-.0165
1.00	0.10	0.1091	0.0537	0.0266	0.0126	-.0085	-.0265	-.0389	-.0326
	0.20	0.0986	0.0426	0.0172	0.0063	-.0110	-.0320	-.0441	-.0368
	0.40	0.0888	0.0346	0.0103	0.0010	-.0122	-.0346	-.0453	-.0376
	2.00	0.0634	0.0244	0.0047	-.0032	-.0062	-.0248	-.0313	-.0254
1.50	0.10	0.1067	0.0505	0.0241	0.0114	-.0096	-.0289	-.0419	-.0350
	0.20	0.0952	0.0382	0.0136	0.0044	-.0129	-.0356	-.0484	-.0402
	0.40	0.0845	0.0292	0.0056	-.0017	-.0149	-.0394	-.0507	-.0418
	2.00	0.0583	0.0185	-.0008	-.0068	-.0098	-.0307	-.0374	-.0299

BENDING MOMENT AT POINT 3

ϕ	ζ	2	3	4	5	8	9	10	11
0.10	0.10	0.0738	0.1620	0.0911	0.0424	0.0369	0.0454	0.0312	0.0128
	0.20	0.0695	0.1539	0.0862	0.0400	0.0411	0.0496	0.0341	0.0145
	0.40	0.0662	0.1469	0.0826	0.0382	0.0428	0.0511	0.0354	0.0157
	2.00	0.0569	0.1249	0.0711	0.0324	0.0351	0.0435	0.0319	0.0153
0.30	0.10	0.0590	0.1399	0.0730	0.0336	0.0391	0.0445	0.0252	0.0064
	0.20	0.0528	0.1286	0.0664	0.0305	0.0449	0.0495	0.0279	0.0078
	0.40	0.0499	0.1200	0.0626	0.0288	0.0483	0.0519	0.0294	0.0092
	2.00	0.0419	0.0986	0.0537	0.0241	0.0428	0.0460	0.0275	0.0106
0.50	0.10	0.0535	0.1322	0.0668	0.0306	0.0387	0.0424	0.0213	0.0029
	0.20	0.0464	0.1195	0.0591	0.0271	0.0446	0.0470	0.0233	0.0038
	0.40	0.0421	0.1101	0.0552	0.0252	0.0484	0.0495	0.0247	0.0052
	2.00	0.0358	0.0883	0.0470	0.0206	0.0438	0.0440	0.0233	0.0071
1.00	0.10	0.0481	0.1247	0.0607	0.0276	0.0379	0.0396	0.0169	-.0008
	0.20	0.0398	0.1102	0.0518	0.0234	0.0436	0.0435	0.0177	-.0008
	0.40	0.0349	0.0998	0.0473	0.0212	0.0475	0.0456	0.0187	0.0002
	2.00	0.0290	0.0772	0.0394	0.0164	0.0434	0.0401	0.0173	0.0024
1.50	0.10	0.0460	0.1217	0.0583	0.0265	0.0375	0.0383	0.0149	-.0025
	0.20	0.0371	0.1064	0.0487	0.0219	0.0429	0.0417	0.0152	-.0029
	0.40	0.0318	0.0955	0.0439	0.0195	0.0468	0.0436	0.0159	-.0022
	2.00	0.0258	0.0722	0.0358	0.0144	0.0428	0.0378	0.0142	0.0000

BENDING MOMENT AT POINT 4

ϕ	ζ	2	3	4	5	8	9	10	11
0.10	0.10	0.0409	0.0885	0.1583	0.0702	0.0392	0.0664	0.0595	0.0298
	0.20	0.0384	0.0837	0.1505	0.0661	0.0402	0.0698	0.0625	0.0312
	0.40	0.0369	0.0805	0.1440	0.0631	0.0395	0.0698	0.0626	0.0313
	2.00	0.0319	0.0695	0.1222	0.0540	0.0330	0.0569	0.0523	0.0276
0.30	0.10	0.0312	0.0725	0.1413	0.0603	0.0436	0.0739	0.0648	0.0309
	0.20	0.0274	0.0653	0.1296	0.0541	0.0440	0.0778	0.0679	0.0317
	0.40	0.0255	0.0613	0.1206	0.0501	0.0419	0.0778	0.0674	0.0309
	2.00	0.0227	0.0529	0.0983	0.0419	0.0334	0.0651	0.0565	0.0264
0.50	0.10	0.0280	0.0675	0.1362	0.0574	0.0442	0.0748	0.0649	0.0303
	0.20	0.0233	0.0589	0.1229	0.0503	0.0441	0.0784	0.0675	0.0305
	0.40	0.0210	0.0542	0.1124	0.0456	0.0411	0.0779	0.0663	0.0290
	2.00	0.0185	0.0462	0.0889	0.0374	0.0313	0.0648	0.0546	0.0236
1.00	0.10	0.0249	0.0629	0.1316	0.0549	0.0445	0.0751	0.0644	0.0294
	0.20	0.0191	0.0527	0.1164	0.0467	0.0436	0.0779	0.0661	0.0286
	0.40	0.0159	0.0468	0.1041	0.0410	0.0395	0.0764	0.0637	0.0260
	2.00	0.0132	0.0383	0.0783	0.0321	0.0277	0.0621	0.0503	0.0191
1.50	0.10	0.0237	0.0611	0.1299	0.0539	0.0445	0.0750	0.0641	0.0289
	0.20	0.0174	0.0502	0.1139	0.0453	0.0433	0.0775	0.0652	0.0277
	0.40	0.0137	0.0436	0.1007	0.0391	0.0387	0.0754	0.0622	0.0245
	2.00	0.0106	0.0345	0.0734	0.0296	0.0257	0.0601	0.0477	0.0167

BENDING MOMENT AT POINT 5

ϕ	ζ	2	3	4	5	8	9	10	11
0.10	0.10	0.0216	0.0449	0.0744	0.1219	0.0226	0.0421	0.0496	0.0287
	0.20	0.0190	0.0405	0.0682	0.1143	0.0232	0.0440	0.0543	0.0319
	0.40	0.0167	0.0368	0.0630	0.1070	0.0230	0.0443	0.0564	0.0340
	2.00	0.0127	0.0285	0.0507	0.0872	0.0199	0.0385	0.0481	0.0311
0.30	0.10	0.0198	0.0411	0.0683	0.1162	0.0252	0.0480	0.0575	0.0332
	0.20	0.0157	0.0350	0.0595	0.1055	0.0244	0.0486	0.0627	0.0365
	0.40	0.0120	0.0295	0.0520	0.0949	0.0227	0.0468	0.0650	0.0384
	2.00	0.0071	0.0199	0.0383	0.0711	0.0179	0.0384	0.0572	0.0362
0.50	0.10	0.0194	0.0404	0.0669	0.1149	0.0258	0.0494	0.0594	0.0344
	0.20	0.0146	0.0333	0.0570	0.1030	0.0244	0.0492	0.0643	0.0373
	0.40	0.0100	0.0267	0.0482	0.0908	0.0217	0.0460	0.0660	0.0386
	2.00	0.0038	0.0155	0.0329	0.0645	0.0155	0.0354	0.0575	0.0359
1.00	0.10	0.0192	0.0398	0.0658	0.1138	0.0262	0.0506	0.0610	0.0353
	0.20	0.0135	0.0317	0.0547	0.1008	0.0241	0.0493	0.0653	0.0376
	0.40	0.0076	0.0235	0.0442	0.0870	0.0202	0.0444	0.0659	0.0380
	2.00	-.0008	0.0095	0.0262	0.0571	0.0119	0.0303	0.0555	0.0340
1.50	0.10	0.0191	0.0396	0.0654	0.1134	0.0264	0.0510	0.0616	0.0356
	0.20	0.0131	0.0310	0.0538	0.1000	0.0240	0.0493	0.0655	0.0377
	0.40	0.0065	0.0220	0.0425	0.0854	0.0195	0.0434	0.0655	0.0376
	2.00	-.0032	0.0063	0.0229	0.0538	0.0099	0.0275	0.0539	0.0325

TABLE 2 - SIMPLY-SUPPORTED SKEW GIRDER BRIDGE

INFLUENCE COEFICIENT OF BENDING MOMENT IN MAIN GIRDER

BENDING MOMENT = COEF.x

(b/) = 0.10 ANGLE OF SKEW=ARCTAN(1.33)

φ	ζ	UNIT VERTICAL LOAD APPLIED AT POINT:															
		2	3	4	5	8	9	10	11	2	3	4	5	8	9	10	11
		BENDING MOMENT AT POINT 2								BENDING MOMENT AT POINT 3							
0.10	0.10	0.1274	0.0811	0.0472	0.0213	-.0209	-.0338	-.0359	-.0250	0.0697	0.1517	0.0828	0.0368	0.0172	0.0069	-.0056	-.0093
	0.20	0.1204	0.0750	0.0429	0.0188	-.0193	-.0307	-.0323	-.0225	0.0644	0.1421	0.0764	0.0336	0.0196	0.0094	-.0027	-.0071
	0.40	0.1105	0.0668	0.0376	0.0163	-.0153	-.0242	-.0254	-.0176	0.0585	0.1315	0.0696	0.0304	0.0201	0.0114	0.0007	-.0042
	2.00	0.0778	0.0430	0.0243	0.0108	-.0010	-.0035	-.0047	-.0036	0.0394	0.0950	0.0476	0.0206	0.0122	0.0116	0.0064	0.0020
0.30	0.10	0.1138	0.0635	0.0314	0.0118	-.0333	-.0536	-.0570	-.0401	0.0527	0.1236	0.0595	0.0243	0.0163	-.0024	-.0191	-.0198
	0.20	0.1055	0.0557	0.0261	0.0084	-.0339	-.0529	-.0554	-.0389	0.0466	0.1115	0.0523	0.0208	0.0202	-.0001	-.0164	-.0177
	0.40	0.0949	0.0491	0.0215	0.0060	-.0310	-.0471	-.0484	-.0338	0.0410	0.1004	0.0465	0.0182	0.0221	0.0022	-.0125	-.0143
	2.00	0.0614	0.0287	0.0131	0.0041	-.0130	-.0192	-.0191	-.0129	0.0264	0.0698	0.0309	0.0122	0.0168	0.0061	-.0017	-.0040
0.50	0.10	0.1089	0.0571	0.0256	0.0083	-.0375	-.0603	-.0643	-.0453	0.0472	0.1148	0.0522	0.0204	0.0154	-.0062	-.0242	-.0236
	0.20	0.0999	0.0497	0.0196	0.0043	-.0392	-.0609	-.0637	-.0449	0.0407	0.1015	0.0447	0.0167	0.0197	-.0042	-.0217	-.0216
	0.40	0.0890	0.0421	0.0149	0.0017	-.0370	-.0557	-.0572	-.0401	0.0352	0.0900	0.0391	0.0142	0.0222	-.0020	-.0177	-.0181
	2.00	0.0550	0.0230	0.0081	0.0008	-.0185	-.0263	-.0258	-.0173	0.0218	0.0606	0.0252	0.0092	0.0178	0.0027	-.0058	-.0069
1.00	0.10	0.1044	0.0512	0.0202	0.0051	-.0414	-.0666	-.0710	-.0501	0.0423	0.1069	0.0457	0.0169	0.0143	-.0099	-.0290	-.0271
	0.20	0.0946	0.0430	0.0133	0.0003	-.0442	-.0684	-.0715	-.0507	0.0353	0.0925	0.0378	0.0130	0.0191	-.0082	-.0268	-.0254
	0.40	0.0831	0.0352	0.0082	-.0028	-.0429	-.0641	-.0656	-.0463	0.0297	0.0804	0.0323	0.0105	0.0220	-.0062	-.0228	-.0219
	2.00	0.0484	0.0170	0.0025	-.0029	-.0245	-.0339	-.0330	-.0223	0.0173	0.0515	0.0198	0.0062	0.0184	-.0013	-.0102	-.0100
1.50	0.10	0.1027	0.0489	0.0182	0.0038	-.0429	-.0689	-.0735	-.0519	0.0405	0.1040	0.0433	0.0156	0.0138	-.0114	-.0308	-.0285
	0.20	0.0925	0.0404	0.0109	-.0013	-.0461	-.0713	-.0746	-.0529	0.0333	0.0891	0.0352	0.0116	0.0188	-.0098	-.0287	-.0268
	0.40	0.0808	0.0324	0.0055	-.0045	-.0452	-.0673	-.0690	-.0487	0.0276	0.0767	0.0298	0.0091	0.0219	-.0079	-.0247	-.0233
	2.00	0.0456	0.0145	0.0000	-.0045	-.0271	-.0371	-.0361	-.0244	0.0156	0.0478	0.0177	0.0049	0.0186	-.0030	-.0120	-.0113
		BENDING MOMENT AT POINT 4								BENDING MOMENT AT POINT 5							
0.10	0.10	0.0350	0.0779	0.1438	0.0620	0.0311	0.0466	0.0290	0.0091	0.0142	0.0331	0.0612	0.1092	0.0226	0.0403	0.0425	0.0172
	0.20	0.0319	0.0719	0.1348	0.0572	0.0313	0.0479	0.0300	0.0101	0.0119	0.0290	0.0553	0.1019	0.0223	0.0406	0.0442	0.0181
	0.40	0.0290	0.0658	0.1253	0.0523	0.0295	0.0458	0.0293	0.0108	0.0102	0.0255	0.0497	0.0945	0.0209	0.0384	0.0427	0.0182
	2.00	0.0202	0.0455	0.0912	0.0357	0.0172	0.0258	0.0198	0.0093	0.0071	0.0169	0.0331	0.0691	0.0127	0.0227	0.0242	0.0128
0.30	0.10	0.0214	0.0553	0.1182	0.0473	0.0334	0.0503	0.0266	0.0049	0.0068	0.0215	0.0470	0.0961	0.0239	0.0445	0.0486	0.0178
	0.20	0.0178	0.0483	0.1065	0.0416	0.0335	0.0525	0.0268	0.0052	0.0031	0.0157	0.0389	0.0854	0.0225	0.0441	0.0514	0.0182
	0.40	0.0155	0.0432	0.0964	0.0370	0.0314	0.0510	0.0256	0.0054	0.0012	0.0119	0.0328	0.0760	0.0202	0.0412	0.0505	0.0178
	2.00	0.0114	0.0295	0.0678	0.0242	0.0199	0.0334	0.0183	0.0061	0.0014	0.0078	0.0207	0.0529	0.0127	0.0264	0.0337	0.0135
0.50	0.10	0.0172	0.0485	0.1106	0.0430	0.0334	0.0503	0.0248	0.0030	0.0044	0.0179	0.0428	0.0923	0.0237	0.0450	0.0497	0.0175
	0.20	0.0131	0.0410	0.0977	0.0369	0.0332	0.0526	0.0245	0.0028	0.0001	0.0112	0.0337	0.0801	0.0217	0.0440	0.0526	0.0175
	0.40	0.0110	0.0360	0.0870	0.0323	0.0308	0.0512	0.0228	0.0028	-.0023	0.0071	0.0271	0.0696	0.0189	0.0405	0.0518	0.0167
	2.00	0.0082	0.0241	0.0594	0.0205	0.0194	0.0344	0.0158	0.0038	-.0012	0.0040	0.0161	0.0464	0.0114	0.0256	0.0354	0.0123
1.00	0.10	0.0134	0.0425	0.1039	0.0393	0.0331	0.0498	0.0229	0.0011	0.0023	0.0147	0.0392	0.0889	0.0234	0.0450	0.0503	0.0170
	0.20	0.0089	0.0345	0.0899	0.0327	0.0325	0.0522	0.0219	0.0004	-.0028	0.0072	0.0290	0.0753	0.0206	0.0433	0.0531	0.0166
	0.40	0.0068	0.0295	0.0785	0.0280	0.0297	0.0509	0.0196	-.0000	-.0057	0.0023	0.0217	0.0635	0.0172	0.0391	0.0524	0.0154
	2.00	0.0048	0.0189	0.0510	0.0170	0.0182	0.0346	0.0124	0.0010	-.0042	-.0002	0.0112	0.0397	0.0095	0.0238	0.0362	0.0105
1.50	0.10	0.0120	0.0403	0.1015	0.0379	0.0329	0.0496	0.0220	0.0003	0.0015	0.0136	0.0378	0.0877	0.0232	0.0449	0.0504	0.0168
	0.20	0.0074	0.0320	0.0869	0.0311	0.0322	0.0519	0.0208	-.0006	-.0040	0.0056	0.0272	0.0735	0.0202	0.0429	0.0532	0.0161
	0.40	0.0051	0.0271	0.0753	0.0264	0.0292	0.0506	0.0182	-.0012	-.0071	0.0005	0.0196	0.0612	0.0165	0.0384	0.0524	0.0147
	2.00	0.0035	0.0168	0.0476	0.0156	0.0175	0.0344	0.0108	-.0002	-.0056	-.0021	0.0092	0.0369	0.0085	0.0227	0.0363	0.0096

(b/) = 0.10 ANGLE OF SKEW=ARCTAN(2.00)

φ	ζ	UNIT VERTICAL LOAD APPLIED AT POINT:															
		2	3	4	5	8	9	10	11	2	3	4	5	8	9	10	11
		BENDING MOMENT AT POINT 2								BENDING MOMENT AT POINT 3							
0.10	0.10	0.0890	0.0450	0.0232	0.0098	-.0108	-.0158	-.0151	-.0095	0.0426	0.1074	0.0505	0.0206	0.0068	-.0004	-.0054	-.0052
	0.20	0.0736	0.0338	0.0172	0.0074	-.0049	-.0071	-.0068	-.0043	0.0322	0.0875	0.0381	0.0153	0.0056	0.0021	-.0009	-.0015
	0.40	0.0583	0.0247	0.0129	0.0058	0.0001	-.0006	-.0010	-.0008	0.0231	0.0679	0.0273	0.0109	0.0026	0.0027	0.0015	0.0004
	2.00	0.0252	0.0095	0.0057	0.0028	0.0035	0.0030	0.0020	0.0010	0.0085	0.0288	0.0104	0.0045	-.0027	0.0010	0.0011	0.0006
0.30	0.10	0.0761	0.0333	0.0142	0.0046	-.0218	-.0308	-.0290	-.0183	0.0305	0.0848	0.0341	0.0122	0.0066	-.0087	-.0158	-.0124
	0.20	0.0595	0.0227	0.0093	0.0029	-.0148	-.0196	-.0178	-.0109	0.0215	0.0663	0.0243	0.0085	0.0071	-.0042	-.0088	-.0068
	0.40	0.0451	0.0153	0.0066	0.0024	-.0076	-.0096	-.0084	-.0051	0.0146	0.0503	0.0168	0.0060	0.0055	-.0009	-.0033	-.0028
	2.00	0.0204	0.0065	0.0037	0.0018	0.0013	0.0009	0.0005	0.0002	0.0056	0.0224	0.0066	0.0028	-.0002	0.0012	0.0008	0.0003
0.50	0.10	0.0719	0.0295	0.0111	0.0027	-.0256	-.0359	-.0338	-.0214	0.0268	0.0777	0.0291	0.0097	0.0063	-.0119	-.0195	-.0149
	0.20	0.0546	0.0191	0.0065	0.0012	-.0186	-.0244	-.0220	-.0136	0.0181	0.0591	0.0199	0.0064	0.0073	-.0070	-.0119	-.0090
	0.40	0.0399	0.0121	0.0043	0.0011	-.0110	-.0134	-.0116	-.0070	0.0118	0.0437	0.0133	0.0044	0.0062	-.0031	-.0057	-.0043
	2.00	0.0178	0.0050	0.0028	0.0013	-.0001	-.0004	-.0005	-.0004	0.0044	0.0193	0.0051	0.0021	0.0008	0.0007	0.0003	-.0000
1.00	0.10	0.0680	0.0259	0.0082	0.0008	-.0292	-.0406	-.0382	-.0243	0.0235	0.0713	0.0247	0.0074	0.0060	-.0149	-.0229	-.0172
	0.20	0.0498	0.0156	0.0038	-.0005	-.0224	-.0289	-.0261	-.0162	0.0150	0.0523	0.0160	0.0044	0.0074	-.0099	-.0150	-.0110
	0.40	0.0347	0.0089	0.0020	-.0004	-.0144	-.0173	-.0150	-.0091	0.0092	0.0372	0.0101	0.0029	0.0066	-.0056	-.0083	-.0059
	2.00	0.0143	0.0033	0.0016	0.0006	-.0020	-.0022	-.0019	-.0011	0.0031	0.0154	0.0036	0.0014	0.0019	-.0002	-.0006	-.0005
1.50	0.10	0.0665	0.0246	0.0071	0.0001	-.0305	-.0423	-.0398	-.0254	0.0223	0.0689	0.0231	0.0066	0.0058	-.0160	-.0241	-.0180
	0.20	0.0479	0.0143	0.0027	-.0013	-.0238	-.0307	-.0276	-.0173	0.0138	0.0497	0.0145	0.0037	0.0074	-.0111	-.0162	-.0118
	0.40	0.0325	0.0077	0.0010	-.0011	-.0158	-.0189	-.0164	-.0100	0.0082	0.0345	0.0089	0.0022	0.0067	-.0066	-.0093	-.0066
	2.00	0.0125	0.0025	0.0010	0.0003	-.0030	-.0031	-.0026	-.0015	0.0025	0.0136	0.0030	0.0011	0.0023	-.0007	-.0011	-.0008
		BENDING MOMENT AT POINT 4								BENDING MOMENT AT POINT 5							
0.10	0.10	0.0202	0.0488	0.1045	0.0398	0.0150	0.0210	0.0107	0.0025	0.0074	0.0184	0.0386	0.0836	0.0124	0.0215	0.0218	0.0080
	0.20	0.0151	0.0369	0.0853	0.0301	0.0102	0.0146	0.0085	0.0030	0.0055	0.0135	0.0290	0.0697	0.0084	0.0145	0.0149	0.0061
	0.40	0.0108	0.0263	0.0659	0.0211	0.0046	0.0064	0.0051	0.0024	0.0041	0.0094	0.0203	0.0547	0.0041	0.0066	0.0063	0.0035
	2.00	0.0045	0.0099	0.0280	0.0076	-.0021	-.0044	-.0003	0.0001	0.0019	0.0039	0.0072	0.0233	-.0012	-.0031	-.0051	-.0006
0.30	0.10	0.0115	0.0324	0.0822	0.0279	0.0173	0.0244	0.0072	-.0018	0.0020	0.0092	0.0259	0.0690	0.0137	0.0256	0.0274	0.0073
	0.20	0.0081	0.0233	0.0649	0.0200	0.0133	0.0197	0.0054	-.0001	0.0014	0.0062	0.0183	0.0552	0.0100	0.0193	0.0219	0.0059
	0.40	0.0059	0.0162	0.0492	0.0135	0.0084	0.0129	0.0049	0.0009	0.0014	0.0045	0.0124	0.0425	0.0064	0.0123	0.0143	0.0043
	2.00	0.0027	0.0062	0.0216	0.0048	0.0006	0.0002	0.0013	0.0007	0.0010	0.0022	0.0044	0.0187	0.0008	0.0009	0.0001	0.0009
0.50	0.10	0.0088	0.0274	0.0752	0.0243	0.0174	0.0247	0.0053	-.0035	0.0002	0.0062	0.0220	0.0643	0.0136	0.0261	0.0286	0.0066
	0.20	0.0059	0.0191	0.0579	0.0168	0.0135	0.0205	0.0047	-.0017	-.0002	0.0036	0.0146	0.0499	0.0098	0.0158	0.0234	0.0052
	0.40	0.0042	0.0129	0.0430	0.0111	0.0090	0.0143	0.0037	-.0002	0.0002	0.0027	0.0097	0.0375	0.0064	0.0131	0.0162	0.0038
	2.00	0.0020	0.0048	0.0187	0.0038	0.0014	0.0020	0.0015	0.0006	0.0007	0.0016	0.0034	0.0164	0.0013	0.0022	0.0021	0.0012
1.00	0.10	0.0064	0.0230	0.0690	0.0212	0.0173	0.0248	0.0034	-.0052	-.0015	0.0035	0.0184	0.0599	0.0132	0.0262	0.0294	0.0058
	0.20	0.0038	0.0152	0.0513	0.0140	0.0133	0.0208	0.0026	-.0034	-.0019	0.0011	0.0112	0.0447	0.0093	0.0197	0.0243	0.0043
	0.40	0.0026	0.0098	0.0367	0.0088	0.0090	0.0151	0.0020	-.0016	-.0011	0.0007	0.0068	0.0322	0.0060	0.0132	0.0175	0.0030
	2.00	0.0014	0.0034	0.0151	0.0027	0.0021	0.0036	0.0012	0.0003	0.0003	0.0009	0.0024	0.0135	0.0016	0.0032	0.0042	0.0012
1.50	0.10	0.0055	0.0214	0.0667	0.0201	0.0172	0.0247	0.0026	-.0059	-.0022	0.0025	0.0171	0.0582	0.0130	0.0261	0.0297	0.0055
	0.20	0.0030	0.0137	0.0487	0.0129	0.0132	0.0208	0.0017	-.0041	-.0025	0.0001	0.0098	0.0426	0.0090	0.0196	0.0246	0.0038
	0.40	0.0019	0.0086	0.0341	0.0079	0.0088	0.0152	0.0011	-.0022	-.0016	-.0002	0.0057	0.0299	0.0057	0.0130	0.0178	0.0025
	2.00	0.0011	0.0029	0.0134	0.0023	0.0023	0.0042	0.0008	0.0001	0.0001	0.0006	0.0019	0.0119	0.0016	0.0034	0.0049	0.0010

TABLE 3 - SIMPLY-SUPPORTED SKEW GIRDER BRIDGE

INFLUENCE COEFICIENT OF BENDING MOMENT IN MAIN GIRDER

BENDING MOMENT = COEF. x ℓ

$(b/\ell) = 0.20$ ANGLE OF SKEW=ARCTAN(0.0)

		UNIT VERTICAL LOAD APPLIED AT POINT:															
ϕ	ζ	2	3	4	5	8	9	10	11	2	3	4	5	8	9	10	11
		BENDING MOMENT AT POINT 2								BENDING MOMENT AT POINT 3							
0.10	0.10	0.1473	0.1031	0.0659	0.0325	0.0127	0.0169	0.0141	0.0075	0.1005	0.2080	0.1306	0.0634	0.0195	0.0320	0.0294	0.0166
	0.20	0.1433	0.0983	0.0621	0.0304	0.0167	0.0217	0.0179	0.0096	0.0958	0.2003	0.1240	0.0598	0.0242	0.0397	0.0360	0.0202
	0.40	0.1398	0.0945	0.0591	0.0287	0.0202	0.0255	0.0209	0.0113	0.0925	0.1949	0.1195	0.0573	0.0275	0.0451	0.0405	0.0227
	2.00	0.1351	0.0898	0.0555	0.0266	0.0249	0.0302	0.0245	0.0134	0.0891	0.1893	0.1153	0.0549	0.0309	0.0507	0.0447	0.0251
0.30	0.10	0.1440	0.0990	0.0632	0.0315	0.0160	0.0210	0.0168	0.0085	0.0950	0.1992	0.1228	0.0593	0.0250	0.0408	0.0372	0.0207
	0.20	0.1377	0.0917	0.0576	0.0286	0.0223	0.0283	0.0224	0.0114	0.0871	0.1861	0.1116	0.0533	0.0329	0.0539	0.0484	0.0267
	0.40	0.1314	0.0852	0.0530	0.0261	0.0286	0.0348	0.0270	0.0139	0.0809	0.1756	0.1033	0.0490	0.0391	0.0644	0.0567	0.0310
	2.00	0.1205	0.0761	0.0468	0.0227	0.0395	0.0439	0.0332	0.0173	0.0741	0.1634	0.0954	0.0451	0.0459	0.0766	0.0646	0.0349
0.50	0.10	0.1430	0.0979	0.0625	0.0314	0.0170	0.0221	0.0175	0.0086	0.0935	0.1968	0.1207	0.0583	0.0265	0.0432	0.0393	0.0217
	0.20	0.1358	0.0897	0.0566	0.0284	0.0242	0.0303	0.0234	0.0116	0.0844	0.1818	0.1080	0.0515	0.0356	0.0582	0.0520	0.0285
	0.40	0.1285	0.0824	0.0516	0.0259	0.0315	0.0376	0.0284	0.0141	0.0770	0.1694	0.0983	0.0466	0.0430	0.0706	0.0617	0.0334
	2.00	0.1148	0.0718	0.0449	0.0222	0.0452	0.0482	0.0351	0.0178	0.0690	0.1541	0.0892	0.0425	0.0510	0.0859	0.0708	0.0375
1.00	0.10	0.1420	0.0969	0.0621	0.0314	0.0180	0.0231	0.0179	0.0086	0.0922	0.1948	0.1190	0.0575	0.0278	0.0452	0.0410	0.0225
	0.20	0.1340	0.0879	0.0559	0.0286	0.0260	0.0321	0.0241	0.0114	0.0820	0.1781	0.1049	0.0501	0.0380	0.0619	0.0551	0.0299
	0.40	0.1256	0.0797	0.0507	0.0261	0.0344	0.0402	0.0293	0.0139	0.0735	0.1637	0.0940	0.0447	0.0465	0.0763	0.0660	0.0353
	2.00	0.1089	0.0681	0.0439	0.0222	0.0511	0.0519	0.0361	0.0178	0.0642	0.1451	0.0838	0.0406	0.0558	0.0949	0.0762	0.0394
1.50	0.10	0.1417	0.0965	0.0620	0.0314	0.0183	0.0235	0.0180	0.0086	0.0917	0.1941	0.1184	0.0572	0.0283	0.0459	0.0416	0.0228
	0.20	0.1332	0.0871	0.0557	0.0287	0.0268	0.0329	0.0243	0.0113	0.0810	0.1767	0.1039	0.0497	0.0390	0.0633	0.0561	0.0303
	0.40	0.1244	0.0787	0.0505	0.0265	0.0356	0.0413	0.0295	0.0135	0.0721	0.1616	0.0924	0.0442	0.0479	0.0784	0.0676	0.0358
	2.00	0.1063	0.0667	0.0438	0.0225	0.0537	0.0533	0.0362	0.0175	0.0624	0.1415	0.0818	0.0401	0.0576	0.0985	0.0782	0.0399
		BENDING MOMENT AT POINT 4								BENDING MOMENT AT POINT 5							
0.10	0.10	0.0634	0.1306	0.2080	0.1005	0.0166	0.0294	0.0320	0.0195	0.0325	0.0659	0.1031	0.1473	0.0075	0.0141	0.0169	0.0127
	0.20	0.0598	0.1240	0.2003	0.0958	0.0202	0.0360	0.0397	0.0242	0.0304	0.0621	0.0983	0.1433	0.0096	0.0179	0.0217	0.0167
	0.40	0.0573	0.1195	0.1949	0.0925	0.0227	0.0405	0.0451	0.0275	0.0287	0.0591	0.0945	0.1398	0.0113	0.0209	0.0255	0.0202
	2.00	0.0549	0.1153	0.1893	0.0891	0.0251	0.0447	0.0507	0.0309	0.0266	0.0555	0.0898	0.1351	0.0134	0.0245	0.0302	0.0249
0.30	0.10	0.0593	0.1228	0.1992	0.0950	0.0207	0.0372	0.0408	0.0250	0.0315	0.0632	0.0990	0.1440	0.0085	0.0168	0.0210	0.0160
	0.20	0.0533	0.1116	0.1861	0.0871	0.0267	0.0484	0.0539	0.0329	0.0286	0.0576	0.0917	0.1377	0.0114	0.0224	0.0283	0.0223
	0.40	0.0490	0.1033	0.1756	0.0809	0.0310	0.0567	0.0644	0.0391	0.0261	0.0530	0.0852	0.1314	0.0139	0.0270	0.0348	0.0286
	2.00	0.0451	0.0954	0.1634	0.0741	0.0349	0.0646	0.0766	0.0459	0.0227	0.0468	0.0761	0.1205	0.0173	0.0332	0.0439	0.0395
0.50	0.10	0.0583	0.1207	0.1968	0.0935	0.0217	0.0393	0.0432	0.0265	0.0314	0.0625	0.0979	0.1430	0.0086	0.0175	0.0221	0.0170
	0.20	0.0515	0.1080	0.1818	0.0844	0.0285	0.0520	0.0582	0.0356	0.0284	0.0566	0.0897	0.1358	0.0116	0.0234	0.0303	0.0242
	0.40	0.0466	0.0983	0.1694	0.0770	0.0334	0.0617	0.0706	0.0430	0.0259	0.0516	0.0824	0.1285	0.0141	0.0284	0.0376	0.0315
	2.00	0.0425	0.0892	0.1541	0.0690	0.0375	0.0708	0.0859	0.0510	0.0222	0.0449	0.0718	0.1148	0.0178	0.0351	0.0482	0.0452
1.00	0.10	0.0575	0.1190	0.1948	0.0922	0.0225	0.0410	0.0452	0.0278	0.0314	0.0621	0.0969	0.1420	0.0086	0.0179	0.0231	0.0180
	0.20	0.0501	0.1049	0.1781	0.0820	0.0299	0.0551	0.0619	0.0380	0.0286	0.0559	0.0879	0.1340	0.0114	0.0241	0.0321	0.0260
	0.40	0.0447	0.0940	0.1637	0.0735	0.0353	0.0660	0.0763	0.0465	0.0261	0.0507	0.0797	0.1256	0.0139	0.0293	0.0402	0.0344
	2.00	0.0406	0.0838	0.1451	0.0642	0.0394	0.0762	0.0949	0.0558	0.0222	0.0439	0.0681	0.1089	0.0178	0.0361	0.0519	0.0511
1.50	0.10	0.0572	0.1184	0.1941	0.0917	0.0228	0.0416	0.0459	0.0283	0.0314	0.0620	0.0965	0.1417	0.0086	0.0180	0.0235	0.0183
	0.20	0.0497	0.1039	0.1767	0.0810	0.0303	0.0561	0.0633	0.0390	0.0287	0.0557	0.0871	0.1332	0.0113	0.0243	0.0329	0.0268
	0.40	0.0442	0.0924	0.1616	0.0721	0.0358	0.0676	0.0784	0.0479	0.0265	0.0505	0.0787	0.1244	0.0135	0.0295	0.0413	0.0356
	2.00	0.0401	0.0818	0.1415	0.0624	0.0399	0.0782	0.0985	0.0576	0.0225	0.0438	0.0667	0.1063	0.0175	0.0362	0.0533	0.0537

$(b/\ell) = 0.20$ ANGLE OF SKEW=ARCTAN(0.10)

		UNIT VERTICAL LOAD APPLIED AT POINT:															
ϕ	ζ	2	3	4	5	8	9	10	11	2	3	4	5	8	9	10	11
		BENDING MOMENT AT POINT 2								BENDING MOMENT AT POINT 3							
0.10	0.10	0.1483	0.1043	0.0669	0.0330	0.0113	0.0148	0.0120	0.0062	0.1012	0.2090	0.1314	0.0639	0.0190	0.0305	0.0276	0.0153
	0.20	0.1445	0.0997	0.0632	0.0310	0.0150	0.0192	0.0156	0.0082	0.0965	0.2013	0.1246	0.0601	0.0238	0.0383	0.0342	0.0190
	0.40	0.1410	0.0958	0.0601	0.0292	0.0185	0.0230	0.0186	0.0099	0.0930	0.1956	0.1199	0.0575	0.0272	0.0438	0.0388	0.0215
	2.00	0.1356	0.0905	0.0560	0.0269	0.0232	0.0277	0.0224	0.0121	0.0892	0.1890	0.1150	0.0547	0.0307	0.0495	0.0430	0.0239
0.30	0.10	0.1451	0.1002	0.0641	0.0320	0.0140	0.0179	0.0138	0.0067	0.0959	0.2006	0.1239	0.0600	0.0240	0.0385	0.0345	0.0188
	0.20	0.1391	0.0931	0.0587	0.0292	0.0197	0.0245	0.0188	0.0092	0.0879	0.1874	0.1124	0.0537	0.0321	0.0515	0.0455	0.0247
	0.40	0.1330	0.0866	0.0540	0.0267	0.0257	0.0306	0.0231	0.0115	0.0814	0.1765	0.1038	0.0492	0.0387	0.0622	0.0539	0.0290
	2.00	0.1216	0.0770	0.0475	0.0231	0.0364	0.0396	0.0295	0.0151	0.0740	0.1631	0.0950	0.0449	0.0460	0.0746	0.0617	0.0330
0.50	0.10	0.1440	0.0990	0.0634	0.0319	0.0148	0.0187	0.0141	0.0065	0.0944	0.1982	0.1219	0.0590	0.0254	0.0406	0.0362	0.0196
	0.20	0.1371	0.0909	0.0574	0.0289	0.0212	0.0260	0.0193	0.0090	0.0851	0.1831	0.1089	0.0520	0.0347	0.0554	0.0486	0.0261
	0.40	0.1300	0.0835	0.0523	0.0263	0.0280	0.0327	0.0238	0.0112	0.0775	0.1702	0.0987	0.0468	0.0424	0.0679	0.0583	0.0310
	2.00	0.1159	0.0724	0.0453	0.0224	0.0414	0.0429	0.0306	0.0152	0.0687	0.1538	0.0886	0.0422	0.0512	0.0835	0.0674	0.0352
1.00	0.10	0.1430	0.0978	0.0628	0.0318	0.0155	0.0194	0.0142	0.0062	0.0930	0.1962	0.1202	0.0582	0.0267	0.0424	0.0376	0.0202
	0.20	0.1351	0.0887	0.0564	0.0289	0.0227	0.0272	0.0193	0.0083	0.0825	0.1792	0.1058	0.0506	0.0370	0.0587	0.0511	0.0271
	0.40	0.1268	0.0803	0.0509	0.0263	0.0303	0.0343	0.0236	0.0102	0.0736	0.1643	0.0941	0.0449	0.0458	0.0730	0.0619	0.0323
	2.00	0.1097	0.0679	0.0436	0.0221	0.0463	0.0453	0.0303	0.0143	0.0635	0.1444	0.0828	0.0402	0.0560	0.0919	0.0720	0.0366
1.50	0.10	0.1426	0.0974	0.0626	0.0318	0.0158	0.0196	0.0142	0.0061	0.0925	0.1955	0.1196	0.0579	0.0271	0.0430	0.0381	0.0204
	0.20	0.1342	0.0878	0.0560	0.0290	0.0233	0.0276	0.0191	0.0080	0.0815	0.1777	0.1046	0.0502	0.0378	0.0600	0.0519	0.0273
	0.40	0.1253	0.0788	0.0504	0.0265	0.0312	0.0349	0.0233	0.0095	0.0720	0.1619	0.0924	0.0443	0.0472	0.0749	0.0631	0.0326
	2.00	0.1068	0.0658	0.0428	0.0221	0.0483	0.0459	0.0296	0.0133	0.0612	0.1405	0.0805	0.0395	0.0579	0.0951	0.0735	0.0367
		BENDING MOMENT AT POINT 4								BENDING MOMENT AT POINT 5							
0.10	0.10	0.0638	0.1312	0.2087	0.1008	0.0168	0.0294	0.0314	0.0188	0.0327	0.0663	0.1035	0.1477	0.0079	0.0146	0.0172	0.0125
	0.20	0.0600	0.1244	0.2008	0.0960	0.0206	0.0363	0.0392	0.0235	0.0305	0.0623	0.0986	0.1436	0.0101	0.0187	0.0222	0.0166
	0.40	0.0574	0.1196	0.1950	0.0925	0.0233	0.0411	0.0448	0.0268	0.0287	0.0591	0.0944	0.1398	0.0119	0.0219	0.0264	0.0202
	2.00	0.0547	0.1148	0.1884	0.0886	0.0257	0.0454	0.0503	0.0301	0.0263	0.0548	0.0889	0.1342	0.0142	0.0259	0.0315	0.0251
0.30	0.10	0.0599	0.1238	0.2005	0.0958	0.0210	0.0372	0.0398	0.0239	0.0319	0.0639	0.0999	0.1448	0.0092	0.0178	0.0216	0.0158
	0.20	0.0537	0.1123	0.1871	0.0876	0.0274	0.0490	0.0531	0.0318	0.0290	0.0583	0.0925	0.1386	0.0124	0.0238	0.0293	0.0221
	0.40	0.0491	0.1035	0.1762	0.0811	0.0321	0.0578	0.0638	0.0381	0.0264	0.0534	0.0858	0.1321	0.0150	0.0288	0.0362	0.0285
	2.00	0.0448	0.0948	0.1627	0.0735	0.0360	0.0661	0.0762	0.0447	0.0225	0.0464	0.0754	0.1201	0.0185	0.0353	0.0462	0.0397
0.50	0.10	0.0589	0.1219	0.1983	0.0944	0.0221	0.0393	0.0421	0.0253	0.0319	0.0635	0.0990	0.1440	0.0095	0.0186	0.0228	0.0168
	0.20	0.0520	0.1088	0.1831	0.0851	0.0294	0.0527	0.0573	0.0344	0.0290	0.0575	0.0908	0.1370	0.0128	0.0252	0.0316	0.0240
	0.40	0.0467	0.0986	0.1702	0.0774	0.0347	0.0631	0.0700	0.0418	0.0263	0.0523	0.0833	0.1297	0.0156	0.0307	0.0395	0.0314
	2.00	0.0421	0.0884	0.1535	0.0685	0.0389	0.0727	0.0854	0.0497	0.0221	0.0447	0.0714	0.1148	0.0193	0.0377	0.0510	0.0454
1.00	0.10	0.0582	0.1203	0.1965	0.0932	0.0230	0.0410	0.0440	0.0266	0.0320	0.0632	0.0982	0.1432	0.0096	0.0193	0.0240	0.0178
	0.20	0.0506	0.1060	0.1797	0.0830	0.0309	0.0559	0.0610	0.0367	0.0293	0.0571	0.0895	0.1356	0.0130	0.0264	0.0338	0.0260
	0.40	0.0448	0.0944	0.1649	0.0741	0.0369	0.0678	0.0757	0.0452	0.0268	0.0519	0.0813	0.1273	0.0158	0.0323	0.0427	0.0345
	2.00	0.0399	0.0828	0.1446	0.0637	0.0412	0.0786	0.0943	0.0541	0.0224	0.0441	0.0683	0.1096	0.0196	0.0394	0.0554	0.0514
1.50	0.10	0.0579	0.1198	0.1958	0.0928	0.0233	0.0416	0.0448	0.0270	0.0321	0.0632	0.0980	0.1430	0.0096	0.0195	0.0245	0.0182
	0.20	0.0501	0.1050	0.1784	0.0821	0.0315	0.0570	0.0624	0.0376	0.0295	0.0571	0.0890	0.1350	0.0130	0.0268	0.0347	0.0268
	0.40	0.0442	0.0929	0.1629	0.0729	0.0377	0.0695	0.0778	0.0466	0.0273	0.0520	0.0806	0.1264	0.0158	0.0329	0.0441	0.0358
	2.00	0.0392	0.0807	0.1411	0.0619	0.0419	0.0808	0.0978	0.0558	0.0229	0.0443	0.0673	0.1075	0.0197	0.0400	0.0573	0.0540

TABLE 4 - SIMPLY-SUPPORTED SKEW GIRDER BRIDGE

INFLUENCE COEFFICIENT OF BENDING MOMENT IN MAIN GIRDER

BENDING MOMENT = COEF. × ℓ

$(b/\ell) = 0.20$ ANGLE OF SKEW=ARCTAN(0.67)

UNIT VERTICAL LOAD APPLIED AT POINT:

BENDING MOMENT AT POINT 2

φ	ζ	2	3	4	5	8	9	10	11
0.10	0.10	0.1529	0.1099	0.0715	0.0356	0.0012	0.0001	-.0018	-.0023
	0.20	0.1510	0.1075	0.0694	0.0344	0.0022	0.0011	-.0011	-.0020
	0.40	0.1490	0.1051	0.0674	0.0331	0.0033	0.0024	0.0000	-.0014
	2.00	0.1411	0.0979	0.0618	0.0298	0.0071	0.0072	0.0044	0.0014
0.30	0.10	0.1485	0.1040	0.0669	0.0335	0.0003	-.0028	-.0061	-.0058
	0.20	0.1446	0.0987	0.0625	0.0311	0.0009	-.0028	-.0070	-.0069
	0.40	0.1408	0.0941	0.0587	0.0285	0.0018	-.0023	-.0070	-.0073
	2.00	0.1308	0.0848	0.0516	0.0244	0.0057	0.0017	-.0032	-.0049
0.50	0.10	0.1466	0.1015	0.0650	0.0326	-.0003	-.0042	-.0082	-.0074
	0.20	0.1412	0.0943	0.0591	0.0295	-.0001	-.0054	-.0107	-.0098
	0.40	0.1361	0.0878	0.0538	0.0265	0.0003	-.0060	-.0121	-.0113
	2.00	0.1244	0.0766	0.0451	0.0210	0.0033	-.0038	-.0100	-.0102
1.00	0.10	0.1445	0.0988	0.0629	0.0317	-.0010	-.0059	-.0105	-.0093
	0.20	0.1372	0.0889	0.0550	0.0277	-.0015	-.0087	-.0153	-.0135
	0.40	0.1296	0.0793	0.0472	0.0235	-.0020	-.0115	-.0196	-.0172
	2.00	0.1142	0.0637	0.0346	0.0153	-.0014	-.0136	-.0219	-.0195
1.50	0.10	0.1437	0.0976	0.0621	0.0313	-.0012	-.0066	-.0116	-.0101
	0.20	0.1352	0.0864	0.0531	0.0268	-.0022	-.0104	-.0176	-.0153
	0.40	0.1263	0.0750	0.0438	0.0219	-.0033	-.0144	-.0236	-.0204
	2.00	0.1081	0.0559	0.0282	0.0118	-.0046	-.0199	-.0293	-.0253

BENDING MOMENT AT POINT 3

φ	ζ	2	3	4	5	8	9	10	11
0.10	0.10	0.1044	0.2132	0.1347	0.0656	0.0135	0.0184	0.0140	0.0063
	0.20	0.1002	0.2059	0.1280	0.0618	0.0181	0.0244	0.0188	0.0088
	0.40	0.0968	0.1997	0.1229	0.0590	0.0219	0.0291	0.0226	0.0108
	2.00	0.0908	0.1888	0.1152	0.0546	0.0257	0.0339	0.0269	0.0136
0.30	0.10	0.0980	0.2033	0.1257	0.0608	0.0159	0.0207	0.0144	0.0054
	0.20	0.0901	0.1898	0.1136	0.0541	0.0229	0.0297	0.0210	0.0083
	0.40	0.0833	0.1779	0.1036	0.0488	0.0297	0.0379	0.0270	0.0112
	2.00	0.0732	0.1592	0.0909	0.0423	0.0394	0.0483	0.0346	0.0157
0.50	0.10	0.0956	0.1997	0.1227	0.0593	0.0162	0.0207	0.0136	0.0044
	0.20	0.0859	0.1834	0.1081	0.0513	0.0238	0.0300	0.0200	0.0069
	0.40	0.0772	0.1686	0.0956	0.0447	0.0313	0.0389	0.0260	0.0095
	2.00	0.0648	0.1458	0.0805	0.0373	0.0435	0.0513	0.0342	0.0141
1.00	0.10	0.0932	0.1963	0.1198	0.0578	0.0164	0.0202	0.0125	0.0033
	0.20	0.0811	0.1766	0.1023	0.0484	0.0241	0.0293	0.0178	0.0046
	0.40	0.0698	0.1579	0.0866	0.0403	0.0320	0.0380	0.0227	0.0061
	2.00	0.0540	0.1295	0.0679	0.0313	0.0461	0.0512	0.0300	0.0097
1.50	0.10	0.0922	0.1949	0.1186	0.0573	0.0164	0.0200	0.0119	0.0027
	0.20	0.0791	0.1736	0.0998	0.0472	0.0240	0.0287	0.0165	0.0035
	0.40	0.0663	0.1529	0.0825	0.0383	0.0319	0.0369	0.0204	0.0040
	2.00	0.0484	0.1213	0.0616	0.0283	0.0463	0.0496	0.0265	0.0065

BENDING MOMENT AT POINT 4

φ	ζ	2	3	4	5	8	9	10	11
0.10	0.10	0.0652	0.1329	0.2101	0.1015	0.0165	0.0267	0.0241	0.0124
	0.20	0.0614	0.1258	0.2018	0.0963	0.0208	0.0341	0.0310	0.0160
	0.40	0.0586	0.1205	0.1953	0.0923	0.0238	0.0393	0.0358	0.0186
	2.00	0.0544	0.1131	0.1847	0.0865	0.0260	0.0434	0.0400	0.0214
0.30	0.10	0.0605	0.1246	0.2014	0.0962	0.0206	0.0332	0.0296	0.0150
	0.20	0.0534	0.1116	0.1866	0.0871	0.0281	0.0457	0.0410	0.0208
	0.40	0.0477	0.1010	0.1738	0.0793	0.0339	0.0561	0.0504	0.0255
	2.00	0.0412	0.0885	0.1554	0.0691	0.0380	0.0658	0.0593	0.0301
0.50	0.10	0.0590	0.1221	0.1988	0.0947	0.0217	0.0347	0.0308	0.0154
	0.20	0.0506	0.1068	0.1817	0.0842	0.0301	0.0488	0.0434	0.0217
	0.40	0.0434	0.0937	0.1661	0.0747	0.0369	0.0609	0.0543	0.0271
	2.00	0.0354	0.0783	0.1432	0.0621	0.0414	0.0728	0.0648	0.0320
1.00	0.10	0.0576	0.1198	0.1965	0.0934	0.0225	0.0359	0.0316	0.0157
	0.20	0.0478	0.1022	0.1770	0.0815	0.0317	0.0511	0.0450	0.0222
	0.40	0.0389	0.0862	0.1584	0.0703	0.0392	0.0645	0.0568	0.0277
	2.00	0.0283	0.0664	0.1295	0.0543	0.0433	0.0777	0.0679	0.0320
1.50	0.10	0.0571	0.1189	0.1957	0.0929	0.0228	0.0362	0.0318	0.0157
	0.20	0.0466	0.1004	0.1752	0.0805	0.0322	0.0518	0.0454	0.0222
	0.40	0.0369	0.0830	0.1553	0.0685	0.0400	0.0655	0.0573	0.0277
	2.00	0.0247	0.0606	0.1231	0.0507	0.0435	0.0786	0.0680	0.0310

BENDING MOMENT AT POINT 5

φ	ζ	2	3	4	5	8	9	10	11
0.10	0.10	0.0331	0.0666	0.1037	0.1479	0.0097	0.0169	0.0179	0.0101
	0.20	0.0308	0.0624	0.0983	0.1434	0.0123	0.0216	0.0233	0.0133
	0.40	0.0288	0.0587	0.0937	0.1392	0.0142	0.0251	0.0279	0.0161
	2.00	0.0251	0.0522	0.0853	0.1300	0.0164	0.0293	0.0336	0.0204
0.30	0.10	0.0320	0.0641	0.1002	0.1453	0.0124	0.0218	0.0230	0.0131
	0.20	0.0286	0.0575	0.0918	0.1385	0.0166	0.0295	0.0320	0.0182
	0.40	0.0253	0.0515	0.0838	0.1313	0.0198	0.0358	0.0401	0.0230
	2.00	0.0194	0.0414	0.0698	0.1153	0.0224	0.0420	0.0516	0.0307
0.50	0.10	0.0319	0.0636	0.0995	0.1447	0.0132	0.0232	0.0246	0.0141
	0.20	0.0282	0.0564	0.0902	0.1372	0.0180	0.0321	0.0348	0.0200
	0.40	0.0244	0.0496	0.0809	0.1289	0.0216	0.0394	0.0443	0.0254
	2.00	0.0173	0.0378	0.0641	0.1095	0.0236	0.0456	0.0577	0.0341
1.00	0.10	0.0319	0.0634	0.0989	0.1443	0.0139	0.0245	0.0260	0.0150
	0.20	0.0281	0.0558	0.0889	0.1362	0.0193	0.0346	0.0375	0.0216
	0.40	0.0240	0.0482	0.0786	0.1269	0.0233	0.0428	0.0483	0.0279
	2.00	0.0150	0.0340	0.0582	0.1033	0.0240	0.0480	0.0629	0.0368
1.50	0.10	0.0319	0.0633	0.0988	0.1441	0.0142	0.0250	0.0265	0.0153
	0.20	0.0281	0.0556	0.0886	0.1358	0.0198	0.0355	0.0386	0.0223
	0.40	0.0239	0.0479	0.0779	0.1262	0.0240	0.0442	0.0500	0.0289
	2.00	0.0139	0.0322	0.0556	0.1006	0.0238	0.0484	0.0645	0.0376

$(b/\ell) = 0.20$ ANGLE OF SKEW=ARCTAN(1.00)

UNIT VERTICAL LOAD APPLIED AT POINT:

BENDING MOMENT AT POINT 2

φ	ζ	2	3	4	5	8	9	10	11
0.10	0.10	0.1533	0.1109	0.0724	0.0360	-.0040	-.0076	-.0091	-.0067
	0.20	0.1525	0.1099	0.0714	0.0353	-.0047	-.0086	-.0101	-.0075
	0.40	0.1520	0.1093	0.0708	0.0349	-.0051	-.0092	-.0107	-.0080
	2.00	0.1516	0.1089	0.0702	0.0343	-.0057	-.0098	-.0111	-.0084
0.30	0.10	0.1477	0.1032	0.0660	0.0327	-.0073	-.0140	-.0168	-.0123
	0.20	0.1446	0.0991	0.0623	0.0306	-.0094	-.0177	-.0209	-.0154
	0.40	0.1423	0.0962	0.0596	0.0288	-.0112	-.0204	-.0238	-.0177
	2.00	0.1399	0.0934	0.0565	0.0263	-.0137	-.0235	-.0266	-.0201
0.50	0.10	0.1452	0.0997	0.0632	0.0313	-.0087	-.0168	-.0203	-.0148
	0.20	0.1404	0.0934	0.0576	0.0282	-.0118	-.0224	-.0266	-.0196
	0.40	0.1366	0.0884	0.0530	0.0253	-.0147	-.0270	-.0316	-.0234
	2.00	0.1321	0.0831	0.0472	0.0208	-.0192	-.0328	-.0369	-.0279
1.00	0.10	0.1425	0.0961	0.0602	0.0298	-.0102	-.0198	-.0239	-.0175
	0.20	0.1354	0.0866	0.0520	0.0253	-.0147	-.0280	-.0334	-.0246
	0.40	0.1291	0.0783	0.0445	0.0207	-.0193	-.0355	-.0417	-.0309
	2.00	0.1206	0.0679	0.0336	0.0127	-.0273	-.0464	-.0521	-.0394
1.50	0.10	0.1414	0.0945	0.0589	0.0292	-.0108	-.0211	-.0255	-.0186
	0.20	0.1332	0.0835	0.0494	0.0240	-.0160	-.0306	-.0365	-.0268
	0.40	0.1255	0.0734	0.0403	0.0185	-.0215	-.0397	-.0466	-.0345
	2.00	0.1143	0.0596	0.0262	0.0082	-.0318	-.0538	-.0604	-.0457

BENDING MOMENT AT POINT 3

φ	ζ	2	3	4	5	8	9	10	11
0.10	0.10	0.1048	0.2134	0.1348	0.0656	0.0097	0.0103	0.0055	0.0009
	0.20	0.1017	0.2074	0.1294	0.0625	0.0132	0.0143	0.0084	0.0021
	0.40	0.0994	0.2030	0.1257	0.0604	0.0161	0.0173	0.0107	0.0033
	2.00	0.0970	0.1980	0.1218	0.0582	0.0197	0.0208	0.0134	0.0047
0.30	0.10	0.0966	0.2005	0.1231	0.0592	0.0104	0.0093	0.0021	-.0026
	0.20	0.0895	0.1877	0.1116	0.0527	0.0157	0.0147	0.0051	-.0018
	0.40	0.0838	0.1771	0.1026	0.0478	0.0213	0.0199	0.0084	-.0006
	2.00	0.0769	0.1634	0.0928	0.0427	0.0303	0.0273	0.0136	0.0020
0.50	0.10	0.0934	0.1956	0.1188	0.0568	0.0100	0.0080	-.0001	-.0045
	0.20	0.0840	0.1794	0.1042	0.0487	0.0156	0.0129	0.0018	-.0047
	0.40	0.0763	0.1653	0.0924	0.0424	0.0217	0.0182	0.0045	-.0042
	2.00	0.0667	0.1465	0.0795	0.0357	0.0332	0.0266	0.0099	-.0017
1.00	0.10	0.0901	0.1908	0.1145	0.0546	0.0094	0.0062	-.0028	-.0067
	0.20	0.0780	0.1703	0.0963	0.0446	0.0147	0.0099	-.0028	-.0085
	0.40	0.0674	0.1518	0.0807	0.0362	0.0209	0.0142	-.0020	-.0095
	2.00	0.0539	0.1262	0.0636	0.0275	0.0346	0.0225	0.0023	-.0081
1.50	0.10	0.0888	0.1888	0.1128	0.0537	0.0091	0.0054	-.0040	-.0076
	0.20	0.0754	0.1664	0.0929	0.0428	0.0141	0.0084	-.0051	-.0104
	0.40	0.0633	0.1457	0.0755	0.0334	0.0201	0.0119	-.0054	-.0123
	2.00	0.0476	0.1165	0.0560	0.0236	0.0344	0.0194	-.0024	-.0118

BENDING MOMENT AT POINT 4

φ	ζ	2	3	4	5	8	9	10	11
0.10	0.10	0.0651	0.1323	0.2089	0.1006	0.0153	0.0235	0.0186	0.0082
	0.20	0.0619	0.1261	0.2015	0.0961	0.0193	0.0299	0.0238	0.0107
	0.40	0.0597	0.1219	0.1963	0.0929	0.0220	0.0345	0.0274	0.0124
	2.00	0.0576	0.1180	0.1910	0.0898	0.0245	0.0392	0.0309	0.0140
0.30	0.10	0.0586	0.1212	0.1972	0.0935	0.0192	0.0288	0.0220	0.0090
	0.20	0.0517	0.1084	0.1823	0.0844	0.0262	0.0400	0.0307	0.0129
	0.40	0.0463	0.0984	0.1702	0.0771	0.0317	0.0494	0.0378	0.0160
	2.00	0.0407	0.0881	0.1559	0.0692	0.0371	0.0606	0.0453	0.0193
0.50	0.10	0.0563	0.1174	0.1934	0.0913	0.0200	0.0298	0.0223	0.0088
	0.20	0.0477	0.1017	0.1754	0.0803	0.0278	0.0422	0.0317	0.0127
	0.40	0.0406	0.0887	0.1599	0.0710	0.0343	0.0532	0.0397	0.0160
	2.00	0.0328	0.0750	0.1405	0.0605	0.0403	0.0668	0.0481	0.0193
1.00	0.10	0.0542	0.1139	0.1898	0.0893	0.0205	0.0303	0.0222	0.0083
	0.20	0.0435	0.0949	0.1685	0.0763	0.0289	0.0435	0.0317	0.0119
	0.40	0.0342	0.0784	0.1491	0.0648	0.0360	0.0554	0.0400	0.0150
	2.00	0.0233	0.0599	0.1230	0.0508	0.0419	0.0706	0.0480	0.0173
1.50	0.10	0.0533	0.1125	0.1885	0.0885	0.0207	0.0304	0.0221	0.0081
	0.20	0.0418	0.0921	0.1658	0.0747	0.0292	0.0437	0.0314	0.0114
	0.40	0.0313	0.0739	0.1446	0.0621	0.0364	0.0557	0.0395	0.0141
	2.00	0.0187	0.0529	0.1151	0.0464	0.0418	0.0711	0.0467	0.0156

BENDING MOMENT AT POINT 5

φ	ζ	2	3	4	5	8	9	10	11
0.10	0.10	0.0325	0.0654	0.1020	0.1463	0.0104	0.0176	0.0175	0.0085
	0.20	0.0304	0.0615	0.0971	0.1421	0.0128	0.0220	0.0225	0.0109
	0.40	0.0288	0.0586	0.0934	0.1388	0.0145	0.0251	0.0263	0.0126
	2.00	0.0270	0.0555	0.0894	0.1346	0.0162	0.0284	0.0308	0.0147
0.30	0.10	0.0303	0.0611	0.0967	0.1424	0.0136	0.0229	0.0227	0.0111
	0.20	0.0264	0.0539	0.0877	0.1348	0.0179	0.0308	0.0313	0.0151
	0.40	0.0229	0.0478	0.0797	0.1275	0.0210	0.0370	0.0391	0.0185
	2.00	0.0179	0.0398	0.0691	0.1159	0.0236	0.0436	0.0500	0.0231
0.50	0.10	0.0297	0.0599	0.0952	0.1413	0.0145	0.0244	0.0241	0.0118
	0.20	0.0251	0.0516	0.0847	0.1326	0.0194	0.0334	0.0340	0.0163
	0.40	0.0208	0.0440	0.0749	0.1236	0.0229	0.0407	0.0431	0.0203
	2.00	0.0138	0.0332	0.0607	0.1076	0.0251	0.0478	0.0566	0.0255
1.00	0.10	0.0292	0.0589	0.0940	0.1404	0.0152	0.0256	0.0253	0.0124
	0.20	0.0240	0.0494	0.0821	0.1306	0.0207	0.0357	0.0363	0.0174
	0.40	0.0186	0.0403	0.0703	0.1199	0.0245	0.0438	0.0465	0.0217
	2.00	0.0087	0.0256	0.0512	0.0981	0.0252	0.0501	0.0617	0.0267
1.50	0.10	0.0290	0.0585	0.0935	0.1401	0.0155	0.0261	0.0257	0.0126
	0.20	0.0236	0.0486	0.0811	0.1298	0.0212	0.0365	0.0371	0.0178
	0.40	0.0177	0.0388	0.0685	0.1184	0.0251	0.0449	0.0477	0.0222
	2.00	0.0061	0.0220	0.0468	0.0938	0.0246	0.0501	0.0631	0.0267

TABLE 5 – SIMPLY-SUPPORTED SKEW GIRDER BRIDGE

INFLUENCE COEFFICIENT OF BENDING MOMENT IN MAIN GIRDER

BENDING MOMENT = COEF. x ℓ

(b/ℓ) = 0.40										ANGLE OF SKEW=ARCTAN(0.0)							
		UNIT VERTICAL LOAD APPLIED AT POINT:															
φ	ζ	2	3	4	5	8	9	10	11	2	3	4	5	8	9	10	11
		BENDING MOMENT AT POINT 2								BENDING MOMENT AT POINT 3							
0.10	0.10	0.1575	0.1165	0.0770	0.0384	0.0025	0.0035	0.0030	0.0016	0.1158	0.2331	0.1535	0.0763	0.0042	0.0069	0.0065	0.0037
	0.20	0.1561	0.1146	0.0754	0.0375	0.0039	0.0054	0.0046	0.0025	0.1137	0.2297	0.1504	0.0745	0.0063	0.0103	0.0096	0.0055
	0.40	0.1545	0.1125	0.0736	0.0365	0.0055	0.0075	0.0064	0.0035	0.1116	0.2263	0.1473	0.0727	0.0084	0.0137	0.0127	0.0073
	2.00	0.1516	0.1089	0.0705	0.0347	0.0084	0.0111	0.0095	0.0053	0.1085	0.2212	0.1428	0.0701	0.0115	0.0188	0.0172	0.0099
0.30	0.10	0.1569	0.1157	0.0764	0.0382	0.0031	0.0043	0.0036	0.0018	0.1148	0.2315	0.1521	0.0755	0.0052	0.0085	0.0079	0.0045
	0.20	0.1547	0.1128	0.0739	0.0368	0.0053	0.0072	0.0061	0.0032	0.1113	0.2258	0.1467	0.0725	0.0087	0.0142	0.0133	0.0075
	0.40	0.1518	0.1088	0.0706	0.0350	0.0082	0.0112	0.0094	0.0050	0.1069	0.2185	0.1401	0.0687	0.0131	0.0215	0.0199	0.0113
	2.00	0.1441	0.0995	0.0629	0.0307	0.0159	0.0205	0.0171	0.0093	0.0976	0.2033	0.1268	0.0612	0.0224	0.0367	0.0332	0.0188
0.50	0.10	0.1567	0.1155	0.0763	0.0381	0.0033	0.0045	0.0037	0.0019	0.1145	0.2311	0.1517	0.0753	0.0055	0.0089	0.0083	0.0047
	0.20	0.1543	0.1122	0.0735	0.0367	0.0057	0.0078	0.0065	0.0033	0.1106	0.2246	0.1457	0.0719	0.0094	0.0154	0.0143	0.0081
	0.40	0.1508	0.1075	0.0697	0.0346	0.0092	0.0125	0.0103	0.0054	0.1052	0.2157	0.1375	0.0673	0.0148	0.0243	0.0225	0.0127
	2.00	0.1406	0.0952	0.0597	0.0292	0.0194	0.0248	0.0203	0.0108	0.0923	0.1946	0.1190	0.0571	0.0277	0.0454	0.0410	0.0229
1.00	0.10	0.1566	0.1154	0.0762	0.0381	0.0034	0.0046	0.0038	0.0019	0.1143	0.2308	0.1514	0.0752	0.0057	0.0092	0.0086	0.0048
	0.20	0.1539	0.1117	0.0732	0.0366	0.0061	0.0083	0.0068	0.0034	0.1099	0.2235	0.1447	0.0715	0.0101	0.0165	0.0153	0.0085
	0.40	0.1498	0.1063	0.0688	0.0343	0.0102	0.0137	0.0112	0.0057	0.1035	0.2130	0.1351	0.0661	0.0165	0.0270	0.0249	0.0139
	2.00	0.1365	0.0905	0.0566	0.0279	0.0235	0.0295	0.0234	0.0121	0.0862	0.1845	0.1104	0.0526	0.0338	0.0555	0.0496	0.0274
1.50	0.10	0.1566	0.1153	0.0762	0.0381	0.0034	0.0047	0.0038	0.0019	0.1143	0.2306	0.1513	0.0751	0.0057	0.0094	0.0087	0.0049
	0.20	0.1537	0.1115	0.0731	0.0366	0.0063	0.0085	0.0069	0.0034	0.1097	0.2232	0.1444	0.0713	0.0103	0.0168	0.0156	0.0087
	0.40	0.1494	0.1058	0.0686	0.0343	0.0106	0.0142	0.0114	0.0057	0.1028	0.2120	0.1342	0.0656	0.0172	0.0280	0.0258	0.0144
	2.00	0.1346	0.0884	0.0554	0.0276	0.0254	0.0316	0.0246	0.0124	0.0834	0.1800	0.1066	0.0507	0.0366	0.0600	0.0534	0.0293
		BENDING MOMENT AT POINT 4								BENDING MOMENT AT POINT 5							
0.10	0.10	0.0763	0.1535	0.2331	0.1158	0.0037	0.0065	0.0069	0.0042	0.0384	0.0770	0.1165	0.1575	0.0016	0.0030	0.0035	0.0025
	0.20	0.0745	0.1504	0.2297	0.1137	0.0055	0.0096	0.0103	0.0063	0.0375	0.0754	0.1146	0.1561	0.0025	0.0046	0.0054	0.0039
	0.40	0.0727	0.1473	0.2263	0.1116	0.0073	0.0127	0.0137	0.0084	0.0365	0.0736	0.1125	0.1545	0.0035	0.0064	0.0075	0.0055
	2.00	0.0701	0.1428	0.2212	0.1085	0.0099	0.0172	0.0188	0.0115	0.0347	0.0705	0.1089	0.1516	0.0053	0.0095	0.0111	0.0084
0.30	0.10	0.0755	0.1521	0.2315	0.1148	0.0045	0.0079	0.0085	0.0052	0.0382	0.0764	0.1157	0.1569	0.0018	0.0036	0.0043	0.0031
	0.20	0.0725	0.1467	0.2258	0.1113	0.0075	0.0133	0.0142	0.0087	0.0368	0.0739	0.1128	0.1547	0.0032	0.0061	0.0072	0.0053
	0.40	0.0687	0.1401	0.2185	0.1069	0.0113	0.0199	0.0215	0.0131	0.0350	0.0706	0.1088	0.1518	0.0050	0.0094	0.0112	0.0082
	2.00	0.0612	0.1268	0.2033	0.0976	0.0188	0.0332	0.0367	0.0224	0.0307	0.0629	0.0995	0.1441	0.0093	0.0171	0.0205	0.0159
0.50	0.10	0.0753	0.1517	0.2311	0.1145	0.0047	0.0083	0.0089	0.0055	0.0381	0.0763	0.1155	0.1567	0.0019	0.0037	0.0045	0.0033
	0.20	0.0719	0.1457	0.2246	0.1106	0.0081	0.0143	0.0154	0.0094	0.0367	0.0735	0.1122	0.1543	0.0033	0.0065	0.0078	0.0057
	0.40	0.0673	0.1375	0.2157	0.1052	0.0127	0.0225	0.0243	0.0148	0.0346	0.0697	0.1075	0.1508	0.0054	0.0103	0.0125	0.0092
	2.00	0.0571	0.1190	0.1946	0.0923	0.0229	0.0410	0.0454	0.0277	0.0292	0.0597	0.0952	0.1406	0.0108	0.0203	0.0248	0.0194
1.00	0.10	0.0752	0.1514	0.2308	0.1143	0.0048	0.0086	0.0092	0.0057	0.0381	0.0762	0.1154	0.1566	0.0019	0.0038	0.0046	0.0034
	0.20	0.0715	0.1447	0.2235	0.1099	0.0085	0.0153	0.0165	0.0101	0.0366	0.0732	0.1117	0.1539	0.0034	0.0068	0.0083	0.0061
	0.40	0.0661	0.1351	0.2130	0.1035	0.0139	0.0249	0.0270	0.0165	0.0343	0.0688	0.1063	0.1498	0.0057	0.0112	0.0137	0.0102
	2.00	0.0526	0.1104	0.1845	0.0862	0.0274	0.0496	0.0555	0.0338	0.0279	0.0566	0.0905	0.1365	0.0121	0.0234	0.0295	0.0235
1.50	0.10	0.0751	0.1513	0.2306	0.1143	0.0049	0.0087	0.0094	0.0057	0.0381	0.0762	0.1153	0.1566	0.0019	0.0038	0.0047	0.0034
	0.20	0.0713	0.1444	0.2232	0.1097	0.0087	0.0156	0.0168	0.0103	0.0366	0.0731	0.1115	0.1537	0.0034	0.0069	0.0085	0.0063
	0.40	0.0656	0.1342	0.2120	0.1028	0.0144	0.0258	0.0280	0.0172	0.0343	0.0686	0.1058	0.1494	0.0057	0.0114	0.0142	0.0106
	2.00	0.0507	0.1066	0.1800	0.0834	0.0293	0.0534	0.0600	0.0366	0.0276	0.0554	0.0884	0.1346	0.0124	0.0246	0.0316	0.0254

(b/ℓ) = 0.40										ANGLE OF SKEW=ARCTAN(0.17)							
		UNIT VERTICAL LOAD APPLIED AT POINT:															
φ	ζ	2	3	4	5	8	9	10	11	2	3	4	5	8	9	10	11
		BENDING MOMENT AT POINT 2								BENDING MOMENT AT POINT 3							
0.10	0.10	0.1578	0.1170	0.0774	0.0386	0.0020	0.0027	0.0022	0.0011	0.1162	0.2337	0.1540	0.0766	0.0039	0.0062	0.0056	0.0031
	0.20	0.1567	0.1153	0.0760	0.0378	0.0031	0.0042	0.0035	0.0018	0.1142	0.2304	0.1510	0.0748	0.0059	0.0094	0.0085	0.0047
	0.40	0.1553	0.1135	0.0744	0.0369	0.0045	0.0060	0.0050	0.0027	0.1122	0.2270	0.1479	0.0730	0.0080	0.0127	0.0115	0.0064
	2.00	0.1523	0.1098	0.0713	0.0351	0.0073	0.0094	0.0080	0.0044	0.1088	0.2215	0.1430	0.0702	0.0113	0.0180	0.0161	0.0091
0.30	0.10	0.1573	0.1163	0.0769	0.0384	0.0024	0.0031	0.0024	0.0011	0.1153	0.2323	0.1528	0.0759	0.0047	0.0074	0.0067	0.0036
	0.20	0.1555	0.1137	0.0747	0.0373	0.0041	0.0054	0.0043	0.0021	0.1121	0.2269	0.1478	0.0731	0.0079	0.0126	0.0114	0.0062
	0.40	0.1530	0.1103	0.0718	0.0357	0.0065	0.0085	0.0069	0.0034	0.1079	0.2200	0.1413	0.0694	0.0122	0.0195	0.0176	0.0096
	2.00	0.1458	0.1014	0.0645	0.0316	0.0134	0.0168	0.0137	0.0072	0.0985	0.2045	0.1275	0.0616	0.0218	0.0346	0.0306	0.0169
0.50	0.10	0.1572	0.1161	0.0768	0.0384	0.0025	0.0032	0.0024	0.0011	0.1151	0.2319	0.1524	0.0758	0.0049	0.0077	0.0069	0.0038
	0.20	0.1551	0.1132	0.0744	0.0371	0.0044	0.0057	0.0044	0.0020	0.1114	0.2259	0.1468	0.0726	0.0085	0.0135	0.0122	0.0066
	0.40	0.1520	0.1090	0.0709	0.0353	0.0072	0.0094	0.0073	0.0035	0.1063	0.2174	0.1389	0.0682	0.0137	0.0218	0.0196	0.0107
	2.00	0.1428	0.0975	0.0616	0.0302	0.0160	0.0200	0.0158	0.0081	0.0934	0.1961	0.1200	0.0576	0.0268	0.0426	0.0374	0.0205
1.00	0.10	0.1570	0.1159	0.0767	0.0384	0.0025	0.0033	0.0025	0.0011	0.1149	0.2316	0.1522	0.0756	0.0050	0.0080	0.0071	0.0038
	0.20	0.1547	0.1127	0.0740	0.0370	0.0046	0.0060	0.0045	0.0020	0.1108	0.2249	0.1460	0.0722	0.0091	0.0143	0.0128	0.0069
	0.40	0.1510	0.1078	0.0701	0.0350	0.0078	0.0101	0.0076	0.0034	0.1047	0.2149	0.1368	0.0670	0.0151	0.0239	0.0213	0.0115
	2.00	0.1389	0.0928	0.0584	0.0289	0.0190	0.0231	0.0174	0.0084	0.0873	0.1863	0.1115	0.0532	0.0326	0.0515	0.0448	0.0241
1.50	0.10	0.1570	0.1159	0.0766	0.0384	0.0026	0.0033	0.0025	0.0011	0.1148	0.2315	0.1521	0.0756	0.0051	0.0080	0.0072	0.0039
	0.20	0.1545	0.1125	0.0739	0.0370	0.0047	0.0061	0.0045	0.0019	0.1105	0.2246	0.1457	0.0720	0.0093	0.0146	0.0131	0.0070
	0.40	0.1506	0.1072	0.0697	0.0349	0.0081	0.0103	0.0076	0.0033	0.1040	0.2139	0.1359	0.0666	0.0157	0.0247	0.0220	0.0118
	2.00	0.1369	0.0905	0.0569	0.0285	0.0203	0.0242	0.0176	0.0081	0.0845	0.1817	0.1076	0.0513	0.0351	0.0554	0.0478	0.0254
		BENDING MOMENT AT POINT 4								BENDING MOMENT AT POINT 5							
0.10	0.10	0.0766	0.1540	0.2335	0.1160	0.0036	0.0062	0.0065	0.0038	0.0385	0.0772	0.1167	0.1576	0.0017	0.0031	0.0035	0.0024
	0.20	0.0748	0.1508	0.2301	0.1140	0.0055	0.0094	0.0098	0.0058	0.0376	0.0756	0.1148	0.1563	0.0027	0.0048	0.0055	0.0038
	0.40	0.0730	0.1476	0.2266	0.1118	0.0074	0.0127	0.0132	0.0079	0.0366	0.0738	0.1127	0.1547	0.0037	0.0067	0.0076	0.0053
	2.00	0.0702	0.1428	0.2210	0.1083	0.0102	0.0175	0.0185	0.0110	0.0346	0.0703	0.1086	0.1513	0.0057	0.0101	0.0116	0.0084
0.30	0.10	0.0759	0.1527	0.2322	0.1152	0.0044	0.0076	0.0078	0.0046	0.0384	0.0768	0.1161	0.1572	0.0020	0.0037	0.0043	0.0030
	0.20	0.0731	0.1476	0.2267	0.1119	0.0074	0.0128	0.0133	0.0079	0.0371	0.0744	0.1133	0.1552	0.0034	0.0064	0.0073	0.0050
	0.40	0.0694	0.1410	0.2195	0.1075	0.0113	0.0196	0.0204	0.0121	0.0353	0.0712	0.1094	0.1523	0.0054	0.0099	0.0113	0.0079
	2.00	0.0615	0.1270	0.2036	0.0977	0.0194	0.0338	0.0359	0.0213	0.0308	0.0630	0.0995	0.1442	0.0101	0.0183	0.0215	0.0157
0.50	0.10	0.0758	0.1524	0.2319	0.1150	0.0046	0.0079	0.0082	0.0049	0.0384	0.0767	0.1160	0.1571	0.0021	0.0039	0.0045	0.0031
	0.20	0.0726	0.1467	0.2257	0.1112	0.0080	0.0138	0.0143	0.0085	0.0370	0.0741	0.1129	0.1548	0.0036	0.0068	0.0079	0.0055
	0.40	0.0681	0.1387	0.2170	0.1059	0.0127	0.0220	0.0229	0.0136	0.0350	0.0704	0.1084	0.1515	0.0059	0.0109	0.0127	0.0088
	2.00	0.0575	0.1195	0.1952	0.0925	0.0237	0.0416	0.0444	0.0262	0.0294	0.0600	0.0955	0.1411	0.0119	0.0218	0.0260	0.0191
1.00	0.10	0.0756	0.1522	0.2316	0.1148	0.0047	0.0082	0.0085	0.0050	0.0384	0.0767	0.1159	0.1570	0.0021	0.0040	0.0047	0.0032
	0.20	0.0721	0.1459	0.2248	0.1107	0.0084	0.0147	0.0152	0.0090	0.0370	0.0739	0.1125	0.1546	0.0038	0.0072	0.0084	0.0059
	0.40	0.0670	0.1367	0.2148	0.1045	0.0139	0.0243	0.0253	0.0150	0.0349	0.0698	0.1074	0.1507	0.0063	0.0120	0.0141	0.0099
	2.00	0.0530	0.1110	0.1856	0.0867	0.0286	0.0506	0.0541	0.0319	0.0284	0.0573	0.0914	0.1376	0.0136	0.0257	0.0312	0.0231
1.50	0.10	0.0756	0.1521	0.2315	0.1148	0.0048	0.0083	0.0086	0.0051	0.0384	0.0766	0.1158	0.1570	0.0021	0.0041	0.0048	0.0033
	0.20	0.0720	0.1456	0.2245	0.1105	0.0086	0.0150	0.0156	0.0092	0.0370	0.0739	0.1124	0.1544	0.0038	0.0073	0.0086	0.0060
	0.40	0.0666	0.1359	0.2139	0.1040	0.0144	0.0252	0.0263	0.0156	0.0349	0.0696	0.1071	0.1504	0.0065	0.0124	0.0146	0.0103
	2.00	0.0511	0.1074	0.1814	0.0841	0.0307	0.0545	0.0584	0.0345	0.0282	0.0564	0.0897	0.1361	0.0143	0.0274	0.0337	0.0250

TABLE 6 - SIMPLY-SUPPORTED SKEW GIRDER BRIDGE

INFLUENCE COEFICIENT OF BENDING MOMENT IN MAIN GIRDER

BENDING MOMENT = COEF. x ℓ

$(b/\ell) = 0.40$										ANGLE OF SKEW=ARCTAN(0.33)							
		UNIT VERTICAL LOAD APPLIED AT POINT:															
ϕ	ζ	2	3	4	5	8	9	10	11	2	3	4	5	8	9	10	11
		BENDING MOMENT AT POINT 2								BENDING MOMENT AT POINT 3							
0.10	0.10	0.1582	0.1174	0.0778	0.0388	0.0014	0.0018	0.0013	0.0005	0.1165	0.2341	0.1544	0.0768	0.0034	0.0053	0.0047	0.0025
	0.20	0.1572	0.1160	0.0766	0.0382	0.0023	0.0029	0.0022	0.0010	0.1147	0.2311	0.1515	0.0751	0.0054	0.0083	0.0073	0.0039
	0.40	0.1561	0.1145	0.0752	0.0374	0.0033	0.0043	0.0034	0.0017	0.1127	0.2278	0.1484	0.0734	0.0074	0.0114	0.0101	0.0054
	2.00	0.1530	0.1109	0.0722	0.0356	0.0059	0.0074	0.0061	0.0033	0.1092	0.2218	0.1433	0.0703	0.0109	0.0166	0.0145	0.0080
0.30	0.10	0.1576	0.1167	0.0773	0.0386	0.0016	0.0019	0.0012	0.0004	0.1156	0.2328	0.1532	0.0762	0.0041	0.0063	0.0054	0.0028
	0.20	0.1561	0.1145	0.0754	0.0376	0.0028	0.0034	0.0024	0.0009	0.1126	0.2278	0.1485	0.0735	0.0071	0.0108	0.0094	0.0049
	0.40	0.1540	0.1115	0.0729	0.0363	0.0046	0.0057	0.0041	0.0018	0.1087	0.2212	0.1422	0.0699	0.0111	0.0171	0.0148	0.0078
	2.00	0.1477	0.1036	0.0663	0.0325	0.0101	0.0123	0.0096	0.0048	0.0994	0.2055	0.1283	0.0620	0.0207	0.0316	0.0272	0.0146
0.50	0.10	0.1575	0.1165	0.0771	0.0386	0.0016	0.0019	0.0012	0.0003	0.1154	0.2324	0.1529	0.0760	0.0043	0.0065	0.0055	0.0028
	0.20	0.1556	0.1139	0.0750	0.0375	0.0030	0.0035	0.0022	0.0007	0.1120	0.2268	0.1476	0.0730	0.0076	0.0115	0.0099	0.0051
	0.40	0.1530	0.1103	0.0719	0.0359	0.0050	0.0060	0.0041	0.0015	0.1071	0.2187	0.1400	0.0687	0.0123	0.0189	0.0163	0.0084
	2.00	0.1449	0.1000	0.0635	0.0312	0.0119	0.0141	0.0104	0.0048	0.0944	0.1973	0.1208	0.0580	0.0254	0.0386	0.0328	0.0174
1.00	0.10	0.1573	0.1163	0.0770	0.0385	0.0017	0.0019	0.0011	0.0002	0.1152	0.2321	0.1527	0.0759	0.0044	0.0066	0.0056	0.0028
	0.20	0.1552	0.1133	0.0746	0.0373	0.0031	0.0035	0.0021	0.0005	0.1113	0.2258	0.1467	0.0726	0.0080	0.0121	0.0103	0.0052
	0.40	0.1519	0.1088	0.0709	0.0355	0.0053	0.0061	0.0037	0.0010	0.1055	0.2162	0.1378	0.0676	0.0135	0.0204	0.0174	0.0088
	2.00	0.1411	0.0951	0.0600	0.0298	0.0136	0.0153	0.0102	0.0039	0.0882	0.1874	0.1121	0.0534	0.0305	0.0460	0.0385	0.0198
1.50	0.10	0.1572	0.1162	0.0769	0.0385	0.0017	0.0019	0.0010	0.0002	0.1151	0.2320	0.1526	0.0759	0.0044	0.0067	0.0057	0.0028
	0.20	0.1550	0.1131	0.0744	0.0373	0.0031	0.0035	0.0020	0.0004	0.1111	0.2254	0.1464	0.0724	0.0081	0.0122	0.0104	0.0052
	0.40	0.1514	0.1082	0.0705	0.0354	0.0054	0.0061	0.0035	0.0007	0.1048	0.2151	0.1369	0.0672	0.0139	0.0210	0.0177	0.0089
	2.00	0.1389	0.0923	0.0581	0.0291	0.0142	0.0154	0.0094	0.0029	0.0851	0.1825	0.1079	0.0514	0.0327	0.0491	0.0405	0.0205
		BENDING MOMENT AT POINT 4								BENDING MOMENT AT POINT 5							
0.10	0.10	0.0768	0.1543	0.2338	0.1162	0.0035	0.0060	0.0059	0.0034	0.0386	0.0773	0.1168	0.1578	0.0018	0.0032	0.0035	0.0023
	0.20	0.0751	0.1512	0.2305	0.1142	0.0054	0.0091	0.0091	0.0052	0.0377	0.0757	0.1150	0.1564	0.0028	0.0050	0.0055	0.0035
	0.40	0.0733	0.1480	0.2270	0.1120	0.0073	0.0124	0.0125	0.0071	0.0367	0.0739	0.1128	0.1547	0.0039	0.0069	0.0077	0.0050
	2.00	0.0703	0.1428	0.2208	0.1082	0.0103	0.0174	0.0177	0.0103	0.0345	0.0701	0.1082	0.1509	0.0060	0.0106	0.0120	0.0082
0.30	0.10	0.0762	0.1531	0.2326	0.1155	0.0042	0.0072	0.0071	0.0041	0.0385	0.0770	0.1164	0.1574	0.0021	0.0039	0.0043	0.0028
	0.20	0.0735	0.1482	0.2273	0.1122	0.0073	0.0123	0.0122	0.0070	0.0373	0.0747	0.1136	0.1554	0.0037	0.0066	0.0073	0.0048
	0.40	0.0698	0.1417	0.2202	0.1078	0.0112	0.0190	0.0190	0.0108	0.0356	0.0715	0.1098	0.1526	0.0057	0.0103	0.0115	0.0075
	2.00	0.0618	0.1273	0.2037	0.0976	0.0197	0.0337	0.0343	0.0196	0.0309	0.0629	0.0993	0.1441	0.0107	0.0192	0.0220	0.0150
0.50	0.10	0.0760	0.1528	0.2323	0.1153	0.0044	0.0075	0.0074	0.0042	0.0385	0.0770	0.1163	0.1573	0.0022	0.0041	0.0045	0.0029
	0.20	0.0730	0.1474	0.2264	0.1117	0.0078	0.0132	0.0131	0.0075	0.0372	0.0745	0.1133	0.1552	0.0039	0.0071	0.0080	0.0052
	0.40	0.0686	0.1396	0.2179	0.1064	0.0126	0.0213	0.0213	0.0121	0.0353	0.0708	0.1088	0.1519	0.0063	0.0115	0.0129	0.0084
	2.00	0.0578	0.1197	0.1953	0.0925	0.0242	0.0416	0.0423	0.0241	0.0295	0.0600	0.0954	0.1411	0.0127	0.0231	0.0268	0.0182
1.00	0.10	0.0759	0.1526	0.2321	0.1151	0.0046	0.0077	0.0077	0.0044	0.0385	0.0769	0.1162	0.1572	0.0023	0.0042	0.0047	0.0031
	0.20	0.0726	0.1466	0.2256	0.1112	0.0083	0.0140	0.0139	0.0079	0.0372	0.0744	0.1130	0.1549	0.0041	0.0076	0.0085	0.0056
	0.40	0.0675	0.1376	0.2158	0.1051	0.0138	0.0234	0.0234	0.0133	0.0352	0.0703	0.1081	0.1513	0.0069	0.0127	0.0143	0.0094
	2.00	0.0531	0.1111	0.1858	0.0867	0.0293	0.0505	0.0514	0.0291	0.0285	0.0574	0.0915	0.1380	0.0150	0.0277	0.0324	0.0221
1.50	0.10	0.0759	0.1525	0.2320	0.1151	0.0046	0.0078	0.0078	0.0044	0.0385	0.0769	0.1162	0.1572	0.0023	0.0043	0.0048	0.0031
	0.20	0.0724	0.1464	0.2253	0.1110	0.0084	0.0143	0.0142	0.0081	0.0373	0.0743	0.1129	0.1549	0.0042	0.0078	0.0087	0.0057
	0.40	0.0671	0.1368	0.2149	0.1046	0.0143	0.0242	0.0242	0.0136	0.0352	0.0702	0.1078	0.1510	0.0072	0.0132	0.0149	0.0098
	2.00	0.0510	0.1073	0.1816	0.0842	0.0315	0.0545	0.0553	0.0313	0.0283	0.0566	0.0900	0.1367	0.0159	0.0298	0.0351	0.0240

$(b/\ell) = 0.40$										ANGLE OF SKEW=ARCTAN(0.50)							
		UNIT VERTICAL LOAD APPLIED AT POINT:															
ϕ	ζ	2	3	4	5	8	9	10	11	2	3	4	5	8	9	10	11
		BENDING MOMENT AT POINT 2								BENDING MOMENT AT POINT 3							
0.10	0.10	0.1584	0.1177	0.0781	0.0390	0.0008	0.0008	0.0004	-.0000	0.1167	0.2345	0.1547	0.0770	0.0030	0.0045	0.0037	0.0018
	0.20	0.1577	0.1167	0.0771	0.0385	0.0013	0.0015	0.0009	0.0002	0.1151	0.2316	0.1520	0.0754	0.0048	0.0070	0.0059	0.0030
	0.40	0.1568	0.1155	0.0761	0.0379	0.0021	0.0025	0.0017	0.0007	0.1133	0.2285	0.1491	0.0737	0.0067	0.0099	0.0084	0.0043
	2.00	0.1541	0.1123	0.0734	0.0363	0.0041	0.0050	0.0039	0.0019	0.1098	0.2225	0.1439	0.0707	0.0102	0.0148	0.0126	0.0067
0.30	0.10	0.1578	0.1170	0.0775	0.0388	0.0008	0.0007	0.0000	-.0004	0.1158	0.2331	0.1535	0.0763	0.0035	0.0051	0.0041	0.0019
	0.20	0.1565	0.1150	0.0759	0.0379	0.0015	0.0015	0.0004	-.0003	0.1130	0.2283	0.1490	0.0737	0.0062	0.0090	0.0073	0.0035
	0.40	0.1548	0.1126	0.0738	0.0368	0.0026	0.0027	0.0013	0.0000	0.1094	0.2221	0.1430	0.0703	0.0099	0.0144	0.0119	0.0059
	2.00	0.1497	0.1061	0.0683	0.0336	0.0064	0.0073	0.0049	0.0019	0.1005	0.2068	0.1293	0.0625	0.0192	0.0278	0.0230	0.0119
0.50	0.10	0.1576	0.1167	0.0773	0.0387	0.0008	0.0006	-.0001	-.0005	0.1156	0.2327	0.1531	0.0761	0.0036	0.0052	0.0041	0.0019
	0.20	0.1560	0.1144	0.0754	0.0377	0.0015	0.0013	0.0001	-.0006	0.1123	0.2272	0.1480	0.0732	0.0065	0.0094	0.0075	0.0035
	0.40	0.1537	0.1112	0.0727	0.0363	0.0027	0.0026	0.0007	-.0006	0.1077	0.2195	0.1406	0.0691	0.0109	0.0157	0.0128	0.0061
	2.00	0.1471	0.1026	0.0655	0.0323	0.0072	0.0076	0.0044	0.0012	0.0956	0.1986	0.1218	0.0584	0.0234	0.0336	0.0274	0.0138
1.00	0.10	0.1574	0.1164	0.0771	0.0386	0.0008	0.0005	-.0003	-.0007	0.1153	0.2323	0.1528	0.0760	0.0037	0.0053	0.0041	0.0018
	0.20	0.1554	0.1136	0.0748	0.0375	0.0015	0.0011	-.0004	-.0011	0.1116	0.2261	0.1470	0.0728	0.0068	0.0097	0.0076	0.0034
	0.40	0.1524	0.1095	0.0715	0.0358	0.0027	0.0021	-.0002	-.0014	0.1059	0.2167	0.1382	0.0678	0.0117	0.0167	0.0132	0.0060
	2.00	0.1431	0.0971	0.0614	0.0305	0.0076	0.0069	0.0023	-.0010	0.0890	0.1881	0.1124	0.0535	0.0278	0.0394	0.0311	0.0149
1.50	0.10	0.1574	0.1163	0.0771	0.0386	0.0008	0.0005	-.0004	-.0007	0.1152	0.2322	0.1527	0.0759	0.0037	0.0053	0.0041	0.0018
	0.20	0.1552	0.1133	0.0746	0.0374	0.0015	0.0009	-.0006	-.0012	0.1113	0.2257	0.1467	0.0726	0.0069	0.0098	0.0076	0.0033
	0.40	0.1518	0.1087	0.0709	0.0356	0.0026	0.0018	-.0008	-.0019	0.1051	0.2156	0.1372	0.0673	0.0120	0.0170	0.0132	0.0059
	2.00	0.1405	0.0938	0.0589	0.0294	0.0075	0.0058	0.0003	-.0028	0.0854	0.1827	0.1077	0.0512	0.0295	0.0414	0.0320	0.0148
		BENDING MOMENT AT POINT 4								BENDING MOMENT AT POINT 5							
0.10	0.10	0.0769	0.1545	0.2340	0.1163	0.0034	0.0057	0.0054	0.0029	0.0387	0.0774	0.1169	0.1578	0.0019	0.0033	0.0035	0.0021
	0.20	0.0753	0.1515	0.2308	0.1143	0.0053	0.0087	0.0083	0.0046	0.0378	0.0758	0.1150	0.1564	0.0029	0.0051	0.0055	0.0033
	0.40	0.0736	0.1484	0.2273	0.1121	0.0072	0.0120	0.0115	0.0063	0.0368	0.0740	0.1129	0.1548	0.0040	0.0071	0.0076	0.0047
	2.00	0.0707	0.1431	0.2210	0.1083	0.0102	0.0169	0.0165	0.0092	0.0346	0.0701	0.1082	0.1507	0.0062	0.0108	0.0120	0.0076
0.30	0.10	0.0763	0.1533	0.2328	0.1156	0.0041	0.0068	0.0064	0.0035	0.0385	0.0771	0.1164	0.1574	0.0023	0.0040	0.0043	0.0026
	0.20	0.0737	0.1485	0.2276	0.1124	0.0071	0.0117	0.0111	0.0060	0.0374	0.0748	0.1137	0.1555	0.0039	0.0069	0.0074	0.0045
	0.40	0.0702	0.1422	0.2206	0.1080	0.0110	0.0183	0.0174	0.0095	0.0357	0.0716	0.1098	0.1526	0.0061	0.0107	0.0115	0.0070
	2.00	0.0623	0.1277	0.2040	0.0977	0.0196	0.0330	0.0319	0.0175	0.0310	0.0630	0.0992	0.1440	0.0112	0.0198	0.0222	0.0139
0.50	0.10	0.0761	0.1530	0.2325	0.1154	0.0043	0.0070	0.0066	0.0036	0.0385	0.0770	0.1163	0.1574	0.0024	0.0042	0.0045	0.0028
	0.20	0.0732	0.1477	0.2267	0.1118	0.0076	0.0125	0.0118	0.0064	0.0373	0.0746	0.1134	0.1552	0.0042	0.0074	0.0080	0.0049
	0.40	0.0689	0.1399	0.2182	0.1066	0.0123	0.0204	0.0194	0.0105	0.0354	0.0709	0.1089	0.1519	0.0068	0.0120	0.0130	0.0079
	2.00	0.0581	0.1200	0.1954	0.0925	0.0242	0.0408	0.0393	0.0214	0.0295	0.0599	0.0952	0.1409	0.0135	0.0242	0.0272	0.0170
1.00	0.10	0.0760	0.1528	0.2322	0.1152	0.0044	0.0072	0.0068	0.0037	0.0386	0.0770	0.1163	0.1573	0.0025	0.0044	0.0047	0.0029
	0.20	0.0727	0.1469	0.2259	0.1113	0.0080	0.0132	0.0124	0.0067	0.0373	0.0745	0.1131	0.1550	0.0045	0.0080	0.0086	0.0053
	0.40	0.0677	0.1378	0.2160	0.1053	0.0135	0.0223	0.0211	0.0114	0.0353	0.0704	0.1081	0.1514	0.0075	0.0134	0.0145	0.0089
	2.00	0.0530	0.1108	0.1854	0.0864	0.0295	0.0496	0.0476	0.0257	0.0283	0.0570	0.0911	0.1377	0.0162	0.0293	0.0331	0.0207
1.50	0.10	0.0759	0.1527	0.2322	0.1152	0.0045	0.0073	0.0069	0.0037	0.0386	0.0770	0.1162	0.1573	0.0025	0.0045	0.0048	0.0029
	0.20	0.0726	0.1466	0.2256	0.1111	0.0082	0.0134	0.0127	0.0068	0.0373	0.0744	0.1131	0.1550	0.0046	0.0082	0.0088	0.0054
	0.40	0.0673	0.1370	0.2152	0.1048	0.0140	0.0230	0.0218	0.0117	0.0353	0.0703	0.1079	0.1512	0.0078	0.0139	0.0151	0.0093
	2.00	0.0506	0.1065	0.1809	0.0837	0.0317	0.0533	0.0510	0.0275	0.0280	0.0561	0.0895	0.1364	0.0174	0.0317	0.0360	0.0225

TABLE 7 - SIMPLY-SUPPORTED SKEW GIRDER BRIDGE

INFLUENCE COEFICIENT OF TWISTING MOMENT IN MAIN GIRDER

TWISTING MOMENT = COEF. x ℓ

(b/ℓ) = 0.10 ANGLE OF SKEW=ARCTAN(0.0)

φ	ζ	UNIT VERTICAL LOAD APPLIED AT POINT:															
		2	3	4	5	8	9	10	11	2	3	4	5	8	9	10	11
		TWISTING MOMENT AT POINT 2								TWISTING MOMENT AT POINT 3							
0.10	0.10	-.0017	-.0082	-.0088	-.0054	0.0017	0.0082	0.0088	0.0054	0.0034	0.0031	-.0031	-.0034	-.0034	-.0031	0.0031	0.0034
	0.20	-.0013	-.0086	-.0087	-.0052	0.0013	0.0086	0.0087	0.0052	0.0035	0.0035	-.0035	-.0035	-.0035	-.0035	0.0035	0.0035
	0.40	-.0009	-.0088	-.0086	-.0049	0.0009	0.0088	0.0086	0.0049	0.0035	0.0038	-.0038	-.0035	-.0035	-.0038	0.0038	0.0035
	2.00	-.0004	-.0090	-.0083	-.0046	0.0004	0.0090	0.0083	0.0046	0.0034	0.0041	-.0041	-.0034	-.0034	-.0041	0.0041	0.0034
0.30	0.10	-.0007	-.0093	-.0110	-.0074	0.0007	0.0093	0.0110	0.0074	0.0054	0.0045	-.0045	-.0054	-.0054	-.0045	0.0045	0.0054
	0.20	-.0001	-.0102	-.0109	-.0070	0.0001	0.0102	0.0109	0.0070	0.0055	0.0053	-.0053	-.0055	-.0055	-.0053	0.0053	0.0055
	0.40	0.0006	-.0108	-.0105	-.0063	-.0006	0.0108	0.0105	0.0063	0.0053	0.0058	-.0058	-.0053	-.0053	-.0058	0.0058	0.0053
	2.00	0.0015	-.0115	-.0098	-.0053	-.0015	0.0115	0.0098	0.0053	0.0048	0.0065	-.0065	-.0048	-.0048	-.0065	0.0065	0.0048
0.50	0.10	-.0001	-.0094	-.0118	-.0083	0.0001	0.0094	0.0118	0.0083	0.0063	0.0051	-.0051	-.0063	-.0063	-.0051	0.0051	0.0063
	0.20	0.0008	-.0104	-.0118	-.0079	-.0008	0.0104	0.0118	0.0079	0.0065	0.0060	-.0060	-.0065	-.0065	-.0060	0.0060	0.0065
	0.40	0.0015	-.0113	-.0113	-.0070	-.0015	0.0113	0.0113	0.0070	0.0063	0.0066	-.0066	-.0063	-.0063	-.0066	0.0066	0.0063
	2.00	0.0024	-.0123	-.0102	-.0056	-.0024	0.0123	0.0102	0.0056	0.0053	0.0074	-.0074	-.0053	-.0053	-.0074	0.0074	0.0053
1.00	0.10	0.0008	-.0093	-.0126	-.0094	-.0008	0.0093	0.0126	0.0094	0.0074	0.0058	-.0058	-.0074	-.0074	-.0058	0.0058	0.0074
	0.20	0.0020	-.0104	-.0127	-.0092	-.0020	0.0104	0.0127	0.0092	0.0079	0.0068	-.0068	-.0079	-.0079	-.0068	0.0068	0.0079
	0.40	0.0029	-.0114	-.0121	-.0082	-.0029	0.0114	0.0121	0.0082	0.0076	0.0076	-.0076	-.0076	-.0076	-.0076	0.0076	0.0076
	2.00	0.0036	-.0130	-.0106	-.0061	-.0036	0.0130	0.0106	0.0061	0.0060	0.0084	-.0084	-.0060	-.0060	-.0084	0.0084	0.0060
1.50	0.10	0.0012	-.0092	-.0129	-.0099	-.0012	0.0092	0.0129	0.0099	0.0079	0.0060	-.0060	-.0079	-.0079	-.0060	0.0060	0.0079
	0.20	0.0027	-.0103	-.0131	-.0098	-.0027	0.0103	0.0131	0.0098	0.0086	0.0073	-.0073	-.0086	-.0086	-.0073	0.0073	0.0086
	0.40	0.0037	-.0113	-.0126	-.0090	-.0037	0.0113	0.0126	0.0090	0.0084	0.0081	-.0081	-.0084	-.0084	-.0081	0.0081	0.0084
	2.00	0.0044	-.0132	-.0109	-.0065	-.0044	0.0132	0.0109	0.0065	0.0064	0.0089	-.0089	-.0064	-.0064	-.0089	0.0089	0.0064
		TWISTING MOMENT AT POINT 4								TWISTING MOMENT AT POINT 5							
0.10	0.10	0.0054	0.0088	0.0082	0.0017	-.0054	-.0038	-.0082	-.0017	0.0046	0.0082	0.0101	0.0085	-.0046	-.0082	-.0101	-.0085
	0.20	0.0052	0.0087	0.0086	0.0013	-.0052	-.0087	-.0086	-.0013	0.0048	0.0087	0.0112	0.0099	-.0048	-.0087	-.0112	-.0099
	0.40	0.0049	0.0086	0.0088	0.0009	-.0049	-.0086	-.0088	-.0009	0.0048	0.0090	0.0119	0.0110	-.0048	-.0090	-.0119	-.0110
	2.00	0.0046	0.0083	0.0090	0.0004	-.0046	-.0083	-.0090	-.0004	0.0048	0.0092	0.0125	0.0121	-.0048	-.0092	-.0125	-.0121
0.30	0.10	0.0074	0.0110	0.0093	0.0007	-.0074	-.0110	-.0093	-.0007	0.0056	0.0091	0.0109	0.0091	-.0056	-.0091	-.0109	-.0091
	0.20	0.0070	0.0109	0.0102	0.0001	-.0070	-.0109	-.0102	-.0001	0.0057	0.0096	0.0122	0.0112	-.0057	-.0096	-.0122	-.0112
	0.40	0.0063	0.0105	0.0108	-.0006	-.0063	-.0105	-.0108	0.0006	0.0055	0.0097	0.0132	0.0131	-.0055	-.0097	-.0132	-.0131
	2.00	0.0053	0.0098	0.0115	-.0015	-.0053	-.0098	-.0115	0.0015	0.0052	0.0099	0.0141	0.0154	-.0052	-.0099	-.0141	-.0154
0.50	0.10	0.0083	0.0118	0.0094	0.0001	-.0083	-.0118	-.0094	-.0001	0.0061	0.0095	0.0109	0.0089	-.0061	-.0095	-.0109	-.0089
	0.20	0.0079	0.0118	0.0104	-.0008	-.0079	-.0118	-.0104	0.0008	0.0062	0.0099	0.0123	0.0112	-.0062	-.0099	-.0123	-.0112
	0.40	0.0070	0.0113	0.0113	-.0015	-.0070	-.0113	-.0113	0.0015	0.0060	0.0100	0.0133	0.0133	-.0060	-.0100	-.0133	-.0133
	2.00	0.0056	0.0102	0.0123	-.0024	-.0056	-.0102	-.0123	0.0024	0.0054	0.0100	0.0144	0.0163	-.0054	-.0100	-.0144	-.0163
1.00	0.10	0.0094	0.0126	0.0093	-.0008	-.0094	-.0126	-.0093	0.0008	0.0067	0.0099	0.0108	0.0086	-.0067	-.0099	-.0108	-.0086
	0.20	0.0092	0.0127	0.0104	-.0020	-.0092	-.0127	-.0104	0.0020	0.0071	0.0103	0.0121	0.0108	-.0071	-.0103	-.0121	-.0108
	0.40	0.0082	0.0121	0.0114	-.0029	-.0082	-.0121	-.0114	0.0029	0.0069	0.0104	0.0131	0.0130	-.0069	-.0104	-.0131	-.0130
	2.00	0.0061	0.0106	0.0130	-.0036	-.0061	-.0106	-.0130	0.0036	0.0058	0.0102	0.0144	0.0169	-.0058	-.0102	-.0144	-.0169
1.50	0.10	0.0099	0.0129	0.0092	-.0012	-.0099	-.0129	-.0092	0.0012	0.0070	0.0100	0.0107	0.0084	-.0070	-.0100	-.0107	-.0084
	0.20	0.0098	0.0131	0.0103	-.0027	-.0098	-.0131	-.0103	0.0027	0.0075	0.0105	0.0119	0.0105	-.0075	-.0105	-.0119	-.0105
	0.40	0.0090	0.0126	0.0113	-.0037	-.0090	-.0126	-.0113	0.0037	0.0075	0.0106	0.0129	0.0126	-.0075	-.0106	-.0129	-.0126
	2.00	0.0065	0.0109	0.0132	-.0044	-.0065	-.0109	-.0132	0.0044	0.0062	0.0103	0.0143	0.0168	-.0062	-.0103	-.0143	-.0168

(b/ℓ) = 0.10 ANGLE OF SKEW=ARCTAN(0.67)

φ	ζ	UNIT VERTICAL LOAD APPLIED AT POINT:															
		2	3	4	5	8	9	10	11	2	3	4	5	8	9	10	11
		TWISTING MOMENT AT POINT 2								TWISTING MOMENT AT POINT 3							
0.10	0.10	-.0004	-.0048	-.0051	-.0029	0.0116	0.0176	0.0165	0.0104	0.0064	0.0077	0.0020	-.0003	0.0034	0.0105	0.0133	0.0091
	0.20	-.0002	-.0055	-.0051	-.0026	0.0128	0.0189	0.0172	0.0108	0.0070	0.0086	0.0018	-.0002	0.0030	0.0108	0.0137	0.0092
	0.40	0.0002	-.0058	-.0048	-.0022	0.0133	0.0193	0.0171	0.0107	0.0072	0.0094	0.0015	-.0001	0.0026	0.0108	0.0137	0.0090
	2.00	0.0014	-.0058	-.0042	-.0017	0.0123	0.0176	0.0151	0.0090	0.0067	0.0094	0.0008	0.0000	0.0019	0.0100	0.0126	0.0079
0.30	0.10	0.0034	-.0008	-.0020	-.0013	0.0155	0.0245	0.0240	0.0159	0.0118	0.0145	0.0064	0.0016	0.0061	0.0168	0.0213	0.0150
	0.20	0.0045	-.0007	-.0007	0.0001	0.0182	0.0276	0.0262	0.0175	0.0133	0.0166	0.0067	0.0020	0.0059	0.0181	0.0228	0.0159
	0.40	0.0056	-.0007	0.0006	0.0015	0.0201	0.0295	0.0272	0.0181	0.0142	0.0184	0.0066	0.0026	0.0055	0.0188	0.0233	0.0160
	2.00	0.0077	-.0014	0.0018	0.0028	0.0200	0.0286	0.0252	0.0161	0.0137	0.0199	0.0055	0.0035	0.0049	0.0185	0.0222	0.0144
0.50	0.10	0.0052	0.0014	-.0003	-.0004	0.0170	0.0271	0.0270	0.0181	0.0142	0.0174	0.0086	0.0025	0.0072	0.0194	0.0246	0.0175
	0.20	0.0070	0.0023	0.0019	0.0016	0.0205	0.0313	0.0302	0.0205	0.0163	0.0204	0.0094	0.0033	0.0074	0.0214	0.0269	0.0190
	0.40	0.0088	0.0030	0.0041	0.0037	0.0231	0.0342	0.0320	0.0219	0.0176	0.0228	0.0097	0.0042	0.0072	0.0226	0.0278	0.0193
	2.00	0.0119	0.0025	0.0064	0.0060	0.0239	0.0343	0.0308	0.0202	0.0176	0.0256	0.0087	0.0059	0.0071	0.0232	0.0273	0.0181
1.00	0.10	0.0072	0.0038	0.0017	0.0005	0.0184	0.0297	0.0300	0.0204	0.0167	0.0205	0.0109	0.0036	0.0084	0.0220	0.0280	0.0201
	0.20	0.0101	0.0060	0.0050	0.0034	0.0228	0.0353	0.0346	0.0239	0.0196	0.0246	0.0125	0.0049	0.0091	0.0251	0.0313	0.0223
	0.40	0.0129	0.0077	0.0085	0.0064	0.0264	0.0395	0.0377	0.0262	0.0216	0.0279	0.0134	0.0063	0.0094	0.0270	0.0329	0.0232
	2.00	0.0178	0.0082	0.0128	0.0104	0.0288	0.0416	0.0381	0.0258	0.0226	0.0329	0.0134	0.0092	0.0104	0.0293	0.0336	0.0228
1.50	0.10	0.0081	0.0049	0.0025	0.0009	0.0190	0.0308	0.0313	0.0214	0.0177	0.0219	0.0118	0.0040	0.0089	0.0231	0.0294	0.0211
	0.20	0.0114	0.0076	0.0064	0.0042	0.0238	0.0370	0.0365	0.0254	0.0210	0.0264	0.0139	0.0056	0.0099	0.0266	0.0331	0.0237
	0.40	0.0148	0.0099	0.0106	0.0077	0.0279	0.0419	0.0402	0.0281	0.0234	0.0302	0.0151	0.0073	0.0104	0.0290	0.0351	0.0249
	2.00	0.0208	0.0113	0.0161	0.0126	0.0311	0.0450	0.0417	0.0286	0.0252	0.0365	0.0158	0.0109	0.0121	0.0323	0.0367	0.0251
		TWISTING MOMENT AT POINT 4								TWISTING MOMENT AT POINT 5							
0.10	0.10	0.0099	0.0151	0.0140	0.0056	-.0014	-.0009	0.0038	0.0046	0.0092	0.0147	0.0163	0.0120	-.0029	-.0053	-.0061	-.0023
	0.20	0.0099	0.0153	0.0147	0.0052	-.0011	-.0009	0.0045	0.0053	0.0099	0.0157	0.0179	0.0140	-.0026	-.0053	-.0070	-.0027
	0.40	0.0095	0.0150	0.0149	0.0046	-.0008	-.0008	0.0050	0.0058	0.0100	0.0161	0.0186	0.0153	-.0023	-.0052	-.0074	-.0029
	2.00	0.0082	0.0134	0.0142	0.0034	-.0007	-.0011	0.0049	0.0056	0.0087	0.0147	0.0175	0.0153	-.0020	-.0050	-.0075	-.0026
0.30	0.10	0.0159	0.0234	0.0210	0.0088	0.0003	0.0029	0.0096	0.0095	0.0138	0.0210	0.0222	0.0157	-.0014	-.0026	-.0029	0.0006
	0.20	0.0168	0.0249	0.0232	0.0089	0.0012	0.0036	0.0114	0.0111	0.0157	0.0236	0.0257	0.0194	-.0000	-.0012	-.0030	0.0008
	0.40	0.0166	0.0250	0.0244	0.0083	0.0022	0.0041	0.0129	0.0124	0.0168	0.0253	0.0282	0.0226	0.0013	0.0002	-.0028	0.0010
	2.00	0.0146	0.0229	0.0247	0.0061	0.0032	0.0042	0.0135	0.0129	0.0158	0.0247	0.0285	0.0254	0.0027	0.0014	-.0027	0.0016
0.50	0.10	0.0184	0.0268	0.0238	0.0102	0.0012	0.0049	0.0123	0.0117	0.0157	0.0235	0.0244	0.0170	-.0006	-.0011	-.0012	0.0021
	0.20	0.0199	0.0291	0.0268	0.0106	0.0026	0.0062	0.0149	0.0139	0.0184	0.0271	0.0290	0.0215	0.0014	0.0012	-.0004	0.0029
	0.40	0.0201	0.0298	0.0288	0.0103	0.0041	0.0072	0.0171	0.0158	0.0203	0.0298	0.0326	0.0258	0.0035	0.0036	0.0005	0.0037
	2.00	0.0182	0.0280	0.0304	0.0080	0.0059	0.0080	0.0186	0.0169	0.0201	0.0307	0.0348	0.0307	0.0060	0.0064	0.0017	0.0049
1.00	0.10	0.0210	0.0302	0.0267	0.0115	0.0022	0.0070	0.0152	0.0140	0.0176	0.0261	0.0266	0.0183	0.0002	0.0005	0.0008	0.0037
	0.20	0.0233	0.0337	0.0308	0.0126	0.0042	0.0092	0.0189	0.0171	0.0213	0.0310	0.0325	0.0238	0.0030	0.0040	0.0028	0.0055
	0.40	0.0242	0.0353	0.0339	0.0127	0.0064	0.0111	0.0220	0.0197	0.0244	0.0351	0.0377	0.0292	0.0062	0.0080	0.0049	0.0071
	2.00	0.0230	0.0348	0.0378	0.0110	0.0099	0.0137	0.0253	0.0222	0.0262	0.0389	0.0433	0.0376	0.0108	0.0138	0.0086	0.0098
1.50	0.10	0.0221	0.0317	0.0278	0.0120	0.0027	0.0079	0.0165	0.0150	0.0185	0.0271	0.0275	0.0188	0.0006	0.0012	0.0017	0.0044
	0.20	0.0248	0.0357	0.0325	0.0134	0.0049	0.0106	0.0207	0.0185	0.0227	0.0327	0.0341	0.0247	0.0038	0.0053	0.0042	0.0066
	0.40	0.0261	0.0377	0.0362	0.0139	0.0075	0.0129	0.0242	0.0215	0.0263	0.0376	0.0400	0.0308	0.0074	0.0100	0.0069	0.0088
	2.00	0.0255	0.0382	0.0415	0.0126	0.0120	0.0167	0.0287	0.0247	0.0294	0.0432	0.0476	0.0410	0.0133	0.0177	0.0124	0.0124

TABLE 8 – SIMPLY-SUPPORTED SKEW GIRDER BRIDGE

INFLUENCE COEFFICIENT OF TWISTING MOMENT IN MAIN GIRDER

TWISTING MOMENT = COEF. x ℓ

$(b/\ell) = 0.10$ ANGLE OF SKEW=ARCTAN(1.33)

ϕ	ζ	UNIT VERTICAL LOAD APPLIED AT POINT: 2	3	4	5	8	9	10	11	2	3	4	5	8	9	10	11
		TWISTING MOMENT AT POINT 2								TWISTING MOMENT AT POINT 3							
0.10	0.10	0.0010	-.0044	-.0039	-.0018	0.0141	0.0178	0.0159	0.0098	0.0067	0.0091	0.0024	0.0006	0.0079	0.0175	0.0170	0.0105
	0.20	0.0011	-.0051	-.0040	-.0017	0.0150	0.0184	0.0163	0.0101	0.0069	0.0097	0.0021	0.0005	0.0077	0.0179	0.0170	0.0105
	0.40	0.0012	-.0055	-.0041	-.0016	0.0152	0.0183	0.0159	0.0097	0.0069	0.0099	0.0018	0.0005	0.0074	0.0177	0.0165	0.0101
	2.00	0.0006	-.0064	-.0049	-.0021	0.0135	0.0154	0.0128	0.0075	0.0057	0.0082	0.0004	-.0002	0.0057	0.0148	0.0134	0.0078
0.30	0.10	0.0035	-.0026	-.0018	-.0002	0.0192	0.0242	0.0221	0.0141	0.0109	0.0151	0.0058	0.0024	0.0110	0.0246	0.0240	0.0152
	0.20	0.0042	-.0033	-.0014	0.0004	0.0212	0.0258	0.0233	0.0150	0.0117	0.0167	0.0055	0.0025	0.0108	0.0257	0.0244	0.0155
	0.40	0.0049	-.0039	-.0011	0.0009	0.0221	0.0260	0.0233	0.0150	0.0120	0.0177	0.0049	0.0026	0.0104	0.0259	0.0240	0.0152
	2.00	0.0052	-.0051	-.0016	0.0007	0.0207	0.0231	0.0199	0.0122	0.0109	0.0168	0.0031	0.0020	0.0088	0.0235	0.0209	0.0127
0.50	0.10	0.0045	-.0017	-.0008	0.0005	0.0208	0.0263	0.0241	0.0155	0.0124	0.0172	0.0071	0.0031	0.0120	0.0269	0.0263	0.0168
	0.20	0.0056	-.0023	-.0001	0.0014	0.0233	0.0282	0.0257	0.0168	0.0134	0.0192	0.0068	0.0034	0.0118	0.0283	0.0268	0.0171
	0.40	0.0067	-.0028	0.0005	0.0022	0.0245	0.0287	0.0260	0.0170	0.0140	0.0207	0.0062	0.0035	0.0114	0.0286	0.0265	0.0169
	2.00	0.0078	-.0040	0.0004	0.0023	0.0235	0.0262	0.0229	0.0144	0.0132	0.0208	0.0044	0.0033	0.0101	0.0269	0.0238	0.0148
1.00	0.10	0.0055	-.0008	0.0002	0.0012	0.0222	0.0281	0.0259	0.0169	0.0137	0.0191	0.0084	0.0038	0.0130	0.0289	0.0284	0.0182
	0.20	0.0069	-.0011	0.0014	0.0025	0.0253	0.0305	0.0280	0.0184	0.0151	0.0217	0.0082	0.0042	0.0128	0.0306	0.0290	0.0186
	0.40	0.0085	-.0016	0.0022	0.0035	0.0268	0.0313	0.0285	0.0189	0.0160	0.0237	0.0076	0.0045	0.0122	0.0311	0.0286	0.0184
	2.00	0.0110	-.0028	0.0027	0.0041	0.0259	0.0291	0.0260	0.0168	0.0158	0.0254	0.0057	0.0046	0.0114	0.0300	0.0266	0.0169
1.50	0.10	0.0059	-.0004	0.0007	0.0015	0.0227	0.0288	0.0266	0.0174	0.0143	0.0199	0.0089	0.0041	0.0133	0.0297	0.0292	0.0187
	0.20	0.0075	-.0007	0.0019	0.0029	0.0260	0.0314	0.0288	0.0191	0.0158	0.0227	0.0087	0.0046	0.0131	0.0315	0.0298	0.0192
	0.40	0.0093	-.0010	0.0030	0.0040	0.0277	0.0322	0.0295	0.0197	0.0168	0.0250	0.0081	0.0049	0.0126	0.0320	0.0293	0.0190
	2.00	0.0126	-.0024	0.0036	0.0048	0.0266	0.0300	0.0272	0.0177	0.0170	0.0274	0.0061	0.0052	0.0120	0.0311	0.0275	0.0177
		TWISTING MOMENT AT POINT 4								TWISTING MOMENT AT POINT 5							
0.10	0.10	0.0102	0.0163	0.0160	0.0059	0.0022	0.0058	0.0117	0.0080	0.0117	0.0190	0.0211	0.0163	-.0014	-.0028	-.0024	0.0017
	0.20	0.0101	0.0163	0.0164	0.0055	0.0022	0.0058	0.0123	0.0083	0.0119	0.0194	0.0219	0.0174	-.0011	-.0027	-.0026	0.0019
	0.40	0.0097	0.0158	0.0163	0.0050	0.0021	0.0056	0.0124	0.0082	0.0114	0.0187	0.0215	0.0177	-.0010	-.0025	-.0025	0.0023
	2.00	0.0075	0.0128	0.0136	0.0034	0.0011	0.0037	0.0103	0.0067	0.0082	0.0142	0.0171	0.0148	-.0013	-.0029	-.0026	0.0027
0.30	0.10	0.0150	0.0236	0.0231	0.0087	0.0043	0.0099	0.0181	0.0123	0.0170	0.0266	0.0290	0.0223	0.0006	0.0001	0.0003	0.0046
	0.20	0.0152	0.0241	0.0244	0.0081	0.0045	0.0100	0.0196	0.0130	0.0180	0.0282	0.0312	0.0251	0.0016	0.0009	0.0004	0.0053
	0.40	0.0148	0.0238	0.0248	0.0072	0.0047	0.0100	0.0204	0.0134	0.0179	0.0283	0.0319	0.0266	0.0022	0.0017	0.0007	0.0060
	2.00	0.0124	0.0207	0.0229	0.0051	0.0039	0.0083	0.0189	0.0121	0.0139	0.0231	0.0273	0.0247	0.0020	0.0015	0.0011	0.0074
0.50	0.10	0.0167	0.0260	0.0255	0.0097	0.0050	0.0113	0.0203	0.0138	0.0187	0.0292	0.0316	0.0242	0.0015	0.0014	0.0016	0.0058
	0.20	0.0170	0.0268	0.0271	0.0090	0.0054	0.0116	0.0222	0.0147	0.0202	0.0313	0.0345	0.0277	0.0028	0.0026	0.0018	0.0067
	0.40	0.0167	0.0267	0.0280	0.0080	0.0058	0.0117	0.0233	0.0152	0.0205	0.0319	0.0357	0.0300	0.0038	0.0038	0.0024	0.0076
	2.00	0.0146	0.0241	0.0271	0.0058	0.0054	0.0106	0.0225	0.0143	0.0168	0.0272	0.0320	0.0293	0.0040	0.0044	0.0036	0.0097
1.00	0.10	0.0182	0.0283	0.0276	0.0106	0.0058	0.0127	0.0223	0.0151	0.0204	0.0315	0.0339	0.0259	0.0024	0.0026	0.0028	0.0069
	0.20	0.0188	0.0293	0.0297	0.0099	0.0063	0.0131	0.0246	0.0162	0.0224	0.0343	0.0376	0.0301	0.0041	0.0044	0.0034	0.0080
	0.40	0.0186	0.0294	0.0310	0.0088	0.0069	0.0133	0.0260	0.0168	0.0232	0.0356	0.0396	0.0333	0.0056	0.0062	0.0043	0.0091
	2.00	0.0165	0.0278	0.0318	0.0064	0.0074	0.0133	0.0262	0.0167	0.0201	0.0321	0.0375	0.0348	0.0066	0.0082	0.0068	0.0120
1.50	0.10	0.0188	0.0291	0.0284	0.0109	0.0061	0.0132	0.0230	0.0156	0.0210	0.0324	0.0348	0.0265	0.0027	0.0031	0.0033	0.0073
	0.20	0.0194	0.0303	0.0307	0.0102	0.0067	0.0137	0.0255	0.0168	0.0233	0.0355	0.0388	0.0311	0.0046	0.0051	0.0040	0.0086
	0.40	0.0194	0.0306	0.0323	0.0091	0.0073	0.0139	0.0270	0.0174	0.0242	0.0371	0.0411	0.0346	0.0063	0.0072	0.0050	0.0098
	2.00	0.0180	0.0295	0.0340	0.0067	0.0083	0.0145	0.0275	0.0176	0.0216	0.0345	0.0401	0.0374	0.0079	0.0101	0.0084	0.0129

$(b/\ell) = 0.10$ ANGLE OF SKEW=ARCTAN(2.00)

ϕ	ζ	UNIT VERTICAL LOAD APPLIED AT POINT: 2	3	4	5	8	9	10	11	2	3	4	5	8	9	10	11
		TWISTING MOMENT AT POINT 2								TWISTING MOMENT AT POINT 3							
0.10	0.10	0.0008	-.0072	-.0061	-.0030	0.0103	0.0121	0.0103	0.0061	0.0058	0.0081	-.0005	-.0010	0.0071	0.0142	0.0128	0.0075
	0.20	0.0002	-.0082	-.0068	-.0034	0.0099	0.0113	0.0094	0.0054	0.0050	0.0070	-.0016	-.0016	0.0063	0.0130	0.0115	0.0066
	0.40	-.0004	-.0086	-.0071	-.0036	0.0090	0.0100	0.0080	0.0045	0.0038	0.0054	-.0025	-.0020	0.0052	0.0113	0.0097	0.0055
	2.00	-.0010	-.0059	-.0051	-.0028	0.0054	0.0056	0.0043	0.0023	0.0012	0.0017	-.0026	-.0018	0.0025	0.0060	0.0049	0.0026
0.30	0.10	0.0039	-.0073	-.0054	-.0021	0.0141	0.0162	0.0140	0.0086	0.0099	0.0142	0.0010	-.0002	0.0093	0.0194	0.0172	0.0103
	0.20	0.0041	-.0090	-.0063	-.0024	0.0138	0.0154	0.0132	0.0081	0.0094	0.0140	-.0008	-.0009	0.0086	0.0185	0.0161	0.0096
	0.40	0.0033	-.0103	-.0071	-.0029	0.0131	0.0142	0.0119	0.0071	0.0080	0.0124	-.0024	-.0016	0.0076	0.0170	0.0145	0.0085
	2.00	0.0002	-.0098	-.0075	-.0038	0.0097	0.0096	0.0075	0.0041	0.0034	0.0057	-.0040	-.0024	0.0045	0.0114	0.0091	0.0050
0.50	0.10	0.0052	-.0070	-.0049	-.0016	0.0154	0.0174	0.0152	0.0095	0.0115	0.0166	0.0017	0.0002	0.0099	0.0210	0.0184	0.0111
	0.20	0.0060	-.0089	-.0057	-.0018	0.0151	0.0167	0.0146	0.0091	0.0114	0.0171	-.0002	-.0005	0.0093	0.0201	0.0174	0.0105
	0.40	0.0056	-.0105	-.0065	-.0022	0.0144	0.0156	0.0134	0.0082	0.0101	0.0160	-.0021	-.0012	0.0085	0.0189	0.0161	0.0096
	2.00	0.0017	-.0113	-.0079	-.0037	0.0117	0.0115	0.0091	0.0052	0.0050	0.0087	-.0044	-.0024	0.0056	0.0141	0.0113	0.0063
1.00	0.10	0.0065	-.0067	-.0043	-.0011	0.0165	0.0185	0.0163	0.0103	0.0131	0.0189	0.0024	0.0007	0.0104	0.0223	0.0194	0.0117
	0.20	0.0081	-.0086	-.0049	-.0010	0.0162	0.0179	0.0159	0.0101	0.0136	0.0205	0.0004	0.0000	0.0098	0.0214	0.0184	0.0112
	0.40	0.0086	-.0105	-.0057	-.0013	0.0154	0.0169	0.0150	0.0095	0.0128	0.0204	-.0017	-.0006	0.0092	0.0204	0.0174	0.0107
	2.00	0.0047	-.0126	-.0076	-.0029	0.0137	0.0138	0.0114	0.0067	0.0077	0.0137	-.0047	-.0019	0.0070	0.0172	0.0140	0.0081
1.50	0.10	0.0071	-.0065	-.0040	-.0009	0.0169	0.0189	0.0167	0.0106	0.0137	0.0198	0.0027	0.0008	0.0106	0.0227	0.0197	0.0119
	0.20	0.0091	-.0084	-.0045	-.0007	0.0166	0.0182	0.0163	0.0104	0.0145	0.0220	0.0007	0.0003	0.0099	0.0218	0.0186	0.0114
	0.40	0.0101	-.0104	-.0052	-.0009	0.0157	0.0173	0.0156	0.0099	0.0141	0.0225	-.0014	-.0003	0.0095	0.0207	0.0177	0.0110
	2.00	0.0068	-.0130	-.0071	-.0023	0.0144	0.0149	0.0126	0.0076	0.0093	0.0167	-.0047	-.0015	0.0078	0.0185	0.0153	0.0090
		TWISTING MOMENT AT POINT 4								TWISTING MOMENT AT POINT 5							
0.10	0.10	0.0080	0.0138	0.0146	0.0037	0.0032	0.0070	0.0112	0.0071	0.0092	0.0162	0.0198	0.0170	0.0001	0.0002	0.0012	0.0036
	0.20	0.0068	0.0119	0.0130	0.0025	0.0026	0.0060	0.0102	0.0064	0.0077	0.0138	0.0173	0.0156	-.0002	-.0002	0.0011	0.0037
	0.40	0.0053	0.0095	0.0106	0.0014	0.0017	0.0045	0.0086	0.0053	0.0059	0.0109	0.0139	0.0131	-.0008	-.0011	0.0002	0.0033
	2.00	0.0022	0.0041	0.0047	0.0000	0.0002	0.0014	0.0040	0.0023	0.0026	0.0049	0.0064	0.0062	-.0014	-.0022	-.0014	0.0012
0.30	0.10	0.0122	0.0208	0.0223	0.0054	0.0051	0.0104	0.0164	0.0101	0.0141	0.0242	0.0291	0.0254	0.0021	0.0028	0.0034	0.0059
	0.20	0.0111	0.0194	0.0216	0.0037	0.0047	0.0097	0.0159	0.0098	0.0125	0.0219	0.0273	0.0254	0.0022	0.0031	0.0039	0.0067
	0.40	0.0093	0.0167	0.0193	0.0021	0.0038	0.0083	0.0145	0.0089	0.0102	0.0183	0.0235	0.0231	0.0014	0.0021	0.0034	0.0068
	2.00	0.0047	0.0087	0.0106	-.0001	0.0009	0.0034	0.0087	0.0050	0.0052	0.0095	0.0126	0.0131	-.0013	-.0019	-.0006	0.0038
0.50	0.10	0.0138	0.0234	0.0250	0.0060	0.0057	0.0114	0.0180	0.0109	0.0159	0.0270	0.0323	0.0283	0.0030	0.0039	0.0043	0.0067
	0.20	0.0129	0.0224	0.0252	0.0042	0.0056	0.0111	0.0178	0.0108	0.0146	0.0253	0.0314	0.0294	0.0034	0.0048	0.0052	0.0076
	0.40	0.0112	0.0200	0.0235	0.0024	0.0049	0.0100	0.0168	0.0102	0.0124	0.0219	0.0280	0.0279	0.0029	0.0042	0.0052	0.0081
	2.00	0.0062	0.0115	0.0143	-.0002	0.0017	0.0049	0.0114	0.0066	0.0067	0.0123	0.0163	0.0174	-.0005	-.0008	0.0007	0.0057
1.00	0.10	0.0153	0.0258	0.0276	0.0066	0.0063	0.0123	0.0194	0.0116	0.0177	0.0298	0.0354	0.0310	0.0038	0.0050	0.0050	0.0073
	0.20	0.0149	0.0257	0.0290	0.0047	0.0065	0.0122	0.0194	0.0115	0.0169	0.0290	0.0357	0.0335	0.0048	0.0066	0.0065	0.0084
	0.40	0.0136	0.0241	0.0285	0.0028	0.0063	0.0118	0.0187	0.0112	0.0151	0.0263	0.0335	0.0335	0.0048	0.0069	0.0074	0.0093
	2.00	0.0086	0.0158	0.0202	-.0003	0.0032	0.0074	0.0149	0.0087	0.0092	0.0166	0.0220	0.0241	0.0012	0.0019	0.0035	0.0083
1.50	0.10	0.0160	0.0268	0.0286	0.0068	0.0065	0.0126	0.0198	0.0118	0.0185	0.0309	0.0366	0.0321	0.0042	0.0054	0.0053	0.0076
	0.20	0.0158	0.0272	0.0306	0.0050	0.0069	0.0126	0.0198	0.0117	0.0180	0.0306	0.0375	0.0352	0.0054	0.0073	0.0070	0.0087
	0.40	0.0148	0.0261	0.0309	0.0030	0.0069	0.0125	0.0193	0.0115	0.0164	0.0285	0.0360	0.0361	0.0057	0.0082	0.0083	0.0097
	2.00	0.0101	0.0185	0.0238	-.0003	0.0043	0.0090	0.0165	0.0098	0.0108	0.0193	0.0255	0.0282	0.0026	0.0039	0.0055	0.0096

TABLE 9 – SIMPLY-SUPPORTED SKEW GIRDER BRIDGE

INFLUENCE COEFICIENT OF TWISTING MOMENT IN MAIN GIRDER

TWISTING MOMENT = COEF.xℓ

$(b/\ell) = 0.20$ ANGLE OF SKEW=ARCTAN(0.0)

UNIT VERTICAL LOAD APPLIED AT POINT:

φ	ζ	2	3	4	5	8	9	10	11	2	3	4	5	8	9	10	11
		TWISTING MOMENT AT POINT 2								TWISTING MOMENT AT POINT 3							
0.10	0.10	-.0029	-.0073	-.0080	-.0051	0.0029	0.0073	0.0080	0.0051	0.0020	0.0016	-.0016	-.0020	-.0020	-.0016	0.0016	0.0020
	0.20	-.0033	-.0088	-.0093	-.0058	0.0033	0.0088	0.0093	0.0058	0.0024	0.0021	-.0021	-.0024	-.0024	-.0021	0.0021	0.0024
	0.40	-.0033	-.0096	-.0099	-.0060	0.0033	0.0096	0.0099	0.0060	0.0027	0.0025	-.0025	-.0027	-.0027	-.0025	0.0025	0.0027
	2.00	-.0029	-.0102	-.0101	-.0060	0.0029	0.0102	0.0101	0.0060	0.0030	0.0030	-.0030	-.0030	-.0030	-.0030	0.0030	0.0030
0.30	0.10	-.0032	-.0092	-.0109	-.0073	0.0032	0.0092	0.0109	0.0073	0.0034	0.0025	-.0025	-.0034	-.0034	-.0025	0.0025	0.0034
	0.20	-.0039	-.0120	-.0138	-.0090	0.0039	0.0120	0.0138	0.0090	0.0045	0.0035	-.0035	-.0045	-.0045	-.0035	0.0035	0.0045
	0.40	-.0040	-.0141	-.0155	-.0098	0.0040	0.0141	0.0155	0.0098	0.0053	0.0045	-.0045	-.0053	-.0053	-.0045	0.0045	0.0053
	2.00	-.0027	-.0161	-.0160	-.0093	0.0027	0.0161	0.0160	0.0093	0.0060	0.0062	-.0062	-.0060	-.0060	-.0062	0.0062	0.0060
0.50	0.10	-.0031	-.0096	-.0118	-.0082	0.0031	0.0096	0.0118	0.0082	0.0040	0.0029	-.0029	-.0040	-.0040	-.0029	0.0029	0.0040
	0.20	-.0037	-.0128	-.0154	-.0104	0.0037	0.0128	0.0154	0.0104	0.0055	0.0041	-.0041	-.0055	-.0055	-.0041	0.0041	0.0055
	0.40	-.0038	-.0154	-.0177	-.0116	0.0038	0.0154	0.0177	0.0116	0.0068	0.0055	-.0055	-.0068	-.0068	-.0055	0.0055	0.0068
	2.00	-.0019	-.0184	-.0183	-.0108	0.0019	0.0184	0.0183	0.0108	0.0077	0.0080	-.0080	-.0077	-.0077	-.0080	0.0080	0.0077
1.00	0.10	-.0029	-.0099	-.0127	-.0090	0.0029	0.0099	0.0127	0.0090	0.0047	0.0033	-.0033	-.0047	-.0047	-.0033	0.0033	0.0047
	0.20	-.0032	-.0134	-.0170	-.0120	0.0032	0.0134	0.0170	0.0120	0.0069	0.0050	-.0050	-.0069	-.0069	-.0050	0.0050	0.0069
	0.40	-.0029	-.0163	-.0201	-.0139	0.0029	0.0163	0.0201	0.0139	0.0089	0.0068	-.0068	-.0089	-.0089	-.0068	0.0068	0.0089
	2.00	-.0002	-.0205	-.0210	-.0129	0.0002	0.0205	0.0210	0.0129	0.0103	0.0103	-.0103	-.0103	-.0103	-.0103	0.0103	0.0103
1.50	0.10	-.0028	-.0100	-.0130	-.0093	0.0028	0.0100	0.0130	0.0093	0.0050	0.0034	-.0034	-.0050	-.0050	-.0034	0.0034	0.0050
	0.20	-.0029	-.0135	-.0177	-.0127	0.0029	0.0135	0.0177	0.0127	0.0075	0.0054	-.0054	-.0075	-.0075	-.0054	0.0054	0.0075
	0.40	-.0022	-.0164	-.0212	-.0151	0.0022	0.0164	0.0212	0.0151	0.0100	0.0075	-.0075	-.0100	-.0100	-.0075	0.0075	0.0100
	2.00	0.0011	-.0212	-.0224	-.0142	-.0011	0.0212	0.0224	0.0142	0.0118	0.0116	-.0116	-.0118	-.0118	-.0116	0.0116	0.0118
		TWISTING MOMENT AT POINT 4								TWISTING MOMENT AT POINT 5							
0.10	0.10	0.0051	0.0080	0.0073	0.0029	-.0051	-.0080	-.0073	-.0029	0.0043	0.0073	0.0082	0.0058	-.0043	-.0073	-.0082	-.0058
	0.20	0.0058	0.0093	0.0088	0.0033	-.0058	-.0093	-.0088	-.0033	0.0053	0.0092	0.0106	0.0079	-.0053	-.0092	-.0106	-.0079
	0.40	0.0060	0.0099	0.0096	0.0033	-.0060	-.0099	-.0096	-.0033	0.0060	0.0106	0.0126	0.0098	-.0060	-.0106	-.0126	-.0098
	2.00	0.0060	0.0101	0.0102	0.0029	-.0060	-.0101	-.0102	-.0029	0.0068	0.0123	0.0151	0.0123	-.0068	-.0123	-.0151	-.0123
0.30	0.10	0.0073	0.0109	0.0092	0.0032	-.0073	-.0109	-.0092	-.0032	0.0055	0.0091	0.0098	0.0068	-.0055	-.0091	-.0098	-.0068
	0.20	0.0090	0.0138	0.0120	0.0039	-.0090	-.0138	-.0120	-.0039	0.0071	0.0119	0.0134	0.0098	-.0071	-.0119	-.0134	-.0098
	0.40	0.0098	0.0155	0.0141	0.0040	-.0098	-.0155	-.0141	-.0040	0.0082	0.0142	0.0167	0.0131	-.0082	-.0142	-.0167	-.0131
	2.00	0.0093	0.0160	0.0161	0.0027	-.0093	-.0160	-.0161	-.0027	0.0091	0.0168	0.0217	0.0192	-.0091	-.0168	-.0217	-.0192
0.50	0.10	0.0082	0.0118	0.0096	0.0031	-.0082	-.0118	-.0096	-.0031	0.0059	0.0096	0.0102	0.0069	-.0059	-.0096	-.0102	-.0069
	0.20	0.0104	0.0154	0.0128	0.0037	-.0104	-.0154	-.0128	-.0037	0.0078	0.0128	0.0141	0.0101	-.0078	-.0128	-.0141	-.0101
	0.40	0.0116	0.0177	0.0154	0.0038	-.0116	-.0177	-.0154	-.0038	0.0090	0.0153	0.0178	0.0138	-.0090	-.0153	-.0178	-.0138
	2.00	0.0108	0.0183	0.0184	0.0019	-.0108	-.0183	-.0184	-.0019	0.0099	0.0180	0.0236	0.0216	-.0099	-.0180	-.0236	-.0216
1.00	0.10	0.0090	0.0127	0.0099	0.0029	-.0090	-.0127	-.0099	-.0029	0.0063	0.0101	0.0104	0.0069	-.0063	-.0101	-.0104	-.0069
	0.20	0.0120	0.0170	0.0134	0.0032	-.0120	-.0170	-.0134	-.0032	0.0085	0.0136	0.0145	0.0102	-.0085	-.0136	-.0145	-.0102
	0.40	0.0139	0.0201	0.0163	0.0029	-.0139	-.0201	-.0163	-.0029	0.0101	0.0164	0.0184	0.0140	-.0101	-.0164	-.0184	-.0140
	2.00	0.0129	0.0210	0.0205	0.0002	-.0129	-.0210	-.0205	-.0002	0.0110	0.0190	0.0250	0.0235	-.0110	-.0190	-.0250	-.0235
1.50	0.10	0.0093	0.0130	0.0100	0.0028	-.0093	-.0130	-.0100	-.0028	0.0065	0.0103	0.0105	0.0069	-.0065	-.0103	-.0105	-.0069
	0.20	0.0127	0.0177	0.0135	0.0029	-.0127	-.0177	-.0135	-.0029	0.0089	0.0139	0.0147	0.0102	-.0089	-.0139	-.0147	-.0102
	0.40	0.0151	0.0212	0.0164	0.0022	-.0151	-.0212	-.0164	-.0022	0.0107	0.0169	0.0185	0.0139	-.0107	-.0169	-.0185	-.0139
	2.00	0.0142	0.0224	0.0212	-.0011	-.0142	-.0224	-.0212	0.0011	0.0118	0.0195	0.0252	0.0238	-.0118	-.0195	-.0252	-.0238

$(b/\ell) = 0.20$ ANGLE OF SKEW=ARCTAN(0.10)

UNIT VERTICAL LOAD APPLIED AT POINT:

φ	ζ	2	3	4	5	8	9	10	11	2	3	4	5	8	9	10	11
		TWISTING MOMENT AT POINT 2								TWISTING MOMENT AT POINT 3							
0.10	0.10	-.0027	-.0069	-.0076	-.0049	0.0036	0.0081	0.0086	0.0054	0.0022	0.0018	-.0012	-.0018	-.0013	-.0004	0.0026	0.0026
	0.20	-.0032	-.0085	-.0090	-.0056	0.0042	0.0098	0.0101	0.0062	0.0026	0.0023	-.0017	-.0022	-.0017	-.0007	0.0033	0.0031
	0.40	-.0033	-.0094	-.0097	-.0059	0.0044	0.0109	0.0109	0.0066	0.0029	0.0027	-.0021	-.0025	-.0020	-.0010	0.0038	0.0034
	2.00	-.0028	-.0100	-.0099	-.0058	0.0041	0.0115	0.0111	0.0065	0.0032	0.0034	-.0027	-.0027	-.0023	-.0015	0.0044	0.0036
0.30	0.10	-.0027	-.0082	-.0099	-.0068	0.0043	0.0105	0.0120	0.0079	0.0038	0.0032	-.0016	-.0028	-.0022	-.0005	0.0043	0.0044
	0.20	-.0034	-.0109	-.0128	-.0084	0.0055	0.0139	0.0154	0.0100	0.0051	0.0044	-.0023	-.0038	-.0030	-.0008	0.0058	0.0058
	0.40	-.0036	-.0130	-.0145	-.0092	0.0062	0.0166	0.0175	0.0111	0.0060	0.0055	-.0031	-.0045	-.0037	-.0014	0.0072	0.0068
	2.00	-.0022	-.0149	-.0148	-.0085	0.0054	0.0191	0.0183	0.0107	0.0070	0.0077	-.0047	-.0051	-.0044	-.0028	0.0093	0.0077
0.50	0.10	-.0025	-.0083	-.0106	-.0074	0.0044	0.0112	0.0131	0.0089	0.0046	0.0038	-.0016	-.0032	-.0026	-.0005	0.0050	0.0052
	0.20	-.0030	-.0112	-.0139	-.0095	0.0057	0.0152	0.0174	0.0117	0.0064	0.0055	-.0025	-.0045	-.0037	-.0009	0.0070	0.0072
	0.40	-.0029	-.0136	-.0160	-.0106	0.0064	0.0186	0.0204	0.0133	0.0080	0.0073	-.0034	-.0055	-.0046	-.0015	0.0091	0.0088
	2.00	-.0009	-.0162	-.0162	-.0094	0.0057	0.0226	0.0218	0.0130	0.0095	0.0104	-.0054	-.0062	-.0054	-.0032	0.0123	0.0102
1.00	0.10	-.0021	-.0083	-.0111	-.0080	0.0044	0.0117	0.0142	0.0099	0.0055	0.0046	-.0017	-.0037	-.0031	-.0005	0.0057	0.0061
	0.20	-.0021	-.0111	-.0148	-.0107	0.0056	0.0163	0.0196	0.0136	0.0082	0.0071	-.0026	-.0054	-.0046	-.0009	0.0086	0.0090
	0.40	-.0014	-.0133	-.0173	-.0122	0.0063	0.0206	0.0239	0.0163	0.0109	0.0098	-.0035	-.0069	-.0059	-.0014	0.0117	0.0118
	2.00	0.0022	-.0160	-.0167	-.0102	0.0058	0.0271	0.0269	0.0167	0.0136	0.0149	-.0054	-.0074	-.0065	-.0029	0.0171	0.0143
1.50	0.10	-.0019	-.0082	-.0113	-.0083	0.0043	0.0119	0.0147	0.0103	0.0059	0.0049	-.0017	-.0039	-.0033	-.0005	0.0061	0.0065
	0.20	-.0015	-.0109	-.0152	-.0112	0.0055	0.0167	0.0206	0.0145	0.0091	0.0078	-.0026	-.0058	-.0050	-.0009	0.0094	0.0099
	0.40	-.0003	-.0127	-.0177	-.0130	0.0061	0.0214	0.0256	0.0179	0.0125	0.0112	-.0035	-.0076	-.0066	-.0014	0.0131	0.0134
	2.00	0.0047	-.0148	-.0164	-.0104	0.0058	0.0296	0.0300	0.0193	0.0164	0.0179	-.0049	-.0079	-.0070	-.0023	0.0202	0.0172
		TWISTING MOMENT AT POINT 4								TWISTING MOMENT AT POINT 5							
0.10	0.10	0.0053	0.0083	0.0075	0.0032	-.0047	-.0072	-.0063	-.0023	0.0044	0.0076	0.0083	0.0058	-.0042	-.0071	-.0078	-.0054
	0.20	0.0060	0.0097	0.0091	0.0036	-.0054	-.0085	-.0076	-.0026	0.0055	0.0095	0.0109	0.0080	-.0052	-.0090	-.0102	-.0074
	0.40	0.0063	0.0104	0.0100	0.0037	-.0056	-.0092	-.0084	-.0025	0.0062	0.0110	0.0129	0.0099	-.0059	-.0104	-.0122	-.0092
	2.00	0.0062	0.0105	0.0106	0.0031	-.0055	-.0093	-.0088	-.0019	0.0070	0.0127	0.0154	0.0125	-.0066	-.0120	-.0147	-.0117
0.30	0.10	0.0078	0.0116	0.0099	0.0038	-.0066	-.0095	-.0075	-.0022	0.0059	0.0096	0.0102	0.0068	-.0053	-.0087	-.0091	-.0060
	0.20	0.0098	0.0149	0.0130	0.0047	-.0082	-.0122	-.0099	-.0026	0.0077	0.0128	0.0141	0.0100	-.0068	-.0115	-.0126	-.0088
	0.40	0.0108	0.0170	0.0154	0.0051	-.0089	-.0137	-.0116	-.0025	0.0090	0.0153	0.0177	0.0134	-.0079	-.0136	-.0159	-.0119
	2.00	0.0105	0.0176	0.0176	0.0038	-.0082	-.0140	-.0130	-.0007	0.0102	0.0183	0.0231	0.0199	-.0085	-.0159	-.0207	-.0178
0.50	0.10	0.0088	0.0128	0.0105	0.0038	-.0073	-.0101	-.0076	-.0019	0.0064	0.0103	0.0107	0.0070	-.0057	-.0091	-.0094	-.0061
	0.20	0.0115	0.0170	0.0143	0.0049	-.0093	-.0133	-.0101	-.0021	0.0086	0.0139	0.0150	0.0104	-.0074	-.0121	-.0131	-.0089
	0.40	0.0132	0.0199	0.0174	0.0053	-.0103	-.0152	-.0121	-.0017	0.0102	0.0169	0.0191	0.0143	-.0086	-.0144	-.0165	-.0122
	2.00	0.0128	0.0212	0.0209	0.0038	-.0091	-.0153	-.0140	0.0009	0.0116	0.0205	0.0259	0.0228	-.0088	-.0164	-.0219	-.0195
1.00	0.10	0.0098	0.0139	0.0111	0.0038	-.0079	-.0107	-.0075	-.0014	0.0069	0.0109	0.0111	0.0071	-.0060	-.0094	-.0095	-.0060
	0.20	0.0136	0.0192	0.0154	0.0047	-.0105	-.0142	-.0099	-.0011	0.0096	0.0151	0.0158	0.0107	-.0080	-.0127	-.0132	-.0087
	0.40	0.0163	0.0235	0.0193	0.0051	-.0120	-.0165	-.0117	-.0001	0.0118	0.0188	0.0204	0.0148	-.0094	-.0150	-.0166	-.0119
	2.00	0.0166	0.0263	0.0253	0.0037	-.0099	-.0159	-.0135	0.0042	0.0141	0.0235	0.0292	0.0257	-.0089	-.0159	-.0217	-.0200
1.50	0.10	0.0103	0.0144	0.0113	0.0037	-.0082	-.0109	-.0074	-.0012	0.0071	0.0111	0.0112	0.0072	-.0062	-.0096	-.0095	-.0059
	0.20	0.0145	0.0202	0.0158	0.0046	-.0111	-.0146	-.0096	-.0006	0.0100	0.0156	0.0160	0.0107	-.0083	-.0129	-.0131	-.0086
	0.40	0.0179	0.0252	0.0201	0.0049	-.0128	-.0169	-.0111	0.0010	0.0127	0.0197	0.0210	0.0149	-.0097	-.0151	-.0163	-.0115
	2.00	0.0193	0.0296	0.0278	0.0036	-.0102	-.0155	-.0122	0.0067	0.0160	0.0255	0.0309	0.0269	-.0089	-.0151	-.0206	-.0193

TABLE 10 – SIMPLY-SUPPORTED SKEW GIRDER BRIDGE

INFLUENCE COEFICIENT OF TWISTING MOMENT IN MAIN GIRDER

TWISTING MOMENT = COEF. x ℓ

$(b/\ell) = 0.20$										ANGLE OF SKEW=ARCTAN(0.67)							
		UNIT VERTICAL LOAD APPLIED AT POINT:															
ϕ	ζ	2	3	4	5	8	9	10	11	2	3	4	5	8	9	10	11
		TWISTING MOMENT AT POINT 2								TWISTING MOMENT AT POINT 3							
0.10	0.10	-.0017	-.0050	-.0058	-.0038	0.0074	0.0118	0.0113	0.0069	0.0030	0.0032	0.0003	-.0008	0.0027	0.0068	0.0084	0.0057
	0.20	-.0026	-.0071	-.0077	-.0048	0.0096	0.0148	0.0138	0.0083	0.0034	0.0036	-.0002	-.0013	0.0029	0.0079	0.0099	0.0066
	0.40	-.0033	-.0088	-.0090	-.0053	0.0112	0.0169	0.0154	0.0092	0.0038	0.0041	-.0006	-.0016	0.0027	0.0085	0.0106	0.0070
	2.00	-.0032	-.0102	-.0096	-.0054	0.0125	0.0183	0.0161	0.0095	0.0043	0.0053	-.0010	-.0015	0.0020	0.0086	0.0109	0.0070
0.30	0.10	-.0003	-.0040	-.0057	-.0041	0.0101	0.0166	0.0167	0.0105	0.0062	0.0070	0.0027	-.0001	0.0045	0.0112	0.0140	0.0098
	0.20	-.0010	-.0064	-.0081	-.0055	0.0141	0.0227	0.0222	0.0139	0.0079	0.0090	0.0028	-.0005	0.0057	0.0144	0.0182	0.0125
	0.40	-.0016	-.0088	-.0100	-.0062	0.0179	0.0278	0.0265	0.0166	0.0093	0.0107	0.0026	-.0009	0.0060	0.0168	0.0212	0.0145
	2.00	-.0017	-.0123	-.0110	-.0056	0.0230	0.0336	0.0301	0.0186	0.0114	0.0143	0.0017	-.0010	0.0046	0.0183	0.0232	0.0154
0.50	0.10	0.0005	-.0031	-.0052	-.0040	0.0110	0.0184	0.0187	0.0120	0.0077	0.0089	0.0040	0.0004	0.0054	0.0130	0.0164	0.0115
	0.20	0.0005	-.0049	-.0073	-.0053	0.0158	0.0259	0.0259	0.0166	0.0105	0.0122	0.0050	0.0003	0.0071	0.0176	0.0223	0.0156
	0.40	0.0004	-.0068	-.0088	-.0058	0.0207	0.0329	0.0320	0.0205	0.0130	0.0153	0.0055	0.0001	0.0079	0.0213	0.0271	0.0188
	2.00	0.0013	-.0100	-.0087	-.0040	0.0285	0.0419	0.0381	0.0243	0.0166	0.0209	0.0050	0.0003	0.0067	0.0245	0.0311	0.0210
1.00	0.10	0.0015	-.0019	-.0045	-.0038	0.0118	0.0201	0.0208	0.0135	0.0094	0.0111	0.0054	0.0009	0.0062	0.0149	0.0189	0.0134
	0.20	0.0025	-.0025	-.0058	-.0048	0.0177	0.0295	0.0302	0.0196	0.0139	0.0164	0.0079	0.0014	0.0087	0.0214	0.0273	0.0194
	0.40	0.0038	-.0030	-.0062	-.0047	0.0240	0.0389	0.0390	0.0255	0.0183	0.0219	0.0100	0.0019	0.0106	0.0274	0.0349	0.0247
	2.00	0.0076	-.0035	-.0026	-.0001	0.0360	0.0537	0.0501	0.0332	0.0250	0.0316	0.0115	0.0034	0.0105	0.0342	0.0430	0.0297
1.50	0.10	0.0020	-.0014	-.0042	-.0037	0.0122	0.0208	0.0217	0.0141	0.0101	0.0120	0.0061	0.0012	0.0066	0.0156	0.0199	0.0142
	0.20	0.0036	-.0013	-.0050	-.0045	0.0185	0.0311	0.0321	0.0210	0.0155	0.0184	0.0093	0.0020	0.0095	0.0232	0.0296	0.0211
	0.40	0.0058	-.0007	-.0046	-.0040	0.0255	0.0418	0.0424	0.0280	0.0210	0.0254	0.0125	0.0029	0.0119	0.0305	0.0389	0.0276
	2.00	0.0121	0.0015	0.0020	0.0026	0.0401	0.0604	0.0572	0.0385	0.0301	0.0381	0.0160	0.0056	0.0130	0.0399	0.0499	0.0349
		TWISTING MOMENT AT POINT 4								TWISTING MOMENT AT POINT 5							
0.10	0.10	0.0065	0.0101	0.0093	0.0044	-.0021	-.0022	0.0003	0.0015	0.0060	0.0099	0.0107	0.0072	-.0036	-.0058	-.0055	-.0024
	0.20	0.0075	0.0119	0.0112	0.0051	-.0027	-.0032	-.0000	0.0016	0.0074	0.0123	0.0136	0.0096	-.0045	-.0077	-.0078	-.0036
	0.40	0.0080	0.0128	0.0122	0.0051	-.0030	-.0038	0.0000	0.0018	0.0084	0.0141	0.0159	0.0117	-.0052	-.0091	-.0097	-.0047
	2.00	0.0078	0.0128	0.0127	0.0042	-.0029	-.0040	0.0008	0.0026	0.0091	0.0156	0.0181	0.0144	-.0056	-.0103	-.0119	-.0059
0.30	0.10	0.0107	0.0161	0.0143	0.0068	-.0019	-.0008	0.0031	0.0040	0.0089	0.0143	0.0147	0.0095	-.0040	-.0060	-.0051	-.0016
	0.20	0.0138	0.0210	0.0189	0.0087	-.0027	-.0017	0.0037	0.0051	0.0119	0.0193	0.0203	0.0137	-.0053	-.0084	-.0078	-.0028
	0.40	0.0159	0.0244	0.0224	0.0097	-.0032	-.0025	0.0043	0.0061	0.0144	0.0233	0.0254	0.0180	-.0060	-.0102	-.0106	-.0041
	2.00	0.0165	0.0260	0.0254	0.0085	-.0027	-.0030	0.0066	0.0085	0.0172	0.0280	0.0322	0.0257	-.0057	-.0116	-.0149	-.0065
0.50	0.10	0.0125	0.0186	0.0162	0.0077	-.0016	0.0002	0.0047	0.0054	0.0101	0.0160	0.0162	0.0103	-.0039	-.0057	-.0045	-.0010
	0.20	0.0169	0.0253	0.0224	0.0103	-.0022	-.0001	0.0063	0.0073	0.0140	0.0223	0.0230	0.0152	-.0051	-.0078	-.0068	-.0018
	0.40	0.0204	0.0306	0.0276	0.0121	-.0025	-.0004	0.0079	0.0092	0.0176	0.0279	0.0296	0.0205	-.0056	-.0093	-.0092	-.0027
	2.00	0.0222	0.0343	0.0330	0.0114	-.0013	-.0004	0.0118	0.0131	0.0222	0.0350	0.0397	0.0315	-.0041	-.0093	-.0133	-.0046
1.00	0.10	0.0143	0.0211	0.0182	0.0086	-.0011	0.0014	0.0065	0.0069	0.0112	0.0176	0.0176	0.0110	-.0038	-.0052	-.0037	-.0003
	0.20	0.0207	0.0304	0.0264	0.0122	-.0013	0.0023	0.0099	0.0103	0.0165	0.0257	0.0260	0.0168	-.0048	-.0068	-.0051	-.0002
	0.40	0.0263	0.0387	0.0341	0.0152	-.0010	0.0033	0.0136	0.0139	0.0217	0.0335	0.0347	0.0234	-.0047	-.0073	-.0063	-.0001
	2.00	0.0312	0.0467	0.0443	0.0162	0.0020	0.0057	0.0212	0.0209	0.0301	0.0456	0.0504	0.0391	-.0003	-.0034	-.0078	0.0002
1.50	0.10	0.0151	0.0221	0.0190	0.0089	-.0010	0.0019	0.0073	0.0075	0.0117	0.0183	0.0181	0.0113	-.0037	-.0050	-.0033	0.0001
	0.20	0.0224	0.0327	0.0282	0.0130	-.0009	0.0035	0.0117	0.0117	0.0176	0.0272	0.0273	0.0174	-.0046	-.0062	-.0042	0.0005
	0.40	0.0293	0.0427	0.0373	0.0166	-.0001	0.0055	0.0167	0.0164	0.0238	0.0363	0.0371	0.0247	-.0042	-.0060	-.0046	0.0014
	2.00	0.0365	0.0540	0.0509	0.0191	0.0044	0.0100	0.0272	0.0258	0.0349	0.0519	0.0565	0.0433	0.0023	0.0009	-.0034	0.0038

$(b/\ell) = 0.20$										ANGLE OF SKEW=ARCTAN(1.00)							
		UNIT VERTICAL LOAD APPLIED AT POINT:															
ϕ	ζ	2	3	4	5	8	9	10	11	2	3	4	5	8	9	10	11
		TWISTING MOMENT AT POINT 2								TWISTING MOMENT AT POINT 3							
0.10	0.10	-.0009	-.0042	-.0050	-.0032	0.0089	0.0128	0.0118	0.0071	0.0035	0.0040	0.0009	-.0004	0.0049	0.0104	0.0111	0.0070
	0.20	-.0017	-.0062	-.0067	-.0041	0.0113	0.0157	0.0143	0.0085	0.0038	0.0044	0.0003	-.0009	0.0054	0.0121	0.0127	0.0080
	0.40	-.0023	-.0078	-.0080	-.0047	0.0132	0.0179	0.0160	0.0096	0.0041	0.0048	-.0001	-.0012	0.0055	0.0132	0.0137	0.0085
	2.00	-.0031	-.0098	-.0093	-.0053	0.0155	0.0202	0.0178	0.0107	0.0045	0.0055	-.0005	-.0013	0.0052	0.0141	0.0143	0.0089
0.30	0.10	0.0006	-.0029	-.0044	-.0031	0.0125	0.0187	0.0179	0.0110	0.0072	0.0087	0.0040	0.0008	0.0080	0.0168	0.0184	0.0120
	0.20	0.0002	-.0052	-.0066	-.0042	0.0173	0.0250	0.0235	0.0145	0.0088	0.0108	0.0042	0.0006	0.0099	0.0215	0.0233	0.0151
	0.40	-.0004	-.0076	-.0083	-.0049	0.0218	0.0304	0.0280	0.0174	0.0101	0.0126	0.0040	0.0003	0.0108	0.0250	0.0266	0.0171
	2.00	-.0015	-.0117	-.0100	-.0050	0.0289	0.0372	0.0334	0.0211	0.0119	0.0157	0.0033	0.0001	0.0102	0.0284	0.0291	0.0187
0.50	0.10	0.0015	-.0019	-.0038	-.0029	0.0137	0.0208	0.0202	0.0126	0.0089	0.0110	0.0057	0.0016	0.0093	0.0193	0.0214	0.0141
	0.20	0.0016	-.0037	-.0055	-.0038	0.0196	0.0288	0.0275	0.0172	0.0116	0.0145	0.0068	0.0017	0.0121	0.0258	0.0283	0.0185
	0.40	0.0015	-.0058	-.0069	-.0041	0.0256	0.0360	0.0338	0.0213	0.0138	0.0175	0.0072	0.0017	0.0136	0.0310	0.0334	0.0218
	2.00	0.0012	-.0098	-.0075	-.0030	0.0358	0.0460	0.0419	0.0270	0.0170	0.0227	0.0069	0.0020	0.0131	0.0365	0.0376	0.0244
1.00	0.10	0.0026	-.0007	-.0029	-.0025	0.0149	0.0229	0.0225	0.0142	0.0108	0.0135	0.0076	0.0024	0.0107	0.0220	0.0245	0.0163
	0.20	0.0036	-.0014	-.0039	-.0030	0.0221	0.0330	0.0320	0.0203	0.0150	0.0190	0.0101	0.0032	0.0145	0.0308	0.0340	0.0225
	0.40	0.0046	-.0024	-.0042	-.0026	0.0297	0.0426	0.0407	0.0261	0.0188	0.0241	0.0119	0.0039	0.0172	0.0383	0.0418	0.0277
	2.00	0.0063	-.0048	-.0018	0.0011	0.0446	0.0576	0.0532	0.0353	0.0244	0.0329	0.0129	0.0053	0.0173	0.0472	0.0489	0.0324
1.50	0.10	0.0030	-.0001	-.0025	-.0023	0.0154	0.0238	0.0235	0.0148	0.0116	0.0146	0.0084	0.0028	0.0112	0.0231	0.0258	0.0172
	0.20	0.0045	-.0003	-.0030	-.0026	0.0231	0.0347	0.0339	0.0216	0.0166	0.0211	0.0117	0.0040	0.0156	0.0329	0.0365	0.0243
	0.40	0.0062	-.0005	-.0026	-.0018	0.0315	0.0456	0.0439	0.0284	0.0213	0.0274	0.0144	0.0051	0.0189	0.0418	0.0458	0.0305
	2.00	0.0095	-.0014	0.0019	0.0036	0.0490	0.0635	0.0592	0.0398	0.0284	0.0384	0.0164	0.0073	0.0196	0.0528	0.0548	0.0366
		TWISTING MOMENT AT POINT 4								TWISTING MOMENT AT POINT 5							
0.10	0.10	0.0070	0.0111	0.0104	0.0049	-.0004	0.0009	0.0040	0.0035	0.0071	0.0118	0.0128	0.0089	-.0032	-.0050	-.0042	-.0009
	0.20	0.0080	0.0127	0.0121	0.0054	-.0009	0.0003	0.0044	0.0038	0.0085	0.0143	0.0157	0.0113	-.0041	-.0067	-.0062	-.0017
	0.40	0.0085	0.0137	0.0132	0.0055	-.0012	-.0001	0.0048	0.0041	0.0096	0.0160	0.0179	0.0132	-.0047	-.0080	-.0078	-.0023
	2.00	0.0089	0.0143	0.0141	0.0052	-.0013	-.0005	0.0055	0.0045	0.0107	0.0178	0.0202	0.0155	-.0053	-.0093	-.0098	-.0031
0.30	0.10	0.0120	0.0184	0.0168	0.0080	0.0008	0.0040	0.0087	0.0072	0.0110	0.0179	0.0187	0.0125	-.0031	-.0044	-.0029	0.0006
	0.20	0.0151	0.0233	0.0215	0.0099	0.0006	0.0042	0.0108	0.0088	0.0145	0.0235	0.0250	0.0173	-.0042	-.0066	-.0052	0.0002
	0.40	0.0171	0.0266	0.0250	0.0108	0.0003	0.0040	0.0126	0.0101	0.0174	0.0280	0.0304	0.0218	-.0049	-.0083	-.0076	-.0004
	2.00	0.0187	0.0291	0.0284	0.0102	0.0001	0.0033	0.0157	0.0119	0.0211	0.0334	0.0372	0.0289	-.0050	-.0100	-.0117	-.0015
0.50	0.10	0.0141	0.0214	0.0193	0.0093	0.0016	0.0057	0.0110	0.0089	0.0126	0.0202	0.0208	0.0137	-.0029	-.0038	-.0019	0.0015
	0.20	0.0185	0.0283	0.0258	0.0121	0.0017	0.0068	0.0145	0.0116	0.0172	0.0275	0.0288	0.0196	-.0038	-.0055	-.0037	0.0016
	0.40	0.0218	0.0334	0.0310	0.0136	0.0017	0.0072	0.0175	0.0138	0.0213	0.0338	0.0360	0.0256	-.0041	-.0069	-.0058	0.0015
	2.00	0.0244	0.0376	0.0365	0.0131	0.0020	0.0069	0.0227	0.0170	0.0270	0.0419	0.0460	0.0358	-.0030	-.0075	-.0098	0.0012
1.00	0.10	0.0163	0.0245	0.0220	0.0107	0.0024	0.0076	0.0135	0.0108	0.0142	0.0225	0.0229	0.0149	-.0025	-.0029	-.0007	0.0026
	0.20	0.0225	0.0340	0.0308	0.0145	0.0032	0.0101	0.0190	0.0150	0.0203	0.0320	0.0330	0.0221	-.0030	-.0039	-.0014	0.0036
	0.40	0.0277	0.0418	0.0383	0.0172	0.0039	0.0119	0.0241	0.0188	0.0261	0.0407	0.0426	0.0297	-.0026	-.0042	-.0024	0.0046
	2.00	0.0324	0.0489	0.0472	0.0173	0.0053	0.0129	0.0329	0.0244	0.0353	0.0532	0.0576	0.0446	0.0011	-.0018	-.0048	0.0063
1.50	0.10	0.0172	0.0258	0.0231	0.0112	0.0028	0.0084	0.0146	0.0116	0.0148	0.0235	0.0238	0.0154	-.0023	-.0025	-.0001	0.0030
	0.20	0.0243	0.0365	0.0329	0.0156	0.0040	0.0117	0.0211	0.0166	0.0216	0.0339	0.0347	0.0231	-.0026	-.0030	-.0003	0.0045
	0.40	0.0305	0.0458	0.0418	0.0189	0.0051	0.0144	0.0274	0.0213	0.0284	0.0439	0.0456	0.0315	-.0018	-.0026	-.0005	0.0062
	2.00	0.0366	0.0548	0.0528	0.0196	0.0073	0.0164	0.0384	0.0284	0.0398	0.0592	0.0635	0.0490	0.0036	0.0019	-.0014	0.0095

TABLE 11 - SIMPLY-SUPPORTED SKEW GIRDER BRIDGE

INFLUENCE COEFFICIENT OF TWISTING MOMENT IN MAIN GIRDER

TWISTING MOMENT = COEF.× ℓ

(b/ℓ) = 0.40										ANGLE OF SKEW=ARCTAN(0.0)							
		UNIT VERTICAL LOAD APPLIED AT POINT:															
φ	ζ	2	3	4	5	8	9	10	11	2	3	4	5	8	9	10	11
		TWISTING MOMENT AT POINT 2								TWISTING MOMENT AT POINT 3							
0.10	0.10	-.0014	-.0032	-.0036	-.0023	0.0014	0.0032	0.0036	0.0023	0.0008	0.0006	-.0006	-.0008	-.0008	-.0006	0.0006	0.0008
	0.20	-.0021	-.0048	-.0051	-.0032	0.0021	0.0048	0.0051	0.0032	0.0011	0.0009	-.0009	-.0011	-.0011	-.0009	0.0009	0.0011
	0.40	-.0027	-.0061	-.0065	-.0040	0.0027	0.0061	0.0065	0.0040	0.0014	0.0011	-.0011	-.0014	-.0014	-.0011	0.0011	0.0014
	2.00	-.0030	-.0077	-.0078	-.0047	0.0030	0.0077	0.0078	0.0047	0.0017	0.0016	-.0016	-.0017	-.0017	-.0016	0.0016	0.0017
0.30	0.10	-.0016	-.0039	-.0046	-.0031	0.0016	0.0039	0.0046	0.0031	0.0012	0.0009	-.0009	-.0012	-.0012	-.0009	0.0009	0.0012
	0.20	-.0027	-.0066	-.0076	-.0050	0.0027	0.0066	0.0076	0.0050	0.0019	0.0014	-.0014	-.0019	-.0019	-.0014	0.0014	0.0019
	0.40	-.0041	-.0099	-.0110	-.0071	0.0041	0.0099	0.0110	0.0071	0.0027	0.0020	-.0020	-.0027	-.0027	-.0020	0.0020	0.0027
	2.00	-.0059	-.0158	-.0165	-.0100	0.0059	0.0158	0.0165	0.0100	0.0041	0.0037	-.0037	-.0041	-.0041	-.0037	0.0037	0.0041
0.50	0.10	-.0016	-.0041	-.0049	-.0034	0.0016	0.0041	0.0049	0.0034	0.0014	0.0010	-.0010	-.0014	-.0014	-.0010	0.0010	0.0014
	0.20	-.0028	-.0071	-.0084	-.0056	0.0028	0.0071	0.0084	0.0056	0.0023	0.0016	-.0016	-.0023	-.0023	-.0016	0.0016	0.0023
	0.40	-.0045	-.0112	-.0128	-.0084	0.0045	0.0112	0.0128	0.0084	0.0034	0.0025	-.0025	-.0034	-.0034	-.0025	0.0025	0.0034
	2.00	-.0072	-.0200	-.0212	-.0132	0.0072	0.0200	0.0212	0.0132	0.0058	0.0050	-.0050	-.0058	-.0058	-.0050	0.0050	0.0058
1.00	0.10	-.0016	-.0042	-.0052	-.0036	0.0016	0.0042	0.0052	0.0036	0.0015	0.0010	-.0010	-.0015	-.0015	-.0010	0.0010	0.0015
	0.20	-.0028	-.0075	-.0091	-.0063	0.0028	0.0075	0.0091	0.0063	0.0027	0.0019	-.0019	-.0027	-.0027	-.0019	0.0019	0.0027
	0.40	-.0046	-.0123	-.0147	-.0100	0.0046	0.0123	0.0147	0.0100	0.0044	0.0031	-.0031	-.0044	-.0044	-.0031	0.0031	0.0044
	2.00	-.0081	-.0247	-.0275	-.0176	0.0081	0.0247	0.0275	0.0176	0.0087	0.0070	-.0070	-.0087	-.0087	-.0070	0.0070	0.0087
1.50	0.10	-.0016	-.0042	-.0053	-.0037	0.0016	0.0042	0.0053	0.0037	0.0016	0.0011	-.0011	-.0016	-.0016	-.0011	0.0011	0.0016
	0.20	-.0028	-.0076	-.0094	-.0066	0.0028	0.0076	0.0094	0.0066	0.0029	0.0020	-.0020	-.0029	-.0029	-.0020	0.0020	0.0029
	0.40	-.0045	-.0126	-.0155	-.0107	0.0045	0.0126	0.0155	0.0107	0.0048	0.0034	-.0034	-.0048	-.0048	-.0034	0.0034	0.0048
	2.00	-.0080	-.0266	-.0306	-.0201	0.0080	0.0266	0.0306	0.0201	0.0106	0.0083	-.0083	-.0106	-.0106	-.0083	0.0083	0.0106
		TWISTING MOMENT AT POINT 4								TWISTING MOMENT AT POINT 5							
0.10	0.10	0.0023	0.0036	0.0032	0.0014	-.0023	-.0036	-.0032	-.0014	0.0019	0.0032	0.0034	0.0023	-.0019	-.0032	-.0034	-.0023
	0.20	0.0032	0.0051	0.0048	0.0021	-.0032	-.0051	-.0048	-.0021	0.0028	0.0048	0.0053	0.0037	-.0028	-.0048	-.0053	-.0037
	0.40	0.0040	0.0065	0.0061	0.0027	-.0040	-.0065	-.0061	-.0027	0.0038	0.0065	0.0073	0.0052	-.0038	-.0065	-.0073	-.0052
	2.00	0.0047	0.0078	0.0077	0.0030	-.0047	-.0078	-.0077	-.0030	0.0054	0.0095	0.0110	0.0083	-.0054	-.0095	-.0110	-.0083
0.30	0.10	0.0031	0.0046	0.0039	0.0016	-.0031	-.0046	-.0039	-.0016	0.0023	0.0039	0.0040	0.0026	-.0023	-.0039	-.0040	-.0026
	0.20	0.0050	0.0076	0.0066	0.0027	-.0050	-.0076	-.0066	-.0027	0.0039	0.0065	0.0069	0.0046	-.0039	-.0065	-.0069	-.0046
	0.40	0.0071	0.0110	0.0099	0.0041	-.0071	-.0110	-.0099	-.0041	0.0058	0.0098	0.0107	0.0074	-.0058	-.0098	-.0107	-.0074
	2.00	0.0100	0.0165	0.0158	0.0059	-.0100	-.0165	-.0158	-.0059	0.0099	0.0174	0.0202	0.0153	-.0099	-.0174	-.0202	-.0153
0.50	0.10	0.0034	0.0049	0.0041	0.0016	-.0034	-.0049	-.0041	-.0016	0.0025	0.0040	0.0041	0.0027	-.0025	-.0040	-.0041	-.0027
	0.20	0.0056	0.0084	0.0071	0.0028	-.0056	-.0084	-.0071	-.0028	0.0042	0.0070	0.0073	0.0048	-.0042	-.0070	-.0073	-.0048
	0.40	0.0084	0.0128	0.0112	0.0045	-.0084	-.0128	-.0112	-.0045	0.0066	0.0110	0.0118	0.0080	-.0066	-.0110	-.0118	-.0080
	2.00	0.0132	0.0212	0.0200	0.0072	-.0132	-.0212	-.0200	-.0072	0.0119	0.0208	0.0243	0.0183	-.0119	-.0208	-.0243	-.0183
1.00	0.10	0.0036	0.0052	0.0042	0.0016	-.0036	-.0052	-.0042	-.0016	0.0026	0.0042	0.0042	0.0027	-.0026	-.0042	-.0042	-.0027
	0.20	0.0063	0.0091	0.0075	0.0028	-.0063	-.0091	-.0075	-.0028	0.0046	0.0074	0.0076	0.0049	-.0046	-.0074	-.0076	-.0049
	0.40	0.0100	0.0147	0.0123	0.0046	-.0100	-.0147	-.0123	-.0046	0.0074	0.0121	0.0127	0.0085	-.0074	-.0121	-.0127	-.0085
	2.00	0.0176	0.0275	0.0247	0.0081	-.0176	-.0275	-.0247	-.0081	0.0144	0.0246	0.0283	0.0212	-.0144	-.0246	-.0283	-.0212
1.50	0.10	0.0037	0.0053	0.0042	0.0016	-.0037	-.0053	-.0042	-.0016	0.0026	0.0042	0.0043	0.0027	-.0026	-.0042	-.0043	-.0027
	0.20	0.0066	0.0094	0.0076	0.0028	-.0066	-.0094	-.0076	-.0028	0.0047	0.0076	0.0078	0.0050	-.0047	-.0076	-.0078	-.0050
	0.40	0.0107	0.0155	0.0126	0.0045	-.0107	-.0155	-.0126	-.0045	0.0078	0.0126	0.0131	0.0086	-.0078	-.0126	-.0131	-.0086
	2.00	0.0201	0.0306	0.0266	0.0080	-.0201	-.0306	-.0266	-.0080	0.0157	0.0264	0.0299	0.0222	-.0157	-.0264	-.0299	-.0222

(b/ℓ) = 0.40										ANGLE OF SKEW=ARCTAN(0.17)							
		UNIT VERTICAL LOAD APPLIED AT POINT:															
φ	ζ	2	3	4	5	8	9	10	11	2	3	4	5	8	9	10	11
		TWISTING MOMENT AT POINT 2								TWISTING MOMENT AT POINT 3							
0.10	0.10	-.0012	-.0028	-.0032	-.0021	0.0018	0.0037	0.0039	0.0025	0.0009	0.0007	-.0004	-.0007	-.0003	0.0003	0.0013	0.0012
	0.20	-.0019	-.0044	-.0048	-.0031	0.0027	0.0054	0.0056	0.0035	0.0012	0.0010	-.0006	-.0010	-.0004	0.0003	0.0018	0.0016
	0.40	-.0026	-.0059	-.0063	-.0039	0.0035	0.0071	0.0072	0.0044	0.0014	0.0012	-.0010	-.0013	-.0006	0.0003	0.0023	0.0020
	2.00	-.0031	-.0078	-.0078	-.0047	0.0043	0.0091	0.0088	0.0052	0.0018	0.0017	-.0015	-.0017	-.0009	-.0000	0.0030	0.0024
0.30	0.10	-.0012	-.0032	-.0039	-.0027	0.0021	0.0045	0.0051	0.0034	0.0015	0.0012	-.0004	-.0009	-.0005	0.0004	0.0020	0.0019
	0.20	-.0022	-.0056	-.0066	-.0044	0.0036	0.0076	0.0083	0.0054	0.0022	0.0019	-.0007	-.0015	-.0007	0.0006	0.0031	0.0029
	0.40	-.0036	-.0088	-.0100	-.0065	0.0056	0.0115	0.0123	0.0078	0.0030	0.0025	-.0012	-.0022	-.0011	0.0007	0.0044	0.0040
	2.00	-.0059	-.0154	-.0161	-.0098	0.0088	0.0190	0.0189	0.0114	0.0045	0.0042	-.0029	-.0037	-.0021	0.0003	0.0071	0.0060
0.50	0.10	-.0011	-.0032	-.0041	-.0029	0.0022	0.0048	0.0055	0.0036	0.0017	0.0014	-.0003	-.0010	-.0005	0.0005	0.0022	0.0021
	0.20	-.0021	-.0058	-.0071	-.0049	0.0039	0.0083	0.0093	0.0061	0.0027	0.0023	-.0007	-.0017	-.0009	0.0007	0.0037	0.0034
	0.40	-.0036	-.0096	-.0113	-.0075	0.0062	0.0131	0.0144	0.0093	0.0040	0.0034	-.0012	-.0026	-.0014	0.0010	0.0055	0.0051
	2.00	-.0069	-.0188	-.0202	-.0125	0.0111	0.0243	0.0247	0.0151	0.0066	0.0061	-.0034	-.0049	-.0029	0.0007	0.0099	0.0085
1.00	0.10	-.0011	-.0032	-.0042	-.0030	0.0022	0.0050	0.0058	0.0039	0.0019	0.0016	-.0003	-.0011	-.0006	0.0005	0.0024	0.0023
	0.20	-.0019	-.0059	-.0076	-.0053	0.0040	0.0089	0.0102	0.0069	0.0033	0.0029	-.0006	-.0019	-.0011	0.0009	0.0043	0.0041
	0.40	-.0033	-.0099	-.0124	-.0086	0.0067	0.0148	0.0167	0.0111	0.0053	0.0046	-.0011	-.0031	-.0018	0.0013	0.0070	0.0066
	2.00	-.0068	-.0216	-.0247	-.0160	0.0136	0.0310	0.0327	0.0207	0.0105	0.0097	-.0036	-.0067	-.0040	0.0015	0.0144	0.0129
1.50	0.10	-.0010	-.0032	-.0043	-.0031	0.0022	0.0050	0.0059	0.0040	0.0020	0.0017	-.0003	-.0011	-.0006	0.0005	0.0025	0.0024
	0.20	-.0018	-.0059	-.0077	-.0055	0.0041	0.0091	0.0106	0.0072	0.0036	0.0031	-.0006	-.0020	-.0012	0.0009	0.0045	0.0044
	0.40	-.0031	-.0099	-.0128	-.0091	0.0068	0.0154	0.0177	0.0119	0.0060	0.0053	-.0011	-.0034	-.0020	0.0015	0.0077	0.0073
	2.00	-.0059	-.0221	-.0265	-.0177	0.0145	0.0342	0.0371	0.0241	0.0132	0.0123	-.0034	-.0076	-.0048	0.0022	0.0174	0.0158
		TWISTING MOMENT AT POINT 4								TWISTING MOMENT AT POINT 5							
0.10	0.10	0.0024	0.0037	0.0033	0.0015	-.0020	-.0030	-.0024	-.0009	0.0019	0.0033	0.0034	0.0023	-.0018	-.0029	-.0031	-.0019
	0.20	0.0033	0.0053	0.0049	0.0022	-.0028	-.0044	-.0037	-.0015	0.0029	0.0049	0.0053	0.0036	-.0027	-.0046	-.0049	-.0032
	0.40	0.0041	0.0067	0.0063	0.0028	-.0036	-.0056	-.0050	-.0019	0.0039	0.0067	0.0075	0.0052	-.0037	-.0063	-.0069	-.0047
	2.00	0.0048	0.0080	0.0079	0.0031	-.0043	-.0069	-.0063	-.0021	0.0056	0.0098	0.0112	0.0084	-.0053	-.0093	-.0106	-.0076
0.30	0.10	0.0033	0.0049	0.0042	0.0018	-.0026	-.0036	-.0027	-.0008	0.0025	0.0040	0.0041	0.0026	-.0022	-.0035	-.0035	-.0021
	0.20	0.0053	0.0079	0.0069	0.0031	-.0042	-.0061	-.0048	-.0016	0.0041	0.0067	0.0070	0.0046	-.0036	-.0060	-.0061	-.0038
	0.40	0.0075	0.0116	0.0104	0.0046	-.0061	-.0091	-.0075	-.0026	0.0061	0.0103	0.0110	0.0074	-.0055	-.0092	-.0098	-.0063
	2.00	0.0107	0.0175	0.0167	0.0067	-.0090	-.0143	-.0126	-.0039	0.0105	0.0183	0.0210	0.0156	-.0096	-.0168	-.0193	-.0138
0.50	0.10	0.0036	0.0052	0.0044	0.0019	-.0027	-.0038	-.0027	-.0008	0.0026	0.0042	0.0043	0.0027	-.0023	-.0036	-.0036	-.0021
	0.20	0.0060	0.0089	0.0076	0.0033	-.0046	-.0065	-.0049	-.0015	0.0045	0.0073	0.0075	0.0048	-.0039	-.0063	-.0064	-.0039
	0.40	0.0091	0.0137	0.0120	0.0052	-.0071	-.0103	-.0081	-.0026	0.0071	0.0117	0.0123	0.0081	-.0062	-.0102	-.0106	-.0067
	2.00	0.0145	0.0231	0.0216	0.0086	-.0116	-.0181	-.0154	-.0044	0.0130	0.0224	0.0256	0.0187	-.0115	-.0200	-.0228	-.0161
1.00	0.10	0.0039	0.0056	0.0046	0.0019	-.0029	-.0039	-.0027	-.0007	0.0028	0.0044	0.0044	0.0027	-.0024	-.0037	-.0036	-.0021
	0.20	0.0068	0.0099	0.0082	0.0034	-.0051	-.0069	-.0049	-.0012	0.0049	0.0079	0.0080	0.0050	-.0042	-.0067	-.0066	-.0039
	0.40	0.0109	0.0161	0.0135	0.0056	-.0082	-.0114	-.0083	-.0021	0.0081	0.0131	0.0134	0.0086	-.0069	-.0111	-.0111	-.0068
	2.00	0.0202	0.0311	0.0279	0.0106	-.0150	-.0224	-.0176	-.0038	0.0164	0.0275	0.0307	0.0220	-.0136	-.0231	-.0259	-.0179
1.50	0.10	0.0040	0.0057	0.0045	0.0019	-.0029	-.0039	-.0027	-.0006	0.0028	0.0045	0.0045	0.0027	-.0024	-.0038	-.0036	-.0021
	0.20	0.0071	0.0103	0.0084	0.0034	-.0052	-.0071	-.0049	-.0011	0.0051	0.0081	0.0081	0.0051	-.0043	-.0068	-.0066	-.0039
	0.40	0.0118	0.0171	0.0142	0.0057	-.0087	-.0118	-.0082	-.0018	0.0086	0.0137	0.0139	0.0088	-.0072	-.0114	-.0113	-.0068
	2.00	0.0237	0.0356	0.0310	0.0114	-.0168	-.0241	-.0179	-.0027	0.0183	0.0301	0.0330	0.0233	-.0146	-.0243	-.0267	-.0182

TABLE 12 - SIMPLY-SUPPORTED SKEW GIRDER BRIDGE

INFLUENCE COEFFICIENT OF TWISTING MOMENT IN MAIN GIRDER

TWISTING MOMENT = COEF. × ℓ

$(b/\ell) = 0.40$ ANGLE OF SKEW=ARCTAN(0.33)

UNIT VERTICAL LOAD APPLIED AT POINT:

φ	ζ	2	3	4	5	8	9	10	11	2	3	4	5	8	9	10	11
		TWISTING MOMENT AT POINT 2								TWISTING MOMENT AT POINT 3							
0.10	0.10	-.0010	-.0025	-.0029	-.0019	0.0022	0.0041	0.0042	0.0026	0.0010	0.0009	-.0002	-.0005	0.0002	0.0011	0.0021	0.0016
	0.20	-.0017	-.0040	-.0045	-.0029	0.0033	0.0060	0.0061	0.0037	0.0012	0.0011	-.0004	-.0008	0.0002	0.0015	0.0028	0.0022
	0.40	-.0025	-.0057	-.0061	-.0038	0.0044	0.0080	0.0078	0.0047	0.0014	0.0012	-.0008	-.0012	0.0002	0.0018	0.0035	0.0026
	2.00	-.0032	-.0079	-.0079	-.0047	0.0057	0.0104	0.0097	0.0057	0.0019	0.0018	-.0014	-.0016	-.0001	0.0017	0.0044	0.0031
0.30	0.10	-.0008	-.0025	-.0033	-.0023	0.0026	0.0051	0.0055	0.0036	0.0017	0.0017	0.0001	-.0006	0.0003	0.0017	0.0031	0.0025
	0.20	-.0017	-.0047	-.0058	-.0039	0.0045	0.0086	0.0091	0.0058	0.0025	0.0024	-.0000	-.0011	0.0004	0.0026	0.0048	0.0038
	0.40	-.0031	-.0079	-.0091	-.0060	0.0070	0.0130	0.0134	0.0083	0.0033	0.0031	-.0005	-.0017	0.0006	0.0036	0.0068	0.0053
	2.00	-.0059	-.0151	-.0158	-.0096	0.0119	0.0220	0.0211	0.0126	0.0049	0.0047	-.0022	-.0033	0.0001	0.0046	0.0105	0.0077
0.50	0.10	-.0007	-.0025	-.0034	-.0024	0.0028	0.0054	0.0059	0.0039	0.0020	0.0020	0.0003	-.0006	0.0003	0.0019	0.0035	0.0028
	0.20	-.0015	-.0047	-.0060	-.0042	0.0049	0.0094	0.0102	0.0066	0.0032	0.0031	0.0002	-.0011	0.0005	0.0031	0.0057	0.0046
	0.40	-.0028	-.0081	-.0099	-.0067	0.0079	0.0150	0.0158	0.0101	0.0045	0.0044	-.0001	-.0019	0.0007	0.0046	0.0086	0.0068
	2.00	-.0065	-.0178	-.0192	-.0119	0.0152	0.0284	0.0278	0.0169	0.0074	0.0072	-.0020	-.0041	0.0003	0.0068	0.0147	0.0111
1.00	0.10	-.0006	-.0024	-.0034	-.0025	0.0029	0.0057	0.0063	0.0042	0.0023	0.0023	0.0004	-.0006	0.0003	0.0021	0.0038	0.0031
	0.20	-.0011	-.0045	-.0062	-.0045	0.0052	0.0102	0.0113	0.0074	0.0039	0.0039	0.0006	-.0011	0.0006	0.0036	0.0067	0.0054
	0.40	-.0022	-.0078	-.0104	-.0074	0.0088	0.0171	0.0185	0.0121	0.0063	0.0062	0.0007	-.0019	0.0009	0.0058	0.0109	0.0087
	2.00	-.0056	-.0190	-.0222	-.0144	0.0191	0.0368	0.0374	0.0235	0.0122	0.0122	-.0005	-.0048	0.0009	0.0105	0.0218	0.0170
1.50	0.10	-.0005	-.0023	-.0034	-.0025	0.0029	0.0058	0.0065	0.0043	0.0024	0.0024	0.0004	-.0006	0.0003	0.0021	0.0039	0.0032
	0.20	-.0010	-.0043	-.0062	-.0045	0.0053	0.0106	0.0117	0.0078	0.0043	0.0043	0.0008	-.0011	0.0006	0.0038	0.0071	0.0058
	0.40	-.0017	-.0075	-.0105	-.0076	0.0091	0.0180	0.0198	0.0130	0.0072	0.0072	0.0011	-.0020	0.0010	0.0064	0.0120	0.0097
	2.00	-.0041	-.0183	-.0228	-.0154	0.0211	0.0413	0.0430	0.0276	0.0157	0.0161	0.0010	-.0049	0.0013	0.0131	0.0265	0.0209

φ	ζ	2	3	4	5	8	9	10	11	2	3	4	5	8	9	10	11
		TWISTING MOMENT AT POINT 4								TWISTING MOMENT AT POINT 5							
0.10	0.10	0.0025	0.0038	0.0035	0.0016	-.0016	-.0023	-.0016	-.0004	0.0021	0.0034	0.0036	0.0023	-.0017	-.0027	-.0027	-.0016
	0.20	0.0034	0.0054	0.0050	0.0024	-.0024	-.0035	-.0026	-.0008	0.0030	0.0051	0.0055	0.0037	-.0026	-.0043	-.0044	-.0027
	0.40	0.0042	0.0068	0.0065	0.0030	-.0031	-.0047	-.0037	-.0012	0.0041	0.0070	0.0077	0.0054	-.0036	-.0060	-.0064	-.0040
	2.00	0.0049	0.0081	0.0080	0.0032	-.0038	-.0059	-.0046	-.0012	0.0058	0.0101	0.0116	0.0087	-.0052	-.0090	-.0102	-.0068
0.30	0.10	0.0035	0.0052	0.0045	0.0021	-.0020	-.0025	-.0015	-.0001	0.0027	0.0043	0.0044	0.0027	-.0020	-.0031	-.0029	-.0016
	0.20	0.0056	0.0084	0.0074	0.0034	-.0033	-.0045	-.0029	-.0005	0.0044	0.0072	0.0075	0.0048	-.0034	-.0054	-.0053	-.0030
	0.40	0.0079	0.0122	0.0110	0.0051	-.0050	-.0071	-.0049	-.0011	0.0066	0.0110	0.0117	0.0077	-.0053	-.0086	-.0088	-.0052
	2.00	0.0114	0.0185	0.0176	0.0074	-.0078	-.0119	-.0089	-.0018	0.0113	0.0195	0.0222	0.0162	-.0093	-.0162	-.0182	-.0119
0.50	0.10	0.0038	0.0057	0.0048	0.0022	-.0021	-.0026	-.0013	0.0001	0.0029	0.0046	0.0046	0.0028	-.0021	-.0032	-.0030	-.0016
	0.20	0.0064	0.0096	0.0083	0.0038	-.0036	-.0046	-.0027	-.0001	0.0049	0.0080	0.0081	0.0051	-.0036	-.0057	-.0054	-.0030
	0.40	0.0097	0.0147	0.0129	0.0059	-.0057	-.0077	-.0048	-.0006	0.0077	0.0126	0.0132	0.0085	-.0058	-.0094	-.0093	-.0053
	2.00	0.0157	0.0250	0.0233	0.0098	-.0099	-.0146	-.0102	-.0015	0.0143	0.0244	0.0274	0.0197	-.0111	-.0191	-.0212	-.0136
1.00	0.10	0.0042	0.0061	0.0051	0.0022	-.0021	-.0025	-.0012	0.0003	0.0031	0.0048	0.0048	0.0029	-.0021	-.0032	-.0029	-.0015
	0.20	0.0074	0.0108	0.0091	0.0040	-.0038	-.0047	-.0023	0.0004	0.0055	0.0087	0.0087	0.0054	-.0038	-.0059	-.0054	-.0029
	0.40	0.0119	0.0176	0.0150	0.0067	-.0063	-.0079	-.0042	0.0004	0.0090	0.0144	0.0147	0.0092	-.0063	-.0099	-.0095	-.0051
	2.00	0.0227	0.0348	0.0312	0.0131	-.0122	-.0168	-.0100	0.0006	0.0187	0.0309	0.0338	0.0236	-.0128	-.0215	-.0232	-.0143
1.50	0.10	0.0043	0.0062	0.0052	0.0023	-.0022	-.0025	-.0011	0.0003	0.0031	0.0049	0.0048	0.0029	-.0022	-.0033	-.0029	-.0015
	0.20	0.0077	0.0113	0.0094	0.0041	-.0039	-.0046	-.0021	0.0006	0.0057	0.0090	0.0089	0.0054	-.0039	-.0059	-.0054	-.0028
	0.40	0.0129	0.0189	0.0159	0.0070	-.0065	-.0079	-.0037	0.0009	0.0096	0.0153	0.0153	0.0095	-.0065	-.0101	-.0094	-.0050
	2.00	0.0270	0.0406	0.0356	0.0147	-.0131	-.0170	-.0085	0.0027	0.0213	0.0346	0.0371	0.0254	-.0135	-.0221	-.0233	-.0139

$(b/\ell) = 0.40$ ANGLE OF SKEW=ARCTAN(0.50)

UNIT VERTICAL LOAD APPLIED AT POINT:

φ	ζ	2	3	4	5	8	9	10	11	2	3	4	5	8	9	10	11
		TWISTING MOMENT AT POINT 2								TWISTING MOMENT AT POINT 3							
0.10	0.10	-.0008	-.0022	-.0026	-.0017	0.0026	0.0044	0.0044	0.0027	0.0011	0.0011	0.0000	-.0004	0.0007	0.0020	0.0028	0.0020
	0.20	-.0015	-.0037	-.0042	-.0027	0.0039	0.0065	0.0064	0.0039	0.0013	0.0012	-.0003	-.0007	0.0009	0.0027	0.0038	0.0027
	0.40	-.0024	-.0055	-.0059	-.0037	0.0052	0.0087	0.0083	0.0050	0.0015	0.0014	-.0007	-.0011	0.0010	0.0033	0.0047	0.0032
	2.00	-.0034	-.0081	-.0081	-.0048	0.0071	0.0116	0.0106	0.0062	0.0019	0.0020	-.0013	-.0015	0.0007	0.0036	0.0056	0.0037
0.30	0.10	-.0005	-.0020	-.0028	-.0020	0.0032	0.0057	0.0059	0.0038	0.0020	0.0021	0.0006	-.0003	0.0011	0.0030	0.0042	0.0031
	0.20	-.0012	-.0039	-.0050	-.0035	0.0054	0.0094	0.0097	0.0061	0.0029	0.0029	0.0005	-.0007	0.0016	0.0046	0.0065	0.0048
	0.40	-.0025	-.0070	-.0083	-.0055	0.0083	0.0143	0.0143	0.0088	0.0037	0.0037	0.0001	-.0013	0.0022	0.0065	0.0092	0.0066
	2.00	-.0059	-.0148	-.0154	-.0093	0.0149	0.0246	0.0230	0.0137	0.0052	0.0052	-.0017	-.0030	0.0023	0.0090	0.0137	0.0094
0.50	0.10	-.0003	-.0018	-.0027	-.0020	0.0033	0.0061	0.0064	0.0041	0.0023	0.0025	0.0008	-.0002	0.0012	0.0033	0.0047	0.0035
	0.20	-.0009	-.0037	-.0051	-.0036	0.0059	0.0105	0.0109	0.0070	0.0037	0.0039	0.0011	-.0006	0.0019	0.0055	0.0078	0.0057
	0.40	-.0021	-.0068	-.0087	-.0059	0.0095	0.0167	0.0170	0.0107	0.0052	0.0053	0.0010	-.0012	0.0028	0.0081	0.0116	0.0084
	2.00	-.0061	-.0169	-.0183	-.0113	0.0191	0.0319	0.0305	0.0185	0.0080	0.0082	-.0008	-.0034	0.0036	0.0129	0.0193	0.0135
1.00	0.10	-.0001	-.0017	-.0027	-.0020	0.0035	0.0064	0.0069	0.0045	0.0027	0.0029	0.0011	-.0002	0.0013	0.0036	0.0052	0.0039
	0.20	-.0004	-.0033	-.0050	-.0037	0.0063	0.0115	0.0122	0.0079	0.0046	0.0050	0.0017	-.0004	0.0023	0.0064	0.0091	0.0068
	0.40	-.0011	-.0061	-.0086	-.0063	0.0107	0.0192	0.0201	0.0129	0.0072	0.0077	0.0024	-.0009	0.0036	0.0103	0.0147	0.0108
	2.00	-.0045	-.0169	-.0200	-.0130	0.0244	0.0419	0.0414	0.0259	0.0136	0.0146	0.0021	-.0031	0.0058	0.0195	0.0289	0.0208
1.50	0.10	-.0001	-.0016	-.0026	-.0020	0.0036	0.0065	0.0070	0.0046	0.0028	0.0030	0.0012	-.0002	0.0013	0.0037	0.0054	0.0040
	0.20	-.0002	-.0030	-.0049	-.0037	0.0065	0.0119	0.0128	0.0083	0.0050	0.0054	0.0020	-.0003	0.0024	0.0068	0.0097	0.0072
	0.40	-.0006	-.0055	-.0085	-.0063	0.0113	0.0204	0.0216	0.0140	0.0083	0.0090	0.0031	-.0007	0.0039	0.0113	0.0162	0.0120
	2.00	-.0025	-.0153	-.0196	-.0133	0.0272	0.0475	0.0478	0.0304	0.0178	0.0194	0.0048	-.0025	0.0074	0.0238	0.0351	0.0256

φ	ζ	2	3	4	5	8	9	10	11	2	3	4	5	8	9	10	11
		TWISTING MOMENT AT POINT 4								TWISTING MOMENT AT POINT 5							
0.10	0.10	0.0026	0.0040	0.0036	0.0018	-.0012	-.0016	-.0007	0.0001	0.0022	0.0037	0.0039	0.0025	-.0016	-.0025	-.0024	-.0012
	0.20	0.0036	0.0056	0.0052	0.0025	-.0019	-.0026	-.0015	-.0001	0.0032	0.0055	0.0059	0.0039	-.0025	-.0041	-.0040	-.0022
	0.40	0.0044	0.0070	0.0066	0.0031	-.0026	-.0037	-.0023	-.0004	0.0043	0.0073	0.0081	0.0056	-.0034	-.0058	-.0060	-.0033
	2.00	0.0050	0.0083	0.0082	0.0033	-.0032	-.0048	-.0028	-.0003	0.0060	0.0104	0.0119	0.0089	-.0050	-.0087	-.0096	-.0057
0.30	0.10	0.0038	0.0056	0.0049	0.0023	-.0014	-.0015	-.0002	0.0007	0.0030	0.0048	0.0048	0.0030	-.0018	-.0028	-.0024	-.0011
	0.20	0.0059	0.0090	0.0080	0.0038	-.0025	-.0029	-.0009	0.0007	0.0048	0.0079	0.0082	0.0052	-.0032	-.0049	-.0046	-.0022
	0.40	0.0084	0.0129	0.0117	0.0056	-.0039	-.0049	-.0022	0.0005	0.0072	0.0119	0.0126	0.0083	-.0050	-.0081	-.0078	-.0040
	2.00	0.0121	0.0194	0.0185	0.0080	-.0066	-.0093	-.0049	0.0002	0.0122	0.0208	0.0235	0.0171	-.0090	-.0156	-.0170	-.0098
0.50	0.10	0.0042	0.0062	0.0053	0.0025	-.0014	-.0013	0.0001	0.0009	0.0032	0.0051	0.0051	0.0031	-.0019	-.0028	-.0024	-.0010
	0.20	0.0069	0.0104	0.0090	0.0043	-.0025	-.0027	-.0004	0.0013	0.0055	0.0088	0.0090	0.0056	-.0033	-.0051	-.0045	-.0021
	0.40	0.0104	0.0158	0.0140	0.0066	-.0042	-.0049	-.0014	0.0014	0.0085	0.0139	0.0145	0.0093	-.0054	-.0086	-.0080	-.0039
	2.00	0.0169	0.0268	0.0249	0.0109	-.0080	-.0109	-.0047	0.0015	0.0158	0.0266	0.0296	0.0210	-.0106	-.0182	-.0195	-.0108
1.00	0.10	0.0045	0.0067	0.0057	0.0026	-.0014	-.0012	0.0003	0.0012	0.0034	0.0054	0.0054	0.0033	-.0019	-.0028	-.0023	-.0009
	0.20	0.0080	0.0118	0.0101	0.0047	-.0025	-.0023	0.0004	0.0020	0.0061	0.0098	0.0097	0.0060	-.0034	-.0051	-.0043	-.0018
	0.40	0.0129	0.0192	0.0167	0.0078	-.0043	-.0043	0.0001	0.0029	0.0101	0.0162	0.0164	0.0103	-.0058	-.0087	-.0078	-.0034
	2.00	0.0249	0.0382	0.0344	0.0152	-.0092	-.0110	-.0020	0.0050	0.0213	0.0348	0.0376	0.0259	-.0120	-.0199	-.0205	-.0106
1.50	0.10	0.0047	0.0069	0.0058	0.0027	-.0014	-.0011	0.0005	0.0013	0.0035	0.0056	0.0055	0.0033	-.0019	-.0027	-.0022	-.0009
	0.20	0.0085	0.0124	0.0106	0.0049	-.0025	-.0022	0.0007	0.0023	0.0064	0.0101	0.0100	0.0061	-.0035	-.0051	-.0042	-.0017
	0.40	0.0142	0.0209	0.0179	0.0083	-.0043	-.0039	0.0009	0.0037	0.0108	0.0172	0.0173	0.0107	-.0059	-.0087	-.0075	-.0031
	2.00	0.0300	0.0452	0.0400	0.0176	-.0093	-.0098	0.0010	0.0080	0.0246	0.0395	0.0418	0.0283	-.0123	-.0198	-.0198	-.0096

TABLE 13 - SIMPLY-SUPPORTED SKEW GIRDER BRIDGE

BENDING MOMENT, TWISTING MOMENT IN MAIN GIRDERS AND REACTION AT SUPPORTS

DUE TO A UNIFORM LINE LOAD OF UNIT INTENSITY ON MAIN GIRDERS

BENDING MOMENT = COEF. ℓ^2, TWISTING MOMENT = COEF. ℓ^2, REACTION = COEF. ℓ

$(b/\ell) = 0.10$ ANGLE OF SKEW=ARCTAN(0.0)

φ	ζ	BENDING MOMENT AT POINT				TWISTING MOMENTT AT POINT					REACTION AT SUPPORT	
		2	3	4	5	1-2	2-3	3-4	4-5	5-6	1	6
0.10	0.10	0.0800	0.1200	0.1200	0.0800	0.0	0.0	0.0	0.0	0.0	0.50000	0.50000
	0.20	0.0800	0.1200	0.1200	0.0800	0.0	0.0	0.0	0.0	0.0	0.50000	0.50000
	0.40	0.0800	0.1200	0.1200	0.0800	0.0	0.0	0.0	0.0	0.0	0.50000	0.50000
	2.00	0.0800	0.1200	0.1200	0.0800	0.0	0.0	0.0	0.0	0.0	0.50000	0.50000
0.30	0.10	0.0800	0.1200	0.1200	0.0800	0.0	0.0	0.0	0.0	0.0	0.50000	0.50000
	0.20	0.0800	0.1200	0.1200	0.0800	0.0	0.0	0.0	0.0	0.0	0.50000	0.50000
	0.40	0.0800	0.1200	0.1200	0.0800	0.0	0.0	0.0	0.0	0.0	0.50000	0.50000
	2.00	0.0800	0.1200	0.1200	0.0800	0.0	0.0	0.0	0.0	0.0	0.50000	0.50000
0.50	0.10	0.0800	0.1200	0.1200	0.0800	0.0	0.0	0.0	0.0	0.0	0.50000	0.50000
	0.20	0.0800	0.1200	0.1200	0.0800	0.0	0.0	0.0	0.0	0.0	0.50000	0.50000
	0.40	0.0800	0.1200	0.1200	0.0800	0.0	0.0	0.0	0.0	0.0	0.50000	0.50000
	2.00	0.0800	0.1200	0.1200	0.0800	0.0	0.0	0.0	0.0	0.0	0.50000	0.50000
1.00	0.10	0.0800	0.1200	0.1200	0.0800	0.0	0.0	0.0	0.0	0.0	0.50000	0.50000
	0.20	0.0800	0.1200	0.1200	0.0800	0.0	0.0	0.0	0.0	0.0	0.50000	0.50000
	0.40	0.0800	0.1200	0.1200	0.0800	0.0	0.0	0.0	0.0	0.0	0.50000	0.50000
	2.00	0.0800	0.1200	0.1200	0.0800	0.0	0.0	0.0	0.0	0.0	0.50000	0.50000
1.50	0.10	0.0800	0.1200	0.1200	0.0800	0.0	0.0	0.0	0.0	0.0	0.50000	0.50000
	0.20	0.0800	0.1200	0.1200	0.0800	0.0	0.0	0.0	0.0	0.0	0.50000	0.50000
	0.40	0.0800	0.1200	0.1200	0.0800	0.0	0.0	0.0	0.0	0.0	0.50000	0.50000
	2.00	0.0800	0.1200	0.1200	0.0800	0.0	0.0	0.0	0.0	0.0	0.50000	0.50000

$(b/\ell) = 0.10$ ANGLE OF SKEW=ARCTAN(0.67)

φ	ζ	BENDING MOMENT AT POINT				TWISTING MOMENTT AT POINT					REACTION AT SUPPORT	
		2	3	4	5	1-2	2-3	3-4	4-5	5-6	1	6
0.10	0.10	0.0554	0.0991	0.1106	0.0812	0.0015	0.0086	0.0104	0.0101	0.0071	0.34901	0.65100
	0.20	0.0538	0.0978	0.1085	0.0791	0.0017	0.0093	0.0108	0.0106	0.0080	0.33895	0.66105
	0.40	0.0527	0.0958	0.1055	0.0763	0.0018	0.0096	0.0108	0.0106	0.0085	0.33478	0.66522
	2.00	0.0484	0.0822	0.0895	0.0633	0.0015	0.0087	0.0099	0.0096	0.0078	0.35010	0.64999
0.30	0.10	0.0362	0.0842	0.1037	0.0819	0.0029	0.0158	0.0187	0.0183	0.0133	0.22408	0.77592
	0.20	0.0312	0.0817	0.0995	0.0776	0.0037	0.0185	0.0203	0.0202	0.0162	0.18415	0.81585
	0.40	0.0285	0.0798	0.0951	0.0723	0.0045	0.0204	0.0211	0.0212	0.0185	0.15746	0.84253
	2.00	0.0281	0.0690	0.0795	0.0572	0.0058	0.0202	0.0205	0.0204	0.0195	0.15473	0.84534
0.50	0.10	0.0279	0.0777	0.1007	0.0821	0.0035	0.0190	0.0223	0.0219	0.0159	0.16961	0.83039
	0.20	0.0204	0.0742	0.0952	0.0766	0.0047	0.0231	0.0248	0.0248	0.0202	0.10941	0.89059
	0.40	0.0159	0.0721	0.0895	0.0696	0.0060	0.0261	0.0262	0.0266	0.0239	0.06441	0.93559
	2.00	0.0162	0.0620	0.0731	0.0522	0.0086	0.0272	0.0267	0.0268	0.0271	0.03456	0.96551
1.00	0.10	0.0191	0.0709	0.0975	0.0823	0.0042	0.0224	0.0260	0.0256	0.0188	0.11228	0.88773
	0.20	0.0082	0.0658	0.0902	0.0754	0.0058	0.0282	0.0299	0.0300	0.0248	0.02529	0.97470
	0.40	0.0010	0.0630	0.0827	0.0661	0.0077	0.0331	0.0323	0.0331	0.0305	-.04687	1.04687
	2.00	0.0003	0.0530	0.0642	0.0447	0.0125	0.0367	0.0348	0.0355	0.0378	-.12927	1.12933
1.50	0.10	0.0155	0.0681	0.0962	0.0824	0.0045	0.0238	0.0276	0.0271	0.0200	0.08849	0.91152
	0.20	0.0029	0.0622	0.0881	0.0748	0.0063	0.0305	0.0320	0.0322	0.0268	-.01138	1.01138
	0.40	-.0058	0.0590	0.0796	0.0645	0.0085	0.0362	0.0351	0.0360	0.0336	-.09774	1.09773
	2.00	-.0077	0.0486	0.0597	0.0407	0.0145	0.0414	0.0389	0.0400	0.0434	-.21282	1.21286

$(b/\ell) = 0.10$ ANGLE OF SKEW=ARCTAN(1.33)

φ	ζ	BENDING MOMENT AT POINT				TWISTING MOMENTT AT POINT					REACTION AT SUPPORT	
		2	3	4	5	1-2	2-3	3-4	4-5	5-6	1	6
0.10	0.10	0.0323	0.0701	0.0869	0.0681	-.0018	0.0097	0.0144	0.0152	0.0127	0.29935	0.70064
	0.20	0.0304	0.0672	0.0830	0.0647	-.0019	0.0100	0.0145	0.0153	0.0132	0.29523	0.70477
	0.40	0.0297	0.0636	0.0776	0.0600	-.0021	0.0098	0.0142	0.0150	0.0131	0.29977	0.70024
	2.00	0.0286	0.0470	0.0529	0.0397	-.0031	0.0073	0.0112	0.0118	0.0101	0.35102	0.64902
0.30	0.10	0.0073	0.0470	0.0715	0.0613	-.0025	0.0157	0.0218	0.0230	0.0201	0.18750	0.81249
	0.20	0.0031	0.0434	0.0664	0.0559	-.0025	0.0170	0.0225	0.0238	0.0221	0.16797	0.83204
	0.40	0.0022	0.0407	0.0611	0.0503	-.0023	0.0175	0.0225	0.0238	0.0231	0.16158	0.83843
	2.00	0.0086	0.0313	0.0421	0.0338	-.0021	0.0150	0.0198	0.0209	0.0202	0.20493	0.79505
0.50	0.10	-.0015	0.0392	0.0661	0.0587	-.0027	0.0178	0.0244	0.0257	0.0228	0.14847	0.85153
	0.20	-.0070	0.0352	0.0604	0.0522	-.0027	0.0197	0.0254	0.0268	0.0255	0.12112	0.87888
	0.40	-.0085	0.0325	0.0548	0.0459	-.0024	0.0206	0.0256	0.0271	0.0272	0.10797	0.89203
	2.00	-.0002	0.0249	0.0371	0.0300	-.0012	0.0187	0.0235	0.0249	0.0254	0.13513	0.86489
1.00	0.10	-.0096	0.0320	0.0612	0.0562	-.0030	0.0198	0.0267	0.0281	0.0253	0.11216	0.88783
	0.20	-.0167	0.0275	0.0546	0.0484	-.0029	0.0224	0.0280	0.0296	0.0289	0.07632	0.92368
	0.40	-.0190	0.0248	0.0486	0.0412	-.0024	0.0236	0.0284	0.0302	0.0314	0.05520	0.94480
	2.00	-.0098	0.0184	0.0316	0.0253	-.0001	0.0226	0.0273	0.0293	0.0316	0.05729	0.94272
1.50	0.10	-.0127	0.0293	0.0593	0.0552	-.0031	0.0206	0.0276	0.0290	0.0262	0.09835	0.90165
	0.20	-.0205	0.0245	0.0524	0.0469	-.0030	0.0234	0.0291	0.0307	0.0302	0.05894	0.94106
	0.40	-.0232	0.0219	0.0461	0.0392	-.0025	0.0249	0.0295	0.0314	0.0330	0.03431	0.96570
	2.00	-.0138	0.0157	0.0292	0.0231	0.0005	0.0240	0.0288	0.0312	0.0346	0.02358	0.97643

TABLE 14 - SIMPLY-SUPPORTED SKEW GIRDER BRIDGE

BENDING MOMENT, TWISTING MOMENT IN MAIN GIRDERS AND REACTION AT SUPPORTS

DUE TO A UNIFORM LINE LOAD OF UNIT INTENSITY ON MAIN GIRDERS

BENDING MOMENT = COEF. ℓ^2, TWISTING MOMENT = COEF. ℓ^2, REACTION = COEF. ℓ

$(b/\ell) = 0.10$ ANGLE OF SKEW=ARCTAN(2.00)

φ	ζ	BENDING MOMENT AT POINT				TWISTING MOMENTT AT POINT					REACTION AT SUPPORT	
		2	3	4	5	1-2	2-3	3-4	4-5	5-6	1	6
0.10	0.10	0.0232	0.0434	0.0525	0.0423	-.0054	0.0047	0.0108	0.0137	0.0135	0.35089	0.64911
	0.20	0.0218	0.0357	0.0407	0.0323	-.0058	0.0036	0.0092	0.0119	0.0118	0.37752	0.62248
	0.40	0.0199	0.0273	0.0285	0.0218	-.0059	0.0024	0.0073	0.0094	0.0091	0.41102	0.58898
	2.00	0.0105	0.0104	0.0087	0.0053	-.0035	0.0006	0.0029	0.0038	0.0033	0.47192	0.52808
0.30	0.10	0.0056	0.0263	0.0402	0.0361	-.0058	0.0084	0.0163	0.0206	0.0214	0.25680	0.74320
	0.20	0.0063	0.0216	0.0311	0.0276	-.0061	0.0074	0.0149	0.0192	0.0206	0.27616	0.72384
	0.40	0.0078	0.0172	0.0224	0.0196	-.0067	0.0058	0.0128	0.0165	0.0177	0.31499	0.68501
	2.00	0.0071	0.0079	0.0076	0.0058	-.0064	0.0020	0.0065	0.0084	0.0081	0.42567	0.57433
0.50	0.10	-.0003	0.0207	0.0359	0.0335	-.0058	0.0098	0.0181	0.0229	0.0243	0.22300	0.77699
	0.20	0.0006	0.0166	0.0273	0.0252	-.0058	0.0091	0.0170	0.0220	0.0243	0.23363	0.76637
	0.40	0.0029	0.0133	0.0196	0.0179	-.0062	0.0076	0.0152	0.0198	0.0221	0.26599	0.73400
	2.00	0.0051	0.0065	0.0070	0.0058	-.0073	0.0033	0.0088	0.0113	0.0116	0.38952	0.61048
1.00	0.10	-.0059	0.0156	0.0320	0.0310	-.0058	0.0112	0.0198	0.0250	0.0270	0.19119	0.80880
	0.20	-.0050	0.0118	0.0235	0.0225	-.0054	0.0107	0.0191	0.0248	0.0283	0.19009	0.80991
	0.40	-.0021	0.0092	0.0165	0.0156	-.0053	0.0096	0.0177	0.0234	0.0274	0.20903	0.79097
	2.00	0.0025	0.0048	0.0060	0.0054	-.0074	0.0055	0.0122	0.0157	0.0174	0.32671	0.67329
1.50	0.10	-.0080	0.0137	0.0304	0.0300	-.0058	0.0118	0.0204	0.0258	0.0281	0.17899	0.82101
	0.20	-.0072	0.0100	0.0220	0.0214	-.0052	0.0114	0.0198	0.0259	0.0299	0.17239	0.82761
	0.40	-.0042	0.0076	0.0151	0.0145	-.0048	0.0104	0.0187	0.0250	0.0297	0.18361	0.81639
	2.00	0.0012	0.0039	0.0054	0.0051	-.0068	0.0068	0.0141	0.0183	0.0210	0.28648	0.71352

$(b/\ell) = 0.20$ ANGLE OF SKEW=ARCTAN(0.0)

φ	ζ	BENDING MOMENT AT POINT				TWISTING MOMENTT AT POINT					REACTION AT SUPPORT	
		2	3	4	5	1-2	2-3	3-4	4-5	5-6	1	6
0.10	0.10	0.0800	0.1200	0.1200	0.0800	0.0	0.0	0.0	0.0	0.0	0.50000	0.50000
	0.20	0.0800	0.1200	0.1200	0.0800	0.0	0.0	0.0	0.0	0.0	0.50000	0.50000
	0.40	0.0800	0.1200	0.1200	0.0800	0.0	0.0	0.0	0.0	0.0	0.50000	0.50000
	2.00	0.0800	0.1200	0.1200	0.0800	0.0	0.0	0.0	0.0	0.0	0.50000	0.50000
0.30	0.10	0.0800	0.1200	0.1200	0.0800	0.0	0.0	0.0	0.0	0.0	0.50000	0.50000
	0.20	0.0800	0.1200	0.1200	0.0800	0.0	0.0	0.0	0.0	0.0	0.50000	0.50000
	0.40	0.0800	0.1200	0.1200	0.0800	0.0	0.0	0.0	0.0	0.0	0.50000	0.50000
	2.00	0.0800	0.1200	0.1200	0.0800	0.0	0.0	0.0	0.0	0.0	0.50000	0.50000
0.50	0.10	0.0800	0.1200	0.1200	0.0800	0.0	0.0	0.0	0.0	0.0	0.50000	0.50000
	0.20	0.0800	0.1200	0.1200	0.0800	0.0	0.0	0.0	0.0	0.0	0.50000	0.50000
	0.40	0.0800	0.1200	0.1200	0.0800	0.0	0.0	0.0	0.0	0.0	0.50000	0.50000
	2.00	0.0800	0.1200	0.1200	0.0800	0.0	0.0	0.0	0.0	0.0	0.50000	0.50000
1.00	0.10	0.0800	0.1200	0.1200	0.0800	0.0	0.0	0.0	0.0	0.0	0.50000	0.50000
	0.20	0.0800	0.1200	0.1200	0.0800	0.0	0.0	0.0	0.0	0.0	0.50000	0.50000
	0.40	0.0800	0.1200	0.1200	0.0800	0.0	0.0	0.0	0.0	0.0	0.50000	0.50000
	2.00	0.0800	0.1200	0.1200	0.0800	0.0	0.0	0.0	0.0	0.0	0.50000	0.50000
1.50	0.10	0.0800	0.1200	0.1200	0.0800	0.0	0.0	0.0	0.0	0.0	0.50000	0.50000
	0.20	0.0800	0.1200	0.1200	0.0800	0.0	0.0	0.0	0.0	0.0	0.50000	0.50000
	0.40	0.0800	0.1200	0.1200	0.0800	0.0	0.0	0.0	0.0	0.0	0.50000	0.50000
	2.00	0.0800	0.1200	0.1200	0.0800	0.0	0.0	0.0	0.0	0.0	0.50000	0.50000

$(b/\ell) = 0.20$ ANGLE OF SKEW=ARCTAN(0.10)

φ	ζ	BENDING MOMENT AT POINT				TWISTING MOMENTT AT POINT					REACTION AT SUPPORT	
		2	3	4	5	1-2	2-3	3-4	4-5	5-6	1	6
0.10	0.10	0.0794	0.1196	0.1202	0.0805	0.0003	0.0007	0.0009	0.0008	0.0003	0.49401	0.50599
	0.20	0.0793	0.1195	0.1202	0.0805	0.0003	0.0008	0.0010	0.0009	0.0004	0.49315	0.50685
	0.40	0.0792	0.1195	0.1201	0.0805	0.0004	0.0009	0.0011	0.0009	0.0005	0.49259	0.50740
	2.00	0.0789	0.1190	0.1196	0.0802	0.0004	0.0009	0.0011	0.0010	0.0005	0.49207	0.50793
0.30	0.10	0.0788	0.1193	0.1204	0.0810	0.0006	0.0014	0.0017	0.0015	0.0007	0.48829	0.51171
	0.20	0.0784	0.1191	0.1204	0.0812	0.0008	0.0019	0.0022	0.0019	0.0009	0.48455	0.51544
	0.40	0.0782	0.1189	0.1203	0.0812	0.0010	0.0022	0.0026	0.0023	0.0012	0.48143	0.51856
	2.00	0.0779	0.1185	0.1198	0.0808	0.0014	0.0026	0.0029	0.0027	0.0017	0.47739	0.52260
0.50	0.10	0.0785	0.1191	0.1205	0.0812	0.0007	0.0018	0.0021	0.0018	0.0008	0.48554	0.51446
	0.20	0.0780	0.1188	0.1205	0.0816	0.0010	0.0025	0.0029	0.0026	0.0013	0.47939	0.52060
	0.40	0.0776	0.1186	0.1205	0.0818	0.0015	0.0031	0.0036	0.0033	0.0018	0.47350	0.52649
	2.00	0.0772	0.1181	0.1198	0.0813	0.0023	0.0041	0.0044	0.0042	0.0028	0.46423	0.53577
1.00	0.10	0.0782	0.1189	0.1206	0.0815	0.0008	0.0021	0.0026	0.0022	0.0010	0.48244	0.51756
	0.20	0.0773	0.1184	0.1207	0.0821	0.0014	0.0033	0.0039	0.0034	0.0017	0.47253	0.52746
	0.40	0.0766	0.1180	0.1208	0.0826	0.0022	0.0046	0.0053	0.0048	0.0026	0.46105	0.53894
	2.00	0.0759	0.1175	0.1199	0.0820	0.0044	0.0072	0.0075	0.0074	0.0052	0.43675	0.56325
1.50	0.10	0.0780	0.1188	0.1206	0.0816	0.0009	0.0023	0.0028	0.0024	0.0011	0.48108	0.51892
	0.20	0.0770	0.1182	0.1208	0.0824	0.0016	0.0037	0.0044	0.0039	0.0019	0.46910	0.53089
	0.40	0.0760	0.1177	0.1209	0.0830	0.0026	0.0055	0.0062	0.0057	0.0031	0.45384	0.54615
	2.00	0.0749	0.1170	0.1198	0.0826	0.0060	0.0096	0.0099	0.0098	0.0071	0.41511	0.58489

TABLE 15 – SIMPLY-SUPPORTED SKEW GIRDER BRIDGE

BENDING MOMENT, TWISTING MOMENT IN MAIN GIRDERS AND REACTION AT SUPPORTS

DUE TO A UNIFORM LINE LOAD OF UNIT INTENSITY ON MAIN GIRDERS

BENDING MOMENT = COEF.ℓ^2, TWISTING MOMENT = COEF.ℓ^2, REACTION = COEF.ℓ

(b/ℓ) = 0.20 ANGLE OF SKEW=ARCTAN(0.67)

ϕ	ζ	BENDING MOMENT AT POINT 2	3	4	5	TWISTING MOMENTT AT POINT 1-2	2-3	3-4	4-5	5-6	REACTION AT SUPPORT 1	6
0.10	0.10	0.0734	0.1140	0.1179	0.0812	0.0006	0.0042	0.0059	0.0056	0.0033	0.46084	0.53915
	0.20	0.0725	0.1132	0.1174	0.0811	0.0007	0.0048	0.0066	0.0063	0.0039	0.45551	0.54449
	0.40	0.0718	0.1126	0.1169	0.0807	0.0008	0.0053	0.0069	0.0066	0.0043	0.45226	0.54773
	2.00	0.0701	0.1099	0.1139	0.0785	0.0006	0.0056	0.0071	0.0068	0.0047	0.45034	0.54966
0.30	0.10	0.0677	0.1088	0.1162	0.0824	0.0012	0.0079	0.0111	0.0105	0.0062	0.42622	0.57378
	0.20	0.0642	0.1059	0.1149	0.0826	0.0017	0.0104	0.0140	0.0134	0.0082	0.40476	0.59524
	0.40	0.0615	0.1039	0.1135	0.0821	0.0020	0.0124	0.0160	0.0154	0.0101	0.38808	0.61192
	2.00	0.0582	0.1007	0.1095	0.0785	0.0026	0.0149	0.0176	0.0172	0.0129	0.36971	0.63030
0.50	0.10	0.0651	0.1065	0.1154	0.0830	0.0015	0.0097	0.0134	0.0127	0.0075	0.41037	0.58962
	0.20	0.0596	0.1019	0.1135	0.0834	0.0022	0.0135	0.0181	0.0173	0.0106	0.37668	0.62332
	0.40	0.0550	0.0984	0.1114	0.0829	0.0028	0.0170	0.0218	0.0210	0.0138	0.34718	0.65282
	2.00	0.0493	0.0943	0.1060	0.0780	0.0042	0.0222	0.0252	0.0248	0.0194	0.30814	0.69187
1.00	0.10	0.0622	0.1039	0.1146	0.0836	0.0018	0.0115	0.0160	0.0152	0.0089	0.39317	0.60682
	0.20	0.0539	0.0968	0.1117	0.0844	0.0028	0.0173	0.0233	0.0222	0.0136	0.34169	0.65831
	0.40	0.0459	0.0907	0.1084	0.0840	0.0040	0.0235	0.0299	0.0288	0.0190	0.28962	0.71037
	2.00	0.0343	0.0839	0.0999	0.0765	0.0071	0.0349	0.0378	0.0377	0.0308	0.20358	0.79642
1.50	0.10	0.0610	0.1028	0.1142	0.0838	0.0019	0.0123	0.0171	0.0162	0.0095	0.38587	0.61413
	0.20	0.0512	0.0945	0.1109	0.0849	0.0031	0.0191	0.0257	0.0245	0.0150	0.32516	0.67484
	0.40	0.0411	0.0866	0.1068	0.0846	0.0046	0.0269	0.0341	0.0329	0.0217	0.25947	0.74053
	2.00	0.0250	0.0777	0.0960	0.0753	0.0090	0.0429	0.0455	0.0456	0.0380	0.13804	0.86197

(b/ℓ) = 0.20 ANGLE OF SKEW=ARCTAN(1.00)

ϕ	ζ	BENDING MOMENT AT POINT 2	3	4	5	TWISTING MOMENTT AT POINT 1-2	2-3	3-4	4-5	5-6	REACTION AT SUPPORT 1	6
0.10	0.10	0.0690	0.1090	0.1145	0.0801	0.0	0.0055	0.0082	0.0082	0.0055	0.44521	0.55480
	0.20	0.0677	0.1078	0.1138	0.0799	0.0	0.0062	0.0092	0.0092	0.0062	0.43828	0.56172
	0.40	0.0668	0.1072	0.1134	0.0796	0.0	0.0068	0.0097	0.0097	0.0068	0.43403	0.56597
	2.00	0.0660	0.1067	0.1130	0.0793	0.0	0.0073	0.0101	0.0101	0.0073	0.43006	0.56994
0.30	0.10	0.0598	0.0997	0.1099	0.0801	0.0	0.0100	0.0152	0.0152	0.0100	0.39911	0.60089
	0.20	0.0546	0.0950	0.1073	0.0796	0.0	0.0129	0.0188	0.0188	0.0129	0.37306	0.62694
	0.40	0.0507	0.0920	0.1054	0.0787	0.0	0.0153	0.0213	0.0213	0.0153	0.35373	0.64627
	2.00	0.0464	0.0898	0.1032	0.0766	0.0	0.0185	0.0235	0.0235	0.0185	0.33209	0.66791
0.50	0.10	0.0557	0.0956	0.1079	0.0801	0.0	0.0121	0.0183	0.0183	0.0121	0.37870	0.62130
	0.20	0.0478	0.0884	0.1039	0.0794	0.0	0.0164	0.0239	0.0239	0.0164	0.33906	0.66094
	0.40	0.0413	0.0833	0.1007	0.0780	0.0	0.0203	0.0280	0.0280	0.0203	0.30673	0.69327
	2.00	0.0333	0.0793	0.0967	0.0740	0.0	0.0263	0.0320	0.0320	0.0263	0.26657	0.73343
1.00	0.10	0.0514	0.0912	0.1057	0.0802	0.0	0.0142	0.0215	0.0215	0.0142	0.35701	0.64300
	0.20	0.0397	0.0805	0.0999	0.0792	0.0	0.0205	0.0298	0.0298	0.0205	0.29861	0.70139
	0.40	0.0291	0.0720	0.0945	0.0771	0.0	0.0269	0.0367	0.0367	0.0269	0.24542	0.75458
	2.00	0.0139	0.0645	0.0870	0.0695	0.0	0.0383	0.0443	0.0443	0.0383	0.16972	0.83028
1.50	0.10	0.0496	0.0894	0.1048	0.0802	0.0	0.0151	0.0229	0.0229	0.0151	0.34794	0.65207
	0.20	0.0360	0.0769	0.0980	0.0791	0.0	0.0224	0.0325	0.0325	0.0224	0.28021	0.71979
	0.40	0.0231	0.0664	0.0915	0.0766	0.0	0.0301	0.0410	0.0410	0.0301	0.21533	0.78467
	2.00	0.0033	0.0567	0.0817	0.0667	0.0	0.0450	0.0508	0.0508	0.0450	0.11661	0.88339

(b/ℓ) = 0.40 ANGLE OF SKEW=ARCTAN(0.0)

ϕ	ζ	BENDING MOMENT AT POINT 2	3	4	5	TWISTING MOMENTT AT POINT 1-2	2-3	3-4	4-5	5-6	REACTION AT SUPPORT 1	6
0.10	0.10	0.0800	0.1200	0.1200	0.0800	0.0	0.0	0.0	0.0	0.0	0.50000	0.50000
	0.20	0.0800	0.1200	0.1200	0.0800	0.0	0.0	0.0	0.0	0.0	0.50000	0.50000
	0.40	0.0800	0.1200	0.1200	0.0800	0.0	0.0	0.0	0.0	0.0	0.50000	0.50000
	2.00	0.0800	0.1200	0.1200	0.0800	0.0	0.0	0.0	0.0	0.0	0.50000	0.50000
0.30	0.10	0.0800	0.1200	0.1200	0.0800	0.0	0.0	0.0	0.0	0.0	0.50000	0.50000
	0.20	0.0800	0.1200	0.1200	0.0800	0.0	0.0	0.0	0.0	0.0	0.50000	0.50000
	0.40	0.0800	0.1200	0.1200	0.0800	0.0	0.0	0.0	0.0	0.0	0.50000	0.50000
	2.00	0.0800	0.1200	0.1200	0.0800	0.0	0.0	0.0	0.0	0.0	0.50000	0.50000
0.50	0.10	0.0800	0.1200	0.1200	0.0800	0.0	0.0	0.0	0.0	0.0	0.50000	0.50000
	0.20	0.0800	0.1200	0.1200	0.0800	0.0	0.0	0.0	0.0	0.0	0.50000	0.50000
	0.40	0.0800	0.1200	0.1200	0.0800	0.0	0.0	0.0	0.0	0.0	0.50000	0.50000
	2.00	0.0800	0.1200	0.1200	0.0800	0.0	0.0	0.0	0.0	0.0	0.50000	0.50000
1.00	0.10	0.0800	0.1200	0.1200	0.0800	0.0	0.0	0.0	0.0	0.0	0.50000	0.50000
	0.20	0.0800	0.1200	0.1200	0.0800	0.0	0.0	0.0	0.0	0.0	0.50000	0.50000
	0.40	0.0800	0.1200	0.1200	0.0800	0.0	0.0	0.0	0.0	0.0	0.50000	0.50000
	2.00	0.0800	0.1200	0.1200	0.0800	0.0	0.0	0.0	0.0	0.0	0.50000	0.50000
1.50	0.10	0.0800	0.1200	0.1200	0.0800	0.0	0.0	0.0	0.0	0.0	0.50000	0.50000
	0.20	0.0800	0.1200	0.1200	0.0800	0.0	0.0	0.0	0.0	0.0	0.50000	0.50000
	0.40	0.0800	0.1200	0.1200	0.0800	0.0	0.0	0.0	0.0	0.0	0.50000	0.50000
	2.00	0.0800	0.1200	0.1200	0.0800	0.0	0.0	0.0	0.0	0.0	0.50000	0.50000

TABLE 16 - SIMPLY-SUPPORTED SKEW GIRDER BRIDGE

BENDING MOMENT, TWISTING MOMENT IN MAIN GIRDERS AND REACTION AT SUPPORTS

DUE TO A UNIFORM LINE LOAD OF UNIT INTENSITY ON MAIN GIRDERS

BENDING MOMENT = COEF.ℓ^2, TWISTING MOMENT = COEF.ℓ^2, REACTION = COEF.ℓ

(b/ℓ) = 0.40 ANGLE OF SKEW=ARCTAN(0.17)

ϕ	ζ	BENDING MOMENT AT POINT				TWISTING MOMENTT AT POINT					REACTION AT SUPPORT	
		2	3	4	5	1-2	2-3	3-4	4-5	5-6	1	6
0.10	0.10	0.0798	0.1198	0.1200	0.0802	0.0002	0.0005	0.0006	0.0005	0.0002	0.49795	0.53915
	0.20	0.0797	0.1198	0.1201	0.0802	0.0002	0.0006	0.0008	0.0007	0.0003	0.49744	0.54449
	0.40	0.0796	0.1198	0.1200	0.0802	0.0002	0.0007	0.0009	0.0008	0.0004	0.49709	0.54773
	2.00	0.0795	0.1196	0.1199	0.0801	0.0003	0.0008	0.0010	0.0008	0.0004	0.49670	0.54966
0.30	0.10	0.0796	0.1197	0.1201	0.0803	0.0003	0.0008	0.0010	0.0009	0.0004	0.49659	0.57378
	0.20	0.0794	0.1196	0.1201	0.0804	0.0004	0.0012	0.0015	0.0013	0.0006	0.49492	0.59524
	0.40	0.0792	0.1195	0.1201	0.0805	0.0006	0.0016	0.0020	0.0017	0.0008	0.49326	0.61192
	2.00	0.0789	0.1192	0.1200	0.0806	0.0008	0.0022	0.0027	0.0024	0.0012	0.49081	0.63030
0.50	0.10	0.0795	0.1197	0.1201	0.0803	0.0003	0.0009	0.0012	0.0010	0.0004	0.49607	0.58962
	0.20	0.0793	0.1195	0.1202	0.0805	0.0005	0.0015	0.0019	0.0016	0.0007	0.49366	0.62332
	0.40	0.0789	0.1193	0.1202	0.0807	0.0008	0.0022	0.0027	0.0024	0.0011	0.49087	0.65282
	2.00	0.0784	0.1189	0.1201	0.0809	0.0013	0.0034	0.0041	0.0036	0.0019	0.48573	0.69187
1.00	0.10	0.0795	0.1196	0.1201	0.0804	0.0004	0.0011	0.0014	0.0012	0.0005	0.49555	0.60682
	0.20	0.0791	0.1194	0.1202	0.0807	0.0006	0.0019	0.0024	0.0020	0.0009	0.49222	0.65821
	0.40	0.0786	0.1190	0.1203	0.0810	0.0010	0.0030	0.0037	0.0032	0.0015	0.48756	0.71037
	2.00	0.0774	0.1182	0.1203	0.0816	0.0023	0.0058	0.0069	0.0062	0.0032	0.47566	0.79642
1.50	0.10	0.0794	0.1196	0.1201	0.0804	0.0004	0.0011	0.0014	0.0012	0.0005	0.49535	0.61413
	0.20	0.0790	0.1193	0.1202	0.0807	0.0007	0.0020	0.0026	0.0022	0.0010	0.49158	0.67484
	0.40	0.0784	0.1189	0.1203	0.0812	0.0012	0.0034	0.0043	0.0037	0.0017	0.48584	0.74053
	2.00	0.0766	0.1178	0.1204	0.0822	0.0030	0.0075	0.0090	0.0081	0.0042	0.46821	0.86197

(b/ℓ) = 0.40 ANGLE OF SKEW=ARCTAN(0.33)

ϕ	ζ	BENDING MOMENT AT POINT				TWISTING MOMENTT AT POINT					REACTION AT SUPPORT	
		2	3	4	5	1-2	2-3	3-4	4-5	5-6	1	6
0.10	0.10	0.0794	0.1196	0.1200	0.0803	0.0003	0.0010	0.0013	0.0011	0.0005	0.49587	0.50413
	0.20	0.0793	0.1194	0.1200	0.0803	0.0003	0.0012	0.0016	0.0014	0.0007	0.49484	0.50515
	0.40	0.0792	0.1193	0.1199	0.0803	0.0004	0.0014	0.0018	0.0016	0.0008	0.49411	0.50589
	2.00	0.0789	0.1189	0.1195	0.0801	0.0004	0.0015	0.0020	0.0018	0.0010	0.49336	0.50664
0.30	0.10	0.0791	0.1193	0.1200	0.0805	0.0004	0.0016	0.0021	0.0018	0.0009	0.49316	0.50684
	0.20	0.0786	0.1189	0.1200	0.0807	0.0007	0.0024	0.0031	0.0027	0.0013	0.48979	0.51020
	0.40	0.0782	0.1186	0.1199	0.0809	0.0009	0.0031	0.0041	0.0036	0.0018	0.48646	0.51354
	2.00	0.0774	0.1178	0.1195	0.0808	0.0012	0.0043	0.0054	0.0049	0.0027	0.48155	0.51844
0.50	0.10	0.0789	0.1192	0.1200	0.0806	0.0005	0.0018	0.0024	0.0021	0.0010	0.49212	0.50788
	0.20	0.0783	0.1187	0.1200	0.0809	0.0008	0.0029	0.0039	0.0034	0.0017	0.48731	0.51269
	0.40	0.0775	0.1181	0.1200	0.0812	0.0012	0.0042	0.0055	0.0049	0.0024	0.48171	0.51829
	2.00	0.0762	0.1169	0.1195	0.0814	0.0020	0.0066	0.0083	0.0075	0.0042	0.47148	0.52852
1.00	0.10	0.0788	0.1191	0.1200	0.0806	0.0006	0.0021	0.0027	0.0024	0.0012	0.49111	0.50889
	0.20	0.0779	0.1184	0.1200	0.0811	0.0010	0.0036	0.0047	0.0042	0.0020	0.48447	0.51553
	0.40	0.0767	0.1174	0.1200	0.0817	0.0017	0.0057	0.0075	0.0066	0.0033	0.47518	0.52482
	2.00	0.0738	0.1152	0.1194	0.0825	0.0035	0.0111	0.0139	0.0127	0.0070	0.45179	0.54820
1.50	0.10	0.0787	0.1190	0.1200	0.0807	0.0006	0.0021	0.0028	0.0025	0.0012	0.49071	0.50929
	0.20	0.0777	0.1183	0.1200	0.0812	0.0011	0.0039	0.0051	0.0045	0.0022	0.48321	0.51678
	0.40	0.0762	0.1171	0.1200	0.0819	0.0019	0.0065	0.0085	0.0075	0.0037	0.47183	0.52817
	2.00	0.0720	0.1139	0.1194	0.0833	0.0046	0.0145	0.0179	0.0164	0.0091	0.43744	0.56255

(b/ℓ) = 0.40 ANGLE OF SKEW=ARCTAN(0.50)

ϕ	ζ	BENDING MOMENT AT POINT				TWISTING MOMENTT AT POINT					REACTION AT SUPPORT	
		2	3	4	5	1-2	2-3	3-4	4-5	5-6	1	6
0.10	0.10	0.0791	0.1192	0.1198	0.0803	0.0003	0.0014	0.0019	0.0017	0.0009	0.49380	0.50620
	0.20	0.0788	0.1190	0.1198	0.0804	0.0004	0.0017	0.0023	0.0021	0.0012	0.49226	0.50774
	0.40	0.0786	0.1188	0.1197	0.0804	0.0004	0.0020	0.0027	0.0024	0.0014	0.49116	0.50884
	2.00	0.0782	0.1182	0.1192	0.0801	0.0004	0.0022	0.0029	0.0027	0.0016	0.49007	0.50993
0.30	0.10	0.0784	0.1187	0.1197	0.0806	0.0005	0.0023	0.0031	0.0029	0.0015	0.48976	0.51024
	0.20	0.0777	0.1180	0.1196	0.0808	0.0007	0.0034	0.0046	0.0042	0.0022	0.48474	0.51526
	0.40	0.0769	0.1174	0.1194	0.0810	0.0010	0.0045	0.0061	0.0056	0.0030	0.47978	0.52022
	2.00	0.0757	0.1162	0.1187	0.0808	0.0013	0.0062	0.0080	0.0075	0.0044	0.47257	0.52743
0.50	0.10	0.0782	0.1185	0.1197	0.0806	0.0006	0.0026	0.0036	0.0033	0.0017	0.48822	0.51178
	0.20	0.0771	0.1175	0.1195	0.0810	0.0009	0.0042	0.0058	0.0053	0.0028	0.48106	0.51894
	0.40	0.0759	0.1165	0.1193	0.0814	0.0013	0.0061	0.0082	0.0075	0.0041	0.47277	0.52723
	2.00	0.0736	0.1145	0.1183	0.0815	0.0021	0.0095	0.0123	0.0115	0.0068	0.45784	0.54216
1.00	0.10	0.0780	0.1183	0.1197	0.0807	0.0006	0.0029	0.0041	0.0037	0.0019	0.48672	0.51328
	0.20	0.0765	0.1170	0.1194	0.0812	0.0011	0.0051	0.0071	0.0064	0.0034	0.47687	0.52313
	0.40	0.0745	0.1153	0.1191	0.0819	0.0018	0.0082	0.0111	0.0102	0.0055	0.46320	0.53680
	2.00	0.0696	0.1113	0.1176	0.0827	0.0038	0.0159	0.0204	0.0191	0.0113	0.42954	0.57046
1.50	0.10	0.0779	0.1182	0.1197	0.0808	0.0007	0.0031	0.0042	0.0039	0.0020	0.48613	0.51387
	0.20	0.0762	0.1168	0.1194	0.0813	0.0012	0.0055	0.0076	0.0069	0.0037	0.47503	0.52497
	0.40	0.0737	0.1147	0.1189	0.0822	0.0021	0.0093	0.0126	0.0115	0.0062	0.45832	0.54168
	2.00	0.0667	0.1089	0.1170	0.0835	0.0049	0.0204	0.0263	0.0246	0.0145	0.40929	0.59071

TABLE 17 - SIMPLY-SUPPORTED SKEW GIRDER BRIDGE

INFLUENCE COEFICIENTS OF REACTIONS

REACTION = COEF.

(b/ℓ) = 0.10 — ANGLE OF SKEW=ARCTAN(0.0)

UNIT VERTICAL LOAD APPLIED AT POINT:

φ	ζ	REACTION AT SUPPORT 1: 2	3	4	5	8	9	10	11	REACTION AT SUPPORT 6: 2	3	4	5	8	9	10	11
0.10	0.10	0.7872	0.5935	0.4065	0.2128	0.0128	0.0065	-.0065	-.0128	0.2128	0.4065	0.5935	0.7872	-.0128	-.0065	0.0065	0.0128
	0.20	0.7914	0.5958	0.4042	0.2086	0.0086	0.0042	-.0042	-.0086	0.2086	0.4042	0.5958	0.7914	-.0086	-.0042	0.0042	0.0086
	0.40	0.7948	0.5976	0.4024	0.2052	0.0052	0.0024	-.0024	-.0052	0.2052	0.4024	0.5976	0.7948	-.0052	-.0024	0.0024	0.0052
	2.00	0.7988	0.5995	0.4006	0.2012	0.0012	0.0005	-.0006	-.0012	0.2012	0.4006	0.5995	0.7988	-.0012	-.0006	0.0005	0.0012
0.30	0.10	0.7656	0.5824	0.4176	0.2344	0.0344	0.0176	-.0176	-.0344	0.2344	0.4176	0.5824	0.7656	-.0344	-.0176	0.0176	0.0344
	0.20	0.7724	0.5867	0.4133	0.2276	0.0276	0.0133	-.0133	-.0276	0.2276	0.4133	0.5867	0.7724	-.0276	-.0133	0.0133	0.0276
	0.40	0.7812	0.5915	0.4085	0.2188	0.0188	0.0085	-.0085	-.0188	0.2188	0.4085	0.5915	0.7812	-.0188	-.0085	0.0085	0.0188
	2.00	0.7949	0.5979	0.4021	0.2051	0.0051	0.0021	-.0021	-.0051	0.2051	0.4021	0.5979	0.7949	-.0051	-.0021	0.0021	0.0051
0.50	0.10	0.7531	0.5760	0.4240	0.2470	0.0470	0.0240	-.0240	-.0469	0.2470	0.4240	0.5760	0.7531	-.0469	-.0240	0.0240	0.0470
	0.20	0.7589	0.5803	0.4197	0.2411	0.0411	0.0197	-.0197	-.0411	0.2411	0.4197	0.5803	0.7589	-.0411	-.0197	0.0197	0.0411
	0.40	0.7698	0.5864	0.4136	0.2302	0.0302	0.0136	-.0136	-.0302	0.2302	0.4136	0.5864	0.7698	-.0302	-.0136	0.0136	0.0302
	2.00	0.7909	0.5963	0.4037	0.2091	0.0091	0.0037	-.0037	-.0091	0.2091	0.4037	0.5963	0.7909	-.0091	-.0037	0.0037	0.0091
1.00	0.10	0.7372	0.5678	0.4322	0.2629	0.0628	0.0322	-.0322	-.0628	0.2629	0.4322	0.5678	0.7372	-.0628	-.0322	0.0322	0.0628
	0.20	0.7385	0.5705	0.4295	0.2615	0.0615	0.0295	-.0295	-.0615	0.2615	0.4295	0.5705	0.7385	-.0615	-.0295	0.0295	0.0615
	0.40	0.7493	0.5776	0.4225	0.2507	0.0507	0.0224	-.0225	-.0507	0.2507	0.4225	0.5776	0.7493	-.0507	-.0225	0.0224	0.0507
	2.00	0.7816	0.5929	0.4071	0.2184	0.0184	0.0071	-.0071	-.0184	0.2184	0.4071	0.5929	0.7816	-.0184	-.0071	0.0071	0.0184
1.50	0.10	0.7296	0.5639	0.4361	0.2704	0.0704	0.0361	-.0361	-.0704	0.2704	0.4361	0.5639	0.7296	-.0704	-.0361	0.0361	0.0704
	0.20	0.7272	0.5652	0.4348	0.2728	0.0728	0.0348	-.0348	-.0728	0.2728	0.4348	0.5652	0.7272	-.0728	-.0348	0.0348	0.0728
	0.40	0.7360	0.5718	0.4282	0.2640	0.0640	0.0282	-.0282	-.0640	0.2640	0.4282	0.5718	0.7360	-.0640	-.0282	0.0282	0.0640
	2.00	0.7734	0.5899	0.4101	0.2266	0.0266	0.0101	-.0101	-.0266	0.2266	0.4101	0.5899	0.7734	-.0266	-.0101	0.0101	0.0266

(b/ℓ) = 0.10 — ANGLE OF SKEW=ARCTAN(0.67)

UNIT VERTICAL LOAD APPLIED AT POINT:

φ	ζ	REACTION AT SUPPORT 1: 2	3	4	5	8	9	10	11	REACTION AT SUPPORT 6: 2	3	4	5	8	9	10	11
0.10	0.10	0.7045	0.4766	0.2967	0.1447	-.0553	-.1033	-.1234	-.0955	0.2955	0.5234	0.7033	0.8553	0.0553	0.1033	0.1234	0.0955
	0.20	0.7014	0.4717	0.2880	0.1363	-.0637	-.1120	-.1283	-.0986	0.2986	0.5283	0.7120	0.8637	0.0637	0.1120	0.1283	0.0986
	0.40	0.7024	0.4709	0.2833	0.1303	-.0697	-.1167	-.1291	-.0976	0.2976	0.5291	0.7167	0.8697	0.0697	0.1167	0.1291	0.0976
	2.00	0.7199	0.4857	0.2903	0.1294	-.0707	-.1097	-.1143	-.0801	0.2802	0.5144	0.7098	0.8707	0.0707	0.1097	0.1143	0.0801
0.30	0.10	0.6233	0.3724	0.2124	0.1021	-.0979	-.1876	-.2276	-.1767	0.3767	0.6276	0.7876	0.8979	0.0979	0.1876	0.2276	0.1767
	0.20	0.6038	0.3468	0.1817	0.0780	-.1220	-.2183	-.2532	-.1962	0.3962	0.6532	0.8183	0.9220	0.1220	0.2183	0.2531	0.1962
	0.40	0.5942	0.3323	0.1595	0.0577	-.1423	-.2405	-.2677	-.2058	0.4058	0.6677	0.8405	0.9423	0.1423	0.2405	0.2677	0.2058
	2.00	0.6099	0.3379	0.1495	0.0396	-.1604	-.2505	-.2622	-.1901	0.3901	0.6622	0.8506	0.9605	0.1605	0.2505	0.2622	0.1901
0.50	0.10	0.5878	0.3268	0.1757	0.0837	-.1163	-.2243	-.2732	-.2122	0.4122	0.6732	0.8243	0.9163	0.1163	0.2243	0.2732	0.2122
	0.20	0.5566	0.2865	0.1304	0.0500	-.1500	-.2696	-.3135	-.2434	0.4434	0.7135	0.8696	0.9500	0.1500	0.2696	0.3135	0.2434
	0.40	0.5374	0.2596	0.0945	0.0195	-.1805	-.3055	-.3404	-.2626	0.4626	0.7404	0.9055	0.9805	0.1805	0.3055	0.3404	0.2626
	2.00	0.5419	0.2476	0.0630	-.0160	-.2161	-.3370	-.3524	-.2581	0.4582	0.7525	0.9371	1.0161	0.2161	0.3371	0.3524	0.2581
1.00	0.10	0.5504	0.2788	0.1370	0.0644	-.1356	-.2630	-.3212	-.2496	0.4496	0.7212	0.8630	0.9356	0.1356	0.2630	0.3212	0.2496
	0.20	0.5035	0.2185	0.0727	0.0186	-.1814	-.3273	-.3815	-.2965	0.4965	0.7815	0.9273	0.9814	0.1814	0.3273	0.3815	0.2965
	0.40	0.4695	0.1728	0.0167	-.0262	-.2262	-.3833	-.4272	-.3305	0.5305	0.8272	0.9833	1.0262	0.2262	0.3833	0.4272	0.3305
	2.00	0.4491	0.1250	-.0550	-.0923	-.2923	-.4550	-.4750	-.3509	0.5510	0.8750	1.0551	1.0923	0.2923	0.4550	0.4750	0.3509
1.50	0.10	0.5349	0.2588	0.1210	0.0564	-.1436	-.2790	-.3411	-.2651	0.4651	0.7412	0.8790	0.9436	0.1436	0.2790	0.3412	0.2651
	0.20	0.4803	0.1888	0.0475	0.0049	-.1951	-.3525	-.4112	-.3197	0.5197	0.8112	0.9525	0.9951	0.1951	0.3525	0.4111	0.3197
	0.40	0.4385	0.1332	-.0189	-.0471	-.2471	-.4189	-.4669	-.3616	0.5616	0.8669	1.0189	1.0471	0.2471	0.4189	0.4668	0.3615
	2.00	0.4018	0.0627	-.1152	-.1313	-.3313	-.5152	-.5374	-.3983	0.5983	0.9374	1.1152	1.1313	0.3313	0.5152	0.5374	0.3982

(b/ℓ) = 0.10 — ANGLE OF SKEW=ARCTAN(1.33)

UNIT VERTICAL LOAD APPLIED AT POINT:

φ	ζ	REACTION AT SUPPORT 1: 2	3	4	5	8	9	10	11	REACTION AT SUPPORT 6: 2	3	4	5	8	9	10	11
0.10	0.10	0.6863	0.4411	0.2560	0.1150	-.0850	-.1440	-.1589	-.1137	0.3137	0.5589	0.7440	0.8850	0.0850	0.1440	0.1589	0.1137
	0.20	0.6857	0.4393	0.2521	0.1109	-.0891	-.1479	-.1607	-.1143	0.3143	0.5607	0.7479	0.8891	0.0891	0.1479	0.1607	0.1143
	0.40	0.6907	0.4442	0.2541	0.1104	-.0896	-.1459	-.1558	-.1093	0.3093	0.5558	0.7459	0.8896	0.0896	0.1459	0.1558	0.1093
	2.00	0.7245	0.4863	0.2884	0.1284	-.0716	-.1116	-.1138	-.0756	0.2756	0.5138	0.7117	0.8716	0.0716	0.1116	0.1137	0.0755
0.30	0.10	0.6221	0.3527	0.1762	0.0677	-.1323	-.2238	-.2473	-.1779	0.3779	0.6473	0.8238	0.9322	0.1323	0.2238	0.2473	0.1779
	0.20	0.6131	0.3404	0.1612	0.0552	-.1448	-.2388	-.2596	-.1869	0.3869	0.6596	0.8388	0.9448	0.1448	0.2388	0.2596	0.1869
	0.40	0.6126	0.3380	0.1551	0.0483	-.1517	-.2450	-.2620	-.1874	0.3874	0.6620	0.8450	0.9517	0.1517	0.2450	0.2620	0.1874
	2.00	0.6460	0.3752	0.1815	0.0597	-.1403	-.2185	-.2249	-.1541	0.3541	0.6249	0.8185	0.9403	0.1403	0.2185	0.2248	0.1540
0.50	0.10	0.5997	0.3220	0.1483	0.0512	-.1488	-.2517	-.2780	-.2003	0.4003	0.6780	0.8517	0.9488	0.1488	0.2517	0.2780	0.2003
	0.20	0.5864	0.3043	0.1277	0.0344	-.1656	-.2723	-.2957	-.2136	0.4136	0.6957	0.8723	0.9656	0.1656	0.2723	0.2957	0.2136
	0.40	0.5822	0.2973	0.1167	0.0238	-.1762	-.2833	-.3027	-.2178	0.4178	0.7027	0.8834	0.9762	0.1762	0.2834	0.3027	0.2178
	2.00	0.6080	0.3226	0.1307	0.0266	-.1734	-.2693	-.2775	-.1920	0.3920	0.6775	0.8693	0.9734	0.1734	0.2693	0.2774	0.1920
1.00	0.10	0.5789	0.2934	0.1224	0.0357	-.1643	-.2776	-.3066	-.2211	0.4211	0.7066	0.8776	0.9643	0.1643	0.2776	0.3066	0.2211
	0.20	0.5609	0.2698	0.0957	0.0144	-.1856	-.3043	-.3302	-.2391	0.4391	0.7302	0.9043	0.9856	0.1856	0.3043	0.3302	0.2391
	0.40	0.5524	0.2573	0.0789	-.0006	-.2006	-.3211	-.3427	-.2476	0.4476	0.7427	0.9211	1.0006	0.2006	0.3211	0.3427	0.2476
	2.00	0.5655	0.2643	0.0742	-.0107	-.2107	-.3258	-.3358	-.2345	0.4345	0.7358	0.9258	1.0107	0.2107	0.3258	0.3357	0.2345
1.50	0.10	0.5710	0.2825	0.1126	0.0298	-.1702	-.2875	-.3175	-.2290	0.4290	0.7175	0.8875	0.9702	0.1702	0.2874	0.3175	0.2290
	0.20	0.5510	0.2565	0.0833	0.0066	-.1934	-.3167	-.3435	-.2490	0.4490	0.7436	0.9168	0.9934	0.1934	0.3167	0.3435	0.2490
	0.40	0.5406	0.2416	0.0639	-.0103	-.2103	-.3361	-.3584	-.2594	0.4594	0.7584	0.9361	1.0103	0.2103	0.3361	0.3584	0.2594
	2.00	0.5471	0.2391	0.0497	-.0270	-.2270	-.3503	-.3609	-.2529	0.4529	0.7609	0.9503	1.0270	0.2270	0.3503	0.3609	0.2529

TABLE 18 - SIMPLY-SUPPORTED SKEW GIRDER BRIDGE

INFLUENCE COEFICIENTS OF REACTIONS

REACTION = COEF.

(b/ℓ) = 0.10 ANGLE OF SKEW=ARCTAN(2.00)

UNIT VERTICAL LOAD APPLIED AT POINT:

φ	ζ	REACTION AT SUPPORT 1								REACTION AT SUPPORT 6							
		2	3	4	5	8	9	10	11	2	3	4	5	8	9	10	11
0.10	0.10	0.7235	0.4849	0.2885	0.1304	-.0696	-.1115	-.1151	-.0765	0.2765	0.5151	0.7115	0.8696	0.0696	0.1115	0.1151	0.0765
	0.20	0.7386	0.5063	0.3077	0.1413	-.0587	-.0923	-.0937	-.0614	0.2614	0.4937	0.6923	0.8587	0.0587	0.0923	0.0937	0.0614
	0.40	0.7561	0.5324	0.3326	0.1565	-.0435	-.0674	-.0676	-.0439	0.2439	0.4676	0.6674	0.8435	0.0435	0.0674	0.0676	0.0439
	2.00	0.7862	0.5788	0.3788	0.1860	-.0140	-.0212	-.0212	-.0138	0.2138	0.4212	0.6212	0.8140	0.0140	0.0212	0.0212	0.0138
0.30	0.10	0.6729	0.4123	0.2195	0.0873	-.1127	-.1805	-.1877	-.1271	0.3271	0.5877	0.7805	0.9127	0.1127	0.1805	0.1877	0.1271
	0.20	0.6852	0.4287	0.2328	0.0937	-.1063	-.1672	-.1713	-.1148	0.3148	0.5713	0.7672	0.9063	0.1063	0.1672	0.1713	0.1148
	0.40	0.7067	0.4594	0.2611	0.1103	-.0897	-.1389	-.1406	-.0933	0.2933	0.5406	0.7389	0.8897	0.0897	0.1389	0.1406	0.0933
	2.00	0.7632	0.5440	0.3440	0.1630	-.0369	-.0560	-.0560	-.0369	0.2368	0.4560	0.6560	0.8369	0.0370	0.0560	0.0560	0.0368
0.50	0.10	0.6547	0.3863	0.1948	0.0717	-.1283	-.2052	-.2137	-.1453	0.3453	0.6137	0.8051	0.9283	0.1283	0.2052	0.2137	0.1453
	0.20	0.6626	0.3964	0.2016	0.0735	-.1265	-.1984	-.2036	-.1374	0.3374	0.6036	0.7984	0.9265	0.1265	0.1984	0.2036	0.1374
	0.40	0.6812	0.4223	0.2248	0.0867	-.1133	-.1752	-.1777	-.1188	0.3188	0.5777	0.7752	0.9133	0.1133	0.1752	0.1777	0.1188
	2.00	0.7450	0.5168	0.3168	0.1452	-.0548	-.0832	-.0832	-.0550	0.2550	0.4832	0.6832	0.8548	0.0548	0.0832	0.0832	0.0550
1.00	0.10	0.6374	0.3620	0.1716	0.0569	-.1431	-.2284	-.2380	-.1626	0.3625	0.6380	0.8284	0.9431	0.1431	0.2284	0.2380	0.1626
	0.20	0.6394	0.3634	0.1696	0.0527	-.1473	-.2304	-.2366	-.1606	0.3606	0.6366	0.8304	0.9473	0.1473	0.2304	0.2366	0.1606
	0.40	0.6515	0.3793	0.1827	0.0591	-.1409	-.2173	-.2207	-.1485	0.3485	0.6207	0.8173	0.9409	0.1409	0.2173	0.2207	0.1485
	2.00	0.7134	0.4695	0.2698	0.1141	-.0859	-.1302	-.1305	-.0866	0.2866	0.5305	0.7302	0.8859	0.0859	0.1302	0.1305	0.0866
1.50	0.10	0.6308	0.3527	0.1627	0.0512	-.1488	-.2373	-.2473	-.1692	0.3692	0.6473	0.8373	0.9488	0.1488	0.2373	0.2473	0.1692
	0.20	0.6300	0.3501	0.1566	0.0443	-.1557	-.2434	-.2499	-.1700	0.3700	0.6500	0.8434	0.9557	0.1557	0.2433	0.2499	0.1700
	0.40	0.6382	0.3602	0.1639	0.0467	-.1533	-.2361	-.2398	-.1618	0.3618	0.6398	0.8361	0.9533	0.1533	0.2361	0.2398	0.1618
	2.00	0.6930	0.4393	0.2397	0.0941	-.1059	-.1603	-.1607	-.1070	0.3070	0.5607	0.7603	0.9059	0.1059	0.1603	0.1607	0.1070

(b/ℓ) = 0.20 ANGLE OF SKEW=ARCTAN(0.0)

UNIT VERTICAL LOAD APPLIED AT POINT:

φ	ζ	REACTION AT SUPPORT 1								REACTION AT SUPPORT 6							
		2	3	4	5	8	9	10	11	2	3	4	5	8	9	10	11
0.10	0.10	0.7948	0.5972	0.4028	0.2052	0.0052	0.0028	-.0028	-.0052	0.2052	0.4028	0.5972	0.7948	-.0052	-.0028	0.0028	0.0052
	0.20	0.7956	0.5976	0.4024	0.2044	0.0044	0.0024	-.0024	-.0044	0.2044	0.4024	0.5976	0.7956	-.0044	-.0024	0.0024	0.0044
	0.40	0.7968	0.5984	0.4016	0.2032	0.0032	0.0016	-.0016	-.0032	0.2032	0.4016	0.5984	0.7968	-.0032	-.0016	0.0016	0.0032
	2.00	0.7991	0.5995	0.4005	0.2009	0.0009	0.0005	-.0005	-.0009	0.2009	0.4005	0.5995	0.7991	-.0009	-.0005	0.0005	0.0009
0.30	0.10	0.7876	0.5931	0.4069	0.2125	0.0124	0.0069	-.0069	-.0124	0.2125	0.4069	0.5931	0.7876	-.0124	-.0069	0.0069	0.0124
	0.20	0.7864	0.5926	0.4074	0.2136	0.0136	0.0074	-.0074	-.0136	0.2136	0.4074	0.5926	0.7864	-.0136	-.0074	0.0074	0.0136
	0.40	0.7877	0.5935	0.4065	0.2123	0.0123	0.0065	-.0065	-.0123	0.2123	0.4065	0.5935	0.7877	-.0123	-.0065	0.0065	0.0123
	2.00	0.7950	0.5976	0.4024	0.2050	0.0050	0.0024	-.0024	-.0050	0.2050	0.4024	0.5976	0.7950	-.0050	-.0024	0.0024	0.0050
0.50	0.10	0.7839	0.5910	0.4090	0.2161	0.0161	0.0090	-.0090	-.0161	0.2161	0.4090	0.5910	0.7839	-.0161	-.0090	0.0090	0.0161
	0.20	0.7803	0.5892	0.4108	0.2197	0.0197	0.0108	-.0108	-.0197	0.2197	0.4108	0.5892	0.7803	-.0197	-.0108	0.0108	0.0197
	0.40	0.7803	0.5895	0.4105	0.2197	0.0197	0.0105	-.0105	-.0197	0.2197	0.4105	0.5895	0.7803	-.0197	-.0105	0.0105	0.0197
	2.00	0.7902	0.5953	0.4047	0.2098	0.0098	0.0047	-.0047	-.0098	0.2098	0.4047	0.5953	0.7902	-.0098	-.0047	0.0047	0.0098
1.00	0.10	0.7797	0.5886	0.4114	0.2203	0.0203	0.0114	-.0114	-.0203	0.2203	0.4114	0.5886	0.7797	-.0203	-.0114	0.0114	0.0203
	0.20	0.7720	0.5846	0.4154	0.2280	0.0280	0.0154	-.0154	-.0280	0.2280	0.4154	0.5846	0.7720	-.0280	-.0154	0.0154	0.0280
	0.40	0.7679	0.5829	0.4171	0.2321	0.0321	0.0171	-.0171	-.0321	0.2321	0.4171	0.5829	0.7679	-.0321	-.0171	0.0171	0.0321
	2.00	0.7792	0.5901	0.4099	0.2208	0.0208	0.0099	-.0099	-.0208	0.2208	0.4099	0.5901	0.7792	-.0208	-.0099	0.0099	0.0208
1.50	0.10	0.7778	0.5876	0.4125	0.2222	0.0222	0.0124	-.0124	-.0222	0.2222	0.4125	0.5876	0.7778	-.0222	-.0124	0.0124	0.0222
	0.20	0.7678	0.5822	0.4178	0.2322	0.0322	0.0178	-.0178	-.0322	0.2322	0.4178	0.5822	0.7678	-.0322	-.0178	0.0178	0.0322
	0.40	0.7606	0.5789	0.4211	0.2394	0.0394	0.0211	-.0211	-.0394	0.2394	0.4211	0.5789	0.7606	-.0394	-.0211	0.0211	0.0394
	2.00	0.7698	0.5858	0.4142	0.2302	0.0302	0.0142	-.0142	-.0302	0.2302	0.4142	0.5858	0.7698	-.0302	-.0142	0.0142	0.0302

(b/ℓ) = 0.20 ANGLE OF SKEW=ARCTAN(0.10)

UNIT VERTICAL LOAD APPLIED AT POINT:

φ	ζ	REACTION AT SUPPORT 1								REACTION AT SUPPORT 6							
		2	3	4	5	8	9	10	11	2	3	4	5	8	9	10	11
0.10	0.10	0.7916	0.5924	0.3985	0.2026	0.0026	-.0015	-.0076	-.0084	0.2084	0.4076	0.6015	0.7974	-.0026	0.0015	0.0076	0.0084
	0.20	0.7918	0.5922	0.3974	0.2015	0.0015	-.0026	-.0078	-.0082	0.2082	0.4077	0.6026	0.7985	-.0015	0.0026	0.0077	0.0082
	0.40	0.7928	0.5926	0.3962	0.1999	-.0001	-.0038	-.0074	-.0072	0.2072	0.4074	0.6038	0.8001	0.0001	0.0038	0.0074	0.0072
	2.00	0.7950	0.5935	0.3946	0.1971	-.0029	-.0054	-.0065	-.0050	0.2050	0.4065	0.6054	0.8029	0.0029	0.0054	0.0065	0.0050
0.30	0.10	0.7814	0.5839	0.3982	0.2072	0.0072	-.0018	-.0161	-.0186	0.2186	0.4161	0.6018	0.7928	-.0072	0.0018	0.0161	0.0186
	0.20	0.7781	0.5804	0.3961	0.2069	0.0069	-.0039	-.0196	-.0219	0.2219	0.4196	0.6039	0.7931	-.0069	0.0039	0.0196	0.0219
	0.40	0.7776	0.5785	0.3929	0.2042	0.0042	-.0071	-.0211	-.0224	0.2224	0.4211	0.6071	0.7958	-.0042	0.0071	0.0211	0.0224
	2.00	0.7829	0.5803	0.3858	0.1945	-.0055	-.0142	-.0197	-.0171	0.2171	0.4197	0.6142	0.8055	0.0055	0.0142	0.0197	0.0171
0.50	0.10	0.7764	0.5797	0.3982	0.2095	0.0095	-.0018	-.0203	-.0236	0.2236	0.4203	0.6018	0.7905	-.0095	0.0018	0.0203	0.0236
	0.20	0.7694	0.5730	0.3955	0.2105	0.0105	-.0045	-.0270	-.0306	0.2306	0.4270	0.6045	0.7895	-.0105	0.0045	0.0270	0.0306
	0.40	0.7659	0.5687	0.3910	0.2081	0.0081	-.0090	-.0313	-.0341	0.2341	0.4313	0.6090	0.7919	-.0081	0.0090	0.0313	0.0341
	2.00	0.7711	0.5679	0.3783	0.1932	-.0068	-.0217	-.0321	-.0289	0.2289	0.4321	0.6217	0.8068	0.0068	0.0217	0.0321	0.0289
1.00	0.10	0.7708	0.5749	0.3982	0.2122	0.0122	-.0018	-.0251	-.0292	0.2292	0.4251	0.6018	0.7878	-.0122	0.0018	0.0251	0.0292
	0.20	0.7577	0.5631	0.3949	0.2155	0.0155	-.0051	-.0369	-.0423	0.2423	0.4369	0.6051	0.7845	-.0155	0.0051	0.0369	0.0423
	0.40	0.7472	0.5524	0.3884	0.2147	0.0147	-.0116	-.0476	-.0528	0.2528	0.4476	0.6116	0.7853	-.0147	0.0116	0.0476	0.0528
	2.00	0.7453	0.5416	0.3633	0.1917	-.0083	-.0367	-.0584	-.0547	0.2547	0.4584	0.6367	0.8083	0.0083	0.0367	0.0584	0.0547
1.50	0.10	0.7683	0.5728	0.3982	0.2134	0.0134	-.0018	-.0272	-.0317	0.2317	0.4272	0.6018	0.7866	-.0134	0.0018	0.0272	0.0317
	0.20	0.7519	0.5581	0.3947	0.2181	0.0181	-.0053	-.0419	-.0481	0.2481	0.4419	0.6053	0.7819	-.0181	0.0053	0.0419	0.0481
	0.40	0.7362	0.5428	0.3869	0.2186	0.0186	-.0131	-.0572	-.0638	0.2638	0.4572	0.6131	0.7814	-.0187	0.0130	0.0572	0.0638
	2.00	0.7246	0.5206	0.3516	0.1910	-.0090	-.0484	-.0794	-.0754	0.2754	0.4793	0.6484	0.8090	0.0090	0.0484	0.0794	0.0754

TABLE 19 - SIMPLY-SUPPORTED SKEW GIRDER BRIDGE

INFLUENCE COEFICIENTS OF REACTIONS

REACTION = COEF.

$(b/\ell) = 0.20$ ANGLE OF SKEW=ARCTAN(0.67)

UNIT VERTICAL LOAD APPLIED AT POINT:

φ	ζ	2	3	4	5	8	9	10	11	2	3	4	5	8	9	10	11
		REACTION AT SUPPORT 1								REACTION AT SUPPORT 6							
0.10	0.10	0.7741	0.5665	0.3739	0.1876	-.0124	-.0261	-.0334	-.0259	0.2259	0.4334	0.6261	0.8124	0.0124	0.0261	0.0334	0.0259
	0.20	0.7712	0.5628	0.3700	0.1849	-.0152	-.0300	-.0372	-.0288	0.2288	0.4372	0.6300	0.8152	0.0151	0.0300	0.0372	0.0288
	0.40	0.7699	0.5610	0.3673	0.1825	-.0175	-.0327	-.0390	-.0301	0.2301	0.4390	0.6327	0.8175	0.0175	0.0327	0.0390	0.0301
	2.00	0.7714	0.5612	0.3647	0.1787	-.0213	-.0353	-.0388	-.0286	0.2286	0.4388	0.6353	0.8213	0.0214	0.0353	0.0388	0.0286
0.30	0.10	0.7505	0.5361	0.3512	0.1778	-.0222	-.0488	-.0639	-.0495	0.2494	0.4639	0.6488	0.8222	0.0222	0.0488	0.0639	0.0495
	0.20	0.7371	0.5187	0.3364	0.1697	-.0303	-.0636	-.0813	-.0629	0.2629	0.4813	0.6636	0.8303	0.0303	0.0636	0.0813	0.0629
	0.40	0.7276	0.5066	0.3243	0.1617	-.0383	-.0756	-.0934	-.0724	0.2724	0.4934	0.6756	0.8383	0.0383	0.0756	0.0934	0.0724
	2.00	0.7216	0.4971	0.3087	0.1468	-.0532	-.0913	-.1029	-.0784	0.2784	0.5029	0.6913	0.8532	0.0532	0.0913	0.1029	0.0784
0.50	0.10	0.7397	0.5220	0.3408	0.1733	-.0267	-.0592	-.0779	-.0603	0.2603	0.4779	0.6592	0.8267	0.0267	0.0592	0.0779	0.0603
	0.20	0.7181	0.4942	0.3179	0.1615	-.0385	-.0821	-.1058	-.0819	0.2819	0.5058	0.6821	0.8385	0.0385	0.0821	0.1058	0.0819
	0.40	0.7004	0.4716	0.2971	0.1488	-.0512	-.1029	-.1284	-.0996	0.2995	0.5284	0.7029	0.8512	0.0512	0.1029	0.1284	0.0995
	2.00	0.6833	0.4480	0.2661	0.1229	-.0771	-.1338	-.1520	-.1167	0.3167	0.5520	0.7339	0.8771	0.0771	0.1339	0.1520	0.1167
1.00	0.10	0.7280	0.5068	0.3296	0.1685	-.0315	-.0704	-.0932	-.0720	0.2720	0.4932	0.6704	0.8315	0.0315	0.0704	0.0932	0.0720
	0.20	0.6944	0.4636	0.2949	0.1513	-.0487	-.1051	-.1364	-.1056	0.3056	0.5364	0.7051	0.8487	0.0487	0.1051	0.1364	0.1056
	0.40	0.6621	0.4221	0.2589	0.1309	-.0691	-.1411	-.1779	-.1379	0.3379	0.5779	0.7411	0.8690	0.0691	0.1411	0.1779	0.1379
	2.00	0.6181	0.3646	0.1939	0.0823	-.1177	-.2061	-.2354	-.1819	0.3819	0.6354	0.8061	0.9177	0.1177	0.2061	0.2354	0.1819
1.50	0.10	0.7230	0.5004	0.3248	0.1665	-.0335	-.0752	-.0996	-.0770	0.2770	0.4996	0.6752	0.8335	0.0335	0.0752	0.0996	0.0770
	0.20	0.6832	0.4491	0.2841	0.1465	-.0535	-.1159	-.1509	-.1168	0.3168	0.5509	0.7159	0.8535	0.0535	0.1159	0.1509	0.1168
	0.40	0.6420	0.3962	0.2389	0.1216	-.0784	-.1611	-.2038	-.1580	0.3580	0.6038	0.7611	0.8784	0.0784	0.1611	0.2038	0.1580
	2.00	0.5772	0.3123	0.1487	0.0570	-.1430	-.2513	-.2877	-.2228	0.4228	0.6877	0.8513	0.9430	0.1430	0.2513	0.2877	0.2228

$(b/\ell) = 0.20$ ANGLE OF SKEW=ARCTAN(1.00)

UNIT VERTICAL LOAD APPLIED AT POINT:

φ	ζ	2	3	4	5	8	9	10	11	2	3	4	5	8	9	10	11
		REACTION AT SUPPORT 1								REACTION AT SUPPORT 6							
0.10	0.10	0.7666	0.5547	0.3619	0.1798	-.0202	-.0381	-.0453	-.0334	0.2334	0.4453	0.6381	0.8202	0.0202	0.0381	0.0453	0.0334
	0.20	0.7626	0.5495	0.3570	0.1766	-.0234	-.0430	-.0505	-.0374	0.2374	0.4505	0.6430	0.8234	0.0234	0.0430	0.0505	0.0374
	0.40	0.7602	0.5466	0.3539	0.1743	-.0257	-.0461	-.0534	-.0398	0.2398	0.4534	0.6461	0.8257	0.0257	0.0461	0.0534	0.0398
	2.00	0.7581	0.5443	0.3510	0.1717	-.0283	-.0490	-.0557	-.0419	0.2419	0.4557	0.6490	0.8283	0.0283	0.0490	0.0557	0.0419
0.30	0.10	0.7383	0.5159	0.3299	0.1636	-.0364	-.0701	-.0841	-.0617	0.2617	0.4841	0.6701	0.8364	0.0364	0.0701	0.0841	0.0617
	0.20	0.7228	0.4953	0.3117	0.1529	-.0471	-.0883	-.1047	-.0772	0.2772	0.5047	0.6883	0.8471	0.0471	0.0883	0.1047	0.0772
	0.40	0.7115	0.4809	0.2980	0.1440	-.0560	-.1020	-.1191	-.0885	0.2885	0.5191	0.7020	0.8560	0.0560	0.1020	0.1191	0.0885
	2.00	0.6997	0.4669	0.2823	0.1314	-.0686	-.1177	-.1331	-.1003	0.3003	0.5331	0.7177	0.8686	0.0686	0.1177	0.1331	0.1003
0.50	0.10	0.7258	0.4987	0.3158	0.1565	-.0435	-.0842	-.1013	-.0742	0.2742	0.5013	0.6842	0.8435	0.0435	0.0842	0.1013	0.0742
	0.20	0.7020	0.4668	0.2881	0.1408	-.0592	-.1119	-.1332	-.0980	0.2980	0.5332	0.7119	0.8592	0.0592	0.1119	0.1332	0.0980
	0.40	0.6830	0.4422	0.2652	0.1264	-.0736	-.1348	-.1578	-.1170	0.3170	0.5578	0.7348	0.8736	0.0736	0.1348	0.1578	0.1170
	2.00	0.6607	0.4154	0.2362	0.1041	-.0959	-.1638	-.1846	-.1393	0.3393	0.5846	0.7638	0.8959	0.0959	0.1638	0.1846	0.1393
1.00	0.10	0.7125	0.4803	0.3008	0.1489	-.0511	-.0992	-.1197	-.0876	0.2876	0.5197	0.6992	0.8511	0.0511	0.0992	0.1197	0.0876
	0.20	0.6772	0.4330	0.2600	0.1263	-.0737	-.1400	-.1670	-.1228	0.3228	0.5670	0.7400	0.8737	0.0737	0.1400	0.1670	0.1228
	0.40	0.6457	0.3916	0.2226	0.1037	-.0963	-.1774	-.2084	-.1543	0.3543	0.6084	0.7774	0.8963	0.0963	0.1774	0.2084	0.1543
	2.00	0.6031	0.3396	0.1682	0.0635	-.1365	-.2318	-.2604	-.1969	0.3969	0.6604	0.8318	0.9365	0.1365	0.2318	0.2604	0.1969
1.50	0.10	0.7069	0.4727	0.2945	0.1458	-.0542	-.1055	-.1273	-.0931	0.2931	0.5273	0.7055	0.8542	0.0542	0.1055	0.1273	0.0931
	0.20	0.6659	0.4175	0.2472	0.1198	-.0802	-.1528	-.1825	-.1341	0.3341	0.5825	0.7528	0.8802	0.0802	0.1528	0.1825	0.1341
	0.40	0.6274	0.3668	0.2016	0.0925	-.1075	-.1984	-.2332	-.1726	0.3726	0.6332	0.7984	0.9075	0.1075	0.1984	0.2332	0.1726
	2.00	0.5716	0.2981	0.1308	0.0410	-.1590	-.2692	-.3019	-.2284	0.4284	0.7019	0.8692	0.9590	0.1590	0.2692	0.3019	0.2284

$(b/\ell) = 0.40$ ANGLE OF SKEW=ARCTAN(0.0)

UNIT VERTICAL LOAD APPLIED AT POINT:

φ	ζ	2	3	4	5	8	9	10	11	2	3	4	5	8	9	10	11
		REACTION AT SUPPORT 1								REACTION AT SUPPORT 6							
0.10	0.10	0.7987	0.5993	0.4007	0.2013	0.0013	0.0007	-.0007	-.0013	0.2013	0.4007	0.5993	0.7987	-.0013	-.0007	0.0007	0.0013
	0.20	0.7986	0.5992	0.4008	0.2014	0.0014	0.0008	-.0008	-.0014	0.2014	0.4008	0.5992	0.7986	-.0014	-.0008	0.0008	0.0014
	0.40	0.7988	0.5993	0.4007	0.2012	0.0012	0.0007	-.0007	-.0012	0.2012	0.4007	0.5993	0.7988	-.0012	-.0007	0.0007	0.0012
	2.00	0.7995	0.5998	0.4003	0.2005	0.0005	0.0002	-.0002	-.0005	0.2005	0.4003	0.5998	0.7995	-.0005	-.0002	0.0002	0.0005
0.30	0.10	0.7975	0.5986	0.4014	0.2025	0.0025	0.0014	-.0014	-.0025	0.2025	0.4014	0.5986	0.7975	-.0025	-.0014	0.0014	0.0025
	0.20	0.7965	0.5981	0.4019	0.2035	0.0035	0.0019	-.0019	-.0035	0.2035	0.4019	0.5981	0.7965	-.0035	-.0019	0.0019	0.0035
	0.40	0.7960	0.5978	0.4022	0.2040	0.0040	0.0022	-.0022	-.0040	0.2040	0.4022	0.5978	0.7960	-.0040	-.0022	0.0022	0.0040
	2.00	0.7973	0.5986	0.4014	0.2027	0.0027	0.0014	-.0014	-.0027	0.2027	0.4014	0.5986	0.7973	-.0027	-.0014	0.0014	0.0027
0.50	0.10	0.7970	0.5983	0.4017	0.2030	0.0030	0.0017	-.0017	-.0030	0.2030	0.4017	0.5983	0.7970	-.0030	-.0017	0.0017	0.0030
	0.20	0.7954	0.5974	0.4026	0.2046	0.0046	0.0026	-.0026	-.0046	0.2046	0.4026	0.5974	0.7954	-.0046	-.0026	0.0026	0.0046
	0.40	0.7941	0.5967	0.4033	0.2059	0.0059	0.0033	-.0033	-.0059	0.2059	0.4033	0.5967	0.7941	-.0059	-.0033	0.0033	0.0059
	2.00	0.7946	0.5972	0.4028	0.2054	0.0054	0.0028	-.0028	-.0054	0.2054	0.4028	0.5972	0.7946	-.0054	-.0028	0.0028	0.0054
1.00	0.10	0.7965	0.5980	0.4020	0.2035	0.0035	0.0020	-.0020	-.0035	0.2035	0.4020	0.5980	0.7965	-.0035	-.0020	0.0020	0.0035
	0.20	0.7942	0.5967	0.4033	0.2058	0.0058	0.0033	-.0033	-.0058	0.2058	0.4033	0.5967	0.7942	-.0058	-.0033	0.0033	0.0058
	0.40	0.7913	0.5951	0.4049	0.2087	0.0087	0.0049	-.0049	-.0087	0.2087	0.4049	0.5951	0.7913	-.0087	-.0049	0.0049	0.0087
	2.00	0.7886	0.5939	0.4061	0.2114	0.0114	0.0061	-.0061	-.0114	0.2114	0.4061	0.5939	0.7886	-.0114	-.0061	0.0061	0.0114
1.50	0.10	0.7964	0.5979	0.4021	0.2036	0.0036	0.0021	-.0021	-.0036	0.2036	0.4021	0.5979	0.7964	-.0036	-.0021	0.0021	0.0036
	0.20	0.7936	0.5964	0.4036	0.2064	0.0064	0.0036	-.0036	-.0064	0.2064	0.4036	0.5964	0.7936	-.0064	-.0036	0.0036	0.0064
	0.40	0.7898	0.5942	0.4058	0.2102	0.0102	0.0058	-.0058	-.0102	0.2102	0.4058	0.5942	0.7898	-.0102	-.0058	0.0058	0.0102
	2.00	0.7838	0.5912	0.4088	0.2162	0.0162	0.0088	-.0088	-.0162	0.2162	0.4088	0.5912	0.7838	-.0162	-.0088	0.0088	0.0162

TABLE 20 – SIMPLY-SUPPORTED SKEW GIRDER BRIDGE

INFLUENCE COEFFICIENTS OF REACTIONS

REACTION = COEF.

(b/ℓ) = 0.40 — ANGLE OF SKEW=ARCTAN(0.17)

φ	ζ	Unit vertical load applied at point: 2	3	4	5	8	9	10	11	2	3	4	5	8	9	10	11
		Reaction at support 1								Reaction at support 6							
0.10	0.10	0.7976	0.5976	0.3992	0.2004	0.0004	-.0008	-.0024	-.0024	0.2024	0.4024	0.6008	0.7996	-.0004	0.0008	0.0024	0.0024
	0.20	0.7972	0.5972	0.3989	0.2003	0.0003	-.0011	-.0028	-.0028	0.2028	0.4028	0.6011	0.7997	-.0003	0.0011	0.0028	0.0028
	0.40	0.7972	0.5970	0.3985	0.2000	-.0000	-.0015	-.0030	-.0028	0.2028	0.4030	0.6015	0.8000	0.0000	0.0015	0.0030	0.0028
	2.00	0.7977	0.5972	0.3978	0.1990	-.0010	-.0022	-.0028	-.0023	0.2023	0.4028	0.6022	0.8010	0.0010	0.0022	0.0028	0.0023
0.30	0.10	0.7958	0.5959	0.3988	0.2009	0.0009	-.0012	-.0041	-.0042	0.2042	0.4041	0.6012	0.7991	-.0009	0.0012	0.0041	0.0042
	0.20	0.7939	0.5941	0.3981	0.2012	0.0012	-.0019	-.0059	-.0061	0.2061	0.4059	0.6018	0.7988	-.0012	0.0019	0.0059	0.0061
	0.40	0.7924	0.5925	0.3972	0.2010	0.0010	-.0028	-.0075	-.0076	0.2076	0.4075	0.6028	0.7990	-.0010	0.0028	0.0075	0.0076
	2.00	0.7922	0.5914	0.3947	0.1987	-.0013	-.0052	-.0086	-.0078	0.2078	0.4086	0.6052	0.8013	0.0013	0.0052	0.0086	0.0078
0.50	0.10	0.7951	0.5953	0.3987	0.2011	0.0011	-.0013	-.0048	-.0049	0.2049	0.4048	0.6013	0.7989	-.0011	0.0013	0.0048	0.0049
	0.20	0.7922	0.5925	0.3978	0.2016	0.0016	-.0022	-.0075	-.0078	0.2078	0.4075	0.6022	0.7984	-.0016	0.0022	0.0075	0.0078
	0.40	0.7893	0.5895	0.3965	0.2018	0.0018	-.0035	-.0105	-.0107	0.2107	0.4105	0.6035	0.7982	-.0018	0.0035	0.0105	0.0107
	2.00	0.7868	0.5859	0.3924	0.1991	-.0009	-.0076	-.0141	-.0132	0.2132	0.4141	0.6075	0.8008	0.0008	0.0075	0.0141	0.0132
1.00	0.10	0.7944	0.5946	0.3986	0.2014	0.0014	-.0014	-.0054	-.0056	0.2056	0.4054	0.6014	0.7986	-.0014	0.0014	0.0054	0.0056
	0.20	0.7903	0.5907	0.3974	0.2022	0.0022	-.0026	-.0093	-.0097	0.2097	0.4093	0.6026	0.7978	-.0022	0.0026	0.0093	0.0097
	0.40	0.7849	0.5854	0.3955	0.2030	0.0030	-.0045	-.0146	-.0151	0.2151	0.4146	0.6045	0.7970	-.0030	0.0045	0.0146	0.0151
	2.00	0.7754	0.5747	0.3883	0.2007	0.0007	-.0117	-.0253	-.0246	0.2246	0.4253	0.6117	0.7993	-.0007	0.0117	0.0253	0.0246
1.50	0.10	0.7941	0.5943	0.3985	0.2014	0.0014	-.0015	-.0057	-.0059	0.2059	0.4057	0.6015	0.7986	-.0014	0.0015	0.0057	0.0059
	0.20	0.7894	0.5898	0.3972	0.2024	0.0024	-.0028	-.0102	-.0106	0.2106	0.4101	0.6028	0.7976	-.0024	0.0028	0.0102	0.0106
	0.40	0.7827	0.5832	0.3951	0.2036	0.0036	-.0049	-.0168	-.0173	0.2173	0.4168	0.6049	0.7964	-.0036	0.0049	0.0168	0.0173
	2.00	0.7667	0.5662	0.3854	0.2022	0.0022	-.0146	-.0338	-.0333	0.2333	0.4338	0.6146	0.7978	-.0022	0.0146	0.0338	0.0333

(b/ℓ) = 0.40 — ANGLE OF SKEW=ARCTAN(0.33)

φ	ζ	Unit vertical load applied at point: 2	3	4	5	8	9	10	11	2	3	4	5	8	9	10	11
		Reaction at support 1								Reaction at support 6							
0.10	0.10	0.7965	0.5960	0.3977	0.1995	-.0005	-.0023	-.0040	-.0035	0.2035	0.4040	0.6023	0.8005	0.0005	0.0023	0.0040	0.0035
	0.20	0.7958	0.5952	0.3970	0.1991	-.0009	-.0030	-.0048	-.0042	0.2042	0.4048	0.6030	0.8009	0.0009	0.0030	0.0048	0.0042
	0.40	0.7955	0.5947	0.3964	0.1987	-.0013	-.0036	-.0053	-.0045	0.2045	0.4053	0.6036	0.8013	0.0013	0.0036	0.0053	0.0045
	2.00	0.7959	0.5946	0.3954	0.1975	-.0025	-.0046	-.0054	-.0041	0.2041	0.4054	0.6046	0.8025	0.0025	0.0046	0.0054	0.0041
0.30	0.10	0.7941	0.5933	0.3962	0.1993	-.0007	-.0038	-.0067	-.0059	0.2059	0.4067	0.6038	0.8007	0.0007	0.0038	0.0067	0.0059
	0.20	0.7913	0.5901	0.3943	0.1988	-.0012	-.0057	-.0099	-.0087	0.2087	0.4099	0.6057	0.8012	0.0012	0.0057	0.0099	0.0087
	0.40	0.7889	0.5871	0.3922	0.1980	-.0020	-.0078	-.0129	-.0111	0.2111	0.4129	0.6078	0.8020	0.0020	0.0078	0.0129	0.0111
	2.00	0.7870	0.5841	0.3881	0.1947	-.0053	-.0119	-.0159	-.0130	0.2130	0.4159	0.6119	0.8053	0.0053	0.0119	0.0159	0.0130
0.50	0.10	0.7931	0.5922	0.3957	0.1993	-.0007	-.0043	-.0078	-.0069	0.2069	0.4078	0.6043	0.8007	0.0007	0.0043	0.0078	0.0069
	0.20	0.7891	0.5876	0.3930	0.1987	-.0013	-.0070	-.0124	-.0109	0.2109	0.4124	0.6070	0.8013	0.0013	0.0070	0.0124	0.0109
	0.40	0.7846	0.5824	0.3896	0.1976	-.0024	-.0104	-.0176	-.0154	0.2154	0.4176	0.6104	0.8024	0.0024	0.0104	0.0176	0.0154
	2.00	0.7789	0.5748	0.3821	0.1929	-.0071	-.0179	-.0252	-.0211	0.2211	0.4252	0.6179	0.8071	0.0071	0.0179	0.0252	0.0211
1.00	0.10	0.7922	0.5912	0.3952	0.1992	-.0008	-.0048	-.0088	-.0078	0.2078	0.4088	0.6048	0.8008	0.0008	0.0048	0.0088	0.0078
	0.20	0.7865	0.5847	0.3915	0.1985	-.0015	-.0085	-.0153	-.0135	0.2135	0.4153	0.6085	0.8015	0.0015	0.0085	0.0153	0.0135
	0.40	0.7788	0.5758	0.3862	0.1972	-.0028	-.0138	-.0242	-.0212	0.2212	0.4242	0.6138	0.8028	0.0028	0.0138	0.0242	0.0212
	2.00	0.7626	0.5561	0.3707	0.1900	-.0100	-.0293	-.0439	-.0374	0.2374	0.4439	0.6293	0.8100	0.0100	0.0293	0.0439	0.0374
1.50	0.10	0.7918	0.5908	0.3950	0.1992	-.0008	-.0050	-.0092	-.0082	0.2082	0.4092	0.6050	0.8008	0.0008	0.0050	0.0092	0.0082
	0.20	0.7854	0.5834	0.3908	0.1985	-.0015	-.0092	-.0166	-.0146	0.2146	0.4166	0.6092	0.8015	0.0015	0.0092	0.0166	0.0146
	0.40	0.7758	0.5724	0.3844	0.1970	-.0030	-.0156	-.0276	-.0242	0.2242	0.4276	0.6156	0.8030	0.0030	0.0156	0.0276	0.0242
	2.00	0.7506	0.5423	0.3626	0.1882	-.0118	-.0374	-.0577	-.0494	0.2494	0.4577	0.6374	0.8118	0.0118	0.0374	0.0577	0.0494

(b/ℓ) = 0.40 — ANGLE OF SKEW=ARCTAN(0.50)

φ	ζ	Unit vertical load applied at point: 2	3	4	5	8	9	10	11	2	3	4	5	8	9	10	11
		Reaction at support 1								Reaction at support 6							
0.10	0.10	0.7955	0.5944	0.3961	0.1985	-.0015	-.0039	-.0056	-.0045	0.2045	0.4056	0.6039	0.8015	0.0015	0.0039	0.0056	0.0045
	0.20	0.7945	0.5931	0.3951	0.1980	-.0020	-.0049	-.0069	-.0055	0.2055	0.4069	0.6049	0.8020	0.0020	0.0049	0.0069	0.0055
	0.40	0.7939	0.5924	0.3942	0.1974	-.0026	-.0058	-.0076	-.0061	0.2061	0.4076	0.6058	0.8026	0.0026	0.0058	0.0076	0.0061
	2.00	0.7940	0.5920	0.3931	0.1961	-.0039	-.0069	-.0080	-.0060	0.2060	0.4080	0.6069	0.8039	0.0039	0.0069	0.0080	0.0060
0.30	0.10	0.7924	0.5906	0.3936	0.1977	-.0023	-.0064	-.0094	-.0076	0.2076	0.4094	0.6064	0.8023	0.0023	0.0064	0.0094	0.0076
	0.20	0.7888	0.5862	0.3905	0.1964	-.0036	-.0095	-.0138	-.0112	0.2112	0.4138	0.6095	0.8036	0.0036	0.0095	0.0138	0.0112
	0.40	0.7854	0.5819	0.3872	0.1949	-.0051	-.0128	-.0181	-.0146	0.2146	0.4181	0.6128	0.8051	0.0051	0.0128	0.0181	0.0146
	2.00	0.7819	0.5771	0.3816	0.1908	-.0092	-.0184	-.0229	-.0181	0.2181	0.4229	0.6184	0.8092	0.0092	0.0184	0.0229	0.0181
0.50	0.10	0.7912	0.5892	0.3927	0.1974	-.0026	-.0073	-.0108	-.0088	0.2088	0.4108	0.6073	0.8026	0.0026	0.0073	0.0108	0.0088
	0.20	0.7860	0.5827	0.3882	0.1957	-.0043	-.0118	-.0173	-.0140	0.2140	0.4173	0.6118	0.8043	0.0043	0.0118	0.0173	0.0140
	0.40	0.7801	0.5755	0.3829	0.1934	-.0066	-.0171	-.0245	-.0199	0.2199	0.4245	0.6171	0.8066	0.0066	0.0171	0.0245	0.0199
	2.00	0.7714	0.5641	0.3722	0.1869	-.0131	-.0278	-.0359	-.0286	0.2286	0.4359	0.6278	0.8131	0.0131	0.0278	0.0359	0.0286
1.00	0.10	0.7901	0.5878	0.3918	0.1971	-.0029	-.0082	-.0122	-.0099	0.2099	0.4122	0.6082	0.8029	0.0029	0.0082	0.0122	0.0099
	0.20	0.7828	0.5788	0.3857	0.1949	-.0051	-.0143	-.0212	-.0172	0.2172	0.4212	0.6143	0.8051	0.0051	0.0143	0.0212	0.0172
	0.40	0.7729	0.5666	0.3770	0.1915	-.0085	-.0230	-.0334	-.0271	0.2271	0.4334	0.6230	0.8085	0.0085	0.0230	0.0334	0.0271
	2.00	0.7510	0.5388	0.3543	0.1798	-.0202	-.0457	-.0612	-.0490	0.2490	0.4612	0.6457	0.8202	0.0202	0.0457	0.0612	0.0490
1.50	0.10	0.7896	0.5872	0.3914	0.1970	-.0030	-.0086	-.0128	-.0104	0.2104	0.4128	0.6086	0.8030	0.0030	0.0086	0.0128	0.0104
	0.20	0.7814	0.5771	0.3845	0.1945	-.0055	-.0155	-.0229	-.0186	0.2186	0.4229	0.6155	0.8055	0.0055	0.0155	0.0229	0.0186
	0.40	0.7692	0.5620	0.3740	0.1905	-.0095	-.0260	-.0380	-.0308	0.2308	0.4380	0.6260	0.8095	0.0095	0.0260	0.0380	0.0308
	2.00	0.7362	0.5206	0.3415	0.1749	-.0251	-.0585	-.0794	-.0638	0.2638	0.4794	0.6585	0.8251	0.0251	0.0585	0.0794	0.0638

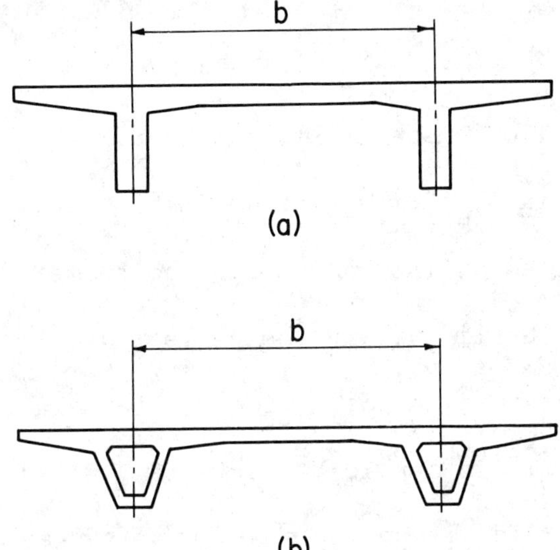

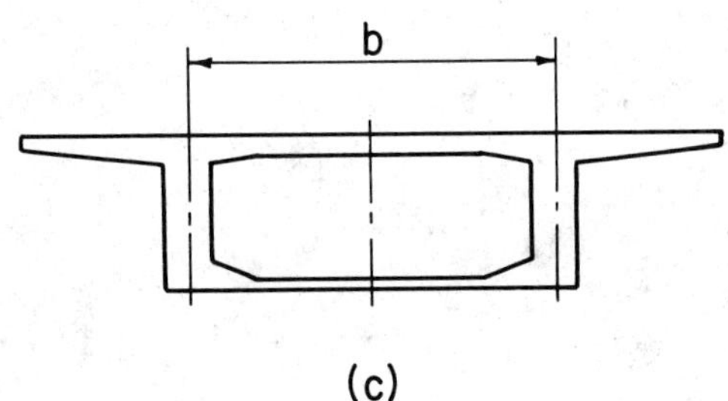

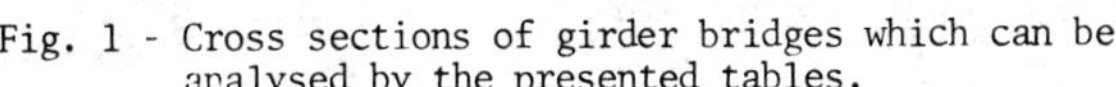

Fig. 1 - Cross sections of girder bridges which can be analysed by the presented tables.

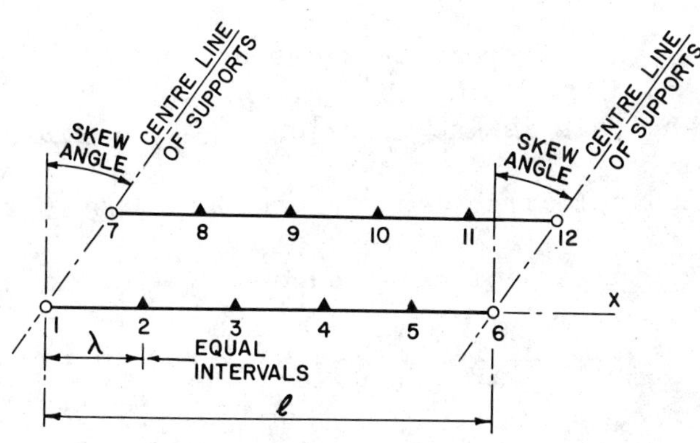

Fig. 2 - Node points used for the analysis of simply supported skew bridge.

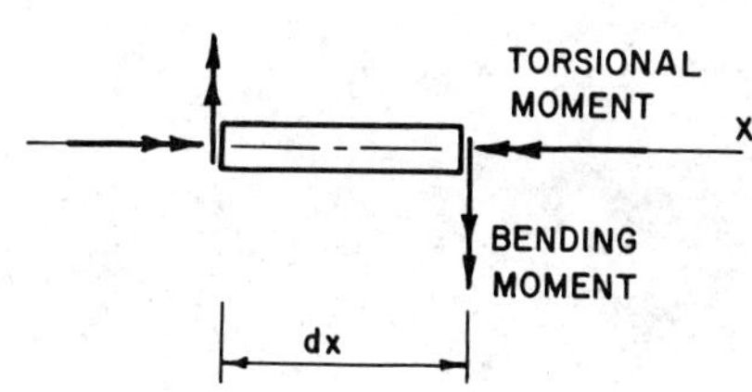

Fig. 3 - Positive directions of bending and torsional moments.

DISCUSSION

By R. P. PAMA

Professor, Department of Civil Engineering, University of Dundee.

It appears that one of the basic assumptions made by Dr. Ghali in his analysis is the omission of the flexural rigidity of the slab in the longtudinal direction. Since the slab is supported at the edges with the beams virtually acting as edge beams, how does Dr. Ghali justify the neglect of the bending resistance of the slab in the longitudinal direction? With this assumption, it is fair to say that the analysis is applicable only if the slab is made of pre-cast units laid side by side along the span, with hinges at the joints so that no bending resistance is offered in the direction of the span.

AUTHOR'S CLOSURE

The author disagrees with the limitation suggested by Mr Pama to the use of the tables presented in this paper. The paper deals with bridges in which the width is small compared to the span, and the slab is monolithic with the main girders. The slab is considered to increase the value of EI and GJ of the main girders, forming T or box sections. Thus, the main contribution of the slab to the rigidity in the direction of the span is not ignored.

The validity of the assumptions adopted in the analysis was verified by experiments on models (1). Elaborate analysis of these models by more accurate idealisation of the actual structure using both finite differences and finite elements methods, showed good agreement with the simple method used in the present paper, but of course these elaborate methods give much more information about the distribution of stresses.

LATERAL DISPLACEMENTS AND ROTATIONS OF SKEW CONTINUOUS PRESTRESSED CONCRETE BRIDGE DECKS

By JACOB SHIMONI

SYNOPSIS

Skew bridge decks, and especially those made of prestressed concrete, are subject to longitudinal and transversal displacements and horizontal rotations due to external forces resulting from:

(a) Longitudinal braking and earthquake forces,
(b) Transversal wind, earthquake and centrifugal forces,
(c) Shortening of deck due to shrinkage, variation of temperature and prestressing forces.

A general solution is presented for determining of these displacements and rotations, and a practical example with numerical evaluation for different types of structures has been given.

Displacements and rotations were found to be dependant mainly on the ratio k_v/k_u and the absolute value of k_u, but also on the stiffnesses of the bearing and the geometry of the supporting system.

The evaluation of these displacements and rotations has considerable importance when determining:

(1) The relative movement of the deck in respect to the abutments near the expansion joints.

(2) The magnitude and direction of the deformations of the elastomeric bearing pads.

(3) The shear forces and bending moments of the columns resulting from them.

Keywords: bridge decks; bridges (structures); displacement; dynamic loads; loads (forces); moving loads; prestressed concrete; shrinkage; skew bridges; structural design; temperature; wind pressure.

JACOB SHIMONI is senior lecturer in prestressed concrete construction at the Technion, Israel Institute of Technology, Haifa, Israel, and since 1963 partner of Yaron-Shimoni, Consulting Engineers Tel-Aviv.

He completed his studies at the Technion in 1952. Since then his experience included several years of structural design work in Europe and in Israel, mainly in the field of prestressed concrete and bridge constructions.

1. INTRODUCTION

Modern design of highways, with roads crossing one, each other, or passing over various obstacles at any desirable angle or curvature in order to fit the modern needs of traffic, has led during the last decade to an ever-increasing application of skew bridges.

Extremely suitable for this purpose are skew slab bridges as they can be given practically every possible shape to fit the required spacing between columns and their inclinations in respect to the longitudinal axis of the bridge, any superelevation, slope, curvature, etc.

As a result, skew overpasses became more and more common practice and a great number of them can be seen all over the world, and mainly in Europe.

Structural analysis of such deck slabs, has so far been practically limited to model analysis only, or--for more usual and simple cases--to the use of influence areas. Since recently, by introducing the use of electronic computors, deck slabs of any shape and with any position of columns and supports could easily be solved by means of finite differences applied on a net with any required density of points.

An excellent summary of the presently existing knowledge in this field has been given recently by Prof. F. Leonhardt.[1]

In all these, attention is given only to displacements perpendicular to the neutral axis of the slab due to loads acting in the same direction.

As far as lateral displacements of deck slabs due to forces acting in the plane of their neutral axis are concerned, very little information has been so far reported.

A rather old booklet of the Portland Cement Association[2] mentions some "lateral creep", and an "observed lengthening of longer diagonals" resulting in lateral deformation of skew bridges up to 4 inches, showing serious damage both in the acute angles of the slab, as well as in the abutments. No explanation has been given in the booklet as to the reasons for this phenomena.

Although lateral displacements of this magnitude have not been reported elsewhere, it is however common practice to provide a certain lateral movability in joint-construction details for skew slabs. (e.g. trapezoidal finger plates, rubber joints of various shapes, etc.)

In this paper, attempt has been made to present an analysis of such lateral displacements and rotations due to forces acting in the plane of the neutral axis of the slab, resulting from the following:

(a) Longitudinal braking and earthquake forces.

(b) Transversal wind, earthquake, or centrifugal forces.

(c) Shortening of the deck due to shrinkage.

(d) Variation of temperature.

(e) Influence of the prestressing force.

Lateral displacements and rotations resulting from loads perpendicular to the plane of neutral axis of skew deck slabs connected rigidly to their columns, e.g. skew portal-type structures[3], are not within the scope of this paper and will be analyzed separately.

2. GENERAL SOLUTION

Let us consider a slab of a rather irregular shape continuous over five supports as shown in Fig. 1.

The intermediate piers "B", "C", "D", are lines of columns, fixed-in in the deck slab. Each column has a certain stiffness against horizontal displacements and rotations, according to its dimensions and its boundary conditions at the foundation.

The exterior supports "A" and "E" are lines of a certain number of elastomeric bearing pads of a given stiffness, resting on fixed abutments.

Any point of support (a column belonging to an intermediate pier, or a bearing pad in the line of the exterior supports), can be defined by its coordinates x_n; y_n; φ_n and by its respective stiffnessess K_u, K_v, K_{uv}

where K_u - the stiffness of the support against displacements in the direction of the principal axis "U".

K_v - the stiffness of the support against displacements in the direction of the principal axis "V".

K_{uv} - Torsional stiffness of support against horizontal rotations of its top in respect to the foundation.

By introducing a displacement $\Delta x = +1$ in the direction of "X", the supports take displacements $\Delta U^x = \Delta x \sin\varphi_n$ $\quad \Delta V^x = \Delta x \cos\varphi_n$ as shown in Fig. 2(a).

Hence the forces exerted are given by:

$$R_{ux} = K_u \sin\varphi_n \, \Delta x$$

$$R_{vx} = K_v \cos\varphi_n \, \Delta x$$

$$R_{xx} = R_{ux} \sin\varphi_n + R_{vx} \cos\varphi_n = (K_u \sin^2\varphi_n + K_v \cos^2\varphi_n)\,\Delta x$$

$$R_{yx} = -R_{ux} \cos\varphi_n + R_{vx} \sin\varphi_n = (K_v - K_u) \sin\varphi_n \cos\varphi_n \,.\, \Delta x \qquad (1)$$

$$R_{mx} = +R_{yx}.\,X_n - R_{xx}.\,y_n = \left\{(K_v - K_u)\sin\varphi_n \cos\varphi_n.\,x_n - (K_u \sin^2\varphi_n + K_v \cos^2\varphi_n)y_n\right\}\Delta x$$

Similarily for a transversal displacement $\Delta y = +1$ (Fig. 2(b)) we get the following displacements:

$$\Delta\, uy = -\Delta\, y \cos\varphi_n \qquad \Delta\, vy = \Delta\, y \,.\, \sin\varphi_n$$

which render in the support the following loads:

$R_{uy} = - K_u . \cos\varphi_n . \Delta y$ $\qquad R_{vy} = K_v \sin\varphi_n . \Delta y$

and at the origin the following imaginary reactions:

$$R_{xy} = R_{uy} . \sin\varphi_n + R_{vy}\cos\varphi_n = (K_v - K_u)\sin\varphi_n\cos\varphi_n . \Delta y$$

$$R_{yy} = - R_{uy} . \cos\varphi_n + R_{vy} . \sin\varphi_n = (K_u\cos^2\varphi_n + K_v\sin^2\varphi_n)\,\Delta y \qquad (2)$$

$$R_{my} = R_{yy} . X_n - R_{xy} . y_n = \left\{(K_u\cos^2\varphi_n + K_v\sin^2\varphi_n)\,x_n - (K_v-K_u)\sin\varphi_n\cos\varphi_n y_n\right\}\Delta y$$

Finally, in the same way, we get for a unit rotation $\Theta = 1$ about the origin "O" (see Fig. 2(c)) the following displacements:

$\Delta_{um} = -(\gamma_n\theta)\cos(\varphi_n - \rho_n)$ $\qquad \Delta_{vm} = (\gamma_n\Theta)\sin(\varphi_n - \rho_n)$

and loads $R_{um} = - K_u . \gamma_n\cos(\varphi_n - \rho_n)\,\theta$ $\qquad R_{vm} = K_v . \gamma_n . \sin(\varphi_n - \rho_n)\,\Theta$

summing up at the origin to

$$R_{xm} = R_{um}\sin\varphi_n + R_{vm}\cos\varphi_n = \left\{-K_u . \gamma_n\cos(\varphi_n-\rho_n)\sin\varphi_n + K_v\gamma_n\sin(\varphi_n-\rho_n)\cos\varphi_n\right\}\theta$$

$$R_{ym} = -R_{um}\cos\varphi_n + R_{vm}\sin\varphi_n = \left\{K_u . \gamma_n\cos(\varphi_n-\rho_n)\cos\varphi_n + K_v\gamma_n\sin(\varphi_n-\rho_n)\sin\varphi_n\right\}\theta \qquad (3)$$

$$R_{mm} = R_{ym} . x_n - R_{xm} . y_n + K_{uv} . (\Theta)$$

Substituting $x_n = \gamma_n . \cos\rho_n$ and $y_n = \gamma_n . \sin\rho_n$ the above equations become:

$$R_{xm} = \left\{(K_v-K_u)\sin\varphi_n . \cos\varphi_n\,x_n - (K_u\sin^2\varphi_n + K_v\cos^2\varphi_n)\,y_n\right\}\theta$$

$$R_{ym} = \left\{(K_u\cos^2\varphi_n + K_v\sin^2\varphi_n)\,x_n - (K_v-K_u)\sin\varphi_n\cos\varphi_n . x_n\right\}\Theta \qquad (4)$$

$$R_{mm} = \left\{(K_u\cos^2\varphi_n + K_v\sin^2\varphi_n)\,x_n^2 + (K_u\sin^2\varphi_n + K_v\cos^2\varphi_n)\,y_n^2 - 2(K_v-K_u)\sin\varphi_n\cos\varphi_n x_n y_n + K_{uv}\right\}\Theta$$

Thus the total horizontal load on a support will be given by:

$$\Sigma R_u = R_{ux} + R_{uy} + R_{um} + R_{u_o}$$

$$\Sigma R_v = R_{vx} + R_{vy} + R_{vm} + R_{v_o}$$

when R_{u_o} and R_{v_o} are loads transmitted directly to the support independent of the displacements Δx, Δy and Θ .

The unknown displacements Δx and Δy and the rotation θ will be calculated from the resultant influences at the origin, where the "imaginary" reactions $[R_{ij}]_{i,j=x,y,m}$ for all the points of support of the system, and all the external loadings have to be in equiliorium.

For a column defined by x_n, y_n and φ_n and its stiffnesses K_u, K_v and K_{uv}, the equations (1), (2) and (4) form the stiffness matrix $[R_{ij}]$

For a point of support made of an elastomeric bearing pad, where the stiffnesses K_u and K_v are equal, the above stiffness equations get a simpler form.

With $K_u=K_v=K_b$ and $K_{uv}=K_s$ we have for a bearing at x_m, y_m and φ_m:

$$R_{xx} = K_b \cdot \Delta x$$

$$R_{yx} = 0$$

$$R_{mx} = - K_b \cdot y_m \cdot \Delta x$$

$$R_{xy} = 0$$

$$R_{yy} = K_b \cdot \Delta y$$

$$R_{my} = + K_b \cdot x_m \cdot \Delta y$$

$$R_{xm} = - K_b \cdot y_m \cdot \theta$$

$$R_{ym} = + K_b \cdot x_m \cdot \theta$$

$$R_{mm} = \left\{K_b(x_m^2 + y_m^2) + K_s\right\} \theta$$

Adding up the stiffness matrix R_{ij} for N columns and M bearing pads, the total stiffness of the system will be given by:

$$\left[R_{ij}\right] = \sum_{1}^{n} \left[R_{ij}\right]_n + \sum_{1}^{m} \left[R_{ij}\right]_m \qquad (i,j = x,y,m)$$

and the following equations will finally lead to the evaluation of the unknown displacements and rotations:

$$R_{xx} \cdot \Delta x + R_{xy} \Delta y + R_{xm} \cdot \theta + H_o = 0$$

$$R_{yx} \cdot \Delta x + R_{yy} \cdot \Delta y + R_{ym} \cdot \theta + V_o = 0$$

$$R_{mx} \cdot \Delta x + R_{my} \cdot \Delta y + R_{mm} \cdot \theta + M_o = 0$$

where H_o, V_o and M_o are the resultant exterior loads at the origin O.

The displacements Δx, Δy and θ are functions of the matrix $\left[R_{ij}\right]$ which involve all the following:

- flexural stiffness of the columns K_u and K_v
- torsional stiffness of the columns K_{uv}
- shear stiffness of the bearings K_b
- torsional stiffness of the bearings K_s
- the geometry of the supporting system and their angle of skew.

3. SOLUTION OF A SPECIFIC CASE:

As a practical example we have analyzed a very frequent type of structure, namely, a continuous three-span deck slab, antisymmetrical about the center point O (Fig. 3), and all lines of supports at angle φ parallel one to each other.

Due to the symmetry the equations get simpler and reduce to:

$$R_{xx} = \{n(K_u \sin^2\varphi + K_v \cos^2\varphi) + m\,K_b\}\,\Delta x$$

$$R_{yx} = n(K_v - K_u)\sin\varphi\,\cos\varphi\,.\Delta x$$

$$R_{mx} = 0$$

$$R_{xy} = n.(K_v - K_u)\,\sin\varphi\,\cos\varphi\,\Delta y$$

$$R_{yy} = \{n(K_u \cos^2\varphi + K_v \sin^2\varphi) + m\,K_b\}\,\Delta y$$

$$R_{my} = 0$$

$$R_{xm} = 0$$

$$R_{ym} = 0$$

$$R_{mm} = \Big\{n(K_u\cos^2\varphi + K_v\sin^2\varphi)x_l^{\,2} + 4\sum_1^j s_j^{\,2}\left[4K_v\sin^2\varphi\cos^2\varphi + K_u(\sin^2\varphi - \cos^2\varphi)^2\right] + {}$$

$$+ n.K_{uv} + m\,K_b x_k^{\,2} + 4K_b\sum_1^i s_i^{\,2} + m.K_s\Big\}\,\Theta$$

Here x_l and x_k are the mean distances of the lines of columns and bearings respectively, and s_j and s_i are the individual distances of the various columns and bearings from the x axis in direction of φ as shown in Fig. 3.

Further we have,

- j - number of columns in one quarter of the coordinate system where $o < j \leq \frac{n}{4}$
- i - number of bearings in one quarter of the coordinate system where $o < i \leq \frac{n}{4}$

In this special case the equations become:

$$\text{(a)}\quad R_{xx} \cdot \Delta X + R_{xy} \cdot \Delta y = H_o$$

$$\text{(b)}\quad R_{yx} \cdot \Delta X + R_{yy} \cdot \Delta y = V_o$$

$$\text{(c)}\quad R_{mm} \cdot \Theta = M_o$$

whence we can deduce:

(a) due to longitudinal forces H_o (breaking force, earthquake, etc.) we get longitudinal displacements Δx_h and transversal displacements Δy_h only.

(b) due to transversal forces V_o (lateral earthquake, centrifugal forces etc.) we get longitudinal displacement Δx_v and transversal Δy_v only.

(c) when the above loading cases are accompanied by an additional moment M_o (e.g. braking force H_o acting excentrically to the longitudinal axis), the rotation Θ can readily be calculated from equation (c) now independent of Δx and Δy.

(d) due to externally imposed displacements, such as due to shrinkage, variation of temperature or due to the introducing of longitudinal and transversal prestressing, all supporting points (columns and bearings) will have to displace according to their relative position to the origin. (Fig. 4)

These displacements will introduce reactions H_ε, V_ε, M_ε in the origin, and additional displacements Δx, ΔY and Θ will have to occur in order to provide equilibrium. Δx, Δy and Θ will be calculated from the equations (a), (b) and (c).

Yet, due to symmetry of all supports about point "O" the imposed external deformations will give the following reactions:

$$H_{O\varepsilon} = 0$$

$$V_{O\varepsilon} = 0$$

$$M_{O\varepsilon} = M_{O\varepsilon_x} + M_{O\varepsilon_y} = \left\{(K_u \sin^2\varphi + K_v \cos\varphi)\sum_1^n x_n y_n - (K_v - K_u)\sum_1^n x_n^2 \sin\varphi\cos\varphi\right\}\varepsilon_x -$$
$$-\left\{(K_u \cos^2\varphi + K_u \sin^2\varphi)\sum_1^n x_n y_n - (K_v - K_u)\sum_1^n y_n^2 \sin\varphi\cos\varphi\right\}\varepsilon_y$$

if $\varepsilon_x = \varepsilon_y$ we get

$$M_{O\varepsilon} = -M(K_v - K_u)\sin\varphi\cos\varphi \cdot x_1^2$$

Hence $\Delta x = 0$ and $\Delta y = 0$ which means that above the induced external displacements, the system does not have any additional deformations, except of the rotation θ

$$\text{and} \quad \theta = \frac{\Sigma(M_{sh} + M_{\Delta t} + M_{prx} + M_{pry})}{R_{mm}}$$

It can be observed that the values of M_{sh}, $M_{\Delta t}$, M_{prx}, M_{pry} are directly proportional to the ratio $\frac{Kv}{Ku}$, the position of the points of support and their number, the angle of skew, and obviously the magnitude of the imposed deformations in both directions.

4. NUMERICAL EXAMPLES

The following numerical examples have been chosen to demonstrate the variations of longitudinal and lateral displacements as well as of rotations when changing the ratio $\frac{Kv}{Ku}$.

In practice this has been achieved, when for a certain type of slab (see Fig. 5) with given dimensions and a constant number and type of bearings, several different arrangements of columns had been adopted. The various cases checked are tabulated in Fig. 6.

The following stiffnesses were considered:

K_u - according to degree of fixity in foundation

$$K_u = \frac{\lambda EJu}{H^3}$$

where $\lambda = 12$ for columns fully fixed-in
$\lambda = 3$ for columns hinged on foundation.

It should be observed that if elastically supported at its foundation can have even smaller values.

The following numerical examples have been made for two groups,

e.g. group "A" → $\lambda = 12$

group "B" → $\lambda = 2$

either of them with the arrangements of columns as shown in Fig. 5.

K_v - in this direction fixing-in both on top and bottom of columns is assumed $K_v = \frac{12EJ_v}{H^3}$

for rectangular columns with $J_u = \frac{bd^3}{12}$ and $J_v = \frac{b^3d}{12}$

$$\frac{J_v}{J_u} = \frac{12}{\lambda} \cdot \frac{b^2}{d^2} .$$

K_{uv} - torsional stiffness of columns is given by

$$K_{uv} = \frac{GJ_{uv}}{H}$$

G - Shear modulus of concrete

ν - Poisson ratio

J_{uv} - Torsional moment of Inertia

$$\frac{K_{uv}}{K_u} = \frac{\frac{GJ_{uv}}{H}}{\frac{X.EJ_u}{H^3}} = \frac{H^2}{2(1+\nu)} \cdot \frac{1}{\lambda} \cdot \frac{J_{uv}}{J_u}$$

K_b - Shear stiffness of bearing pads, is given by $K_b = \frac{A_b.G_b}{T_b}$

A_b - Bearing area $= 0.2m \times 0.3m = 0.06\ m^2$

G_b - Shear modulus $= 200\ ^t/_{m^2}$

t_b - Thickness of bearing = 0.03m

$$K_b = \frac{0.2 \times 0.3 \times 200}{0.03} = 400\ t/m$$

K_s - Torsional stiffness of a bearing is practically a negligible value.

4.1 LONGITUDINAL AND TRANSVERSAL DISPLACEMENTS DUE TO HORIZONTAL FORCES.

In Fig. 7, the stiffnesses R_{xx}, R_{yx}, R_{yy}, R_{mm} for the deck slab shown in Fig. 5 with the various columns arrangements defined in Fig. 6 had been tabulated.

Displacements Δx_h, Δy_h and Δx_v, Δy_v under unit loads $H_u = 1^t$ and $V_o = 1^t$ respectively have been calculated. Their values are given in Fig. 7, and are traced in Fig. 9, according to the variation of the ratio $\frac{K_v}{K_u}$.

4.2 ROTATIONS DUE TO SHRINKAGE, TEMPERATURE AND PRESTRESSING FORCE.

Fig. 8 gives the rotations of the given deck slab due to shrinkage, fall of temperature and prestressing force for the various arrangements of columns as defined in Fig. 6.

The values considered were:

- Shrinkage $\varepsilon_{sh} = 20 \times 10^{-5}$
- Fall of temperature $\alpha_t = 0.00001$ $\Delta t = +20^{\circ}C$ $\varepsilon_{st} = 20 \times 10^{-5}$
- Prestressing force average stress $\sigma_x = \sigma_y = 50\ ^{Kg}/_{cm^2}$

elasticity $E = 250000\ ^{Kg}/_{cm^2}$

$$\varepsilon_{pr_x} = \varepsilon_{pr_y} = 20 \times 10^{-5}$$

Due to these rotations, considerable displacements occur at the joints between the deck slab and the end abutments. Those are traced in Fig. 9, according to the variation of the ratio $\frac{K_v}{K_u}$

4.3 RESULTING LOADS ON COLUMNS AND BEARINGS.

Horizontal shear forces and moments acting on the columns belonging to an intermediate pier, will be calculated from the total displacements ΔX, ΔY and the rotation θ, including the externally induced deformations resulting from shrinkage, fall of temperature, and prestressing forces.

Denoting Δu and Δv the total displacements of a certain column defined by x_n, y_n, φ_n, K_u, K_v, K_{uv}, in the directions of u and v respectively, we have:

$\Delta u = (\Delta_x + \mathcal{E}_x \cdot x_n) \sin \varphi_n = (\Delta_y + \mathcal{E}_y \cdot y_n) \cos \varphi_n - \gamma_n \cos (\varphi_n - \rho_n) \Theta$

$\Delta \; - (\Delta_x + \mathcal{E}_x \cdot x_n) \cos \varphi_n + (\Delta_y + \mathcal{E}_y \cdot y_n) \sin \varphi_n + \gamma_n \sin (\varphi_n - \rho_n) \Theta$

And hence

Shearing forces - $R_u = K_u \cdot \Delta u$

$R_v = K_v \cdot \Delta v$

Bending moments - $M_u = D_u \cdot \Delta u$

$M_v = D_v \cdot \Delta v$

Where D_u and D_v are the flexural stiffnesses of the column in direction of u and v respectively, and according to the degree of fixity on its top and bottom.

Torsional moment - $M_{uv} = K_{uv} \cdot \Theta$

In a similar way, the total displacements of the bearing pads can be calculated and their ability to stand them must be checked.

For a bearing pad defined by x_m, y_m, φ_m, K_b, K_s we have:

$\Delta u = (\Delta_x + \mathcal{E}_x x_m) \sin \varphi_m - (\Delta_y + \mathcal{E}_y \cdot y_m) \cos \varphi_m - \gamma_m \cos (\varphi_m - \rho_m) \Theta$

$\Delta v = (\Delta_x + \mathcal{E}_x X_m) \cos \varphi_m + (\Delta_y + \mathcal{E}_y \cdot y_m) \sin \varphi_m + \gamma_m \sin (\varphi_m - \rho_m) \Theta$

The resultant deformation ΔB is given by

$$\Delta b = \sqrt{(\Delta u)^2 + (\Delta v)^2}$$

and hence the shearing force of the given bearing

$$R_b = K_b \cdot \Delta b$$

4.4 DISPLACEMENTS AT THE JOINTS BETWEEN DECK SLAB AND ABUTMENT.

In order to provide sufficient movability in the construction of the joints between the deck slab and the fixed abutment, it is important to determine the extreme displacements of these joints at various loading cases.

It should be noted that these displacements are composed of:

- the displacements Δx and Δy due to longitudinal and transversal loads Ho and Vo (Fig. 7)
- the externally induced displacements $\varepsilon_x . x_k$ and $\varepsilon_y . y_k$ due to shrinkage, fall of temperature and prestressing forces.
- the displacements resulting from the rotations θ caused by the above influences, which can reach considerable values as shown in the last column of Fig. 8.

5. CONCLUSIONS

A general solution has been presented for determining the longitudinal and transversal displacements, as well as the horizontal rotations of a deck slab supported by any desired arrangement of columns and/or elastomeric bearing pads.

These displacements and rotations have been shown to be dependent on:

- the stiffnesses K_u, K_v and K_{uv} of the individual columns.
- the stiffnesses K_b and K_s of the groups of bearings.

- the geometry of the supporting system and the respective angle of skew of each of its components.
- the intensity of the external forces H_o and V_o and the externally induced deformations due to shrinkage, variation of temperature and the prestressing forces.

From a practical example of a three-span continuous skew deck slab, all antisymmetrical about the central point "O", it has been shown that these displacements and rotations depend on the ratio $\frac{K_v}{K_u}$ and on the absolute value of K_u as traced in Fig. 9.

It is interesting to note that Δx_h and Δy_v increase when decreasing the ratio $\frac{K_v}{K_u}$, their absolute value increasing somewhat less than inversely proportional to the values of K_u.

On the other hand the rotation θ decreases when decreasing the ratio $\frac{K_v}{K_u}$ but is only slightly increasing when reducing K_u six times.

This fact has some important conclusions for the intensity of loads and moments acting on the intermediate columns. These loads were shown to be a function of the total displacements Δu and Δv and the stiffnesses K_u and K_v in the same direction.

Reducing of K_u would however increase Δx_h and Δy_v which are relatively small values, but would only slightly increase the displacements due to the rotation θ. Thus, the total displacements Δu and Δv will not change practically, whereas a reduced stiffness of K_u - without changing the dimensions of the column - would reduce considerably the strains in them.

Furthermore, for a certain ratio of $\frac{K_v}{K_u}$, the rotation θ, and hence the opening of the joints "δ" (see Fig. 8 & 9) would remain practically unchanged, that is to say that no extra influences on the joints and on the bearings should be expected.

Finally, the author asks to recommend more investigations and field observations to be done on this subject.

Nevertheless, it seems that the following can already be concluded; it is generally advantageous and preferable to provide rigid connections between columns and deck slab, their mutual influences should be considered accordingly as shown.

REFERENCES:

1. F. Leonhardt: General Report, Session IVa, Chapter 4 presented at the VIII IABSE Congress New York, 1968. p.p. 415 - 420

2. Concrete Bridge Details: Portland Cement Association. Publication No. T -28 -3M -3 -53 p. 41 - 46

3. P. E. Soutter: Schiefe Strassenunterfuehrung bei Koblenz, Sweiz, Bauzeitung (1950) s. 694 - 703

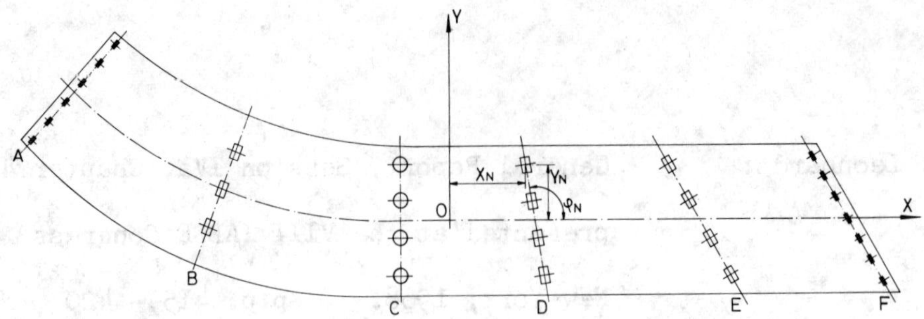

Fig. 1

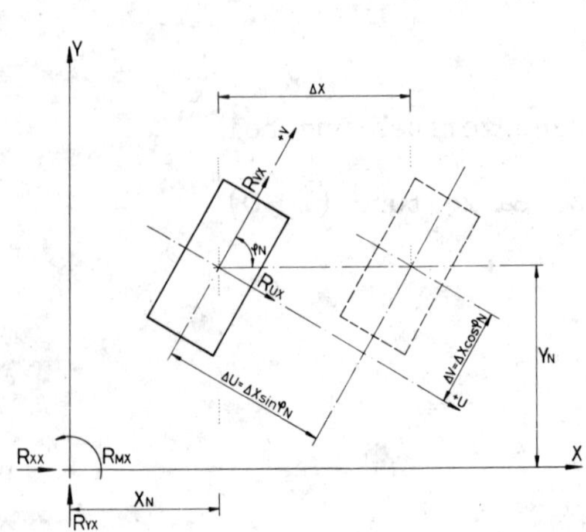

$$R_{XX} = R_{UX} \sin\varphi_N + R_{VX} \cos\varphi_N = (K_U \sin^2\varphi_N + K_V \cos^2\varphi_N)\,\Delta X$$

$$R_{YX} = -R_{UX} \cos\varphi_N + R_{VX} \sin\varphi_N = (K_V - K_U) \sin\varphi_N \cos\varphi_N\,\Delta X$$

$$R_{MX} = +R_{YX} \cdot X_N - R_{XX} \cdot Y_N = \{(K_V - K_U) \sin\varphi_N \cos\varphi_N \cdot X_N - (K_U \sin^2\varphi_N + K_V \cos^2\varphi_N) Y_N\}\,\Delta X$$

Fig. 2a

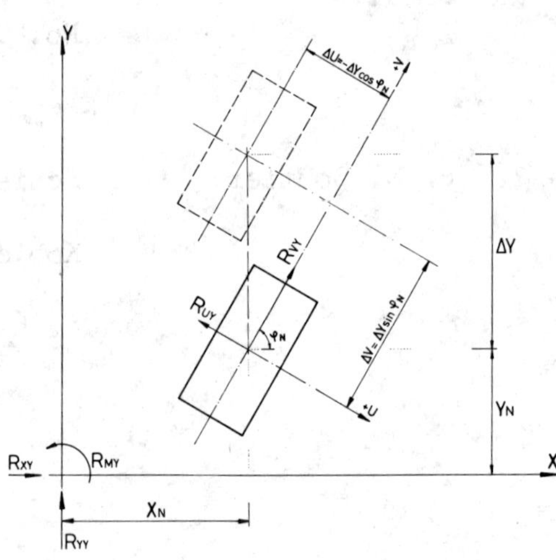

$$R_{XY} = R_{UY} \cdot \sin\varphi_N + R_{VY} \cdot \cos\varphi_N = (K_V - K_U) \sin\varphi_N \cdot \cos\varphi_N \cdot \Delta Y$$

$$R_{YY} = R_{UY} \cdot \cos\varphi_N + R_{VY} \cdot \sin\varphi_N = (K_U \cdot \cos^2\varphi_N + K_V \cdot \sin^2\varphi_N) \cdot \Delta Y$$

$$R_{MY} = R_{YY} \cdot X_N - R_{XY} \cdot Y_N = \{(K_U \cos^2\varphi_N + K_V \sin^2\varphi_N) X_N - (K_V - K_U) \sin\varphi_N \cos\varphi_N \cdot Y_N\}\,\Delta Y$$

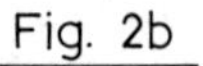

Fig. 2b

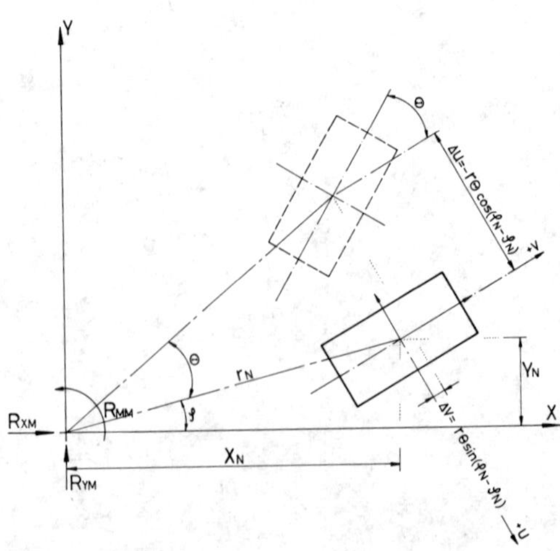

$$R_{XM} = R_{UM} \sin\varphi_N + R_{VM} \cos\varphi_N = \{-K_U \cdot r_N \cos(\varphi_N - \vartheta_N) \sin\varphi_N + K_V \cdot r_N \sin(\varphi_N - \vartheta_N) \cos\varphi_N\}\,\Theta$$

$$R_{YM} = -R_{UM} \cos\varphi_N + R_{VM} \sin\varphi_N = \{K_U \cdot r_N \cos(\varphi_N - \vartheta_N) \cos\varphi_N + K_V \cdot r_N \sin(\varphi_N - \vartheta_N) \sin\varphi_N\}\,\Theta$$

$$R_{MM} = R_{YM} \cdot X_N - R_{XM} \cdot Y_N + K_{UV} \cdot (\Theta)$$

Fig. 2c

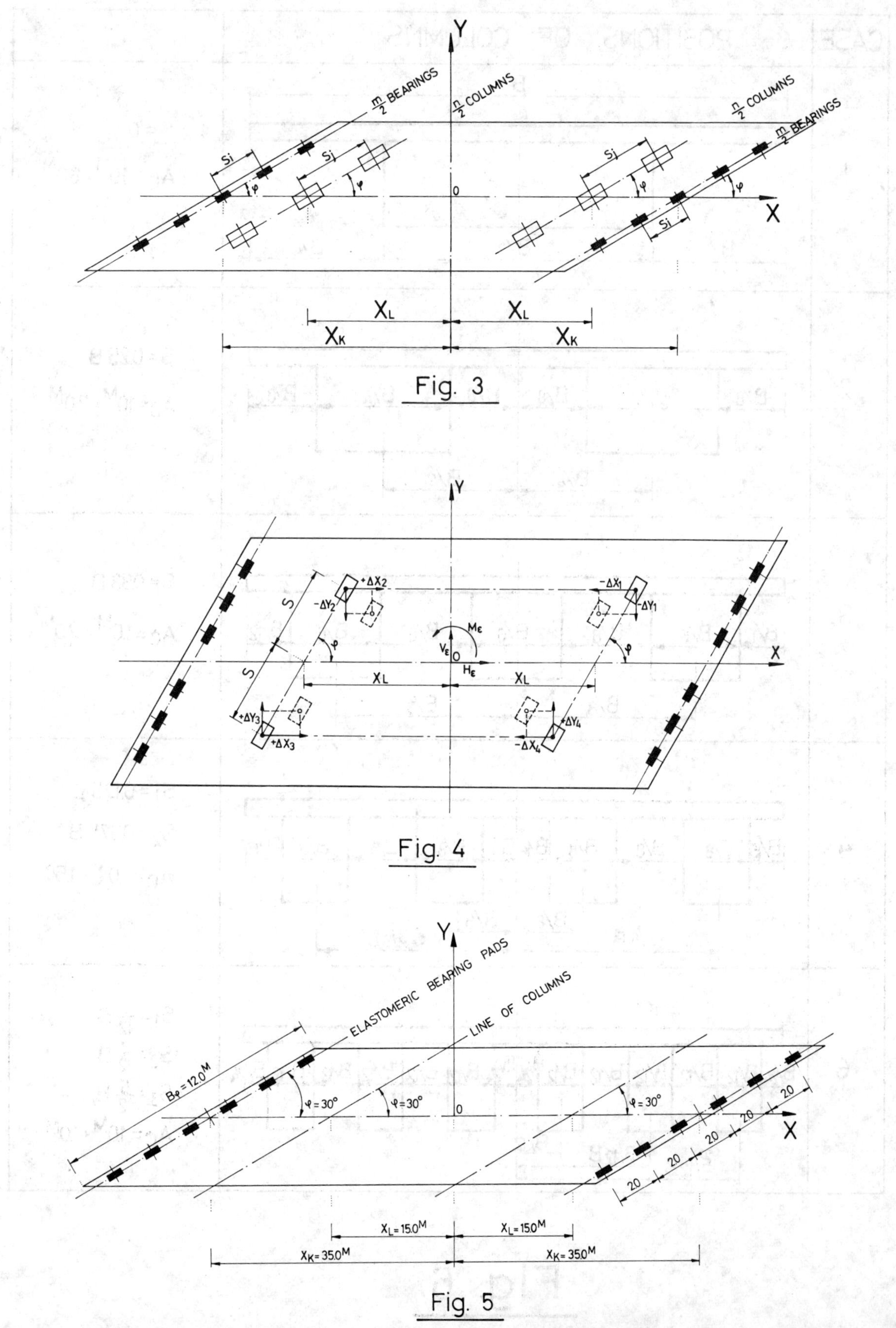

Fig. 3

Fig. 4

Fig. 5

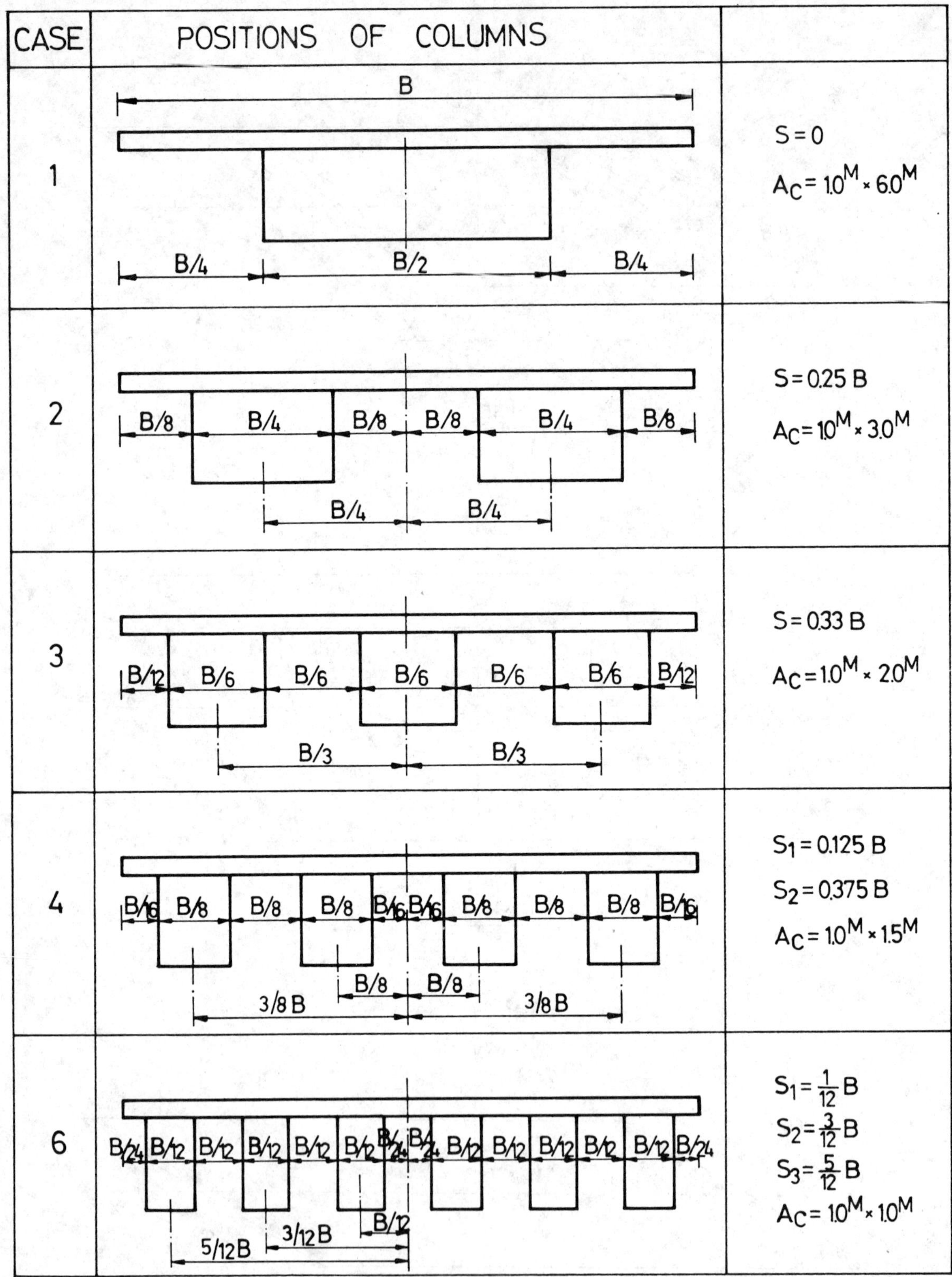
CASE
POSITIONS OF COLUMNS
1
B
B/4 B/2 B/4
S=0
Ac= 1.0M × 6.0M
2
B/8 B/4 B/8 B/8 B/4 B/8
B/4 B/4
S=0.25 B
Ac=1.0M × 3.0M
3
B/12 B/6 B/6 B/6 B/6 B/6 B/12
B/3 B/3
S=0.33 B
Ac=1.0M × 2.0M
4
B/16 B/8 B/8 B/8 B/16 B/16 B/8 B/8 B/8 B/16
B/8 B/8
3/8 B 3/8 B
S1 = 0.125 B
S2 = 0.375 B
Ac = 1.0M × 1.5M
6
B/24 B/12 B/12 B/12 B/12 B/12 B/24 B/24 B/12 B/12 B/12 B/12 B/12 B/24
B/12
3/12B
5/12B
S1 = 1/12 B
S2 = 3/12 B
S3 = 5/12 B
Ac = 1.0M × 1.0M

Fig. 6

	CASE	$\frac{K_v}{10^6}$	$\frac{K_u}{10^6}$	$\frac{K_v}{K_u}$	$\frac{K_{uv}}{K_u}$	$10^4 \frac{K_B}{K_u}$	$\frac{1}{K_u} R_{xx}$	$\frac{1}{K_u} R_{xy}$	$\frac{1}{K_u} R_{yy}$	$\frac{1}{K_u} R_{MM}$	$H_o = 100^t$		$V_o = 100^t$	
											ΔX_H mm	ΔY_H mm	ΔX_V mm	ΔY_V mm
GROUP "A"	1	3	$\frac{1}{12}$	36	5.2	48	54.556	30.30	19.556	4468.54	+0.157	−0.245	−0.245	+0.440
	2	$\frac{3}{8}$	$\frac{1}{24}$	9	5.2	96	28.115	13.86	12.115	3114.08	+0.195	−0.224	−0.224	+0.454
	3	$\frac{1}{9}$	$\frac{1}{36}$	4	5.2	144	19.673	7.80	10.673	2813.42	+0.258	−0.189	−0.189	+0.475
	4	$\frac{9}{192}$	$\frac{1}{48}$	2.25	5.2	192	15.730	4.33	10.730	2861.03	+0.343	−0.138	−0.138	+0.502
	6	$\frac{1}{72}$	$\frac{1}{72}$	1	5.2	288	12.346	0	12.346	3326.24	+0.582	0	0	+0.582
GROUP "B"	1	3	$\frac{1}{72}$	216	31.2	288	324.846	186.19	109.846	25123.74	+0.782	−1.320	−1.320	+2.290
	2	$\frac{3}{8}$	$\frac{1}{144}$	51	31.2	576	163.691	91.80	57.691	15264.48	+0.817	−1.300	−1.300	+2.320
	3	$\frac{1}{9}$	$\frac{1}{216}$	24	31.2	864	110.537	59.75	41.537	11739.22	+0.880	−1.270	−1.270	+2.350
	4	$\frac{9}{192}$	$\frac{1}{288}$	13.5	31.2	1152	84.382	43.30	34.382	10263.71	+0.968	−1.220	−1.220	+2.370
	6	$\frac{1}{72}$	$\frac{1}{432}$	6	31.2	1728	59.074	26.00	29.074	9657.44	+1.220	−1.090	−1.090	+2.480

Fig. 7

	CASE	$\frac{K_v}{10^6}$	$\frac{K_u}{10^6}$	$\frac{K_v}{K_u}$	$\frac{K_{uv}}{K_u}$	$10^4 \frac{K_B}{K_u}$	$(K_v-K_u)\sin\varphi\cos\varphi$	$n X_L^2$	$\frac{1}{K_{u\varepsilon}} M_{o\varepsilon}$	$\frac{1}{K_u} R_{MM}$	$\frac{1}{\varepsilon}\Theta$	$\Theta_{\varepsilon=60\times10^{-5}}$	$\delta_{JOINT}=\Theta(X_K+\frac{B}{2}\cos\varphi)$
GROUP "A"	1	3	$\frac{1}{12}$	36	5.2	48	15.15 K_u	450	6817.50	4468.54	1.525	9.15×10^{-4}	36.7 mm
	2	$\frac{3}{8}$	$\frac{1}{24}$	9	5.2	96	3.46 K_u	900	3114.00	3114.08	1.000	6.00×10^{-4}	24.1 mm
	3	$\frac{1}{9}$	$\frac{1}{36}$	4	5.2	144	1.30 K_u	1350	1755.00	2813.42	0.623	3.74×10^{-4}	15.0 mm
	4	$\frac{9}{192}$	$\frac{1}{48}$	2.25	5.2	192	0.54 K_u	1800	972.00	2861.03	0.339	2.03×10^{-4}	8.1 mm
	6	$\frac{1}{72}$	$\frac{1}{72}$	1	5.2	288	0	2700	0	3326.24	0	0	0
GROUP "B"	1	3	$\frac{1}{72}$	216	31.2	288	93.09 K_u	450	41890.50	25123.74	1.667	10.00×10^{-4}	40.2 mm
	2	$\frac{3}{8}$	$\frac{1}{144}$	54	31.2	576	22.95 K_u	900	20655.00	15264.48	1.353	8.12×10^{-4}	32.5 mm
	3	$\frac{1}{9}$	$\frac{1}{216}$	24	31.2	864	9.96 K_u	1350	13446.00	11739.22	1.145	6.87×10^{-4}	27.6 mm
	4	$\frac{9}{192}$	$\frac{1}{288}$	13.5	31.2	1152	5.41 K_u	1800	9738.00	10263.71	0.948	5.69×10^{-4}	22.8 mm
	6	$\frac{1}{72}$	$\frac{1}{432}$	6	31.2	1728	2.17 K_u	2700	5859.00	9657.44	0.606	3.64×10^{-4}	14.6 mm

Fig 8

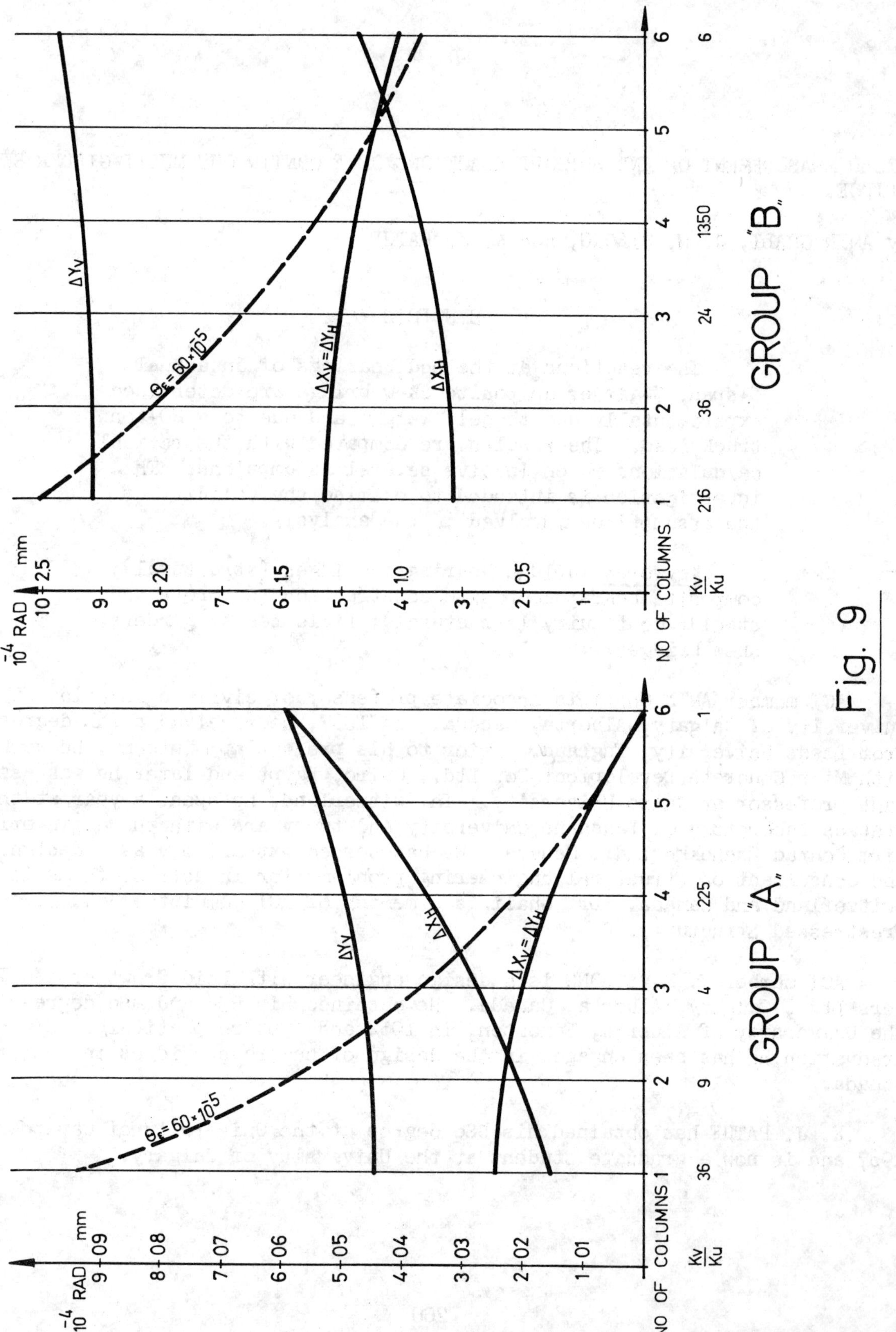
10^-4 RAD
mm
NO OF COLUMNS
Kv/Ku
36
9
4
225
1
ΔYv
ΔXH
ΔXv=ΔYH
Θε=60×10^-5
GROUP "A"
216
36
24
1350
6
GROUP "B"

Fig. 9

FIELD MEASUREMENT OF END SUPPORT REACTIONS OF A CONTINUOUS MULTI-GIRDER SKEW BRIDGE

By AMIN GHALI, J. M. STRONG, and K. J. BATHE

SYNOPSIS

The reactions at the end bearings of an actual 8-span, 7-girder composite skew bridge are determined experimentally due to self weight and due to a 20-ton truck load. The results are compared with theoretical calculations which involve several assumptions. The investigation is intended to examine the validity of the assumptions involved in the analysis.

Keywords: bridge bearings; bridges (structural); composite beams; composite construction (concrete and steel); continuity (structural); field tests; girders; skew bridges.

ACI member AMIN GHALI is associate professor of civil engineering, the University of Calgary, Alberta, Canada. In 1957, he received a PhD degree from Leeds University, England. Prior to his present appointment, he worked with Misr Concrete Development Co. Ltd., Cairo, Egypt and later he was assistant professor at Cairo University. In Switzerland, he spent a year at the Statics Laboratory of Lausanne University and two years with the engineering firm Conrad Zschokke Ltd., Geneva. He has served extensively as a designer and consultant on structural engineering problems for industrial firms in Egypt, Switzerland and Canada. Dr. Ghali is a member of ACI Committee 344, Circular Prestressed Structures.

ACI member J. M. STRONG is a design engineer with Reid Crowther and Partners Ltd., Calgary, Alberta, Canada. He obtained his BSc and MSc degrees from the University of Alberta, Edmonton, in 1962 and 1964 respectively. Since graduation he has been engaged in the design of numerous bridges in Western Canada.

K. J. BATHE has obtained his BSc degree at the University of Capetown in 1967 and is now a graduate student at the University of Calgary.

Analysis and model testing of bridges indicate that the reactions at the supports of skew bridges can be greatly affected by the angle of skew.[1-3] Damage has been reported to bearings and to the bridge deck in cases in which the skew effect has been ignored.[4] On the other hand, accurate evaluation of the reactions permits economic and safe design of the bearings, the deck and the supporting elements.

The analysis of a bridge involves in all cases several assumptions in order to represent the complicated behaviour of the composite material, concrete and steel, by that of an idealized structure for which established theories could be applied.

The present investigation is concerned with a bridge deck composed of a concrete slab acting compositely with 7 steel plate girders (Fig. 1). The deck is continuous over 8 spans supported on laminated rubber bearing pads at the two abutments and on steel rollers at the intermediate supports. The span lengths measured in the direction of the traffic parallel to the girders vary between 65' and 133' (19.8-40.6 m.). Measurements of the actual reactions are taken at the 7 bearings on one end of the deck where the skew angle is 50°. The span at the end where the reactions are measured is 65' (19.8 m.) and the two adjacent spans are 97' and 86' (29.6 and 26.2 m.). A schematic plan of the span at this end is shown in Fig. 2. At the end of the bridge a cross girder is rigidly connected to the main girders immediately above the bearings as shown in Fig. 3. Shear connectors are provided between the main girders and the slab in the portions of positive dead load moment as well as over the whole length of the cross girder over the abutments.

The steel girders were fabricated in segments which were field spliced by bolts at approximately 1/5th of the spans. Starting from one abutment, the girders were erected at the design elevations for the end span (extending over a part of the adjacent span) and the cross girders were connected by bolts. This sequence was repeated for all the spans, then all bolted connections were tightened. Concreting of the deck started in the end span followed by the adjacent span having a part above the intermediate support which was then poured. This sequence was repeated for all spans.

The abutments were founded on piles and the piers were on footings on dense gravel. Settlements were recorded and it was concluded that no differential settlement appreciably affected the measured reactions.

An elastic analysis is made for the bridge deck considered as a grid. The assumptions involved and the method of analysis will be discussed later. The reactions at one of the abutments obtained by this analysis are compared with the measured reactions both for dead loading and a 20-ton (17850 Kg) truck load. No attempt is made to make more refined assumptions in the analysis than what is usually made in practice, since the object of the testing is to check the validity of the assumptions made in a practical case.

EXPERIMENTAL INVESTIGATION

A hydraulic jack was used to lift each main girder in turn from its bearing and the force applied by the jack was measured by a load cell and verified by readings of a pressure gage (Fig. 4). The lifting force was applied on the girder at a distance of 1' - 2" from the centre line of the bearing. This distance was taken as small as practicable so that the measurement represents as close as possible the support reaction. For each reaction measurement, a girder was first lifted until the bearing is cleared. The bearing was then removed and the girder was allowed to move downwards to its original position before lifting. The vertical movement of the girder was controlled by a dial gage.

In order to provide sufficient clearance to insert the jack and the measuring device a recess was provided during the construction of the abutments for this purpose. Also, additional steel stiffners were welded to the girders at the jacking points to permit the application of the reaction at these points.

The procedure of the reaction measurement due to the truck load was slightly different. Each girder was first supported by the jack instead of the bearing and then lowered to the exact level as described above. With the jack in position, the truck load was supplied, the girder level was adjusted back to its original position and the load cell indicated the jacking force. In this way the girder at which the reaction was measured acted as if it were resting on a rigid support which did not allow the small vertical movement which would have occurred at the end of this girder had the bridge been on its elastomeric bearing pads. An alternative method of measurement would be to apply the truck load with the girders on the bearing pads, then transfer the reaction from one bearing to the jack without change in girder level. This process would have required much more time and it was not possible to stop the traffic for such a period.

The actual axle load and wheel spacing of the truck used for testing are shown in Figure 5.

THEORETICAL ANALYSIS

The deck is idealized as an assemblage of beam elements having both torsional and bending rigidities in the form of a gird. The bending and torsional rigidities of the main girders and the end cross girders are calculated for a composite section in the portion where shear connectors are provided. The slab width considered to be acting is 12 times the slab thickness. Where no shear connectors are provided, the flexural rigidity is taken as the sum of the flexural rigidity of a steel girder plus that of a slab strip of width as above.

Intermediate cross bracings are treated as cross girders of moment of inertia = 1.1 times the moment of inertia of the top and bottom chords about a horizontal axis at mid-depth. To this is added the moment of inertia of a strip of the slab of width equal to the spacing between the bracings. The torsional rigidity of the cross bracings is neglected. The ratio of the modulus of elasticity of steel to that of concrete is taken as 8.

The dead load is replaced by line loads on the main girders of uniform intensity between adjacent nodes. For the effect of the moving loads, the values of the reactions are determined for a unit load at the nodes, then these values are used to draw contour lines representing influence surfaces for the reactions. These are then used to calculate the reactions of the wheel loads of the truck used for testing.

The analysis is made by a computer programme for which the continuous deck is partitioned into substructures[5] each composed of one span. The deck is then considered as an assemblage of the 8 spans.

RESULTS OF ANALYSIS AND TESTING

Table 1 gives the values of the reactions due to dead loads obtained by the analysis and by testing. The concrete at the time of measurement had an age of approximately 8 months.

Table 1 : Dead Load Reactions in kips*

Support	A	B	C	D	E	F	G	Sum of End Reactions
Theoretical Values	49.8	51.2	53.3	59.8	60.5	63.7	56.7	395.0
Experimental Values	22.0	57.5	44.5	54.0	85.0	84.5	40.5	388.0

* 1 kip = 454 Kg.

It is worth mentioning that a set of reactions calculated for the main girders acting as separate continuous beams differed only slightly from the theoretical values of the grid analysis.

The elastomeric bearing pads are compressed when the live load is applied, that is - the actual bridge is resting on elastic (spring) supports at the ends of the seven girders. With the method of measurement followed, the support at which the measurement is taken is not allowed to settle. This has an appreciable effect on the value of the reactions because of the relatively high stiffness of the end cross girder. However, the measured values when compared with theoretical values calculated with one rigid end support and the other six flexible represent the elastic behaviour of the structure under the effect of live load.

The theoretical and measured values of the reactions are given in Table 2 for the seven end supports each for 9 loading positions of the truck. The location of the centre of the rear bogie (point A in Fig. 5) for each of the 9 positions is indicated in Fig. 2.

Table 2: Truck Load Reactions in kips*

Load position		1	2	3	4	5	6	7	8	9
Girder A	Theory	18.0	23.7	9.4	5.1	0.7	0.9			
	measured	20.5	28.0	12.5	3.5	-.5	-.5	**	**	**
Girder B	Theory	9.1	14.5	15.4	13.1	5.3	5.7			
	measured	4.5	10.0	15.5	16.5	6.5	6.0	**	**	**
Girder C	Theory	2.9	4.0	7.2	10.6	12.6	17.9			
	measured	0.0	0.0	6.5	11.0	17.5	25.5	**	**	**
Girder D	Theory	0.3	0.6	2.1	4.3	8.9	14.9			
	measured	0.0	0.0	0.0	2.0	7.5	13.5	**	**	**
Girder E	Theory						2.8	6.4	1.9	0.7
	measured	**	**	**	**	**	0.0	11.5	-.5	-.5
Girder F	Theory							16.5	9.2	9.4
	measured	**	**	**	**	**	**	14.0	14.0	13.5
Girder G	Theory							4.5	16.2	23.1
	measured	**	**	**	**	**	**	4.0	17.5	24.0

* 1 Kip = 454 Kg.

** The reaction was not measured

CONCLUSIONS

The sum of the theoretical and experimental values of the dead load reactions differ only by 1.8% while the values of the individual reactions differ considerably. For supports E and F, the measured dead load reactions are as high as 1.4 times the theoretical values. The dead load reactions are affected by the method of erection, sequence of casting and time-dependent deformations of concrete. It is difficult to give justifications for the exact reasons for the discrepancies.

The reactions due to the truck load showed generally better agreement between the measured and theoretical values. In all cases of loading, the measured value of the largest reaction is higher than the theoretical value. The largest discrepancy is for loading positions 4, 5 and 6 where the axis of the truck is midway between two main girders. The main reason for the discrepancies is believed to be caused by idealization of the bridge as a grid. In the actual bridge, the slab tends to transmit the truck load in positions 4, 5 and 6 to the bearing at the obtuse angle in a more effective way than the assumed grid. Excluding these three loading positions, the maximum difference between the theoretical and the measured value of the largest reaction is 18%.

The end cross girder is found to have an appreciable effect on the elastic behaviour of the deck. The advantage gained by the practice of providing a stiff cross girder at the abutments is questionable. However, if such a cross girder is provided, its effect should not be ignored.

ACKNOWLEDGEMENTS

This project was supported by a grant from the National Research Council of Canada which is gratefully acknowledged. Permission to carry out the testing on the bridge was granted from the City of Calgary. Dominion Bridge Co., the Canadian Institute of Steel Construction, and Reid Crowther and Partners Ltd. shared the cost of modifications to the girders. Standard General Construction (International) Ltd. supplied the truck used in obtaining the live load measurements. Thanks are due to Dr. W. Dilger of The University of Calgary for his suggestions all through the investigation.

REFERENCES

1. Andrä, W., and Leonhardt, F., "Influence of the Spacing of the Bearings on Bending Moments and Reactions in Single-Span Skew Slabs," Beton und Stahlbeton, July 1960. Translated into English, Cement and Concrete Association, Library translation no. 99.

2. Homberg, H., "Modell Untersuchung an einem schiefen Kasten," Die Bautechnik, 4/1961, (in German).

3. Ghali, A., "Analysis of Continuous Skew Concrete Girder Bridge," First International Symposium on Concrete Bridge Design, Toronto, Arpil 5, 1967, ACI Publication.

4. Hoeland, G., "Der Kraftverlauf in schiefen Hohlkästen," Der Stahlbau, March 1960 (in German).

5. Przemiensecki, J.S., "Theory of Matrix Structural Analysis," McGraw-Hill Book Co., New York, 1968.

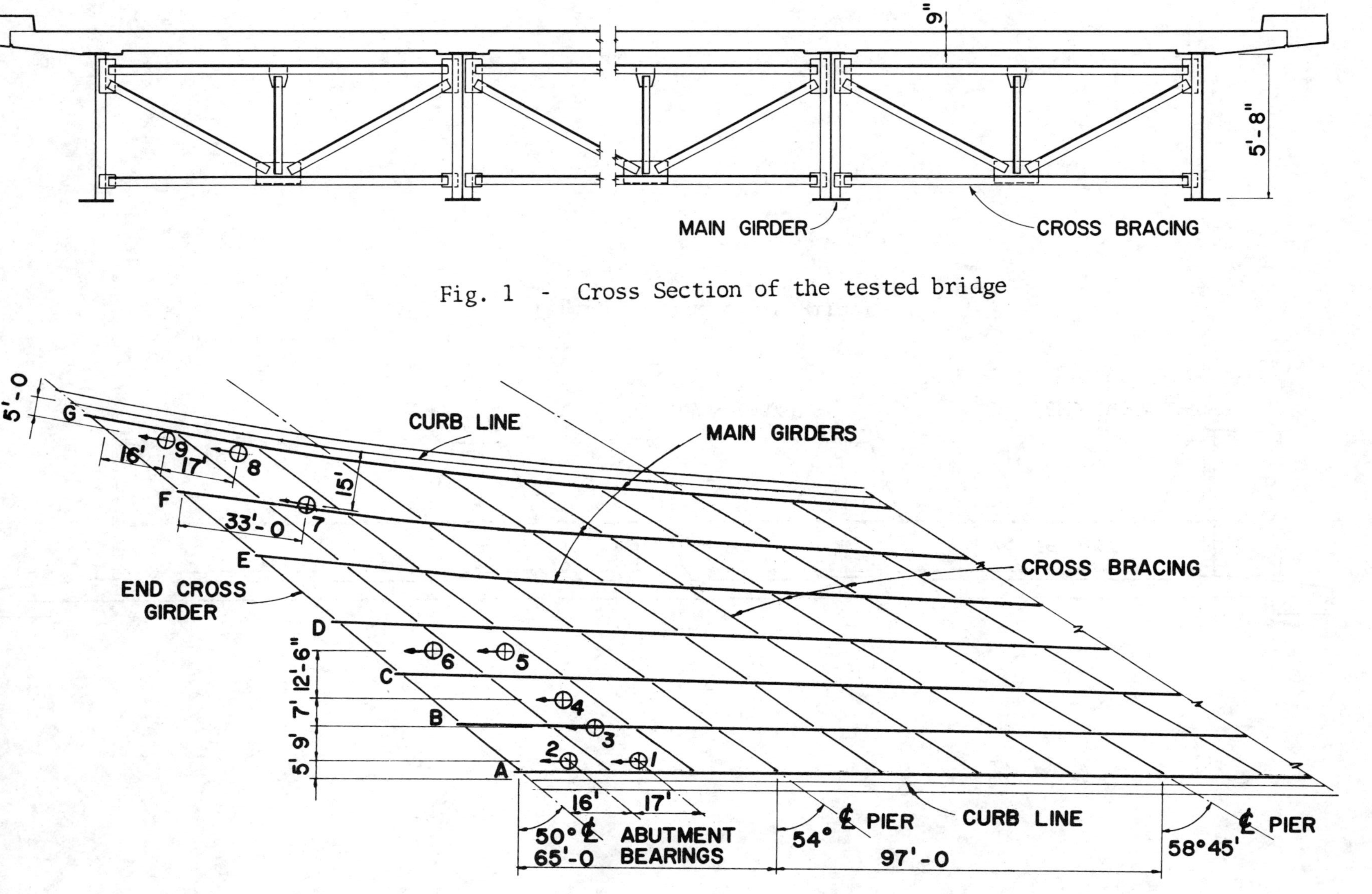

Fig. 1 - Cross Section of the tested bridge

Fig. 2 - Schematic plan of the bridge deck and location of truck loading

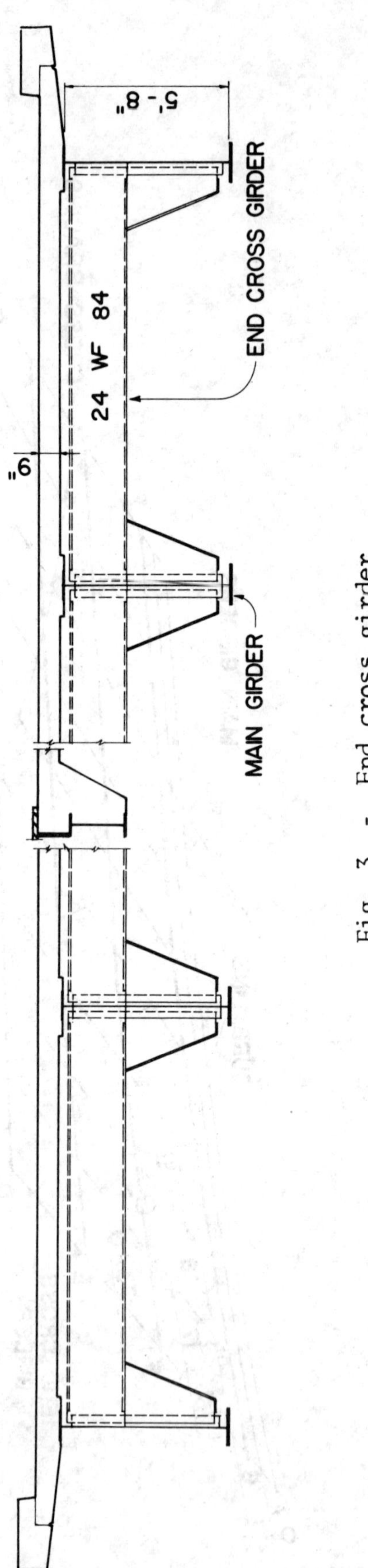

Fig. 3 - End cross girder

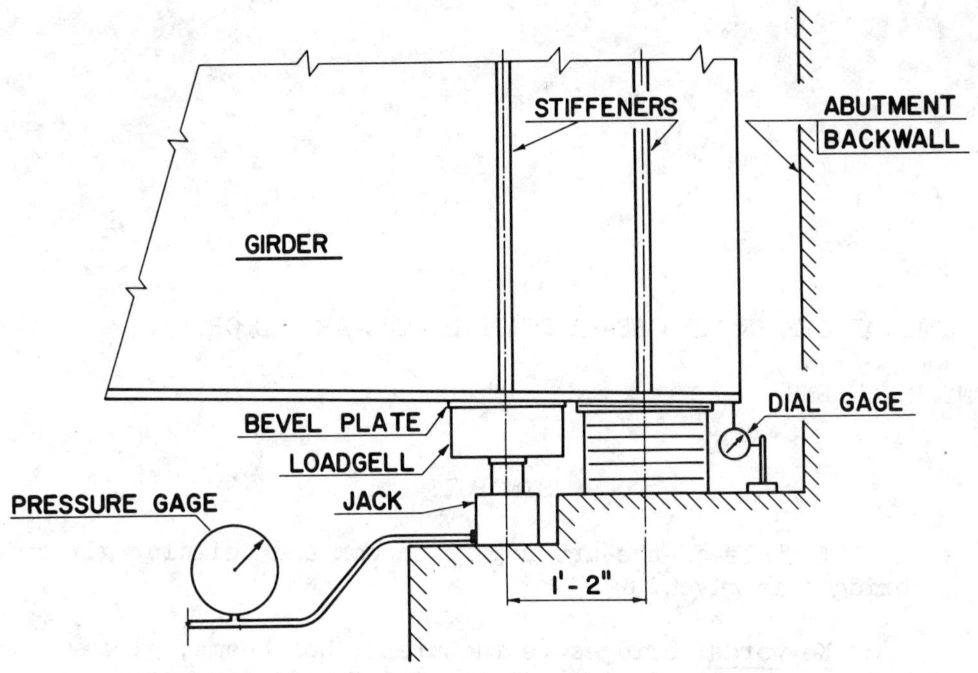

Fig. 4 - Set-up for reaction measurement

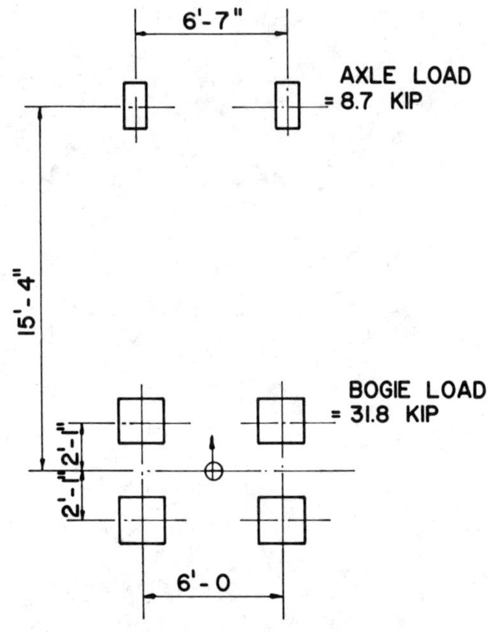

Fig. 5 - Truck load used in testing

BOX AND CELLULAR GIRDER BRIDGES--A STATE-OF-THE-ART REPORT

By ANTHONY R. CUSENS

SYNOPSIS

A state-of-the-art report on box and cellular girder bridges is given.

Keywords: bridges (structures); box beams; girder bridges; prestressed concrete; reinforced concrete.

ACI member ANTHONY R. CUSENS is the head of the civil engineering department at the University of Dundee in Dundee Scotland.

There is a song which emanated from somewhere on this side of the Atlantic which concerns people who live in boxes made of ticky-tacky which all look just the same. Hardly an eulogy of the box structure perhaps - and we know that even for buildings the boxes do not all have to look the same. The box as a living unit has been used imaginatively in building structures such as Habitat in Montreal and the San Antonio Hilton in Texas. However the song is symptomatic of this era of boxes we live in. Looking around at new concrete bridge construction it may be seen that an astonishingly high percentage of current construction falls within the general heading of this session on Box and Cellular Girder Bridges.

There is frequently some semantic confusion when engineers discuss box and cellular bridge decks. It is appropriate therefore to attempt to distinguish between the main types of concrete bridge in this category.

An established form of construction here in the United States, but until recently a rarer occurrence in Europe, is the elevated motorway in urban areas. The increasing construction of elevated motorways has been accompanied by a desire to keep the supports as simple and as unobtrusive as possible. In consequence many recent elevated motorways in Western Europe and North America have been supported on single columns, and the bridge section has been designed as a box form. Intuitively the box form is right for the single supports and the structural designer is well aware of the merits of high torsional and flexural stiffness with comparatively light weight. This type of construction is frequently known as a <u>spine beam</u> and the basic section may be a single cell (as in the curved bridge described in the paper by Dr. Aneja and Dr. Roll) or it may be in a multi-cell form. The spine beam may be cast on site and post-tensioned or conveniently precast in segments and post-tensioned.

The multi cell slab (Fig. 2) is essentially a monolithic slab with voids of some form. In normal circumstances the multi cell slab is cast in situ.

The <u>multi-beam bridge</u> (Fig. 3) consists essentially of precast (usually pretensioned) concrete beams which are placed side by side to form the deck. In its most elementary form the transverse connection may consist only of a concrete or mortar shear key which, as its name implies, will convey shear force between adjoining sections but not bending moment. Various forms of mild steel bar connection are also used. The most effective transverse connection is created with prestressing wires which, if there is sufficient transverse prestress, convert the bridge into a monolithic voided slab. However the bridge designer (at least in Britain) is constantly being told that transverse prestressing and transverse diaphragms are expensive luxuries, to be avoided if possible. In consequence there is an urgent need to find practical values of stiffness parameters for the multi-beam bridge corresponding to common forms of transverse connection.

It is possible to distinguish three basic types of box and cellular bridge deck but of course the picture is not quite as clear as Figs. 1 to 3 imply. The boundaries between the three types is occasionally a little blurred and this may become more obvious in examining some examples of current or recent bridge construction in Europe.

In Scotland there is currently a bridge over the Clyde under construction at Kingston, Glasgow. Kingston Bridge is to carry dual 5-lane carriageways and the main span of 470 ft consists of twin three-cell box beams of varying depths.

It has been designed by W.A. Fairhurst and Partners. The approach roads are two and three cell spine beams.

Fig. 4 shows a section of one of the approach roads to Kingston Bridge. This is a 5-lane elevated highway; the box beams are 4 ft 3 in. deep. Column distances are 70 ft but the construction consists of 100 ft beams with cantilever ends in prestressed concrete, with alternate 40 ft suspended spans in reinforced concrete. In this case, there are two spine beams connected by a solid slab. In other structures on this project there are multiple box beams connected by a solid slab.

The basic shape of the section being used in the Kingston Bridge approach roads bears a strong resemblance to an earlier box section spine beam used in the Mancunian Way completed in 1967. This elevated highway[1] is about 3200 ft long and consists of 32 spans mostly of 105 ft. The structure consists of two spine beams as seen in Fig. 5, linked by a concrete median strip. Each 105 ft span is made up of fourteen segments with 3 in. concrete joints. Individual segments weighed up to 28 tons. A model of one of the Mancunian Way spans in micro-concrete was given extensive tests[2] in the laboratories of the Cement and Concrete Association. The Mancunian Way was designed by Maunsell and Partners of London and this same firm has designed a very interesting elevated highway scheme now under construction in West London - the Western Avenue extension[3]. Here there are three interesting concrete box beams in use on different sections of the work.

The first is a three cell spine beam with cantilever arms (Fig. 6). The total construction width of each beam is 62 ft and the spans of this section of the elevated highway are 115 ft. These beams were also constructed in segments, each weighing 55 tons.

Secondly there is the very large three cell spine beam (Fig. 7 and 8) used in Section 5 of Western Avenue. Designed for spans of 204 ft these beams were constructed in segments which weigh up to 145 tons and are 94 ft wide. Model tests were carried out during the design stage by the Cement and Concrete Association.

The top hat section box beam (Fig. 9) is the third type of interest in the Western Avenue project. Precast pretensioned beams have in situ concrete added at top and bottom to form a second series of boxes in the composite section. Steel bars are left protruding from each side of the bottom flange of these boxes and when the site concrete is added, these provide the transverse rigidity of the deck. At Dundee University tests are about to begin on a quarter scale model of one of these decks in an attempt to evaluate practical values of the torsional and flexural stiffness parameters.

These are just a few examples of current trends in construction. They are all taken from bridges in Britain but they represent current trends in the use of box girders. There are many other examples of interesting construction in other countries in Europe, such as the Oleron viaduct in France and elevated highways at Dusseldorf in Germany. Finally, although it departs from the strict title of this session perhaps it would be appropriate to remember that the largest span concrete bridge in the world is also of box section. Fig. 10 shows the 1000 ft arch of the Gladesville bridge in Sydney completed in 1964.

Before we leave the construction of box and cellular beams it is of interest to note the change in jointing methods for segmental bridges over the past few years. I mentioned the 3 inch wide concrete joints in the Mancunian Way. The Campenon Bernard organization in France has used closed joints sealed with epoxy resins on bridges at Choisy-le -Roi and Oleron. In Britain the Rawcliffe bridge in Yorkshire has also been successfully jointed with epoxy. Doubtless this technique will be used more widely in segmental bridges.

The analysis of some of the more complex box sections is a difficult process. As I mentioned it was found necessary to conduct model studies for both Mancunian Way and Section 5 of Western Avenue. Three of the papers in this session also involve tests on models. For simpler sections a number of design methods have been used; again development and refinement of analytical techniques have proceeded rapidly in the last five years.

At the last Symposium Professor Scordelis presented a paper based on the use of folded plate analysis for the design of box sections and he will have more to say on this subject later in this session when he extends the method to an indeterminate deck and also introduces a finite segment method of analysis. Both he and Dr. Aneja will also refer to the finite element method which has attracted a great deal of attention and a correspondingly large volume of papers recently. There is no doubt that the finite element method is the most general of all the available methods. It is not proposed to discuss its accuracy in a typical design situation but it appears prodigal in terms of computer time for many of the simpler bridge problems which can be solved quickly and accurately by such methods as folded plate analysis, grillage analysis or even orthotropic plate theory. Hybrid methods such as the finite segment method and the finite strip method will clearly help here. A fruitful field for the finite element method in the future appears to lie in solving the three-dimensional problems for which no other method exists and it is to be hoped that the leading exponents of the method will do more work in this direction. A period of sorting-out lies ahead and it is also to be hoped that computer programs for all of the main methods of analysis will be freely available to designers.

The search for sophisticated and accurate techniques for calculating stresses in box beam bridges needs very little prompting - it is clearly proceeding under its own momentum, mainly in University departments around the world. However a plea must be made for more short-cut devices to allow the engineer in the design offices to arrive by a logical process at an approximate section which can then be checked by a more advanced technique. The design process in major bridge construction projects, and perhaps in structural work generally, is to have two main stages (a) approximate design leading to a choice of a small number of alternative solutions; (b) an accurate check of the alternative solutions using computer techniques.

The other plea is for more experimental work on bridges. An analytical method is only as good as the data fed in at the beginning - no computer program will correct poor assumptions however much it is felt that large sheafs of results from the line printer have the ring of truth. Apart from studies on models of specific bridges there is a great deal of general information still lacking on the behaviour of box beam bridges under load. For example, we are still comparatively ignorant as to the precise effects of diaphragms ; the action of certain forms of transverse connection in multi-beam bridges cannot be accurately assessed; it is not possible to place absolutely reliable values on the torsional and flexural stiffnesses of some bridge sections. The number of institutions actually working on experimental studies is comparatively small on both sides of the Atlantic. It is necessary to dispel the view that experimental work is an activity to be saved for the graduate student of lesser ability; a man will never be a good engineer unless he is willing to verify his analytical techniques.

REFERENCES

1. BINGHAM, T.G. and LEE, D.J. "The Mancunian Way Elevated Road Structure", Jnl. Inst. of Civil Engrs., V.42, Paper No. 7186, April 1969 pp. 459-492.

2. SOMERVILLE, G., ROLL, F. and CALDWELL, J.A.D. "Tests on a 1/12 Scale Model of the Mancunian Way", Technical Report TRA 394, Cement and Concrete Association, London, December 1965.

3. HUNTLEY, H.D. "Western Avenue Extension", Structural Engineer, V.47, No. 3, Mar. 1969, pp. 85-97.

FIG. 1 **SPINE BEAM BRIDGES**

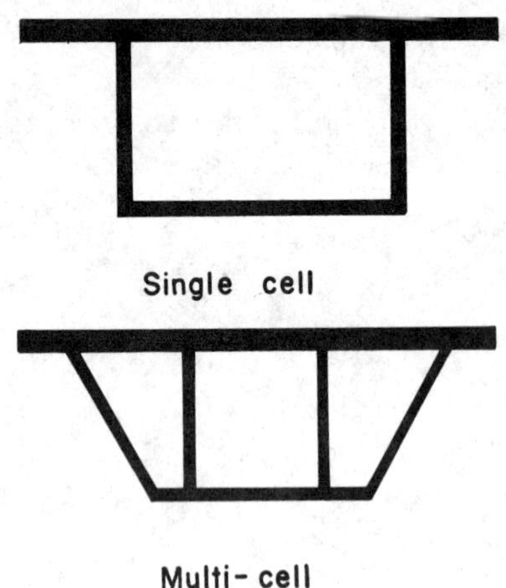

CONSTRUCTION - In-situ or precast in segments

FIG. 2 **MULTI-CELL SLAB BRIDGES**

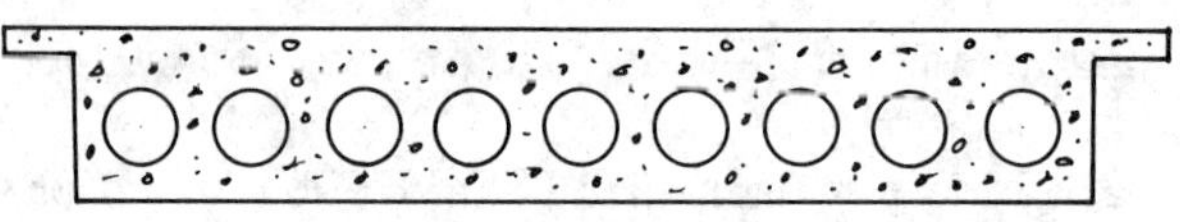

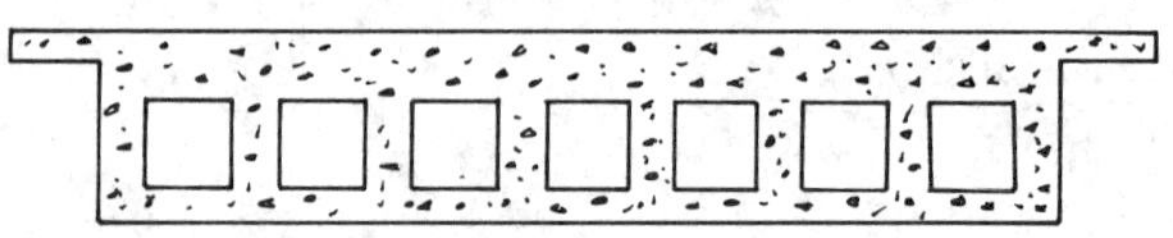

CONSTRUCTION - In-situ

FIG. 3 **MULTI-BEAM BRIDGES**

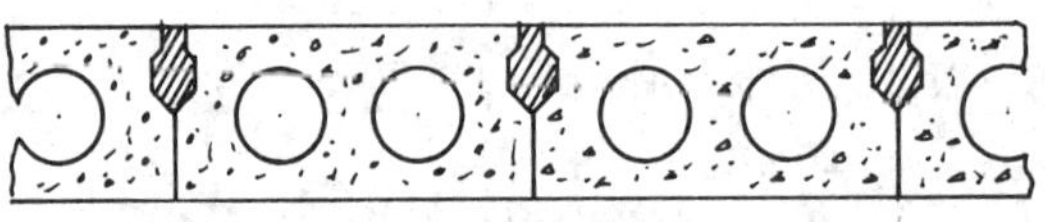

Multi-beam with shear keys

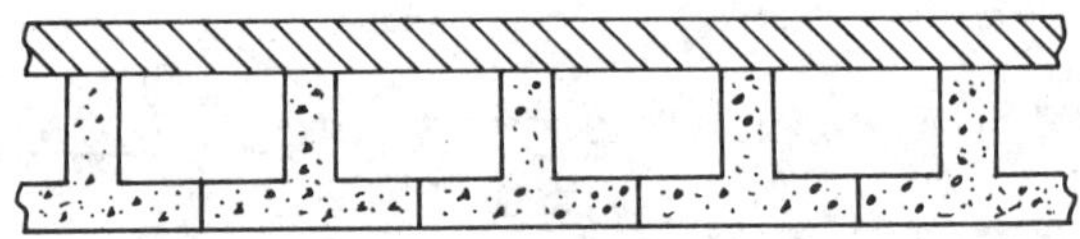

Composite multi-beam

CONSTRUCTION - Precast with possible in-situ addition

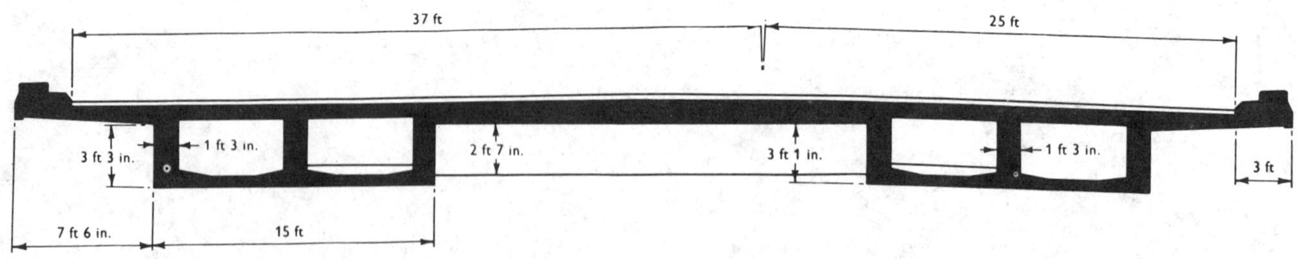

Fig. 4 Kingston Bridge Glasgow: Typical cross-section, five-lane elevated highway.

Fig. 5 Mancunian Way, Manchester, England

Fig. 6 Traffic Intersection on Section I of the Western Avenue Extension, London.

Fig. 7 Bridge Segment of Section 5 of the Western Avenue Extension, London

Fig. 8 Underside of Completed Portion of Section 5 of the Western Avenue Extension, London.

Fig. 9 Top Hat Beams Used in Section 6 of the Western Avenue Extension, London.

Fig. 10 Gladesville Bridge, Sydney, Australia.

STRESSES IN CONTINUOUS CONCRETE BOX GIRDER BRIDGES

By A. C. SCORDELIS and R. E. DAVIS

SYNOPSIS

Three methods for the theoretical assessment of structural behavior of multi-celled box girder bridges with or without interior diaphragms or supports are briefly described. These methods, designated as the folded plate method, the finite segment method and the finite element method, extend the scope of previously reported studies (1) to include the effects of continuity and arbitrary boundary conditions. Relative accuracy of these methods is assessed by comparing selected results for a typical 3-cell bridge. Effects of continuity on load distribution in 3- and 6-cell bridges are evaluated by studying results from twenty-three separate computer analyses performed using general computer programs developed for each of the three methods of analysis.

Keywords: analysis; box beams; bridges (structures); computer programs; continuity (structural); finite element method; folded plates; girder bridges; girders; loads (forces); reinforced concrete; specifications; stresses; structural analysis.

ACI member, A. C. SCORDELIS is professor of civil engineering, department of civil engineering, University of California, Berkeley, where he has been a faculty member since 1949. He has been noted for his research work in reinforced concrete structures, particularly with respect to shell and bridge systems. Currently he is a member of ACI-ASCE Committee 421, Design of Reinforced Concrete Slabs, ACI Committee 435, Deflection of Concrete Building Structures, and the ACI Committee 334, Concrete Shell Design and Construction.

RAYMOND E. DAVIS received a BS in engineering from the California Institute of Technology in 1949 and has been with the California Division of Highways Bridge Department since then, engaged in construction, design and, primarily, research and special studies. As a Senior Bridge Engineer, his recent and current fields of research include studies of structural behavior of box girder bridges; ventilation of large vehicular tunnels; orthotropic steel deck plate bridges; and concrete arch, concrete pipe, and corrugated metal pipe culverts under very high fills.

INTRODUCTION

The box girder bridge has become an established feature of California's highway system. On the basis of deck area, about sixty percent of current California bridge designs incorporate this structural form. Its appreciable torsional rigidity provides structural efficiency, and its unbroken soffit is superior in appearance to that of open web structures.

In California, concrete box girders have proven economical in simple span ranges of 70 to 150 feet, while recently designed continuous box girders of ordinary reinforced concrete have incorporated spans up to 240 ft. Continuous prestressed boxes with spans up to 300 ft. have been designed, and one set of current plans calls for a segmentally constructed prestressed box girder bridge with a 450-foot span in southern California.

In the past decade a new type of structure has come into vogue in which a concrete roadway slab is compositely attached to small single-celled or large multi-celled steel box sections. About fifty such structures of this variety have been built throughout the world during this period. Currently a large, two-celled, composite, comcrete slab and steel box girder bridge is being built across the Sacramento River in California.

Recent trends in aesthetics have resulted in sloping or rounded exterior webs for concrete box girders, while the trend toward longer spans has required the use of haunched girders and, in some instances, parabolic soffits.

While these innovations in form have resulted in unique and beautiful structures, they have also introduced complexities into construction and design techniques.

In general, design of girder bridges, including box girders, has involved taking a typical, repeating I-section from the structure and determining stresses therein as functions of: (1) the influence of a single wheel line or lane load of standard design trucks; (2) the center to center spacing of girders; and (3) a distribution factor which may have evolved as a rule of thumb, some rather crude calculations, or empirical studies of isolated structures.

It is readily apparent that this design method would produce, at best, only an approximate assessment of actual structural behavior; indeed, for the complex box girder geometries currently employed, a designer might experience great difficulty in deciding how to apply the method. It is also difficult to conceive that load distribution in areas of negative moment over supports would be the same as that out in central portions of the spans as indicated by this design method.

In a previous study [1], it was demonstrated for an example structure that a conservatively designed two-lane bridge would change into an under-designed three-lane facility with no more alteration than a small change in width of railing and curb, were the present distribution factor method used in design.

Accurate assessment of structural behavior for the more complex box girder structure geometries requires the employment of much more sophisticated design methods which can take these geometries into account.

GENERAL DESCRIPTION OF THEORETICAL METHODS

Three analytical methods were developed in this investigation and were designated as the folded plate method, the finite segment method and the finite element method. Only a brief description of the methods is possible here, however, complete theoretical derivations may be found in [3]. The folded plate method and the finite element methods are based on "elasticity theory" and the finite segment method on "ordinary theory". The ordinary theory assumes that the membrane stresses in each plate can be calculated by elementary beam theory and that slab bending is defined by means of transverse one-way slab action only. The elasticity theory utilizes plane stress elasticity theory and classical two-way thin plate bending theory to determine the membrane stresses and slab moments in each plate.

Folded Plate Method

This method is restricted to structures simply supported at the two ends. In this analysis the basic structural element used is a single plate having a width equal to the distance between longitudinal joints and a length equal to the overall length of the bridge. A combination of a displacement (stiffness) and a force (flexibility) method is used in the solution, Fig. 1. A primary structure, Fig. 1a, is selected consisting of the loaded structure simply supported at its ends with a large number of unknown redundant forces existing at the interior diaphragm support. Displacements due to each effect are evaluated by a direct stiffness solution in which a harmonic analysis using Fourier series is utilized and then compatibility equations are used to evaluate the unknown redundants. The original structure is then analyzed subjected to the known loading and known redundants to determine the final stresses and displacements in the continuous box girder system.

The redundant forces X are represented by a set of three joint forces at each longitudinal joint, Fig. 1e, consisting of vertical, horizontal and rotational components in the plane of the transverse diaphragm and a set of four plate forces for each plate, Fig. 1f, consisting of distributed normal and tangential forces having triangular variations between the two longitudinal edges of the plate. The 3-cell box girder continuous over one interior support which is shown in Fig. 1 has 8 longitudinal joints and 10 plate elements and thus would have a total of (8 x 3) + (10 x 4) = 64 redundants. For two interior supports, therefore a 3-span continuous bridge, the number of redundants would double. All of the redundant forces are assumed to be uniformly distributed in the longitudinal span direction over a length equal to the transverse diaphragm thickness specified at the interior support. The condition of zero displacement of the entire cross-section at the interior support is closely approximated by requiring that the displacements be zero on this cross-section at each of the longitudinal joints in the vertical, horizontal, and rotational directions and at the third points between joints in directions normal and tangential to the plane of each plate.

Finite Segment Method

This method can be applied to structures with arbitrary boundary conditions at the two ends. The basic structural element used in this method is a finite segment which is formed by dividing each plate element into a finite number of segments longitudinally, Fig. 2. These finite segments each have a width equal to the transverse distance between the longitudinal joints of the plate. In the analysis, the finite segments are first interconnected transversely at one end of the bridge to form a full transverse segment of the entire bridge cross-section, Fig. 2. The solution proceeds by a segment progression method along the span to connect one transverse segment to the next until the far end of the bridge is reached. The boundary conditions at the two ends of the bridge provide sufficient equations to determine all the unknowns needed in the solution of the problem. It should be noted that only joint loads are considered and they are assumed to be uniformly distributed over the length of each segment.

If a single finite segment, Fig. 2c, is taken as a free body it is similar to a rectangular plate on elastic supports along its four sides. The boundary conditions at the two longitudinal ends of the segment require that continuity and equilibrium with the next segment along the span or with a support condition must be satisfied. Along the two longitudinal edges of the segment, line loads are acting on the edges. These line loads produce both transverse one way slab bending and also in-plane membrane stresses. At each longitudinal joint, equilibrium requires that the sum of all the line loads on the segments connected to the joint must be equal to the externally applied line load acting on the joint. In addition these segments must all have the same joint displacements to satisfy compatibility.

A typical finite segment taken from the structure is shown in Fig. 2c with the positive directions of the forces and corresponding displacements shown. At each longitudinal end of the segment, therefore at sections k-1 and k, there exist three stress resultants: an axial force N , a shear force Q , and an in-plane bending moment M_1 . The three corresponding displacements at each end are u_1 , v_1 and Ψ . It is assumed that plane sections remain plane at each end of the segment when satisfying continuity. Along the longitudinal edges i and j , plate edge forces, uniformly distributed along the length of the segment, are assumed to exist. These forces per unit length of edge are: a membrane shear force T along the edge, a transverse membrane force P normal to the edge, a shear force V normal to the plate, and a transverse slab moment M_2 about the longitudinal edge (shown as a vector using the right hand rule). The four corresponding displacements u_2, v_2, w and θ are taken at the midpoint of the two ends of the segments. Thus in the solution compatibility conditions with respect to these displacements on the longitudinal joints are satisfied only at the center points of each segment.

An inspection of Fig. 2c indicates that each finite segment has 14 degrees of displacement freedom and 14 corresponding forces. A segment progression solution based on the transfer matrix method is adopted in the analysis. To describe the segment progression solution, consider a segment k between sections $k-1$ and k taken as a free body from a plate element. This free body is subjected to the actions, forces and displacements, shown in Fig. 2c. The actions at section k depend on the actions at sections $k-1$ and the uniformly distributed line loads at the two longitudinal edges i and j of the segment. The magnitudes of the edge line loads are determined so as to satisfy compatibility and equilibrium conditions of a whole transverse cross-section. They can be expressed in terms of the actions of all plate elements at section $k-1$ and the externally applied joint loads on segment k . After the edge line loads are found in these terms, the actions at section k can then be expressed in terms of the actions at section $k-1$ and the externally applied joint loads on this segment. Repeating this procedure for the first segment at the origin to the last segment at the far end of the structure, the relation between the actions at the two ends of the structure is obtained. Where an interior support condition is encountered at a particular section, proper account is taken of the boundary conditions imposed when passing from one segment to the next. By satisfying the boundary conditions at the two ends, sufficient equations are available to determine the unknown actions at the two ends and then the final internal forces and displacements can be found by progressing along the structure once again.

Finite Element Method

The finite element method can be thought of as a numerical procedure by means of which the solution of a problem in continuum mechanics may be approximated by analyzing a structure consisting of an assemblage of finite elements interconnected at a finite number of nodal points, in which selected internal stress or displacement patterns are assumed in the elements to satisfy certain required conditions. During the past decade this method has been applied successfully to a variety of problems involving plates subjected to in-plane or normal loadings, axi-symmetric solids and axi-symmetric shells. More recently attention has been focused on applying the method to general thin shell problems and to the general three dimensional analysis of solids.

Of particular interest in the present investigation is the application of the finite element method to the analysis of prismatic cellular folded plate structures such as the box girder bridge. The basic structural element used in this method is a finite element which is formed by dividing each rectangular plate element transversely as well as longitudinally into an assemblage of smaller rectangular finite elements, Fig. 3. The size, thickness and material properties of these rectangular finite elements can be varied as desired throughout the structure. Thus in zones near concentrated loads, Fig. 3, a finer mesh can be used to more accurately determine the stresses and moments which are rapidly changing in this vicinity. Arbitrary loading or boundary conditions may be selected at each nodal point.

In the present investigation it is assumed that each nodal point has six degrees of freedom, Fig. 4. For each of these, a known external force or a known displacement may exist. If a certain force is known, the corresponding displacement is unknown, and vice versa. Stiffnesses for individual elements are first formed and then assembled into a structure stiffness matrix. A direct stiffness solution is then used to find all of the unknown nodal point displacements and forces. Once these are known, the internal forces and stresses for each finite element can be determined. The key step in this approach is the development of element stiffness matrices for the individual finite elements which can accurately approximate the behavior of the continuum when they are assembled to form the structure stiffness matrix needed in the direct stiffness solution.

The basic assumptions used for individual finite elements are:

(a) The in-plane displacements within each rectangular finite element (membrane action) are obtained by the superposition of 12 displacement patterns. These patterns are uniquely defined by three nodal point displacement components, Fig. 4a, at each corner of the element, which are taken as two in-plane translations and one rotation about a normal to the plane of the element.

(b) In-plane stresses, Fig. 5a, within each finite element are determined from the in-plane displacements by means of the elasticity equations defining the plane stress problem.

(c) The normal displacements within each rectangular finite element (slab action) are obtained by the superposition of 12 displacement patterns. These patterns can be uniquely defined by three nodal point displacement components, Fig. 4b, at each corner of the element, which are taken as two rotations about in-plane axes and a displacement normal to the plane of the plate.

(d) The plate bending and torsional moments, Fig. 5b, within each finite element are determined from the normal displacements by means of the classical thin plate theory.

It should be remembered that the complete structure assembled from the finite elements only approximates the true continuum since equilibrium and compatibility are satisfied only at the nodal points and not along the entire interfaces of adjacent elements. The independent displacement patterns chosen for the individual elements are selected so as to closely as possible satisfy compatibility across these interfaces.

COMPARISON OF RESULTS

General Remarks

Relative accuracy of the three methods was assessed and the validity of assumptions checked by analyzing a box section by each method and comparing resulting deflections, longitudinal stresses, percentage of total moments taken by each girder and transverse slab moments.

One analysis was made by the folded plate method, and two, each, by the finite element and finite segment methods, using different meshes. Results by the folded plate method are considered exact for purposes of comparison.

The analyzed hypothetical structure comprised two 60 ft. spans continuous over a support. Assumed configurations of the structure and analytical models are depicted in Figs. 6 and 7. A single, 1000 lb. force applied over one exterior girder at the center of each span comprised the loading. Longitudinal symmetry of loading permitted treatment of only one, fixed-simple span by two of the methods. Structural dimensions were similar to those used in a former study of simple spans [1] [2] to permit comparison of resulting behavior and assessments of effects of continuity. Typical results from [3] are presented below.

Vertical Deflections

Vertical deflections at the tops of the girders are shown in Fig. 8. Shaded regions indicate the variations obtained for the five analyses and computed values are tabulated for deflections of the exterior girder under the load. Good agreement exists among results of the five analyses. The vertical deflections are generally the least sensitive of the results obtained and even the coarse Mesh 1 used for the finite element and finite segment methods produced deflections comparing favorably with those of the folded plate method.

Longitudinal Stresses

Longitudinal distribution of longitudinal stress, at the edge of the top slab, is depicted in Fig. 9 for each of the five analyses. The transverse distribution of the same quantity at midspan is shown in Fig. 10.

For all three methods stress plots were based on transversely averaged values from either side of the joints.

The figures indicate general agreement among results for the three methods except in the vicinity of the concentrated load. The improvement in this area which results from employing the finer Mesh 2 for the finite element and finite segment methods is immediately apparent.

Distribution of Girder Resisting Moments

If the box girder cross-section is sub-divided into hypothetical individual girders bounded by vertical planes at the midbays, total stresses in girder components can be integrated and resisting moments computed about neutral axes.

Girder resisting moments computed in this way and percentage of total moments taken by each girder are listed in Table 1. The results of applying the finite segment method for both meshes agree well with those for the folded plate method, as do the results of using Mesh 2 with the finite element method. The latter method with Mesh 1 tends to overestimate resisting moments in girders R1 and R2.

Transverse Slab Moments

A typical plot of the transverse slab moments is shown in Fig. 11. The plot shows that good agreement exists among the results except in the sensitive vicinity of the concentrated load. Results of the finite segment and finite element methods in this area compared more favorably with those of the folded plate method after refinement from Mesh 1 to Mesh 2.

Static equilibrium requires that transverse slab moments in the plates on either side of a joint sum to zero. Such a result was accurately indicated by the folded plate and finite segment methods, but static equilibrium was only approximated by the finite element method.

Studies of transverse distribution of transverse slab moments indicate that the folded plate and finite element methods, which assume two-way slab action, produce distinctly non-linear distributions, with the high moments under the concentrated load especially evident in the folded plate analysis.

The finite segment method, with its assumed one-way slab action, results in linear transverse distributions of slab moments and does not correctly assess these moments under concentrated loads.

Computer Times

The execution times on an IBM 7094 computer using general computer programs developed for each of these methods to perform the analyses were as follows.

Folded Plate Method	4 min. 27 sec.
Finite Element Method - Mesh 1	5 min. 50 sec.
Finite Element Method - Mesh 2	18 min. 17 sec.
Finite Segment Method - Mesh 1	2 min. 35 sec.
Finite Segment Method - Mesh 2	5 min. 48 sec.

For a given mesh size, execution times are much less for the finite segment method than for the finite element method, and the required computer times increase much more rapidly for the latter method than for the former as the mesh size is refined.

STUDY OF 3-CELL AND 6-CELL BRIDGES

General Remarks

To make a rational study of the problem of load distribution in a multi-celled continuous box girder bridge subjected to a single concentrated load at midspan, two basic questions need to be answered.

1. What is the division of the total statical moment in a given span between the total positive moment at the midspan section and the total negative moments at the support sections?

2. What is the transverse distribution of the above total positive or negative moments at a section to each of the independent longitudinal girders?

Many factors may influence the answers to these questions besides the single parameter of the center to center spacing of webs in the cross-section used in the present design method. Among these factors may be the geometry and dimensions of the bridge, the number of cells in the cross-section, the transverse position of the concentrated load on the bridge deck, and the degree of longitudinal continuity at the supports.

In order to answer these questions, 3-cell and 6-cell bridge cross-sections were subjected to parameter studies.

Description of Example Bridges Analyzed

The cross-section of the 3-cell structure is depicted in Fig. 7a. Cell dimensions were the same for the 6-cell structure.

Three end conditions, simple-simple, fixed-simple, and fixed-fixed, were studied.

1,000 lb line loads, spread over 1 ft longitudinally, were assumed at mid-span, placed either over the exterior girder (R_2 for the 3-cell bridge and R_3 for the 6-cell bridge) or at the transverse center of the midspan section.

Twenty-three separate computer analyses were performed by the three methods, eight by the folded plate method, three by the finite element method, and twelve by the finite segment method.

Distribution of Moments to Each Girder

The distributions to each individual longitudinal girder of the total longitudinal moments at the midspan and the fixed end support sections were calculated by the procedure described earlier. The results of these calculations are presented in Tables 2, 3, 4, and 5. The 3-cell bridge had two exterior girders L_2 and R_2 and two interior girders L_1 and R_1 while the 6-cell bridge had two exterior girders L_3 and R_3 and five interior girders L_2, L_1, C, R_1 and R_2. Based on a study of these results a number of points are discussed in the sections that follow.

Comparison of Results by Different Methods

Results obtained by the folded plate and the finite segment methods are close to each other for both the total moment at a section and the percent of this total taken by each girder. Differences between the results by the two methods are of the order of 1 to 2%. Results by the finite element method, given in Table 2, tend to be on the high side especially for the moments taken by Girders R_1 and R_2. A refinement of mesh size is required to obtain more accurate results by this method.

Since the finite segment method gives accurate results, it can be used to make extensive studies of this type for arbitrary end and interior boundary conditions. Further discussion of Tables 2, 3, 4 and 5 will be based on the results by this method.

Longitudinal Division of Total Static Moment Between Positive and Negative Moments

The moment diagrams for a beam subjected to a midspan concentrated load of 1000 lb with end conditions of simple-simple, fixed-simple, and fixed-fixed are shown in Figs. 12, 13, and 14. It is of particular importance to compare the moments at midspan and at the supports given in these figures with those obtained for the total moments at a section given in Tables 2, 3, 4 and 5. It is seen that the results are essentially the same, being within 1 or 2% of each other for all cases. The following conclusions may be drawn:

1. The results from the computer analyses satisfy statics.
2. The division of the total static moment in the box girder bridges between the total positive moment at midspan and the total negative moment at the support is the same as that found in a beam subjected to the same loading. Furthermore, it appears that this is true irrespective of the number of cells in the bridge or of the transverse position of the load on the bridge deck. Thus, only the transverse distribution of these total moments at a section to each girder need be further studied.

The second conclusion could be deduced approximately by the following simplified reasoning. First, assume the continuous box girder bridge to be cut along longitudinal lines in the top and bottom slabs at the midpoints between the webs, thus dividing the bridge into several individual and independent girders. If all of these girders have the same longitudinal variations of flexural and shear stiffness and ratios of these stiffnesses, similar moment diagrams would exist for each of the girders for similar loadings. The loadings on the girders consist of the applied external loading plus equal and opposite interaction forces at the cuts between the girders. The moment diagram due to the applied loading is the same as that in a continuous beam under the same loading, while the moment diagrams due to the equal and opposite interaction forces between the girders will cancel each other out when summed for all the girders. This is what occurs in box girder bridges of usual span lengths. If the individual girders have substantially different longitudinal variations of flexural or shear stiffness or ratios of these stiffnesses then this would not be true.

Transverse Distribution of Moments to Each Girder

The transverse distribution of moments to each girder is influenced by whether the midspan or support section is being considered, the end boundary conditions, the number of cells in the cross-section and the transverse position of the load on the bridge deck. For a uniform distribution across the section, the percentage moment taken by each interior girder would be approximately equal to 100% divided by the number of cells in the bridge, while that for the exterior girders would be half this value. These percentages for interior and exterior girders are thus 33.3 and 16.7% for the 3-cell bridge and 16.7 and 8.3% for the 6-cell bridge. From a study of Tables 2, 3, 4 and 5 the following comments may be made:

1. For a given case, a more uniform and thus a better distribution is

obtained at a support section than at a midspan section. The percentage moment taken by the most highly stressed girder at a support section is from 3 to 17% less than that at a midspan section for the same girder. Thus it would seem that different distribution factors should be used at these two sections.

2. For a given span, the results for different end boundary conditions show that increasing the fixity at the supports gives a poorer distribution of moments. This is to be expected since the ability of a bridge to distribute a concentrated load transversely is a function of the ratio of the relative stiffnesses in the transverse and longitudinal directions. As this ratio is decreased the distribution becomes poorer and vice-versa. An increase in end fixity or a decrease in span length increases the longitudinal stiffness resulting in a poorer distribution. Thus different distribution factors should be used for simple and continuous bridges having the same span lengths between supports.

3. A load over the exterior girder web, is the most severe loading case for the exterior girder. Furthermore, comparing the results for the 3-cell and 6-cell bridges in Tables 2 and 4, for any given set of end boundary conditions the percentages of the total moment taken by the exterior girder are within 1 or 2% of each other. This indicates the localized effect of this loading.

Midspan Deflections

The midspan vertical deflections found from the computer analyses are given in Table 6.

The agreement between the results for a specific case as obtained by the three methods of analysis is generally good for all loading cases.

Comparing the transverse distribution of deflections in Table 6 it is seen that increasing the fixity at the end supports has two distinct and obvious effects.

1. The maximum deflection under the load is decreased.

2. The deflection damps out more rapidly in a transverse direction. While the transverse distribution of deflections and of the total moment at a midspan section to each girder have the same general trend, no relationship was found that would simply and accurately relate these two quantities.

CONCLUSIONS

Three general methods for the elastic analysis of continuous box girder bridges have been presented. Each has been shown to have certain advantages and disadvantages.

The folded plate method:

1. is the most accurate of the three methods;

2. yields a complete solution in a reasonable computer time;

3. is restricted to analyses of continuous, homogeneous, prismatic structures with simple supports at the extreme ends.

The finite segment method:

1. applies to structures with arbitrary end and interior support conditions;

2. requires computer time comparable to the folded plate method for a reasonable mesh size;

3. provides accurate results for deflections and transverse distribution of total moment;

4. provides longitudinal stresses and transverse slab moments approaching those resulting from the folded plate method for a concentrated load over a web (except in the vicinity of the load) if a refined mesh is employed;

5. should not be used to predict local slab moments or deflections directly under a concentrated load applied between webs.

The finite element method:

1. is the most versatile of the three methods, treating aribtrary loadings, boundary conditions, varying dimensional and material properties, and plate cutouts;

2. requires much larger computer times for comparable solutions, especially as finer meshes are used;

3. provides accurate deflections for relatively coarse meshes;

4. requires a refined mesh, especially in the vicinity of concentrated loads, to produce accurate longitudinal stresses, transverse slab moments, and transverse distributions of moments;

5. does not automatically satisfy static equilibrium.

For a continuous box girder bridge the longitudinal distribution of the total statical moment between positive and negative moments is the same as that obtained for a similarly loaded, continuous beam with the same longitudinal configuration, irrespective of the number of cells or transverse load position. The transverse distribution of moment to each girder is dependent upon the section, end boundary conditions, number of cells and transverse load position. These factors should be considered in establishing load distribution criteria.

It is apparent from the results that present design specifications which require consideration of only one parameter, the girder web spacing, oversimplify the problem.

General computer programs which have been developed to apply the three methods may be used: (1) for the design of specific bridges, or, (2) to develop more accurate distribution factors which may be used in simplified design methods.

ACKNOWLEDGMENTS

This research was conducted in the Division of Structural Engineering and Structural Mechanics at the University of California, Berkeley, in cooperation with the Division of Highways, Department of Public Works, State of California and under the sponsorship of the United States Department of Transportation, Federal Highway Administration, Bureau of Public Roads.

The detailed theoretical development for the folded plate and finite segment methods was carried out by K. S. Lo and for the finite element method by B. N. Abu Ghazeleh. C. A. Meyer and D. Ngo participated extensively in various phases of the investigation and especially in the development of the computer programs and the computer analyses carried out as part of the research program.

The opinions, findings and conclusions expressed in this publication are those of the authors and not necessarily those of the Bureau of Public Roads.

REFERENCES

1. Scordelis, A. C., Davis, R. E. and Lo, K. S., "Load Distribution in Concrete Box Girder Bridges," ACI Proceedings of International Symposium on Concrete Bridge Design, Toronto, Canada, April 1967. (to be published)

2. Scordelis, A. C., "Analysis of Simply Supported Box Girder Bridges," Structures and Materials Research Report, SESM 66-17, Division of Structural Engineering and Structural Mechanics, Department of Civil Engineering, University of California, Berkeley, October 1966.

3. Scordelis, A. C., "Analysis of Continuous Box Girder Bridges," Structures and Materials Research Report, SESM 67-25, Division of Structural Engineering and Structural Mechanics, Department of Civil Engineering, University of California, Berkeley, November 1967.

TABLE 1: DISTRIBUTION OF MOMENTS TO EACH GIRDER FOR 3-CELL BRIDGE UNDER ECCENTRIC LOAD (FIXED-SIMPLE END SUPPORT CONDITIONS)

Section	Girder	Folded Plate		Finite Element				Finite Segment			
				Mesh 1		Mesh 2		Mesh 1		Mesh 2	
		M ft-lb	%	M ft-lb	%	M ft-lb	%	M ft-lb	%	M ft-lb	%
Midspan	L_2	412	4.3	424	3.9	412	4.5	383	4.1	421	4.4
	L_1	1265	13.3	1287	11.9	1251	13.6	1150	12.3	1242	13.1
	R_1	2925	30.8	3566	32.9	2829	30.8	2824	30.2	2804	29.5
	R_2	4894	51.6	5568	51.3	4690	51.1	4994	53.4	5045	53.0
	Total	9496	100.0	10845	100.0	9182	100.0	9351	100.0	9512	100.0
Fixed Support	L_2	914	8.3	1040	8.4	1074	9.3	818	7.4	860	7.8
	L_1	1994	18.2	2051	16.6	2258	19.5	1879	17.0	2007	18.2
	R_1	4023	36.7	4383	35.5	4204	36.3	4101	37.1	4140	37.5
	R_2	4040	36.8	4870	39.5	4040	34.9	4256	38.5	4034	36.5
	Total	10971	100.0	12344	100.0	11576	100.0	11054	100.0	11041	100.0

TABLE 2: DISTRIBUTION OF MOMENTS TO EACH GIRDER FOR 3-CELL BRIDGE UNDER ECCENTRIC LOAD

Method	Section	At Midspan						At Support			
	Support Conditions	Simple-Simple		Fixed-Simple		Fixed-Fixed		Fixed-Simple		Fixed-Fixed	
	Girder	M ft-lb	%	M ft-lb	%	M ft-lb	%	M ft-lb	%	M ft-lb	%
Folded Plate	L_2	1324	8.9	412	4.3			914	8.3		
	L_1	3037	20.4	1265	13.3			1994	18.2		
	R_1	4810	32.3	2925	30.8			4023	36.7		
	R_2	5713	38.4	4894	51.6			4040	36.8		
	Total	14884	100.0	9496	100.0			10971	100.0		
Finite Element	L_2	1351	8.2	424	3.9	101	1.1	1040	8.4	385	4.7
	L_1	3032	18.4	1287	11.9	667	7.3	2051	16.6	1030	12.6
	R_1	5431	33.0	3566	32.9	2937	32.3	4383	35.5	3016	36.9
	R_2	6657	40.4	5568	51.3	5394	59.3	4870	39.5	3735	45.8
	Total	16471	100.0	10845	100.0	9099	100.0	12344	100.0	8166	100.0
Finite Segment	L_2	1310	8.8	383	4.1	66	0.9	818	7.4	307	4.1
	L_1	2933	19.7	1150	12.3	538	7.3	1879	17.0	900	12.0
	R_1	4675	31.4	2824	30.2	2125	28.8	4101	37.1	2834	37.8
	R_2	5970	40.1	4994	53.4	4648	63.0	4256	38.5	3456	46.1
	Total	14888	100.0	9351	100.0	7377	100.0	11054	100.0	7497	100.0

TABLE 3: DISTRIBUTION OF MOMENTS TO EACH GIRDER FOR 3-CELL BRIDGE UNDER CENTER LOAD

Method	Section	At Midspan						At Support			
	Support Conditions	Simple-Simple		Fixed-Simple		Fixed-Fixed		Fixed-Simple		Fixed-Fixed	
	Girder	M ft-lb	%	M ft-lb	%	M ft-lb	%	M ft-lb	%	M ft-lb	%
Folded Plate	L_2	2104	14.0	1129	12.0			1682	15.7		
	L_1	5447	36.0	3570	38.0			3682	34.3		
	R_1	5447	36.0	3570	38.0			3682	34.3		
	R_2	2104	14.0	1129	12.0			1682	15.7		
	Total	15102	100.0	9398	100.0			10728	100.0		
Finite Segment	L_2	2110	14.1	1142	12.1	780	10.5	1680	15.2	1036	13.8
	L_1	5372	35.9	3578	37.9	2935	39.5	3846	34.8	2717	36.2
	R_1	5372	35.9	3578	37.9	2935	39.5	3846	34.8	2717	36.2
	R_2	2110	14.1	1142	12.1	780	10.5	1680	15.2	1036	13.8
	Total	14964	100.0	9440	100.0	7430	100.0	11052	100.0	7506	100.0

TABLE 4: DISTRIBUTION OF MOMENTS TO EACH GIRDER FOR 6-CELL BRIDGE UNDER ECCENTRIC LOAD

Method	Section	At Midspan						At Support			
	Support Conditions	Simple-Simple		Fixed-Simple		Fixed-Fixed		Fixed-Simple		Fixed-Fixed	
	Girder	M ft-lb	%	M ft-lb	%	M ft-lb	%	M ft-lb	%	M ft-lb	%
Folded Plate	L_3	239	1.6	26	0.3			78	0.7		
	L_2	551	3.7	92	1.0			169	1.5		
	L_1	807	5.5	197	2.1			350	3.2		
	C	1312	8.9	451	4.7			783	7.1		
	R_1	2236	15.2	1073	11.3			1717	15.7		
	R_2	4214	28.6	2811	29.6			3887	35.5		
	R_3	5381	36.5	4834	51.0			3974	36.3		
	Total	14740	100.0	9484	100.0			10958	100.0		
Finite Segment	L_3	326	2.2	19	0.2	0	0.0	66	0.6	7	0.1
	L_2	830	5.6	66	0.7	0	0.0	121	1.1	7	0.1
	L_1	875	5.9	159	1.7	15	0.2	287	2.6	59	0.8
	C	1260	8.5	433	4.3	110	1.5	684	6.2	259	3.5
	R_1	2046	13.8	985	10.5	501	6.8	1655	15.0	894	12.1
	R_2	3854	26.0	2748	29.3	2115	28.7	3994	36.2	2824	38.2
	R_3	5633	38.0	5000	53.3	4629	62.8	4226	38.3	3341	45.2
	Total	14824	100.0	9380	100.0	7370	100.0	11033	100.0	7391	100.0

TABLE 5: DISTRIBUTION OF MOMENTS TO EACH GIRDER FOR 6-CELL BRIDGE UNDER CENTER LOAD

Method	Section	At Midspan						At Support			
	Support Conditions	Simple-Simple		Fixed-Simple		Fixed-Fixed		Fixed-Simple		Fixed-Fixed	
	Girder	M ft-lb	%	M ft-lb	%	M ft-lb	%	M ft-lb	%	M ft-lb	%
Folded Plate	L_3	700	4.7	243	2.5			487	4.5		
	L_2	1579	10.6	706	7.4			1059	9.7		
	L_1	2490	16.6	1577	16.5			2076	19.0		
	C	5420	36.2	4498	47.2			3678	33.6		
	R_1	2490	16.6	1577	16.5			2076	19.0		
	R_2	1579	10.6	706	7.4			1059	9.7		
	R_3	700	4.7	243	2.5			487	4.5		
	Total	14958	100.0	9550	100.0			10922	100.0		
Finite Segment	L_3	684	4.6	215	2.3	66	0.9	408	3.7	157	2.1
	L_2	1532	10.3	634	6.8	332	4.5	980	8.9	495	6.6
	L_1	2454	16.5	1521	16.3	1172	15.9	2115	19.2	1462	19.5
	C	5533	37.2	4590	49.2	4233	57.4	4009	36.4	3270	43.6
	R_1	2454	16.5	1521	16.3	1172	15.9	2115	19.2	1462	19.5
	R_2	1532	10.3	634	6.8	332	4.5	980	8.9	495	6.6
	R_3	684	4.6	215	2.3	66	0.9	408	3.7	157	2.1
	Total	14873	100.0	9330	100.0	7373	100.0	11015	100.0	7498	100.0

TABLE 6: MIDSPAN VERTICAL DEFLECTIONS IN FT. x 10^4 FOR ECCENTRIC AND CENTER LOADS ON 3 AND 6-CELL BRIDGES

Support Conditions		Simple-Simple			Fixed-Simple			Fixed-Fixed	
Method		Folded Plate	Finite Seg.	Finite Elem.	Folded Plate	Finite Seg.	Finite Elem.	Finite Seg.	Finite Elem.
Case	Gird.								
3-Cell Bridge Eccentric Load	L_2	0.992	0.934	0.994	0.277	0.229	0.244	0.037	0.049
	L_1	1.173	1.122	1.115	0.412	0.359	0.366	0.120	0.131
	R_1	1.736	1.692	1.661	0.856	0.791	0.786	0.442	0.451
	R_2	3.051	3.051	2.933	2.069	2.047	1.956	1.614	1.540
3-Cell Bridge Center Load	L_2	1.431	1.392		0.614	0.561		0.267	
	L_1	1.797	1.806		0.976	0.967		0.663	
	R_1	1.797	1.806		0.976	0.967		0.663	
	R_2	1.431	1.392		0.614	0.561		0.267	
6-Cell Bridge Eccentric Load	L_3	0.180	0.337		0.021	0.015		0.000	
	L_2	0.210	0.286		0.031	0.023		0.000	
	L_1	0.312	0.329		0.066	0.052		0.006	
	C	0.510	0.484		0.150	0.127		0.027	
	R_1	0.871	0.805		0.348	0.301		0.114	
	R_2	1.528	1.414		0.823	0.767		0.440	
	R_3	2.874	2.719		2.054	2.031		1.612	
6-Cell Bridge Center Load	L_3	0.510	0.484		0.151	0.127		0.027	
	L_2	0.604	0.581		0.221	0.195		0.071	
	L_1	0.901	0.883		0.462	0.430		0.254	
	C	1.619	1.639		1.139	1.140		0.925	
	R_1	0.901	0.883		0.462	0.430		0.254	
	R_2	0.604	0.581		0.221	0.195		0.071	
	R_3	0.510	0.484		0.151	0.127		0.027	

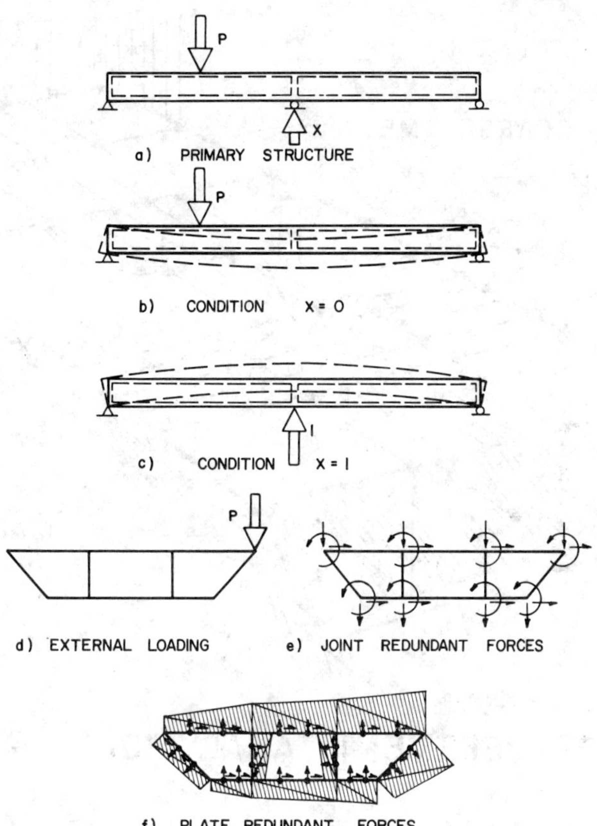

FIG. I FOLDED PLATE METHOD OF ANALYSIS OF CONTINUOUS BOX GIRDER BRIDGE

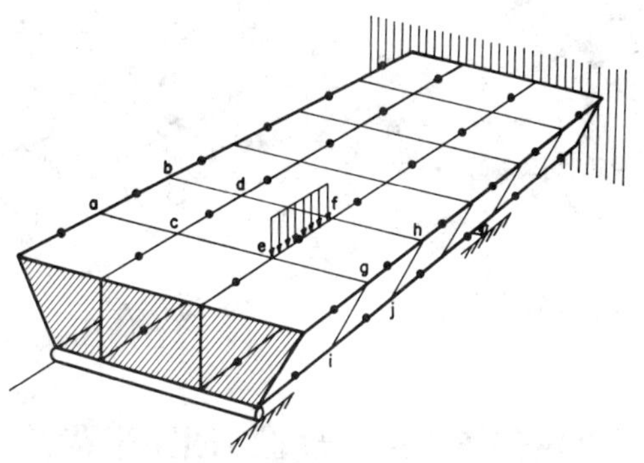

a) TOTAL BRIDGE SYSTEM

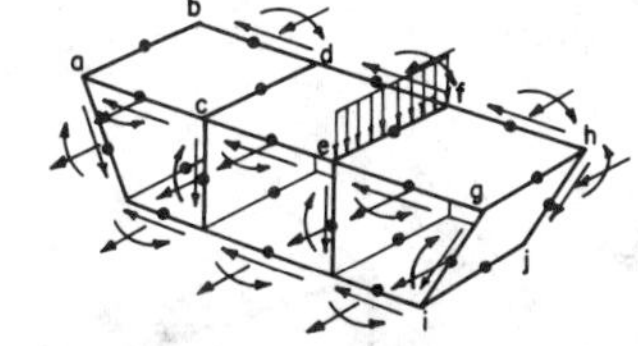

b) TYPICAL FULL TRANSVERSE SEGMENT

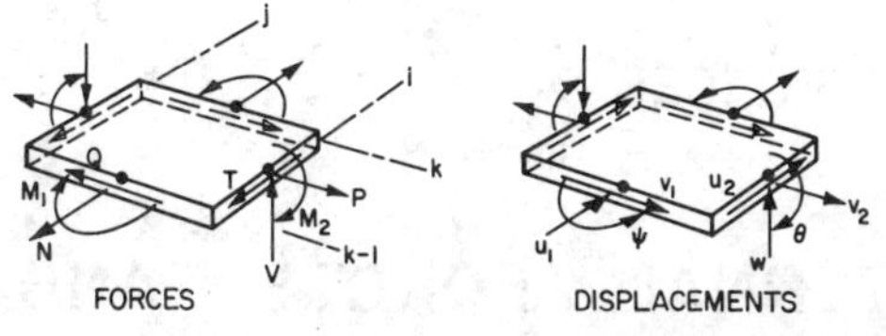

c) FORCES AND DISPLACEMENTS IN TYPICAL FINITE SEGMENT

FIG. 2 FINITE SEGMENT ANALYTICAL MODEL

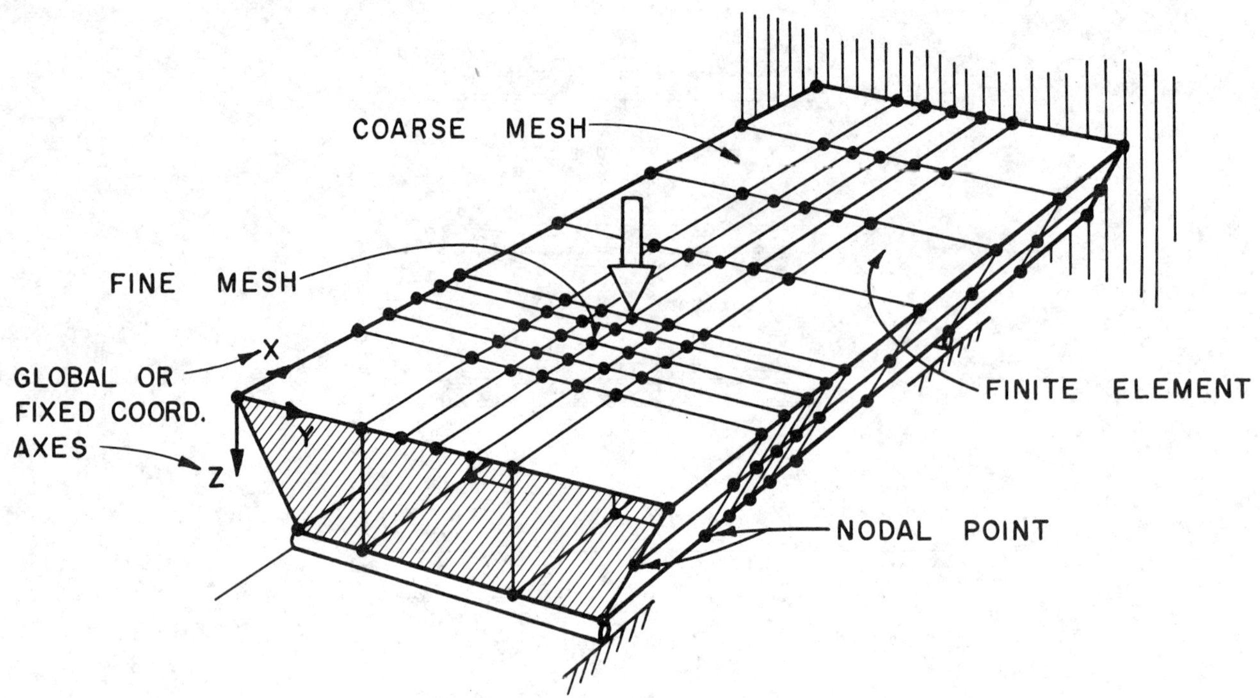

FIG. 3 FINITE ELEMENT ANALYTICAL MODEL

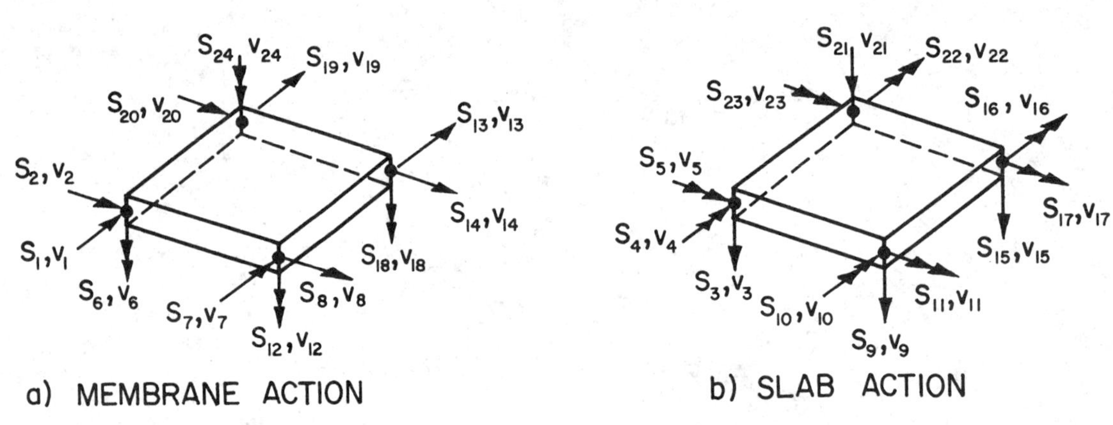

FIG. 4 NODAL POINT FORCES (S) AND DISPLACEMENTS (v) FOR A FINITE ELEMENT

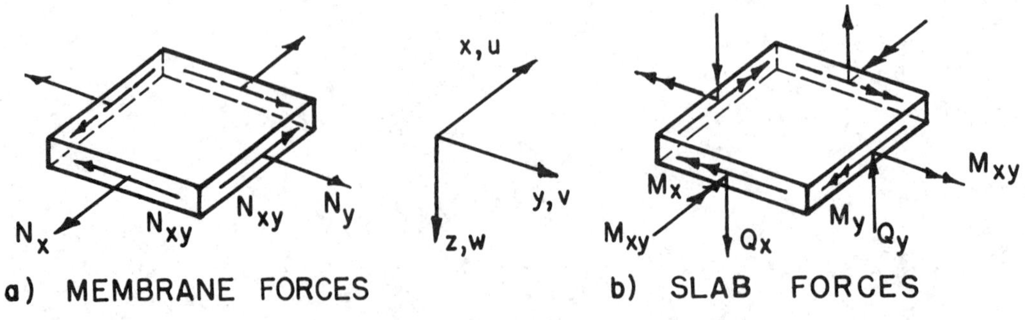

FIG. 5 POSITIVE INTERNAL FORCES AND DISPLACEMENTS IN A FINITE ELEMENT

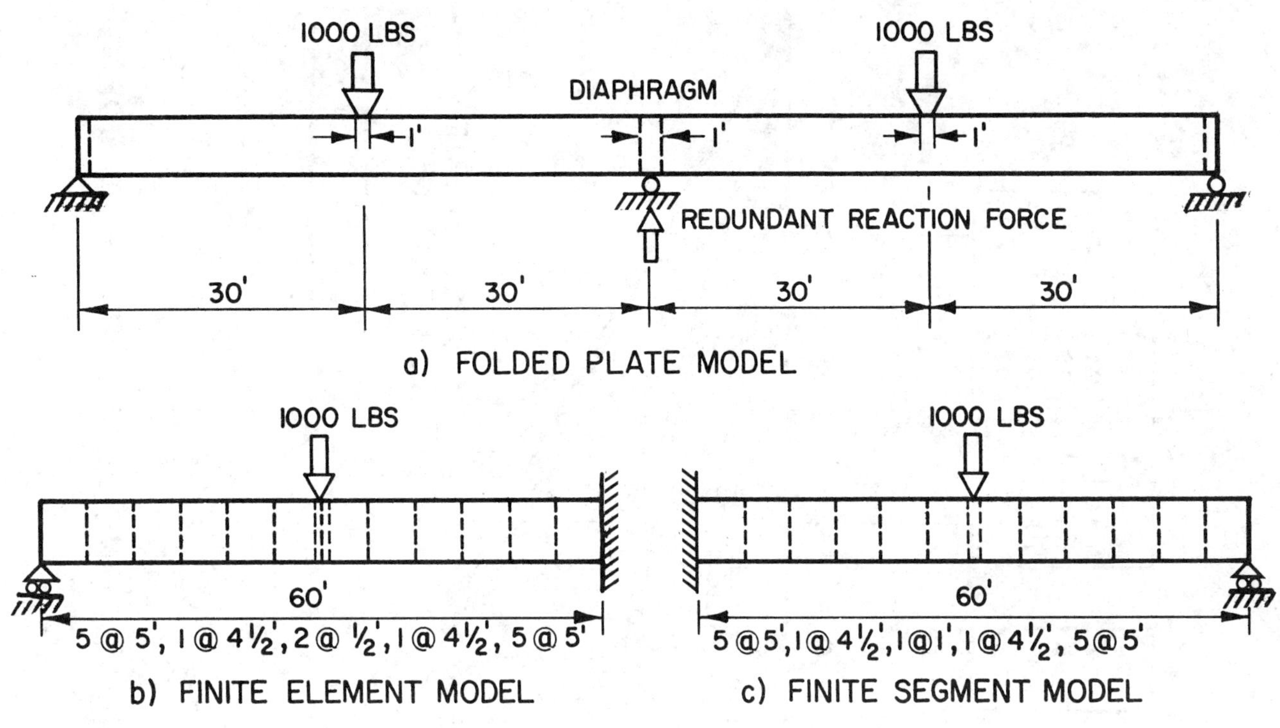

FIG. 6 LONGITUDINAL ELEVATIONS

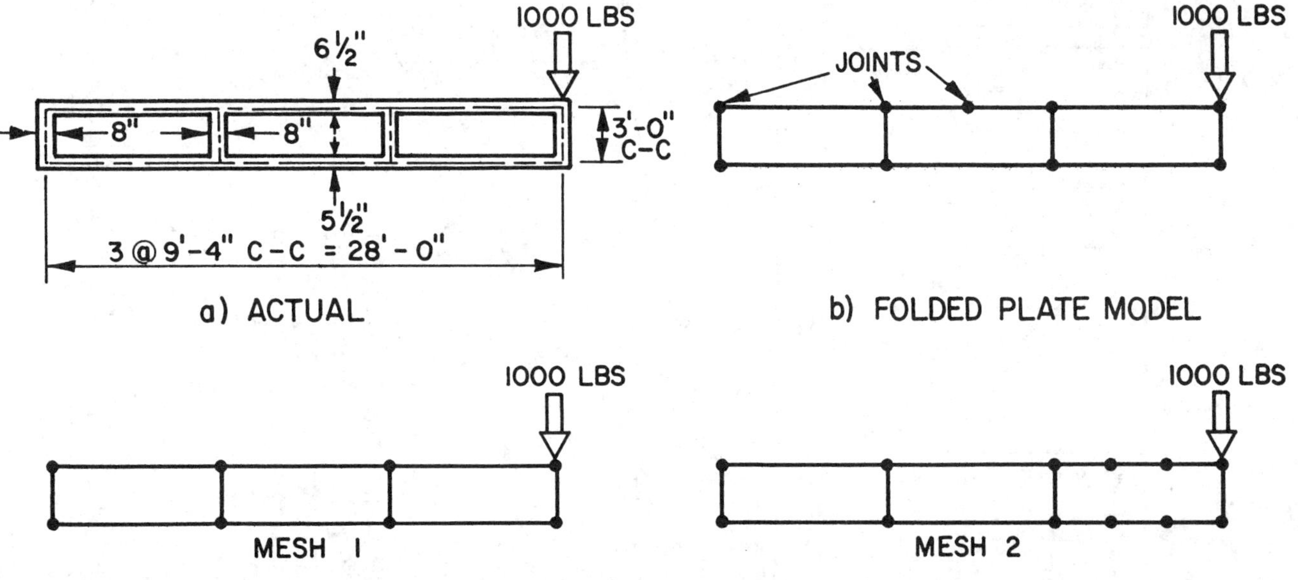

FIG. 7 TYPICAL TRANSVERSE SECTIONS

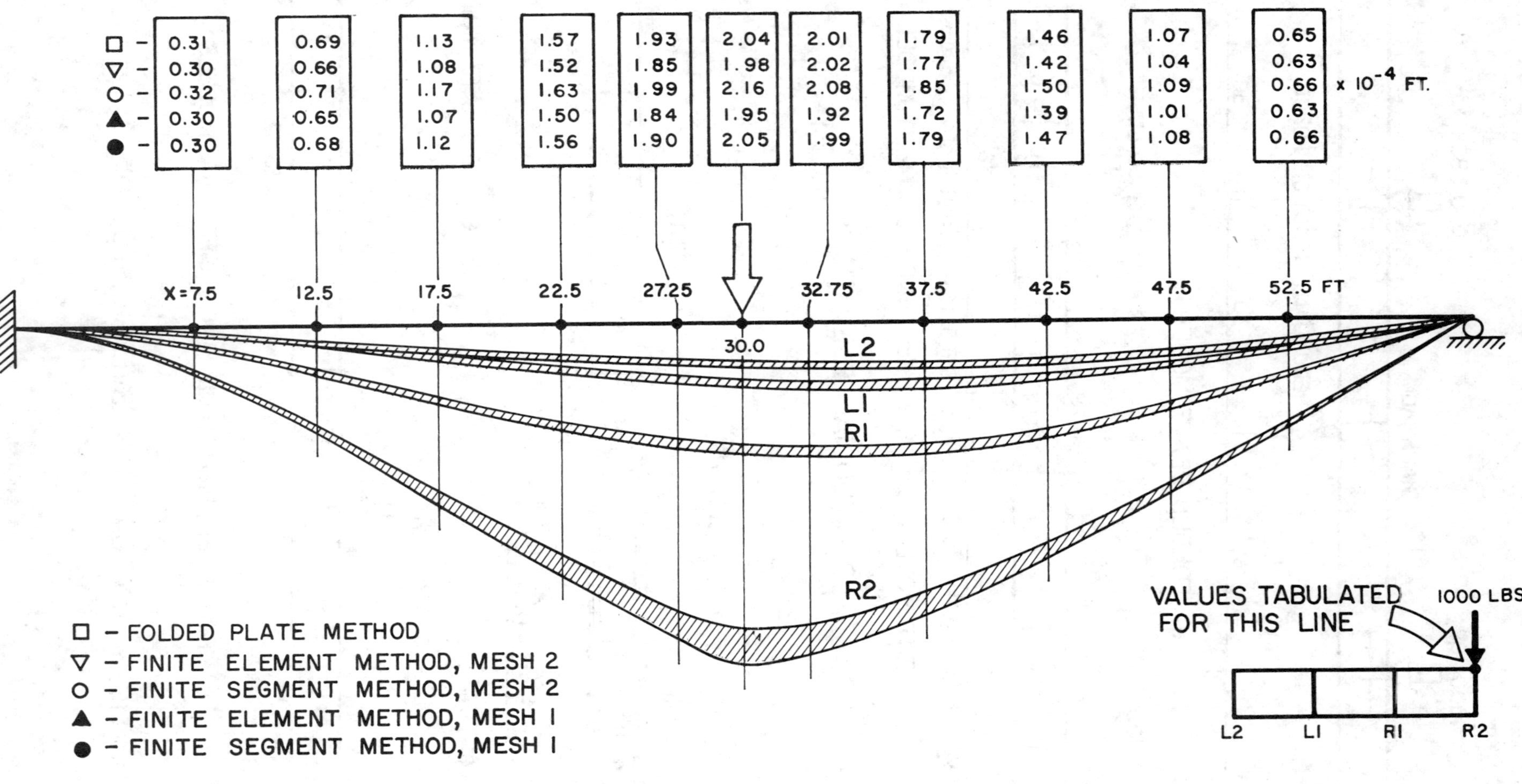

FIG. 8 VERTICAL DEFLECTION ALONG LONGITUDINAL LINE AT TOP OF GIRDERS

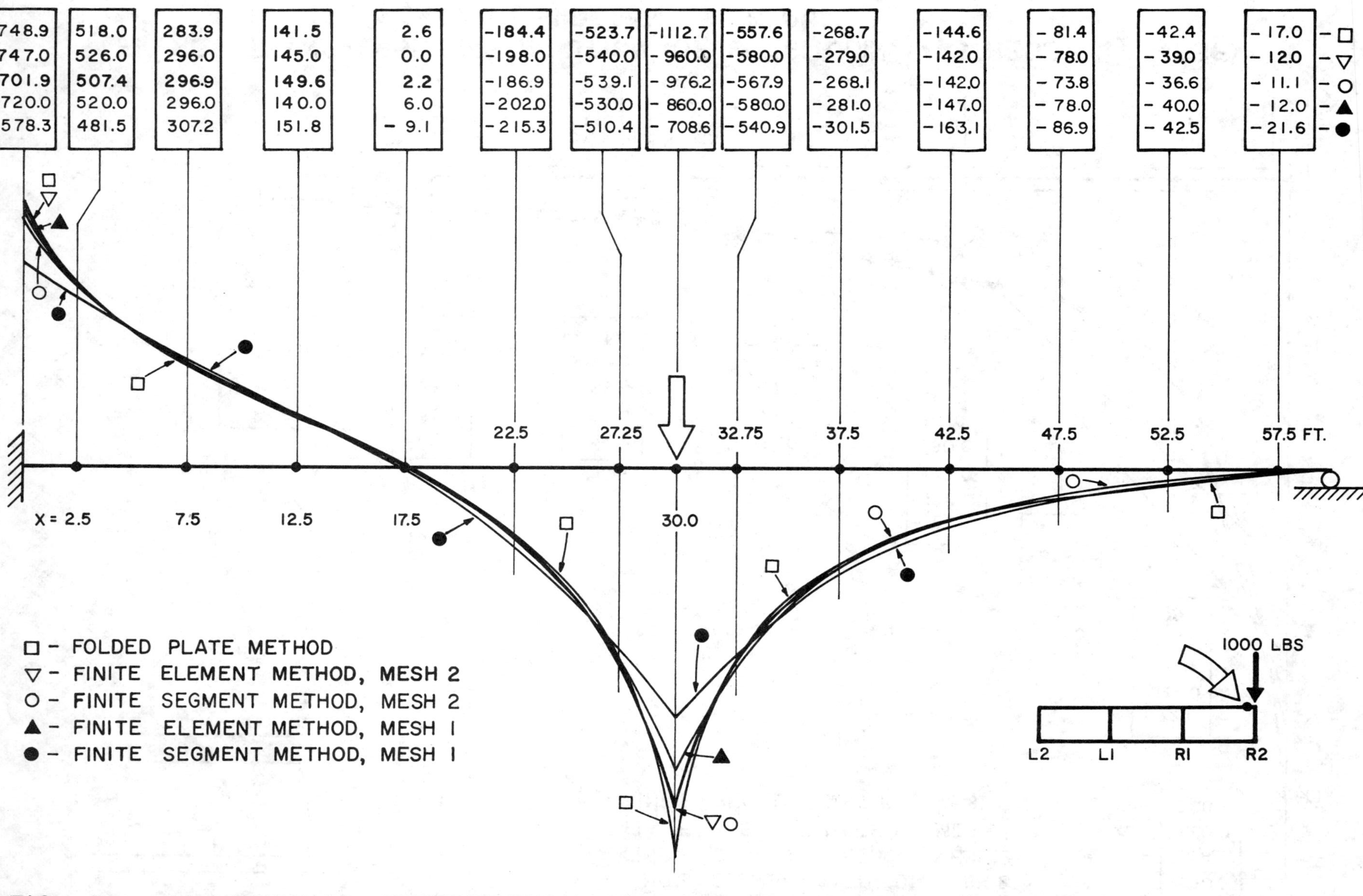

FIG. 9 LONGITUDINAL DISTRIBUTION OF LONGITUDINAL STRESS σ_x (PSF) IN TOP SLAB OVER R2

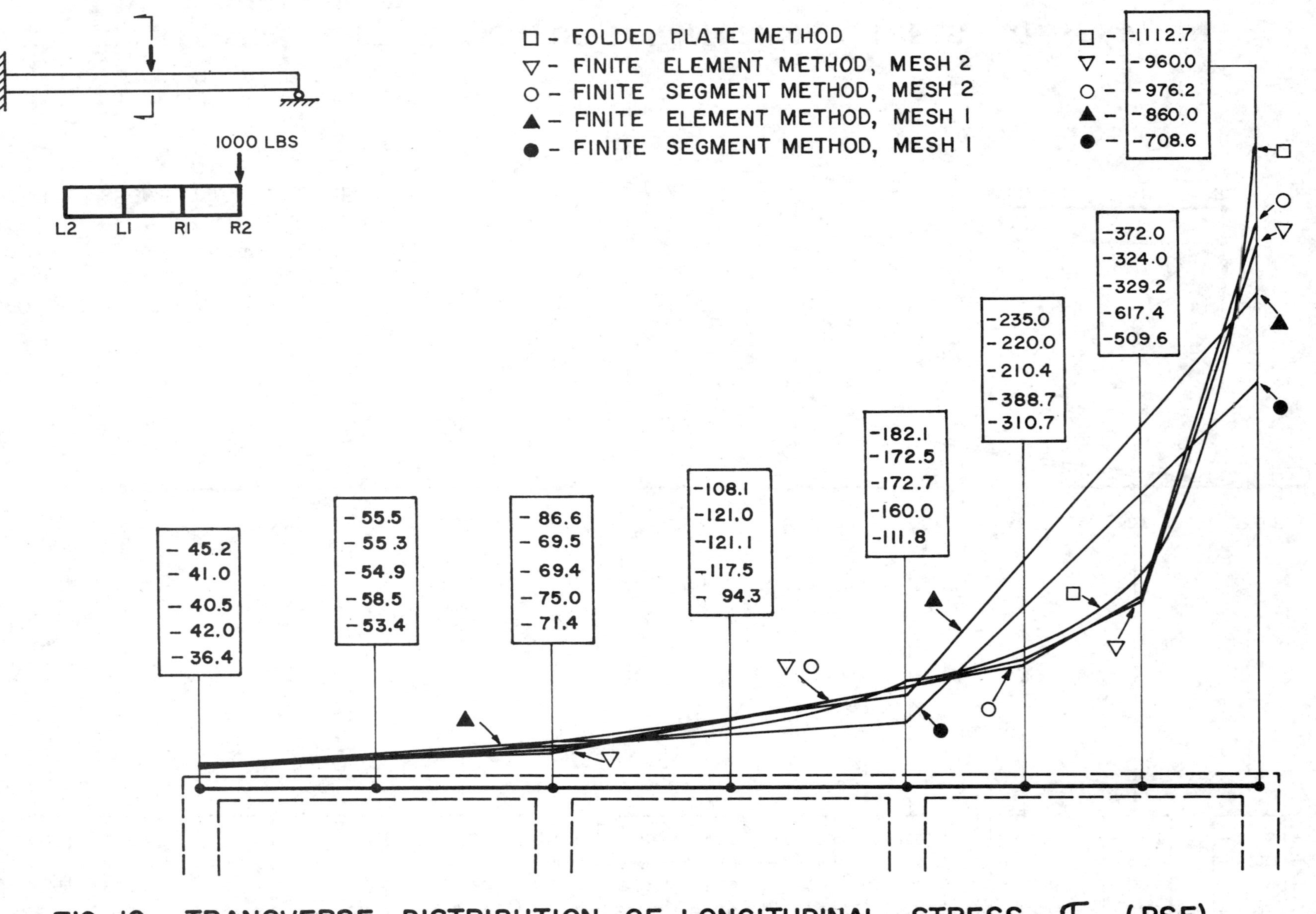

FIG. 10 TRANSVERSE DISTRIBUTION OF LONGITUDINAL STRESS σ_x (PSF) IN TOP SLAB AT MIDSPAN SECTION

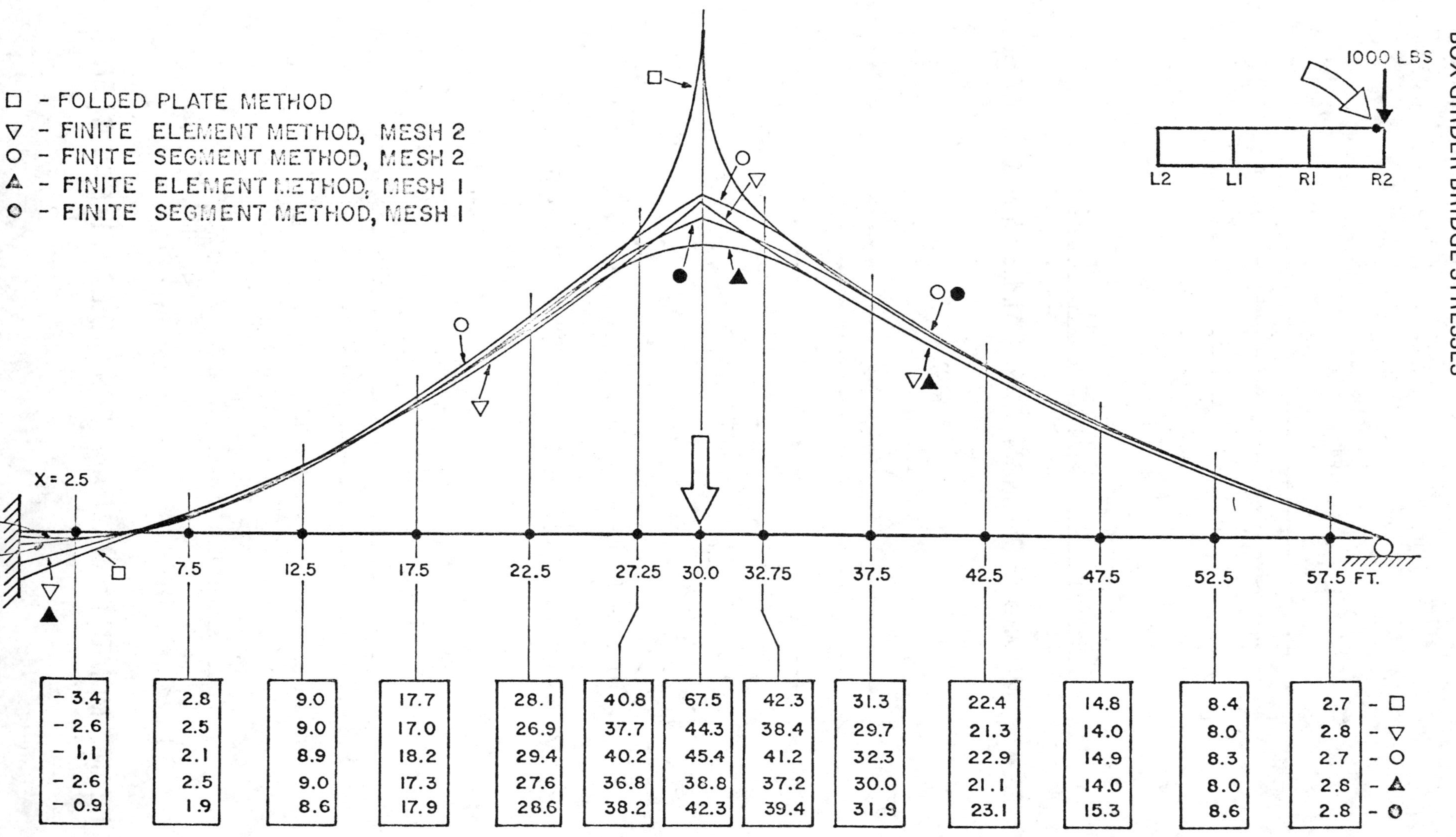

Method	2.5	7.5	12.5	17.5	22.5	27.25	30.0	32.75	37.5	42.5	47.5	52.5	57.5
□	− 3.4	2.8	9.0	17.7	28.1	40.8	67.5	42.3	31.3	22.4	14.8	8.4	2.7
▽	− 2.6	2.5	9.0	17.0	26.9	37.7	44.3	38.4	29.7	21.3	14.0	8.0	2.8
○	− 1.1	2.1	8.9	18.2	29.4	40.2	45.4	41.2	32.3	22.9	14.9	8.3	2.7
▲	− 2.6	2.5	9.0	17.3	27.6	36.8	38.8	37.2	30.0	21.1	14.0	8.0	2.8
●	− 0.9	1.9	8.6	17.9	28.6	38.2	42.3	39.4	31.9	23.1	15.3	8.6	2.8

FIG. 11 LONGITUDINAL DISTRIBUTION OF TRANSVERSE MOMENT M_y (FT-LB/FT) IN TOP SLAB OVER R2

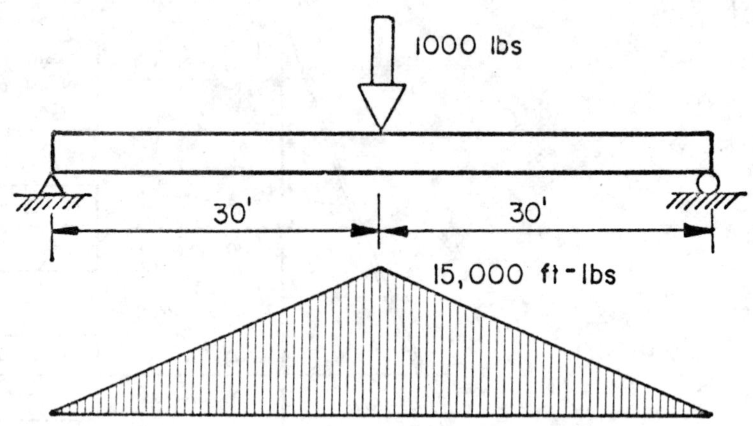

FIG 12 BEAM MOMENT DIAGRAM FOR SIMPLE-SIMPLE CASE

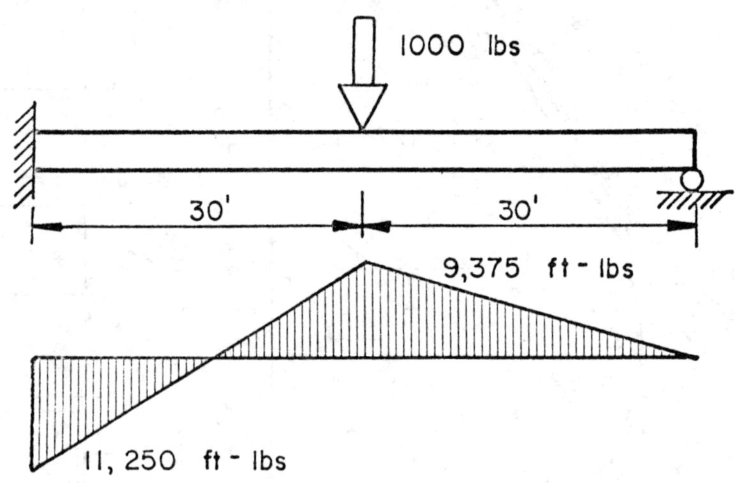

FIG. 13 BEAM MOMENT DIAGRAM FOR FIXED-SIMPLE CASE

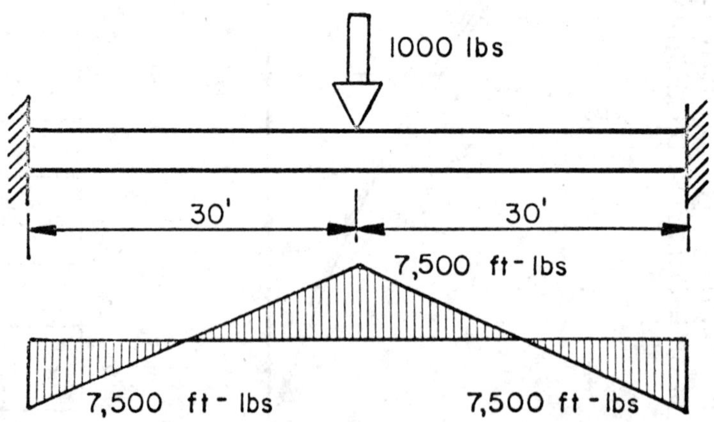

FIG. 14 BEAM MOMENT DIAGRAM FOR FIXED-FIXED CASE

DISCUSSION

By R. P. PAMA

Professor, Department of Civil Engineering, University of Dundee

Professor Scordelis and Mr. R.E. Davis are to be congratulated for their interesting paper on Box Girder Bridges. The comparison between the folded plate method and the finite element and finite segment methods for detailed stress analysis is extremely interesting. In design the most important parameter is usually the longitudinal bending moment and here orthotropic plate theory will also give good results.

At the University of Dundee orthotropic plate theory has been extended to cover statically indeterminate bridge decks and a computer program has been developed for the Ministry of Transport in London. This program was used to analyze the 3-cell bridge described in the paper and the results are tabulated below.

Distribution of longitudinal moment to each girder for 3-cell bridge under a central load at midspan

	Simple-simple case moment at midspan			Simple-fixed case moment at midspan			Simple-fixed case moment at midspan		
	FP	FS	OPT	FP	FS	OPT	FP	FS	OPT
L_2	14%	14.1%	14.9%	12%	12.1%	14.8%	15.7%	15.2%	14.77%
L_1	36	35.9	35.1	38	37.9	35.2	34.3	34.8	35.23
R_1	36	35.9	35.1	38	37.9	35.2	34.3	34.8	35.23
R_2	14	14.1	14.9	12	12.1	14.8	15.7	15.2	14.77

Legend: FP = Folded Plate
FS = Finite Segment
OPT = Orthotropic plate theory

MODEL ANALYSIS OF A CURVED PRESTRESSED CONCRETE CELLULAR BRIDGE

By H. W. CHUNG and N. J. GARDNER

SYNOPSIS

This paper describes a model investigation of a curved prestressed concrete bridge. A 1/24 scale perspex model was used to predict the elastic properties and a 1/6 scale prestressed concrete model to determine the load factor.

Keywords: bending moments; box beams; bridges (structures); curved beams; failure; girder bridges; girders; load factors; models; prestressed concrete; research; structural analysis.

ACI member H. W. CHUNG is a lecturer in the Department of Civil Engineer- University of Hong Kong. Dr. Chung received his BSc and MSc at the University of Hong Kong and his PhD from the University of Leeds. His research interests are in the fields of concrete technology and design and he has co-authored several papers on prestressed composite structures.

ACI member NOEL J. GARDNER is assistant professor, Department of Civil Engineering, University of Ottawa, Canada. During 1967 Dr. Gardner lectured at the University of Hong Kong. Previously he taught at the University of Western Ontario. His research interests are prestressed concrete bridges, prestressed concrete columns and pipe columns.

The Waterfront Road project has been initiated to ease East-West traffic flow on Hong Kong Island. The Waterfront Road has dual three lane carriageways and runs from Harcourt Road in Central District to Kings Road at North Point. Tsing Fung Street takes traffic from Kings Road onto the Waterfront Road. The town bound right-turning traffic on Kings Road is carried over Kings Road into Tsing Fung Street by means of a curved flyover (overpass). Figure 1 shows the flyover superimposed upon the existing street network.

The flyover comprises straight access ramps and a three-span in-situ prestressed concrete cellular bridge curving thru 90° over Kings Road. The bridge has a width of 25 feet (7.7m) widened to 28 feet (8.6m) at the apex of the curve and a total length of 370 feet (114m). Figure 2 shows a center-line elevation of the bridge. The two end spans, 115 feet (35m) between supports have 31 feet (9.5m) cantilevered overhangs which support the 78 foot (24m) central suspended span. Each anchor span is simply supported at its outer end and is monolithic with the 6 foot (1.85) diameter column at its inner end.

The bridge was designed to carry M.O.T. type HA bridge loading on either or both lanes of the bridge. M.O.T. Type HA loading specifies a Uniformly Distributed Load of 220 lbs / sp. ft. (1040 kgf/m^2) plus a Knife Edge Load of 27,000 lbs (12200 kgf) over a 10 ft (3.1m) lane; the Knife Edge Load being located to give the worst effect.

Large torsional effects are present in any curved bridge, aggravated in this case by the necessity to use slender columns which cannot absorb the applied torque.

Unfortunately no rigorous analysis exists to analyse a curved cellular bridge. The flyover was designed by assuming that the bridge deck can be considered as a single curved beam with the appropriate flexural and torsional stiffness.

The authors were asked by the designers to undertake a model investigation of the bridge to determine:

1) the elastic behaviour of the bridge
2) the torsional properties of the deck section
3) if uplift occurs at the supports
4) the effect of a prestressing force on a curved bridge
5) load factor and mode of failure of the bridge

A 1/24 scale perspex model of the central suspended and one anchored span was fabricated and loaded to answer queries (1), (2), (3), and (4). A 1/6th scale prestressed concrete model of the center span was used to answer query (5).

Model Analysis

The basic idea of model analysis is that the deflection of one part of the model relative to any other part of the model has the same relationship as that of the corresponding points on the prototype.

Thus the deflection of any point on the model to the deflection of the corresponding point on the prototype in a constant ratio.

$$\frac{\Delta_j \text{ (prototype)}}{\Delta_j \text{ (model)}} = \frac{\left(\beta_1 \frac{FL^3}{EI} + \beta_2 \frac{FL}{EA} + \beta_3 \frac{FL}{GA} + \beta_4 \frac{FL^3}{GJ}\right)_p}{\left(\beta_1 \frac{FL^3}{EI} + \beta_2 \frac{FL}{EA} + \beta_3 \frac{FL}{GA} + \beta_4 \frac{FL^3}{GJ}\right)_m} = \text{constant}$$

where F is a load typifying the complete system of loads acting on the structure, L is a characteristic length of the structure, and EA, EI, GA, and GJ are the extensional, flexural, shear and torsional regidities respectively; β_1, β_2 β_3, and β_4 are numerical coefficients which depend upon the geometry of the structure. It is necessary that the relationships between L, A, I, and J are the same for both the model and the prototype. This can only be achieved by complete geometric similarity between the model and the prototype.

Abeles (1), Guyon (2), and others have shown that a prestressed concrete structure behaves in a linear elastic manner at loads less than the design working load. Thus to model the elastic behaviour of the bridge it is only necessary that the model material has a linear elastic stress-strain characteristic. However to model the ultimate load behaviour the changes in incremental strain of corresponding points on the model prototype must be in a constant ratio: Practically this means the model must be made of the same material as the prototype.

Thus a perspex model was used to investigate the linear elastic properties and a concrete model to investigate the failure mechanism.

Details of Models

Perspex also known as lucite, was chosen as the elastic model material because of its low modulus of elasticity (0.4×10^6 p.s.i.,

2.8×10^4 kgf/cm^2) and its near linear stress/strain characteristic.

A scale of 1/24th full size, was chosen for the model so that all the members could be simply machined from 3/8" (9.6mm) or 1/2" (12.6 mm) sheet perspex. The modelled structure was simplified by eliminating vertical curvature and superelevation, thus making the deck of the model flat.

The model was fabricated in radial sections; each section consisting of a top flange, a bottom flange, longitudinal and transverse stiffeners. The bottom flange and the stiffeners were solvent welded to the top flange forming, a rigid box. These boxes were then machined to shape and joined together to form the complete model.

As the prototype central suspended span is elastically supported at each end, it was necessary to provide similar supports for the model. Preliminary tests determined that, as far as the central suspended span was concerned, the anchored span behaved as a pair of springs having a specific vertical and torsional stiffness. Two cantilever springs, designed to give the desired vertical and torsional stiffness, were used to support one end of the central suspended span.

A general view of the model, together with the point loading device, is shown in figure 3. The dimensions of the model are shown in figure 4.

Concrete Model

The concrete model of the central span was built to a scale of 1/6 full size and was geometrically similar to the prototype.

The model was prestressed using 17 Nos 0.276 ins (7mm) unbonded high tensile steel wires as being equivalent to the 17 Nos 7/0.7" (18mm) stranded cables in the prototype. Figure 5 shows the dimensions of the model and the steel arrangement.

The scaled dead weight moment in a model is less than in the prototype. To obtain the same stress condition at transfer either the density of the model must be increased or the prestress reduced. To increase the dead weight of the model, magnetite aggregates were used in the concrete and the empty cells in the model were filled with loosely packed magnetite fines. The prestress was also reduced so that the stresses at mid-span of the model at transfer were the same as in the prototype.

Properties of the materials used in the concrete model are given in table 1. The completeted model as set up for testing is shown in figure 6.

Instrumentation

A generalised grid, shown in figure 7, was imposed upon the models to define all points. Dial gauges were used to measure displacements and their locations are shown in Table AI in the Appendix.

Linear strains were measured with electrical resistance strain gauges which were located, in pairs, on the top and bottom surfaces of the model at specific points. Foil type strain gauges were used with active lengths of 0.6 ins (1.5cm) for the perspex model and 1.0 ins (2.5cm) for the concrete model. Gauges to measure strains in the longitudinal direction were located upon the longitudinal stiffeners at the positions shown in table A2.

Gauges to measure strains in the transverse direction were located on the cross stiffeners midway between longitudinal stiffeners and are numbered as in table A3. (eg. D_{3-3} top is a transverse gauge on the top surface on radial line D between longitudinal stiffeners 2 and 3.)

To determine the torsional properties of the bridge strain gauge rosettes were mounted on the outside vertical faces, near the neutral axis, at the mid span of the suspended span.

Testing Procedure

The elastic behaviour of the bridge was determined by applying a point load, in turn, to all the junctions of the longitudinal and transverse stiffeners and recording the strains and deflections.

The response of the structure to a uniformly distributed load was determined by applying a UDL in turn to the suspended span and the anchored span. The UDL was simulated by a layer of steel bars lying on a pad of foam rubber as shown in figure 8,

The torsional properties of the model were determined by applying a known torque and measuring the resulting displacements.

The occurrence, or otherwise, of uplift at the supports was inferred from the displacements of the supports when the model was loaded with a scaled distribution of load.

To examine the possibility of buckling of the curved bridge during prestressing the central suspended span was prestressed to several times the scale prestressing load and the behaviour observed.

The over-load behaviour and the ultimate load of the bridge were determined by testing the concrete model to failure. The UDL and the K.E.L. were simulated by multiple point loads applied through a system of hydraulic jacks and spreader beams. The suspended span was considered critical as it had the largest torque moment ratio.

Accuracy of Results

The accuracy of the results depends upon many factors including accuracy of model dimensions, accuracy of the response gauge being considered and the method of calculation used in analysing the results. The propable limits of accuracy in terms of prototype response, are given in table 2.

Results

The results are presented as answers to the queries stated in the introduction. The measured model and assumed prototype material properties are given in table 1.

(1) Elastic Behaviour of Bridge

The results presented in this section are from the tests on the perspex model except where otherwise stated. All model responses have been scaled up to equivalent prototype response.

A summary only of the test results in given here, a complete set of the results can be obtained from either author. The complete results comprise influence lines for longitudinal stress, transverse stress and the stresses at the base of the column, and the deflected shape of the model under various point loads and a uniformly distributed load.

Because the bridge deck is not symetrical the stresses on the top and bottom surfaces have different magnitudes. To simplyify the graphs the term 'total stress' which is directly proportional to bending moment, has been introduced. This avoids making any assumptions regarding the effectiveness of the section or the position of the neutral axis.

$$\text{Total stress} = \left[\begin{array}{c}\text{stress on top}\\ \text{surface}\end{array}\right] - \left[\begin{array}{c}\text{stress on bottom}\\ \text{surface}\end{array}\right]$$

Summary

The stress and deformation results show that the bridge behaves in a similar manner to a straight bridge; the effect of plan curvature being small.

The deflections of the perspex model show more twist than the concrete model. This is to be expected as the modulus of rigidity, relative to the modulus of elasticity, of perspex is less than that of concrete. However the agreement between the average displacements is within 8%.

Unfortunately the agreement between the longitudinal stress for the two models, shown in table 3, is not too good. An indication of the reliability of the model results can be obtained by comparing the results taken on line B with those taken on line F.(should be identical). The results from the concrete model are not consistent. This demonstrates the difficulty of measuring strains on concrete structures and explains the discrepancy between the two sets of model results.

Rather than direct scaling of model results to obtain prototype results it is preferable to use the model results to verify a theory and use the verified theory to design the prototype.

Influence lines for longitudinal total stress are presented in figures 9 and 10. Figures 9 (a) and (b) show the total longitudinal stress measured on line 1 (please see figure 7 for notation) due to a point load moving along lines 1 and 5 respectively. Figures 10 (a) and 10 (b) are plotted for the stress on line 5. These figures show the extreme stress conditions for the bridge and display a consistent behavior similar to that for a straight bridge.

The stress diagram, analogous to a bending moment diagram, for the longitudinal stress under a uniformly distributed load of 100 psf (488 kgf/m^2) on either the central span of the anchor span is given in figure 11. The prototype stresses obtained by scaling the results from both models are tabulated in table 3.

The stresses induced in the column by a UDL of 100 psf (488 kgf/m^2) on either the center span or the anchor span are given in table 4. Table 4 shows a tensile stress existing on face 2 of the column due to a load on the suspended span. Thus the column is deforming into an "S" shape, the bending moment changing sign between the top and bottom of the column.

The deflection of the prototype under a load of 100 psf (488 kgf/m^2) obtained by scaling the results of both the concrete and perspex models is given in figure (12).

2) Torsional Properties of Deck Section

The torsional behaviour of thin box sections can be analysed using the shear flow concept (3). This analysis assumes that the shear stress is constant through the thickness of any side of the box section.

By consideration of the shear flow in a multiple box it can be seen, in figure (13) that little net shear stress exists in the interior webs. Thus the section can be considered as a single open box and the following expressions used.

$$\tau = \frac{T}{2At} \quad \text{and} \quad \theta = \frac{T}{4A^2G}\int\frac{ds}{t}$$

where

τ = shear stress

A = cross section area of box

G = modulus of rigidity

S = length of side

t = thickness of side

T = torque

θ = twist/unit length

To experimentally verify the validity of the method a torque was applied at mid span of the central suspended span of the perspex model and the resulting displacements and shear stresses measured.

Applied torque = 3640 lbs ins. (420 kgf.m)

The measured experimental shear stresses are compared to the calculated stresses in table 5.

The displacements resulting from the applied torque are shown in figure (14).

Three estimates of the magnitude of J (polar second moment of area) can be found from the differential twists between radial lines D-End 2 , D - F and F - End 2 . The experimental and theoretical results are compared in table 6.

Conclusion

From the close agreement of the experimental and theoretical values of J and the shear stress it can be concluded that the thin tube method can be used to predict torsional properties with acceptable accuracy.

It should be noted from the deflections, due to torsion, in figure (14) that the centre of twist is not along the centre line of the model. This is due to the model being curved in plan.

3) Possibility of Uplift at the Supports

A load applied to the outside edge of a curved bridge exerts a torque plus a vertical reaction at the supports. The relative magnitude of the torque compared with the vertical reactions depends upon the curvature, width, and radius of the bridge. If the downward vertical reactions required by the torque are greater than the upward reactions required by the vertical load then tie-down supports have to be provided.

The Tsing Fung Street Flyover has two supports which may need tie-downs, supporting the central suspended span and supporting the extreme end of the anchor span.

Central Suspended Span

The specified design live load is for either lane of the bridge to be loaded. Consider that a lane load can be represented by a concentrated load at the centre of the lane. A concentrated load was applied to the middle of each lane in turn and no uplift occurred.

Anchored Span

From observations of the deflection results the critical load condition for the anchored span support is Dead Load of suspended span Dead Load of Anchor Span Live Load on both lanes of suspended span.

Reaction measurements were taken, using two load cells for the reactions of the anchored span duc to an uniformly distributed load on either the suspended span or the anchored span. These results are given in columns 2 and 3 of Table 7.

Assuming that the dead load of the bridge is 350 psf (1710 kgf/m^2) the reactions for the critical loading can be calculated. These are given in column (7) of table 7. As both reactions are positive it appears that no uplift occurs at the supports of the anchor span.

Conclusion

The results show that uplift does not occur at any of the supports of the Tsing Fung Street Flyover under the specified design loading conditions.

4 Possibility of Buckling during Prestressing

Theoretically, buckling cannot occur in any system provided that the line of action of the force remains fixed with respect to the centroid of the section. Thus, a prestressed concrete member with post-tensioned steel can only buckle until the tendons come into contact with the ducts; thereafter the member under goes no further instability.

From the theory of buckling, the buckling stress σ_{cr}

is given by:

$$\sigma_{cr} = \frac{\pi^2 E}{\left(\frac{L}{r}\right)^2}$$

Provided $(\frac{l}{r})$ is the same, the buckling stress in any two structures is proportional to the modulus of elasticity.

Mean prestress in prototype = 1330 psi (94 kgf/cm^2)

Scaled mean prestress in perspex model = 1330 x $\frac{Ep}{Ec}$

$$= \frac{1300 \times 415{,}000^*}{5{,}000{,}000} \qquad = 110 \text{ psi } (7.7 \text{ kgf/cm}^2)$$

*(not corrected to 15°)

The central suspended span of the perspex model was provided with five prestressing wires of 0.120" (3 mm) diameter in the appropriate location. The wires were stressed by screw jacks placed at one end of the model, and the prestressing force in each wire was measured with a cylindrical load cell located at the other end of the model, as shown in figure (15). During stressing, the forces in the five wires were increased gradually, until a wire fractured. Owing to friction along the length of the wire, the load measured was somewhat less than the average force in the wire;

Maximum measured mean stress in model = 750 psi (53 kgf/cm^2)

$$\frac{\text{Measured stress}}{\text{Scaled prestress}} = \frac{750}{110} = 6.8$$

Conclusion

The experimental results support the theoretical prediction that no buckling will occur in a post-tensioned concrete member due to prestressing.

5 Load Factor and Mode of Failure of Prestressed Concrete Model

The model representation of the design load for the bridge was achieved using hydraulic jacks loading thru spreader beams to give 10 point loads. The jack pressures were adjusted to simulate a uniformly distributed load over all the span plus a knife edge load at mid span. The loads were increased in ratio and the behaviour observed. Complete results of the destructive test on the concrete model are given in reference (4).

The mid-span deflection of the bridge is shown in figure (16). The behaviour of the model became non-linear beyond $2\frac{1}{4}$ times the design load, when radial cracks occurred at the lower surface. As loading was increaded, the cracks propagated straight up to the soffit of the top flange and widened at such a rate that they rendered the structure unserviceable a 3 3/4 times the design load. With further increase of loading, the model behaved like a "mechanism" with a hinge at mid-span where a very wide crack existed. Nevertheless, the cross-stiffeners functioned satisfactorily at such intensity of loading and there was no great difference in deflection between line 1 and line 5. The model failed in flexure by crushing of the concrete on the top surface at 7 times the design load without any sign of distress due to shear or torsion.

Conclusions

The failure mode was identical to that that would be expected for a straight bridge, the model failing in flexure.

The use of unbonded cables in the model gave a conservative estimate of the failure load of a prototype with bonded cables. The model failed in flexure at 7 times design live load with no distress due to shear or torsion.

General Conclusions

A $\frac{1}{24}$ the scale perspex model of the Tsing Fung Street Flyover enabled the authors to determine the elastic behaviour of the bridge structure, ascertain its torsional properties and to determine that no problems would arise due to uplift at the supports.

The $\frac{1}{6}$ th scale prestressed concrete model gave similar elastic results to the perspex model and predicted the load factor for this particular bridge.

The torsionally stiff box section ensures that all the deck is effective in resisting partial loads. The thin tube method can be used to calculate the torsional properties of cellular decks with acceptable accuracy. Adequate transverse diaphragms should be provided to keep the box cross section from distorting.

It is strongly recommended that all model investigations be carried out in an indirect manner ie. the model is used to verify a theory. If a direct model test is required it is recommended that model and prototype material have the same Poisson's ratio.

Model investigations, such as this one serve as a simple means of verifying design assumptions and of checking the behaviour of complex structures under both service load and over-load.

Acknowledgements

The model investigation is being carried out in the laboratories of the Department of Civil Engineering, University of Hong Kong. The authors wish to thank Professor S. Mackey for his permission to use the laboratory facilities and for his encouragement during the investigation. The flyover is designed by the Architectural Office in liaison with the Roads and Drainage Division(HK) of the Civil Engineering Office of the Public Works Department, Hong Kong. The latter Division will also be responsible for construction of the flyover as part of the overall Water-front Road Scheme.

The authors gratefully acknowledge the co-operation of the P.W.D. which commissioned this investigation.

References

1. Abeles Paul W. 'Introduction to prestressed concrete' concrete Publications Ltd, London 1964 page 266.

2. Guyon Y. 'Prestressed Concrete' Vol, 1 Contractors Record Ltd. London 1960 page 329

3. Timoshanks and Goodier 'Theory of Elastiscity' McGraw-Hill Book Co. Inc. New York page 301.

4. Chung H.W. and Gardner N.J. "Model test on a curved bridge of cellular construction". Civil Engineering and Public Works Review, November 1968.

TABLE 1

Properties of measured model and assumed prototype materials.

Property	Perspex Model	Concrete Model at transfer (7 days)	Concrete Model (28 days)	Concrete Model (test at 152 days)	Assumed prototype properties (28 days)
Modulus of Elasticity	450,000 psi (31,500 kgf/km^2) at 15°C	4,700,000 psi (330,000 kgf/cm^2)	5,000,000 psi (351,000 kgf/cm^2)	5,100,000 psi (360,000 kgf/cm^2)	5,000,000 psi (351,000 kgf/cm^2)
Cube strength	—	7,700 psi (540 kgf/cm^2)	8,950 psi (630 kgf/cm^2)	9,700 psi (680 kgf/cm^2)	7,500 psi (525 kgf/cm^2)
Density of concrete	—	220 lbs/cubic ft. (3,450 kgf/m^3)	—	—	150 lbs/cubic ft. (2,350 kgf/m^3)
Prestressing steel 0.2% proof stress	—	102 Tsi (16,500 kgf/cm^2)	—	—	—
Prestressing steel ultimate strength	—	112 Tsi (17,800 kgf/cm^2)	—	—	—
Prestressing steel Modulus of Elasticity	—	27,600,000 psi (1,800,000 kgf/cm^2)	—	—	—

TABLE 2

EXPECTED ACCURACY OF RESULTS

	Results from Perspex Model	Results from Concrete Model
Longitudinal stress	3%	8%
Transverse stress	± 2%	± 25%
Shear stress	± 10%	—
Reflection	± 1%	± 1%

TABLE 3

Comparison of longitudinal stress scaled from model results for a UDL of 100 psf (488.2 kgf/m^2)

Position	Scaled from perspex model		Scaled from concrete model	
	Stress on Top Surface psi (kgf/cm^2)	Stress on Bottom Surface psi (kgf/cm^2)	Stress on Top Surface psi (kgf/cm^2)	Stress on Bottom Surface psi (kgf/cm^2)
B_1	-110 (- 7.7)	118 (8.3)	--	129 (9.1)
B_2	-114 (- 8.0)	123 (8.7)	--	140 (9.9)
B_3	-118 (- 8.3)	123 (8.7)	--	126 (8.9)
B_4	-117 (- 8.2)	127 (8.9)	--	145 (10.2)
B_5	-127 (- 8.9)	133 (9.4)	--	120 (8.4)
D_1	-152 (-10.7)	182 (12.8)	-139 (9.8)	156 (11.0)
D_2	-158 (-11.1)	178 (12.5)	-- ---	145 (10.2)
D_3	-156 (-11.0)	178 (12.5)	-129 (9.1)	145 (10.2)
D_4	-157 (-11.0)	177 (12.4)	-139 (9.8)	156 (11.0)
D_5	-175 (-12.3)	190 (13.3)	-126 (8.9)	147 (10.3)
F_1	-113 (- 8.0)	118 (8.3)	-77 (-5.4)	112 (7.9)
F_2	-121 (-8.5)	125 (8.8)	-68 (-4.8)	115 (8.1)
F_3	-122 (-8.6)	127 (8.9)	-- ---	109 (7.7)
F_4	-126 (-8.9)	131 (9.2)	-82 (-5.8)	120 (8.4)
F5	-132 (-9.3)	129 (9.1)	-88 (-6.2)	104 (7.3)

TABLE 4

Prototype column stress due to a load of 100 psf. (488.2 kgf/m^2)

	Stress At μ_1 psi (kgf/cm^2)	Stress At μ_2 psi (kgf/cm^2)	Stress At μ_3 psi (kgf/cm^2)	Stress At μ_4 psi (kgf/cm^2)
Load on suspended span	-41.8 (- 2.94)	-56.4 (- 3.96)	-20.9 (- 1.47)	-3.0 (-0.02)
Load on Anchored Span	-8.9 (-0.06)	111.0 (7.80)	-102.5 (-7.2)	-253.0 (-17.70)

TABLE 5

COMPARISION OF THE PREDICTED AND OBSERVED SHEAR STRESS.

	Experiment psi (kgf/cm^2)	Theoretical psi (kgf/cm^2)
Shear stress on line 1	220 (15.5)	254 (17.8)
Shear stress on line 5	267 (18.8)	254 (17.8)

TABLE 6

COMPARISION OF THE PREDICTED AND OBSERVED VALUES OF τ.

	Observed between D - End 2	Observed between D - F	Observed between F - End 2	Theory
J. ins^4 (cm^4)	27 (1122)	38 (1580)	22.5 (940)	29.6 (1230)

TABLE 7

Magnitude of anchored span reactions

Due to → / Reaction ↓	UDL 100 psf ($488.2\ kgf/cm^2$) on suspended span (2)	UDL 100 psf ($488.2\ kgf/cm^2$) on anchored span (3)	DEAD WT of suspended span (4)	DEAD WT of anchored span (5)	LIVE LOAD on suspended span (6)	TOTAL OF columns (4), (5) and (6) (7)
Reaction on line 1 (Force Units)	-12	25	-42.0	87.5	-26.4	19.1
Reaction on line 5	3.9	21.5	13.6	76.4	8.6	98.6

+ ve is upward reaction

- ve is tie down reaction

TABLE A 1

Position of dial gauges.

Longitudinal co-ordinate	Transverse co-ordinate				
End 1	1	—	—	—	5
B	1	2	3	4	5
D	1	2	3	4	5
F	1	2	3	4	5
End 2	1	2	3	4	5
Column	1	—	—	—	5
M	1	2	3	4	5
P	1	2	3	4	5
S	1	2	3	4	5

TABLE A 2

Position of Longitudinal strain gauges.

Longitudinal co-ordinate	Transverse co-ordinate				
B	1	2	3	4	5
D	1	2	3	4	5
F	1	2	3	4	5
I	1	2	3	4	5
Column	1	—	—	—	5
P	1	2	3	4	5

TABLE A3

Position of transverse strain gauges.

Longitudinal co-ordinate	Transverse co-ordinate.			
D	1-2	2-3	3-4	4-5
I	1-2	2-3	3-4	4-5
P	1-2	2-3	3-4	4-5

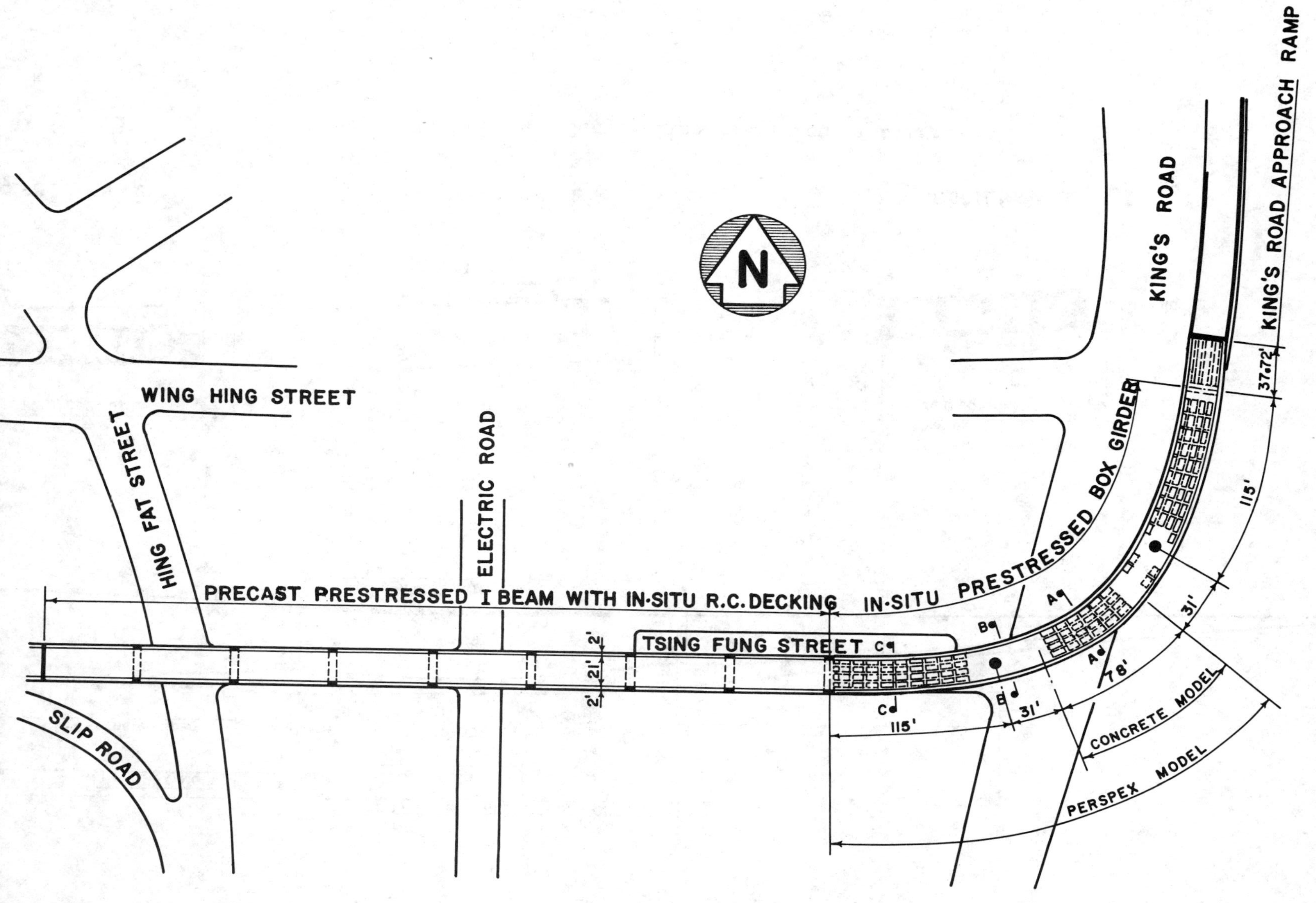

Fig. 1 Flyover superimposed upon existing street network

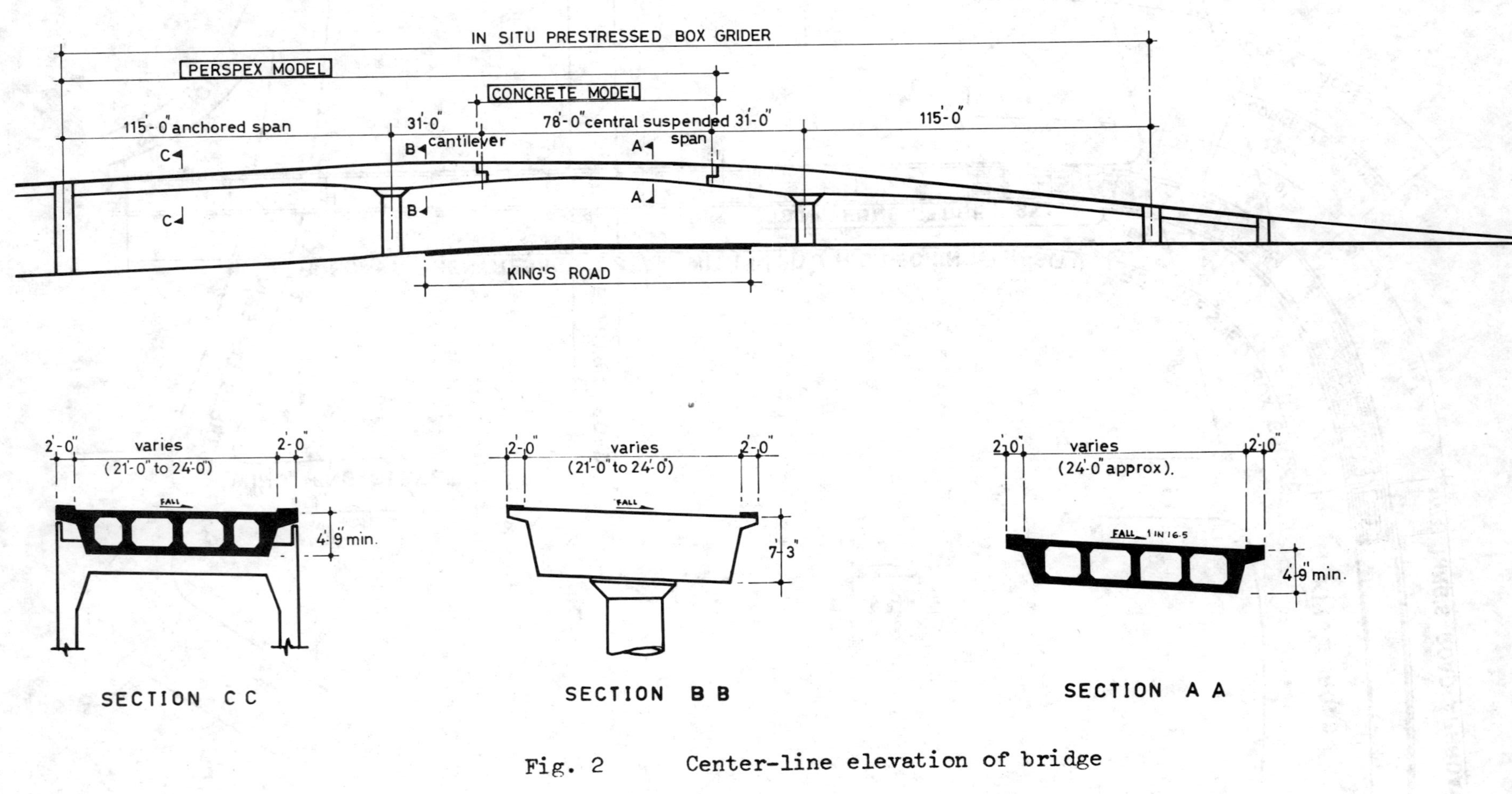

Fig. 2 Center-line elevation of bridge

Fig. 3 Ceneral view of perspex model and point loading device

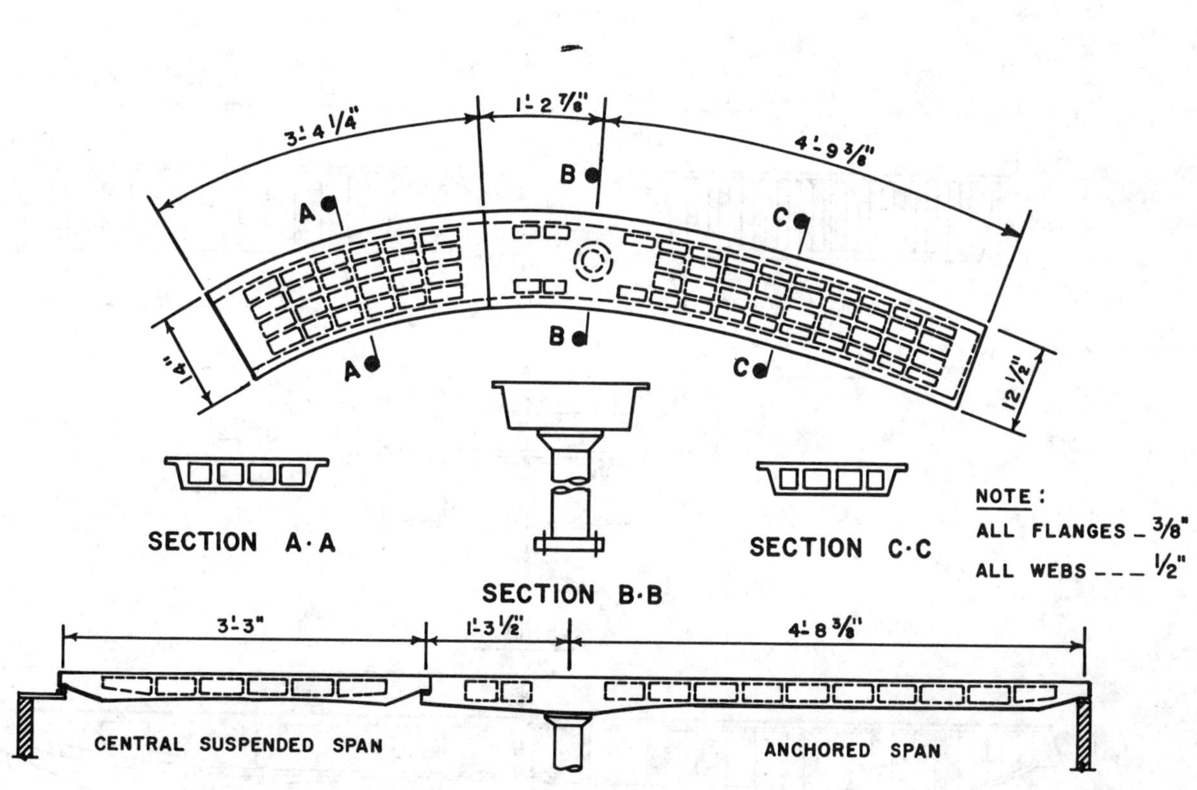

Fig. 4 Dimensions of perspex model

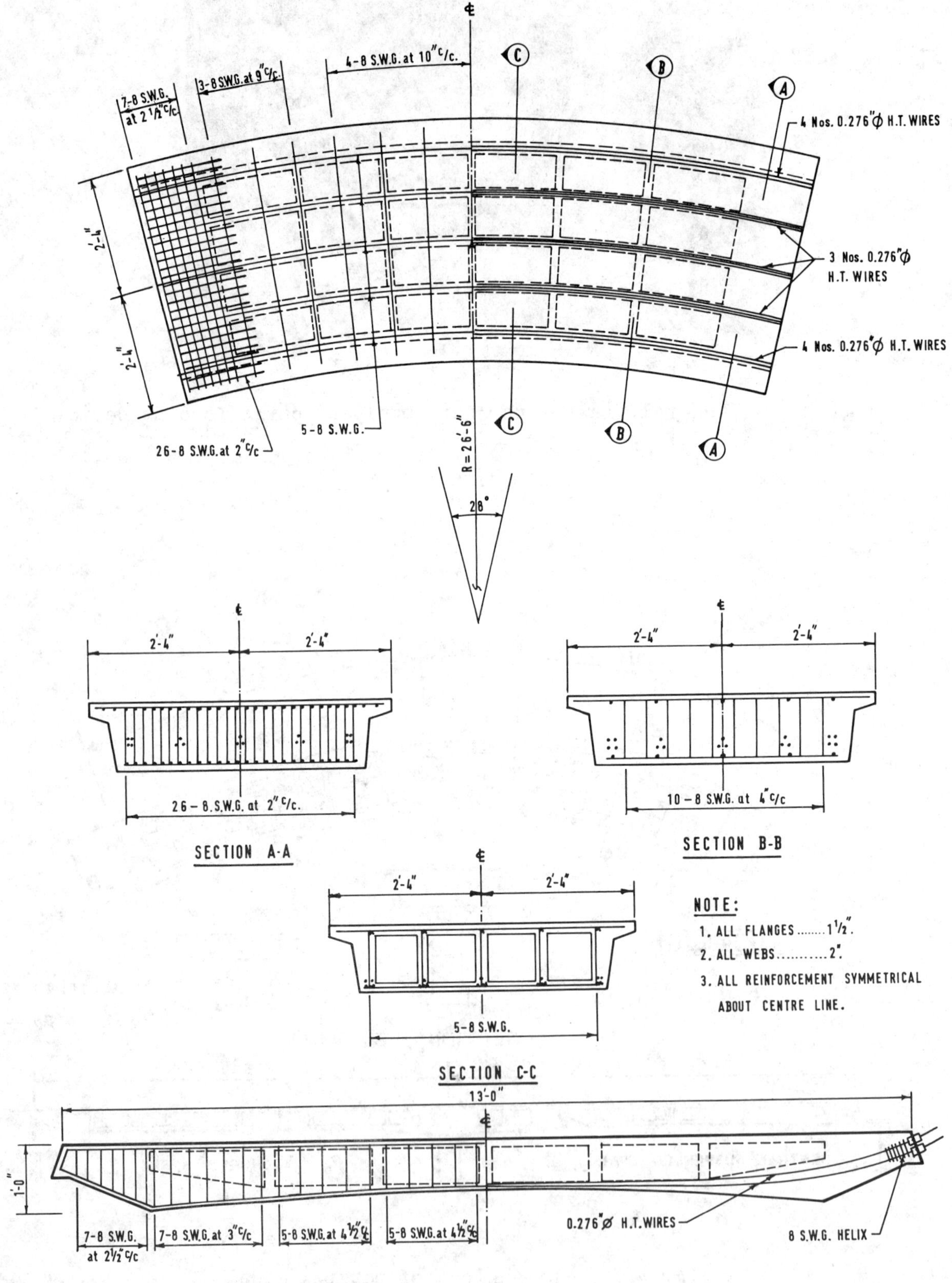

Fig. 5 Dimensions of prestressed concrete model

Fig. 6 Concrete model in test frame

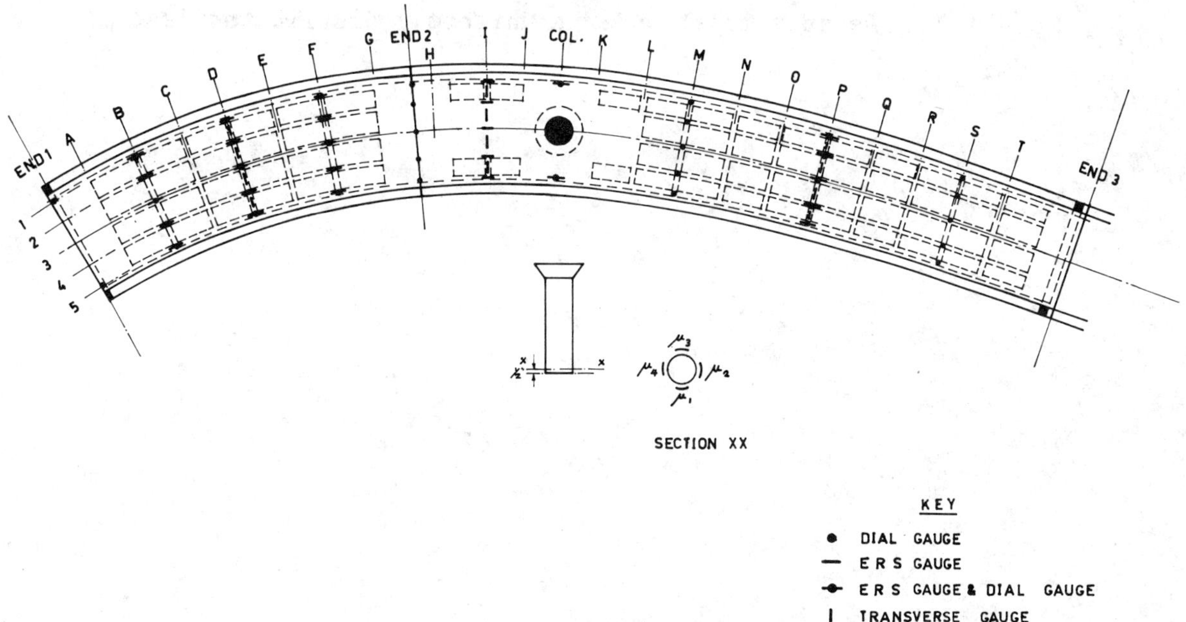

Fig. 7 Grid notation and position of column strain gauges

Fig. 8 Perspex model under a uniformly distributed load

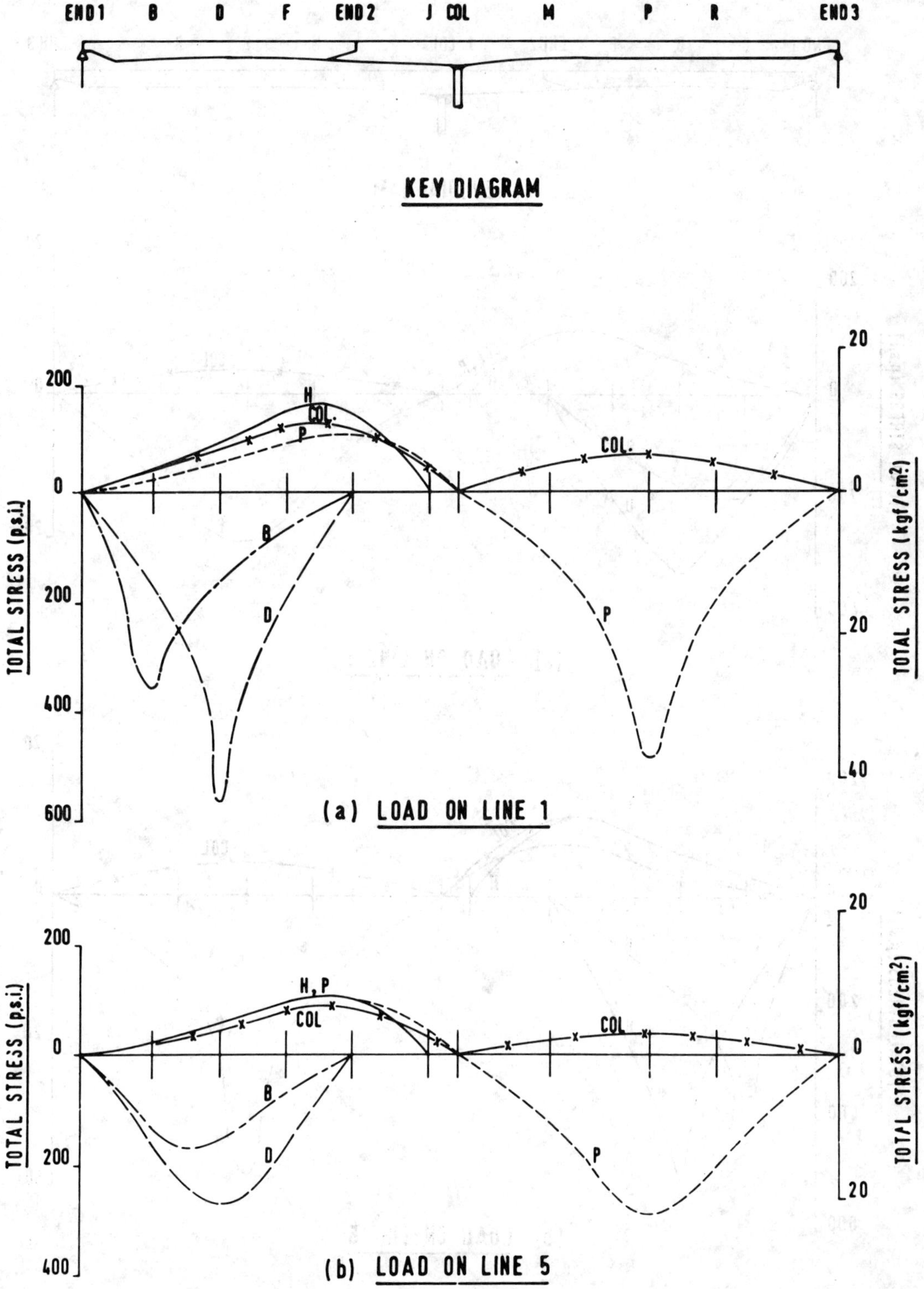

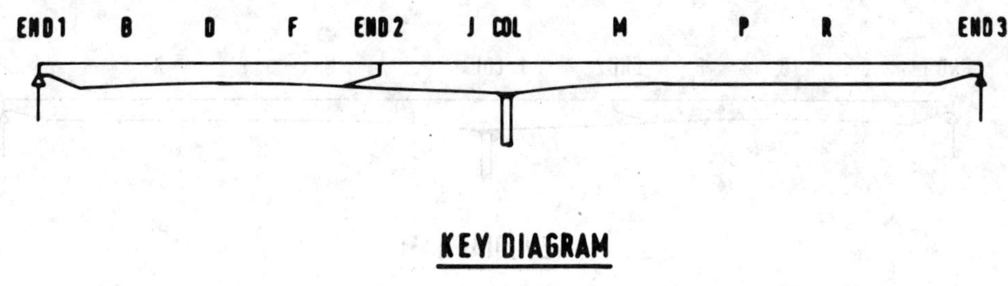

KEY DIAGRAM

(a) LOAD ON LINE 1

(b) LOAD ON LINE 5

Fig. 9 Influence line of total stress on line 1 due to 100,000 lbs (455 kgf) load on line 1 or line 5

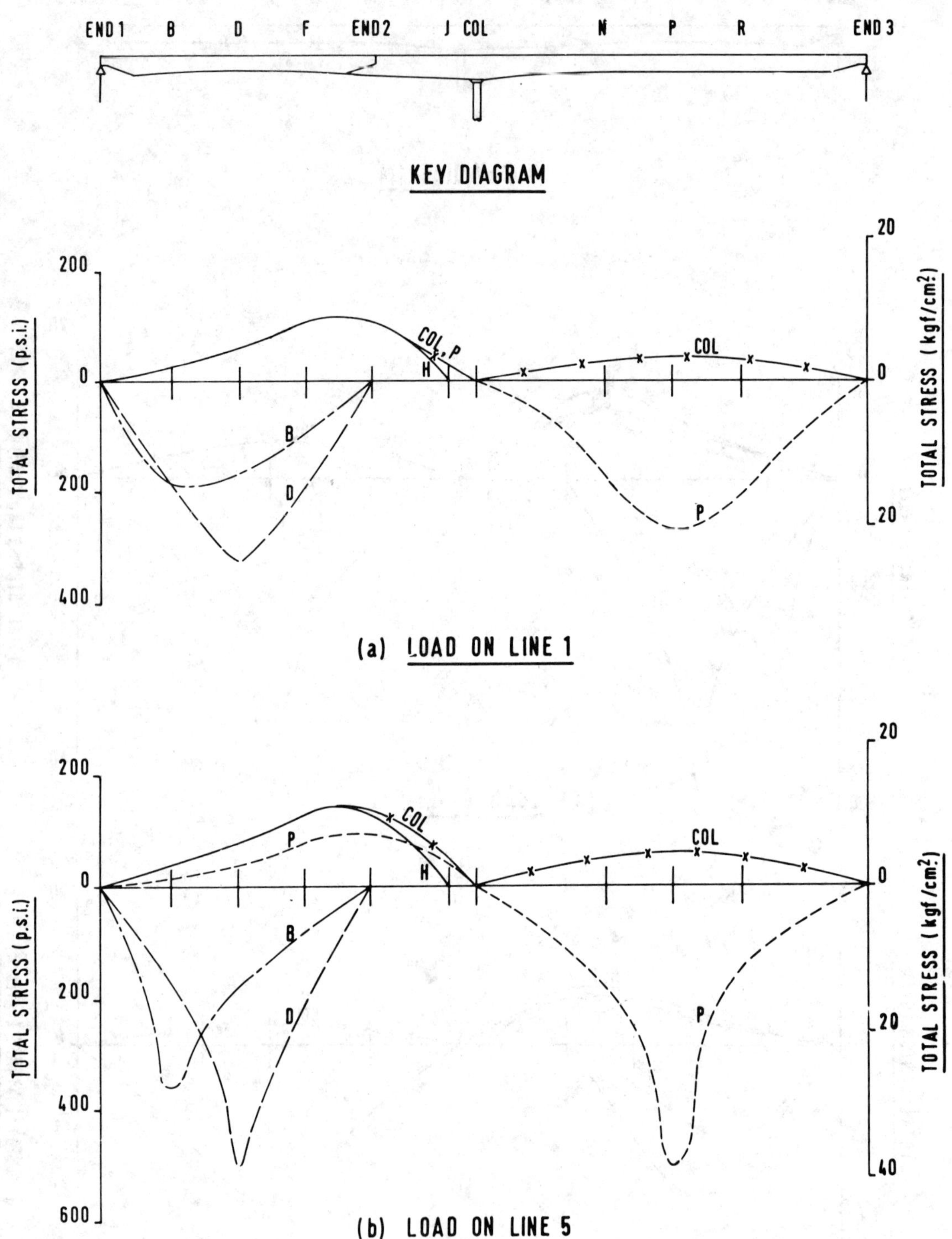

Fig.10 Influence line of total stress on line 5 due to 100,00 lbs (455 kgf) load on line 1 or line 5

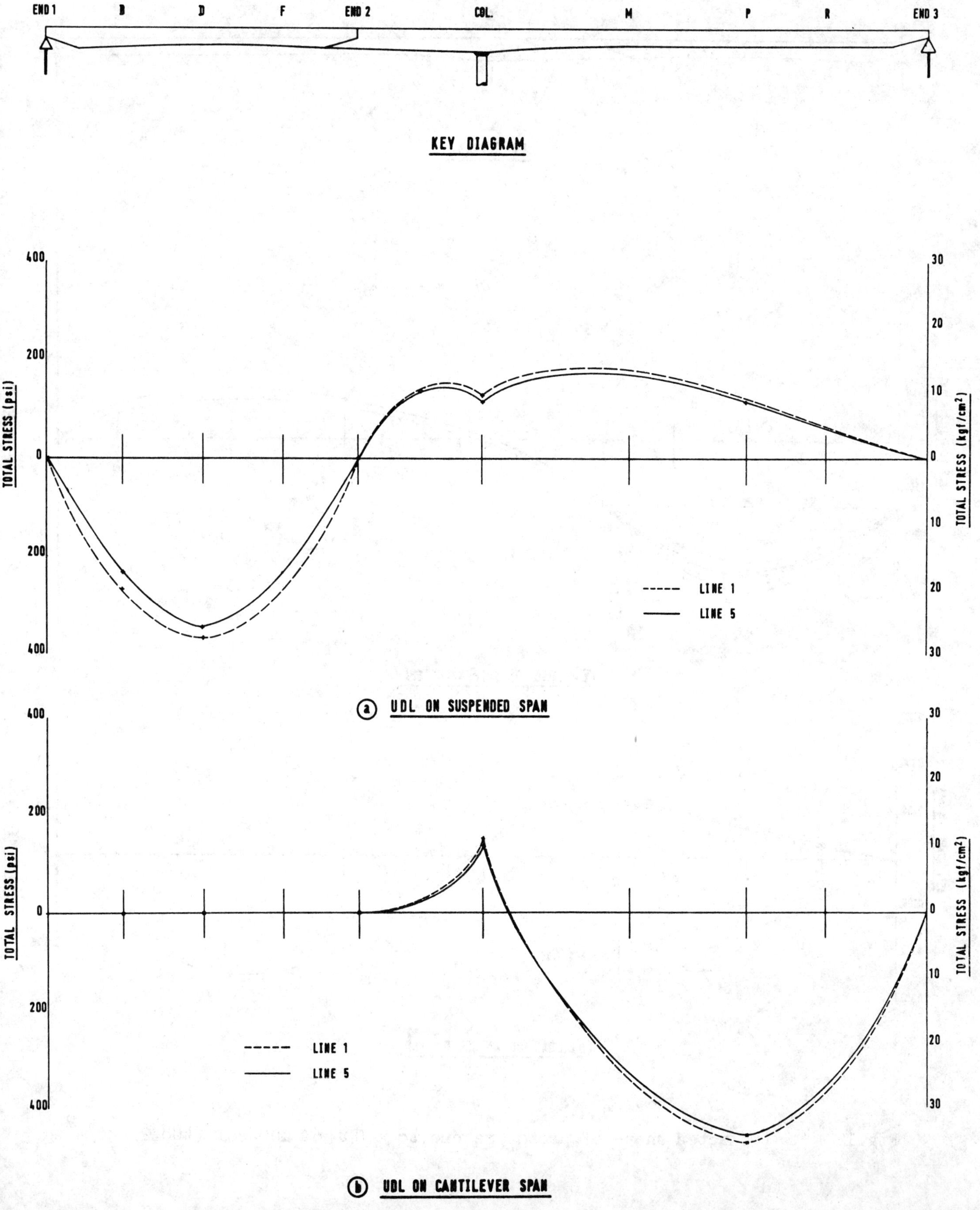

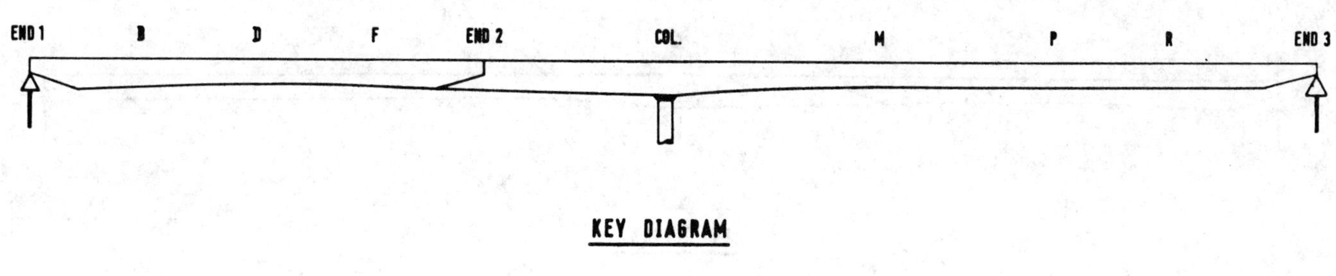

KEY DIAGRAM

(a) **UDL ON SUSPENDED SPAN**

(b) **UDL ON CANTILEVER SPAN**

Fig.11 Total stress diagram of prototype due to a UDL of 100 psf (488.2 kgf/m^2)

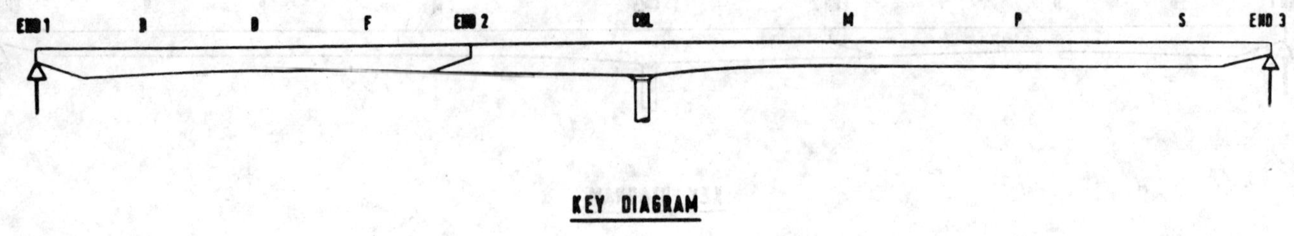

KEY DIAGRAM

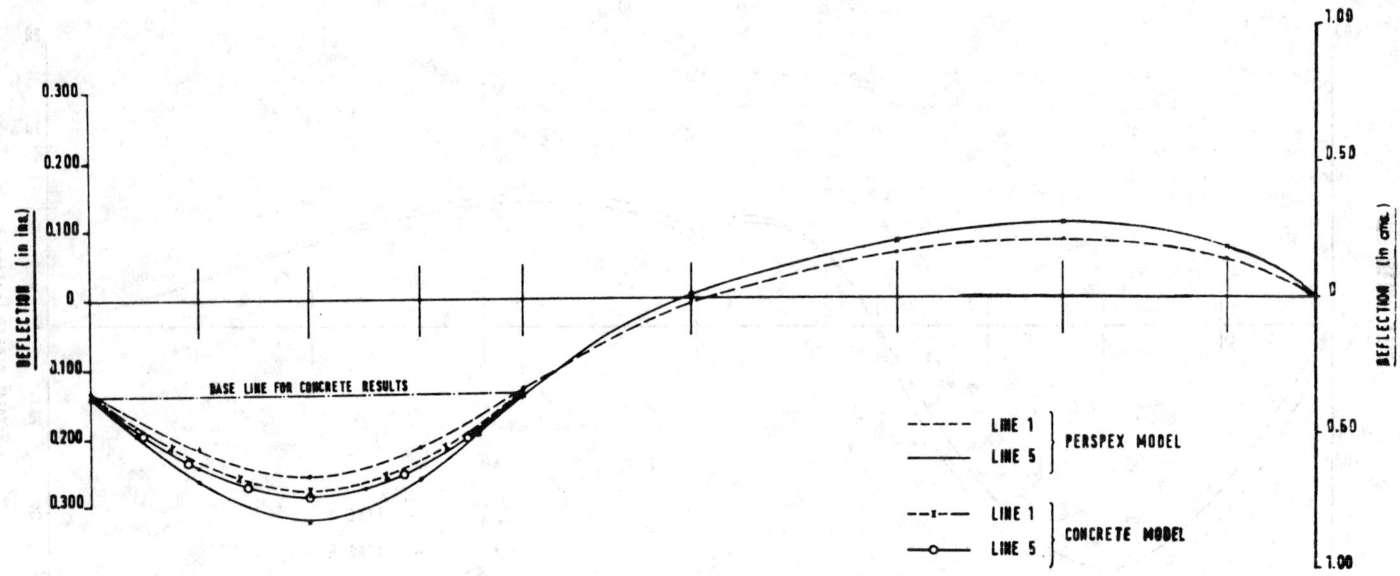

(a) LOAD ON SUSPENDED SPAN

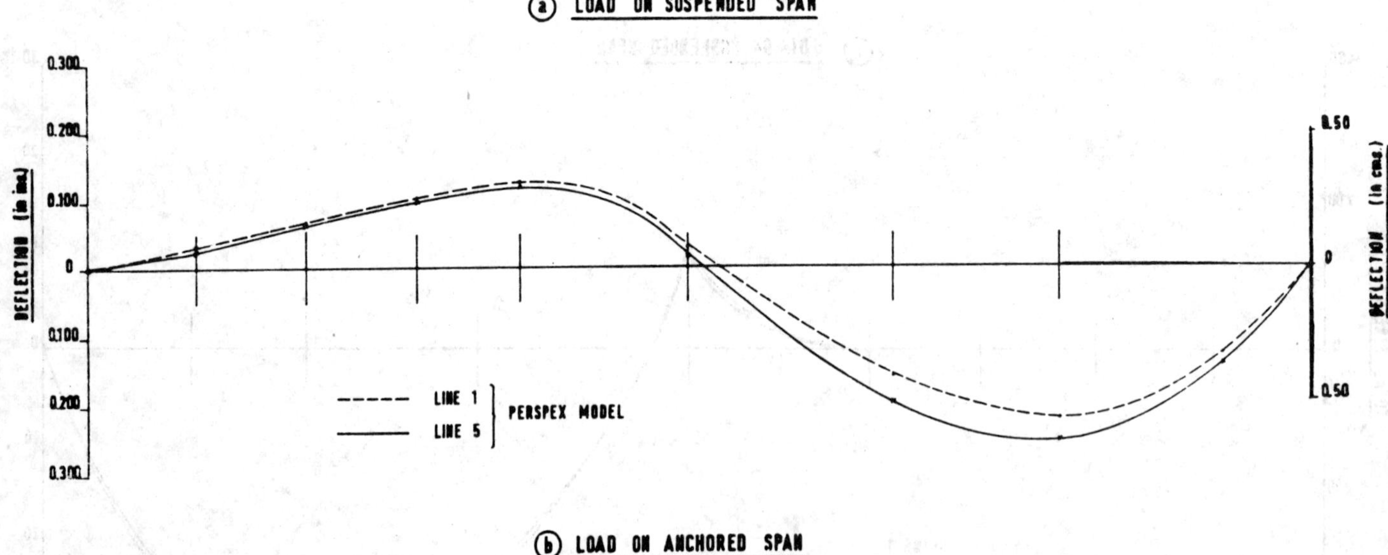

(b) LOAD ON ANCHORED SPAN

Fig.12 Deflected shape of prototype due to a UDL of 100 psf (488.2 kgf/m^2)

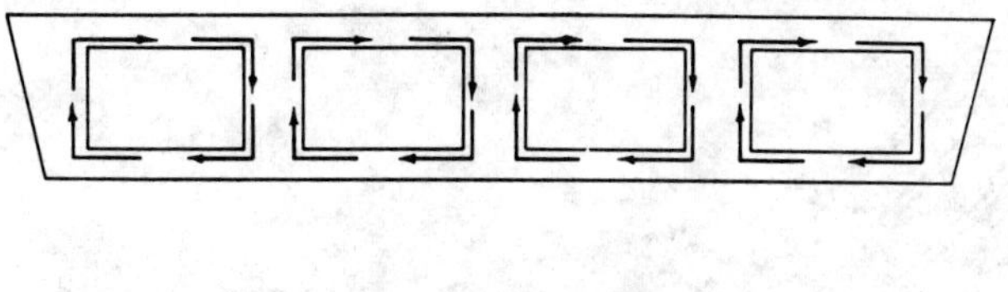

ⓐ SHEAR FLOW IN SECTION

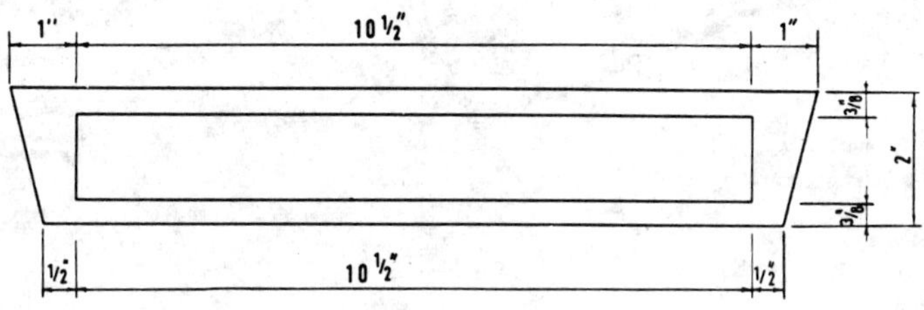

ⓑ EQUIVALENT SINGLE BOX

Fig.13 Cross section of dimensions used in torsion calculations

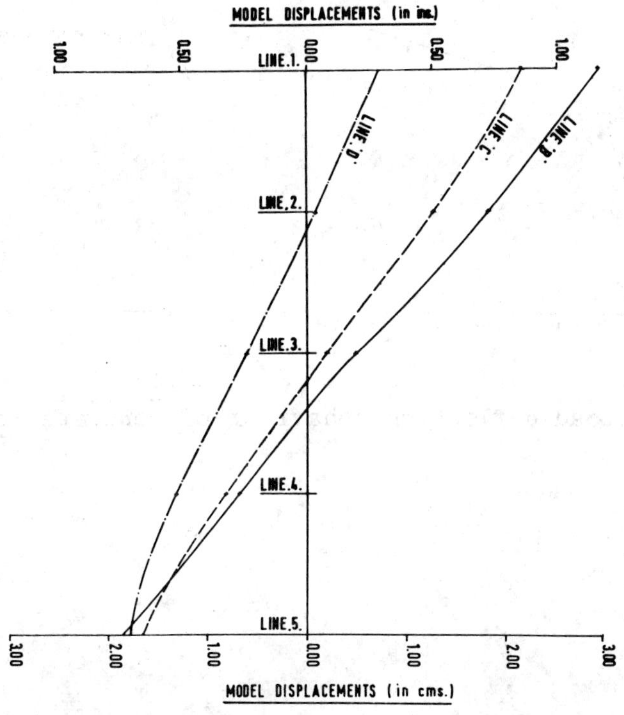

Fig.14 Perspex Model displacements due to an applied torque

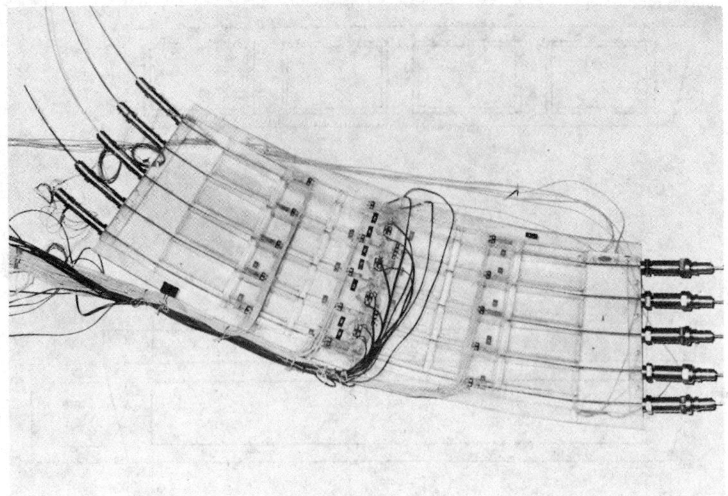

Fig.15 View of prestressing system for perspex model

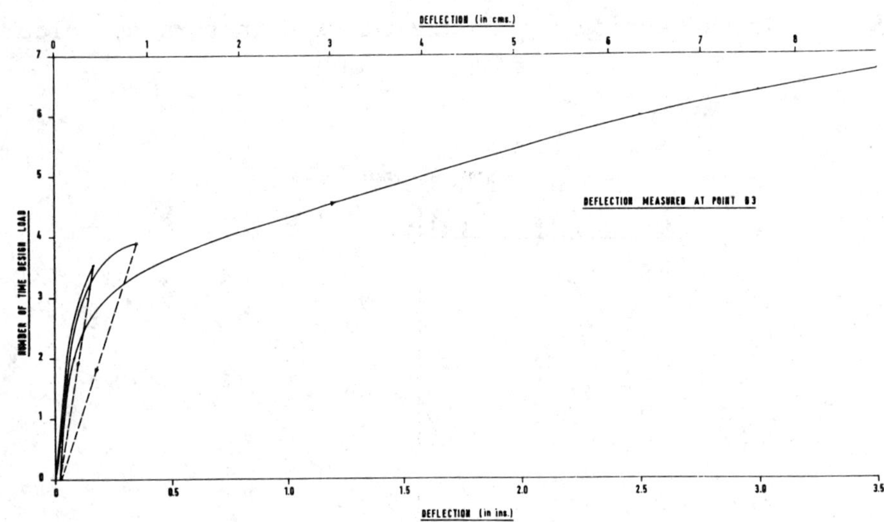

Fig.16 Load deflection behaviour of concrete model to failure.

ANALYSIS OF BOX GIRDER BRIDGES BY THE FINITE STRIP METHOD

By YAU-KAI CHEUNG

SYNOPSIS

The Finite Strip Method is used for the analysis of box girder bridges. In this method harmonic functions which fitted the boundary conditions (bending and in-plane) in the longitudinal direction are used in conjunction with simple polynomials for the transverse direction. Stiffness matrices for both bending and in-plane analysis have developed for a strip with an orthotropic property, and by dividing the box girder into a number of strips any combination of loadings can be easily dealt with. After solving for the joint displacements, the stresses at any point of a strip can be calculated and is a part of the direct printout of the programme. The analysis of a typical box girder bridge was carried out and a very good accuracy has been obtained.

Keywords: box beams; bridges (structures); displacements; finite element method; girder bridges; girders; matrix methods; orthotropic slabs; reinforced concrete; stiffness methods; stresses; structural analysis.

YAU-KAI CHEUNG is associate professor of civil engineering at the University of Calgary, Calgary, Alberta, Canada. He received his PhD degrees in 1964 from the University of Wales, Swansea, where he also worked as senior research fellow and lecturer in civil engineering until 1967. He has made many technical contributions which have appeared in various engineering journals. His main interest is in the development and application of the Finite Element Method.

INTRODUCTION

A concrete box girder bridge may be considered as a multiple folded plate structure, and an analysis based on the elasticity theory originated by Goldberg and Leve(1) has been performed by Chu and Dudnik(2). The results have been compared with those obtained from the beam formula and empirical methods.

The elasticity method has been shown to give accurate results for various types of folded plate structures(2),(3), but it suffers from the drawback of being too complex. For a structure subject to any loadings which do not act at the joints, it is necessary first of all to perform an elastic plate analysis in order to obtain the fixed edge forces. These forces (now with opposite signs) are then used as ridge loads for the analysis of the whole folded plate structure. The final answers are obtained from superposition of these two solutions. Needless to say, such procedures involve extra programming efforts and limit the generality of the computer program because only a certain number of loading cases can be incorporated and stored as subroutines. Furthermore, the method is not applicable to plates with orthotropic properties. Such orthotropy can be the result of two-way reinforcements or stiffening of the slab by ribs in one or two directions.

The finite strip method, which is an extension of the powerful finite element method, has been shown to be a valuable tool for the analysis of orthotropic and isotropic plates with arbitrary boundary conditions(4). This method has also been extended to the analysis of folded plate structures(5), and excellent results have been obtained.

In the present paper it will be shown that this method is also applicable to box girder bridge problems.

The main advantages of the finite strip approach lie in its simplicity, its high accuracy, and to a certain extent, its versatility. The stiffness matrix of a strip with its pre-set end conditions is established in the same way as that for a finite element, and the stress matrix can also be written in terms of the nodal displacement parameters. The loadings can be point loads, longitudinal or transverse line loads, or distributed loads. The loads can act either on the ridges or directly on the surface of the plates.

Development of Stiffness Matrix

The simply-supported box girder bridge is now assumed to be divided into a number of strips in the longitudinal direction in the webs as well as in the flanges. It is necessary to have a finer mesh at the top slabs because this part is usually more heavily loaded. A typical strip is shown in Fig. 1. The properties of each strip are regarded as constant in its own, but can change from strip to strip so as to approximate variable thickness problems.

Each strip is subject to "in-plane" or membrane stresses and to transverse bending forces. Since these two types of forces are not coupled it is convenient to establish the characteristic stiffnesses separately in two stages and then combine them into a comprehensive matrix. In the subsequent formulation the strip is assumed to posses orthotropic properties.

The formulation of both types of matrices has been presented in detail in a separate paper[5]. A somewhat shorter description will be given here.

a) "In-plane" stiffness of a strip.

The end conditions for the in-plane forces and displacements are

$$v = 0$$
$$\sigma_y = 0 \quad \text{or} \quad \left(\frac{\partial v}{\partial y} + \mu_x \frac{\partial u}{\partial x}\right) = 0 \qquad (1)$$

For a strip with sides i and j, the above conditions can be satisfied by the folowing Fourier series:

$$u = \sum_{m=1,2,\ldots r} \left[\left(1 - \frac{x}{b}\right) u_{im} + \frac{x}{b} u_{jm} \right] \sin k_m y$$
$$v = \sum_{m=1,2,\ldots r} \left[\left(1 - \frac{x}{b}\right) v_{im} + \frac{x}{b} v_{jm} \right] \cos k_m y \qquad (2a)$$

$$\text{or} \quad f = \begin{Bmatrix} u \\ v \end{Bmatrix} = \sum_{m=1,2..r} C_{pm}\, \delta_{pm} \qquad (2b)$$

where $k_m = \frac{m\pi}{l}$, and u_{im}, v_{im}, etc. are the diaplacement parameters of the mth term at the nodal lines.

If the loads X and Y are also resolved into Fourier series in the longitudinal direction, i.e.

$$X = \sum_{m=1,2,\ldots r} X_m \sin k_m y$$
$$Y = \sum_{m=1,2,\ldots r} Y_m \cos k_m y \qquad (2c)$$

it is possible to utilize the orthogonal properties of the functions to uncouple the series so that each term can be solved individually and then summed to give the final answers. In the text which follows, the summation sign will be dropped completely.

Using the standard matrix formulation given in a text by Zienkiewicz and Cheung[6], we have for the strain-displacement relationship

$$\varepsilon_m = \begin{Bmatrix} \varepsilon_x \\ \varepsilon_y \\ \gamma_{xy} \end{Bmatrix}_m = \begin{Bmatrix} \frac{\partial u}{\partial x} \\ \frac{\partial v}{\partial y} \\ \frac{\partial u}{\partial y} + \frac{\partial v}{\partial x} \end{Bmatrix}_m = B_{pm}\ \delta_{pm} \qquad (3)$$

for the stress-strain relationship

$$\sigma_m = \begin{Bmatrix} \sigma_x \\ \sigma_y \\ \tau_{xy} \end{Bmatrix}_m = D_p \varepsilon_m = D_p B_{pm}\ \delta_{pm} \qquad (4)$$

in which the property matrix D_p is given by

$$D_p = \begin{bmatrix} \frac{E_x}{1-\mu_x\mu_y} & \frac{\mu_x E_y}{1-\mu_x\mu_y} & 0 \\ \frac{\mu_x E_y}{1-\mu_x\mu_y} & \frac{E_y}{1-\mu_x\mu_y} & 0 \\ 0 & 0 & G \end{bmatrix} \qquad (5)$$

and for the nodal force-displacement relationship

$$\int_o^1 \int_o^b B_{pm}^T\ D_p\ B_{pm}\ dxdy\ \delta_{pm} =$$

$$\int_o^1 \int_o^b C_{pm}^T \begin{Bmatrix} X_m \sin k_m y \\ Y_m \cos k_m y \end{Bmatrix} dxdy$$

or

$$S_{pm}\ \delta_{pm} = F_{pm} \qquad (6)$$

The stiffness S_{pm} (4x4) has been worked out explicitly and can be found in Appendix Ia.

To demonstrate the accuracy of the in-plane stiffness, an isotropic square deep beam under a uniform line load at the top has been analysed and the results are presented in Fig. 2. It can be seen that the longitudinal stresses σ_y agree very well with the values given by Kalmanok(7).

b) Bending stiffness of a strip

The end conditions for the bending forces and displacements are

$$w = 0$$

$$M_y = 0 \quad \text{or} \quad D_1 \frac{\partial^2 w}{\partial x^2} + D_y \frac{\partial^2 w}{\partial y^2} = 0 \qquad (7)$$

A displacement function which satisfies the above conditions can be given as

$$W = \sum_{m=1,2\ldots r} \left[\left(1 - \frac{3x^2}{b^2} + \frac{2x^3}{b^3}\right) w_{im} + \left(x - \frac{2x^2}{b} + \frac{x^3}{b^2}\right) \theta_{im} + \left(\frac{3x^2}{b^2} - \frac{2x^3}{b^3}\right) w_{jm} + \left(\frac{x^3}{b^2} - \frac{x^2}{b}\right) \theta_{jm} \right] \sin k_m y$$

$$= \sum_{m=1,2\ldots r} C_{bm} \delta_{bm} \qquad (8a)$$

in which δ_{bm} is a vector representing the nodal displacement parameters of the mth term.

The normal load $\mathcal{Z}$ is also resolved into a Fourier Series, i.e.

$$\mathcal{Z} = \sum_{m=1,2...r} \mathcal{Z}_m \sin k_m y \tag{8b}$$

Following the reasoning in the previous section we found that in this case the results of each term can also be solved individually and then summed to give the final results. As such the summation sign will also be dropped.

The curvature-displacement relationship can be written as

$$\chi_m = \begin{Bmatrix} -\dfrac{\partial^2 w}{\partial x^2} \\ -\dfrac{\partial^2 w}{\partial y^2} \\ 2\dfrac{\partial^2 w}{\partial x \partial y} \end{Bmatrix}_m = B_{bm}\,\delta_{bm} \tag{9}$$

and the moment-curvature relationship as

$$M_m = \begin{Bmatrix} M_x \\ M_y \\ M_{xy} \end{Bmatrix}_m = D_b\,\chi_m = D_b\,B_{bm}\,\delta_{bm} \tag{10}$$

in which the property matrix D_b is

$$D_b = \begin{bmatrix} D_x & D_1 & 0 \\ D_1 & D_y & 0 \\ 0 & 0 & D_{xy} \end{bmatrix} \tag{11}$$

Finally the nodal force-displacement relationship will be given as

$$\int_{o}^{1}\int_{o}^{b} B_{bm}^{T} D_b B_{bm} \, dxdy \;\; \delta_{bm} = \int_{o}^{1}\int_{o}^{b} C_{bm}^{T} Z_m \sin k_m y \, dxdy$$

or

$$S_{bm} \, \delta_{bm} = F_{bm} \qquad (12)$$

The bending stiffness S_{bm}(4x4) has also been worked out explicitly and can be found in Appendix Ib.

The bending stiffness has been tested thoroughly. In Fig. 3 the moments for an isotropic square plate under a central point load are compared with the values obtained from a 8x8 finite element analysis and from the Method of Distribution Coefficients. It can be seen that the first two sets of values practically coincide with each other, while the third set of values shows the usual underestimation of peak moments.

c) The comprehensive matrix of a strip

If both systems of nodal displacements are acting simultaneously, then at each nodal line four components of forces are developed and these are given in terms of four components of displacement.

We have for the forces

$$F_m = \left\{ U_{im} \; V_{im} \; W_{im} \; M_{im} \; U_{jm} \; V_{jm} \; W_{jm} \; M_{jm} \right\}^T \qquad (13a)$$

and for the corresponding displacements

$$\delta_m = \left\{ u_{im} \; v_{im} \; w_{im} \; \theta_{im} \; u_{jm} \; v_{jm} \; w_{jm} \; \theta_{jm} \right\}^T \qquad (13b)$$

The force-displacement relationship of this system will now be

$$S_m \, \delta_m = F_m \qquad (13c)$$

with the element $(s_m)_{ij}$ of the matrix S_m simply made up of appropriate elements from S_{pm} and S_{bm} matrices

$$\underset{(4x4)}{(s_m)_{ij}} = \begin{bmatrix} (s_{pm})_{ij} & 0 \\ 0 & (s_{bm})_{ij} \end{bmatrix} \qquad (13d)$$

Unlike the stiffness matrix of a generalised finite element, S_m is not singular, and is thus well suited to bridge problems where there are no displacement boundary conditions at the free edges.

Transformation of Coordinate Systems

Since the strips are very often not co-planar, it is necessary to have a common system of coordinates for establishing the equations of equilibrium and compatibility at the nodes. Let this common orthogonal coordinate system be labelled x, y, z and the individual coordinate system x', y', z' as shown in Fig. 4. The transformation of forces and displacements between the two sets of coordinate systems is given by

$$F_m = RF'_m$$

$$S'_m = R^T\delta_m$$

in which the transformation matrix R is simply

$$R = \begin{bmatrix} r & o \\ o & r \end{bmatrix}$$

$$\text{and } r = \begin{bmatrix} \cos\alpha & 0 & \sin\alpha & 0 \\ 0 & 1 & 0 & 0 \\ -\sin\alpha & 0 & \cos\alpha & 0 \\ 0 & 0 & 0 & 1 \end{bmatrix}$$

where α is the angle between x and x' axes.

The final result of the transformation is

$$F_m = (R\, S_m'\, R^T)\delta_m$$

$$= S_m\, \delta_m$$

Analysis of a Box Girder Bridge

A typical box girder bridge (Fig. 5) which was analysed by Chu and Dudnik[2] using the elasticity method is taken as an example to show the accuracy of the finite strip method. In order to compare with the results of reference (2), the sidewalk elements are also replaced by a cantilever slab 8" thick and 3'-9" wide, although unlike the elasticity method, using the actual cross-section will not involve any more effort or computer time.

Three types of loadings are used and their magnitudes and distribution are given in Fig. 6. They are respectively the dead load of the structure and two types of truck loadings (a) (loading 5 in reference 2) and (b) (loading 6 in reference 2).

The box girder is divided into 93 strips, and there are 90 nodal lines altogether. The top slab is given a much finer mesh than the bottom slab because of the concentrated truck loadings.

Eleven terms of the Fourier series have been used for the analysis. For the dead loads which are symmetrical with respect to the centre of the span, only the odd terms of the series are useful, since the even terms produce zero value answers.

The nodes have been numbered to produce a matrix with the narrowest half-band width. This is quite important because the solution time for such band matrices are directly proportional to the square of the band width. The various loadings are solved one after the other, while the elimination procedure of the stiffness matrix is only performed once. The additional computer time required for an extra loading case is thus usually very small compared with the overall solution time. For the present bridge analysis the execution time on the medium speed IBM-360-50 computer is 25 minutes.

The transverse and longitudinal stresses are positive when tensile, while the bending moments M_x and M_y obey the usual sign convention given in Timoshenko and Woinowsky-Krieger[(8)] using the individual coordinate systems of the strips. In this particular example, all the horizontal strips have their x'-axes pointing towards the right and all the vertical strips have their x'- axes pointing downwards.

The longitudinal stresses σ_y, transverse bending moments M_x and longitudinal bending moments M_y at the centre of span for the three loading cases are presented in Figs. 7-9. The transverse stresses σ_x, in-plane shear stresses τ_{xy} and the twisting moments M_{xy} are also included in the output but will not be given here.

The values of longitudinal stresses and transverse moments due to dead load are all slightly below those given by reference (2), although the same pattern of variation can be observed. This might be due to the fact that there is some difference in the total load used for the two analyses. For the finite strip analysis, the maximum bending moment due to the dead weight checked closely with the resisting moment computed from the longitudinal stresses and their respective moment arms. The author feels that the transverse moments given by the elasticity method are probably too high, since the simply-supported maximum moment of all slabs (2.21k-ft/ft for top slab and 1.40 k-ft/ft for bottom slab) exceed those for a corresponding rigid frame analysis (2.14 k-ft/ft for top slab and 1.33 k-ft/ft for bottom slab). Now the values obtained from the rigid frame analysis should be regarded as the maximum values attainable by the elasticity method, i.e., in the case when the slab is bent into a cylindrical surface. In reality, due to the deflection of the webs the values should be somewhat lower than the maximum.

The values of the negative transverse moment M_x due to loading (a) compare very well with those of reference (2), but the positive transverse moments should only be treated in the same way as moment distribution coefficients and used for the design of stiffening ribs when such members are present. The actual maximum positive moment under the wheel loads cannot be adequately supplied by the theory of thin plates, and special methods have to be used.

To find the local stresses under the wheel loads, we should resort to either of two procedures due to Pigeaud and Westergaard. A detailed description of these methods can be found in a text by Rowe[9].

CONCLUSION

It has been shown in this paper that the finite strip method provides a simple and accurate tool for the analysis of box girder bridges. Moreover, apart from the finite element method, it is the only alternative procedure which will solve problems with orthotropic properties. Such orthotropic properties can be due to two-way reinforcement of slabs and stiffening of slabs by ribs in one or two directions.

ACKNOWLEDGEMENT

The author wishes to thank the National Research Council of Canada and the University of Calgary for support of the project.

REFERENCES

(1) Goldberg, J.E. and Leve, H.L.
"Theory of Prismatic Folded Plate Structures", 1 ABSE, Zurich, Switzerland, No. 87, pp 71-72.

(2) Chu, K.H. and Dudnik, E.
"Concrete Box Girder Bridges Analyzed as Folded Plates" Proc. Int. Symp. on Concrete Bridge Design, April 1, 1967, Toronto.

(3) De Fries-Skene, A. and Scordelis, A.C.
"Direct Stiffness Solution for Folded Plates" Jour. of Struct. Div., Proc. ASCE, August 1964, pp 15-47.

(4) Cheung, Y,K.
"Analysis of Elastic Rectangular Slabs by Finite Stip Method". Jour. of Eng. Mech. Div., Proc. ASCE, December 1968.

(5) Cheung, Y.K.
"Folded Plate Structures by the Finite Strip Method" to be published.

(6) Zienkiewicz, D.C. and Cheung, Y.K.
"Finite Element Method in Structural and Continium Mechanics" McGraw-Hill Book Co. Ltd., 1967.

(7) Kalmanok, A.S.
"Calculation of Plates" (In Russian) National Press, Moscow 1959.

(8) Timoshenko, S. and Woinowsky-Krieger, S.
"Theory of Plates and Shells" 2nd edition, McGraw-Hill, New York, 1959.

(9) Rowe, R.E.
"Concrete Bridge Design" John Wiley and Sons, Inc. 1962.

APPENDIX Ia - IN-PLANE STIFFNESS MATRIX

$$S_{pm} = t \begin{bmatrix} \frac{\ell E_1}{2b} + \frac{\ell b k_m^2 G}{6} & & & \text{Symmetrical} \\ \frac{\ell k_m \mu_x E_2}{4} - \frac{\ell k_m G}{4} & \frac{\ell b k_m^2 E_2}{6} + \frac{\ell G}{2b} & & \\ \frac{\ell E_1}{2b} + \frac{\ell b k_m^2 G}{12} & -\frac{\ell k_m \mu_x E_2}{4} - \frac{\ell k_m G}{4} & \frac{\ell E_1}{2b} + \frac{\ell b k_m^2 G}{6} & \\ \frac{\ell k_m \mu_x E_2}{4} + \frac{\ell k_m G}{4} & \frac{\ell b k_m^2 E_2}{12} - \frac{\ell G}{2b} & -\frac{\ell k_m \mu_x E_2}{4} + \frac{\ell k_m G}{4} & \frac{\ell b k_m^2 E_2}{6} + \frac{\ell G}{2b} \end{bmatrix}$$

$$E_1 = \frac{E_x}{1-\mu_x \mu_y}$$

$$E_2 = \frac{E_y}{1-\mu_x \mu_y}$$

APPENDIX Ib - BENDING STIFFNESS OF MATRIX

$\frac{13\ell b}{70} k_m^4 D_y + \frac{12\ell}{5b} k_m^2 D_{xy} + \frac{6\ell}{5b} k_m^2 D_1 + \frac{6\ell}{b^3} D_x$			
$\frac{3\ell}{5} k_m^2 D_1 + \frac{\ell}{5} k_m^2 D_{xy} + \frac{3\ell}{b^3} D_x + \frac{11\ell b^2}{420} k_m^4 D_y$	$\frac{\ell b^3}{210} k_m^4 D_y + \frac{4\ell b}{15} k_m^2 D_{xy} + \frac{2\ell b}{15} k_m^2 D_1 + \frac{2\ell}{b} D_x$		
$\frac{9\ell b}{140} k_m^4 D_y - \frac{12\ell}{5b} k_m^2 D_{xy} - \frac{6\ell}{5b} k_m^2 D_1 - \frac{6\ell}{b^3} D_x$	$\frac{13\ell b^2}{840} k_m^4 D_y - \frac{\ell}{5} k_m^2 D_{xy} - \frac{\ell}{10} k_m^2 D_1 - \frac{3\ell}{b^2} D_x$	$\frac{13\ell b}{70} k_m^4 D_y + \frac{12\ell}{5b} k_m^2 D_y + \frac{6\ell}{5b} k_m^2 D_1 + \frac{6\ell}{b^3} D_x$	
$- \frac{13\ell b^2}{840} k_m^4 D_y + \frac{\ell}{5} k_m^2 D_{xy} + \frac{\ell}{10} k_m^2 D_1 + \frac{3\ell}{b^2} D_x$	$- \frac{3\ell b^3}{840} k_m^4 D_y - \frac{\ell b}{15} k_m^2 D_{xy} - \frac{\ell b}{30} k_m^2 D_1 + \frac{\ell}{b} D_x$	$- \frac{11\ell b^2}{420} k_m^4 D_y - \frac{\ell}{5} k_m^2 D_{xy} - \frac{3\ell}{5} k_m^2 D_1 - \frac{3\ell}{b^2} D_x$	$\frac{\ell b^3}{210} k_m^4 D_y + \frac{4\ell b}{15} k_m^2 D_{xy} + \frac{2\ell b}{15} k_m^2 D_1 + \frac{2\ell}{b} D_x$

APPENDIX II - NOTATION

u = displacement in x direction

v = displacement in y direction

w = displacement in z direction

θ = rotation round y axis

E_x, E_y, μ_x, G = orthotropic elastic constants in the x and y directions

σ_x, σ_y, τ_{xy} = normal and shear stresses

M_x, M_y, M_{xy} = bending and twisting moments

X, Y, Z = loadings in the x, y, z directions respectively.

t = thickness of strip

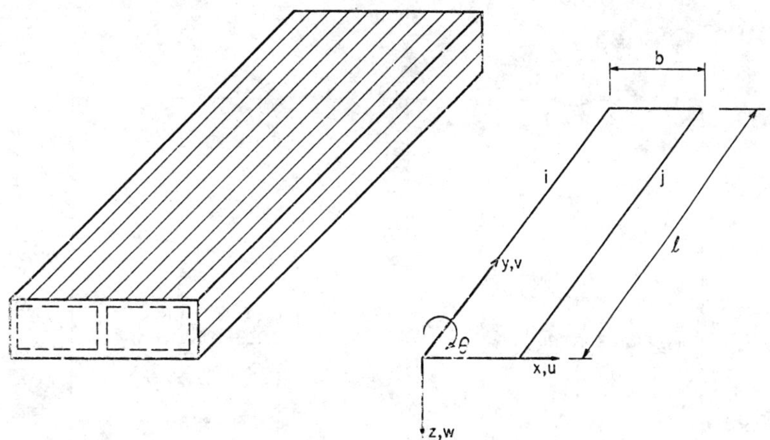

Fig. 1 A typical bridge and a finite strip.

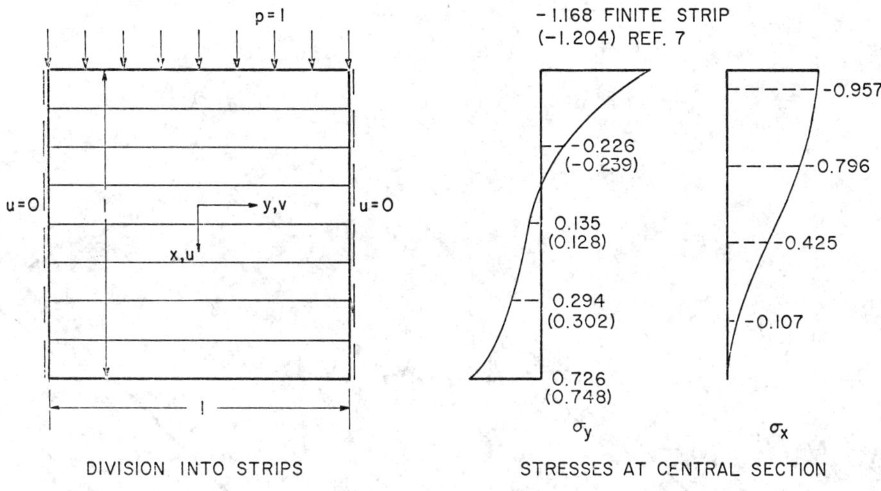

Fig. 2 A deep beam problem.

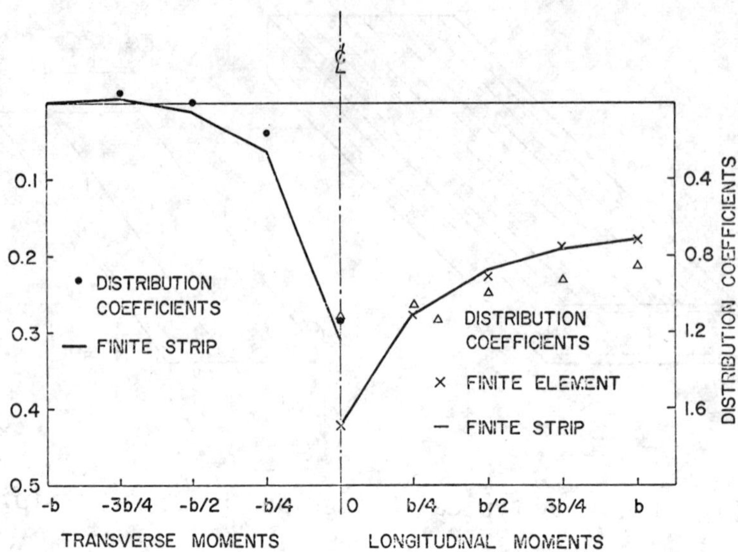

Fig. 3 Distribution of moments for a square isotropic bridge under central point load.

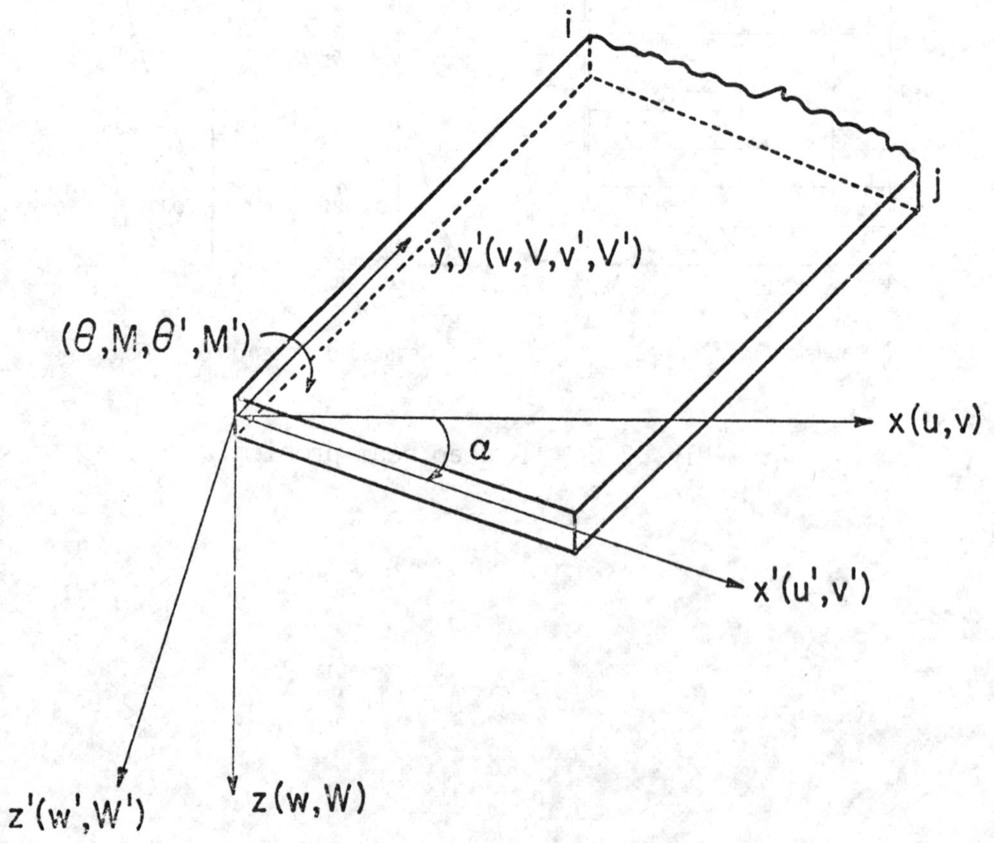

Fig. 4 Individual and common coordinate systems.

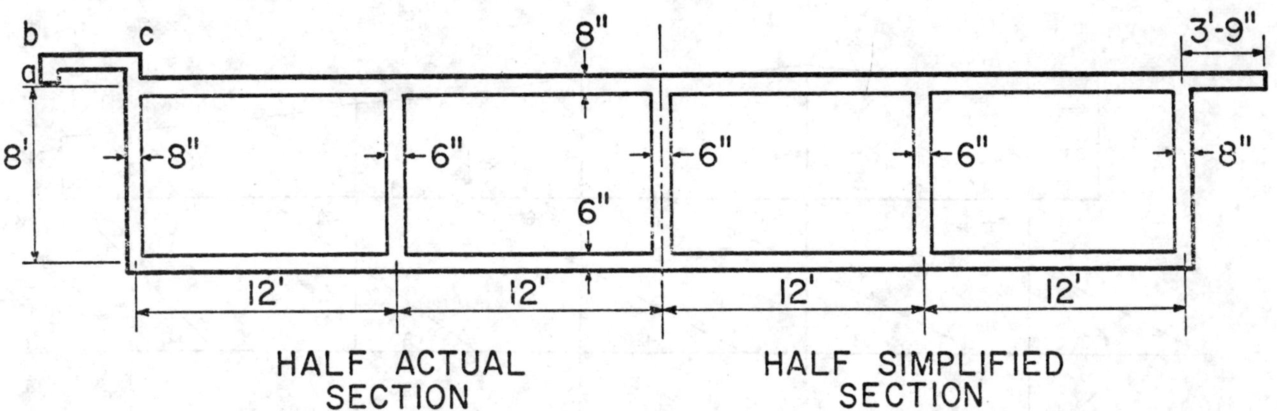

Fig. 5 Cross-sectional dimensions of box girder bridge.

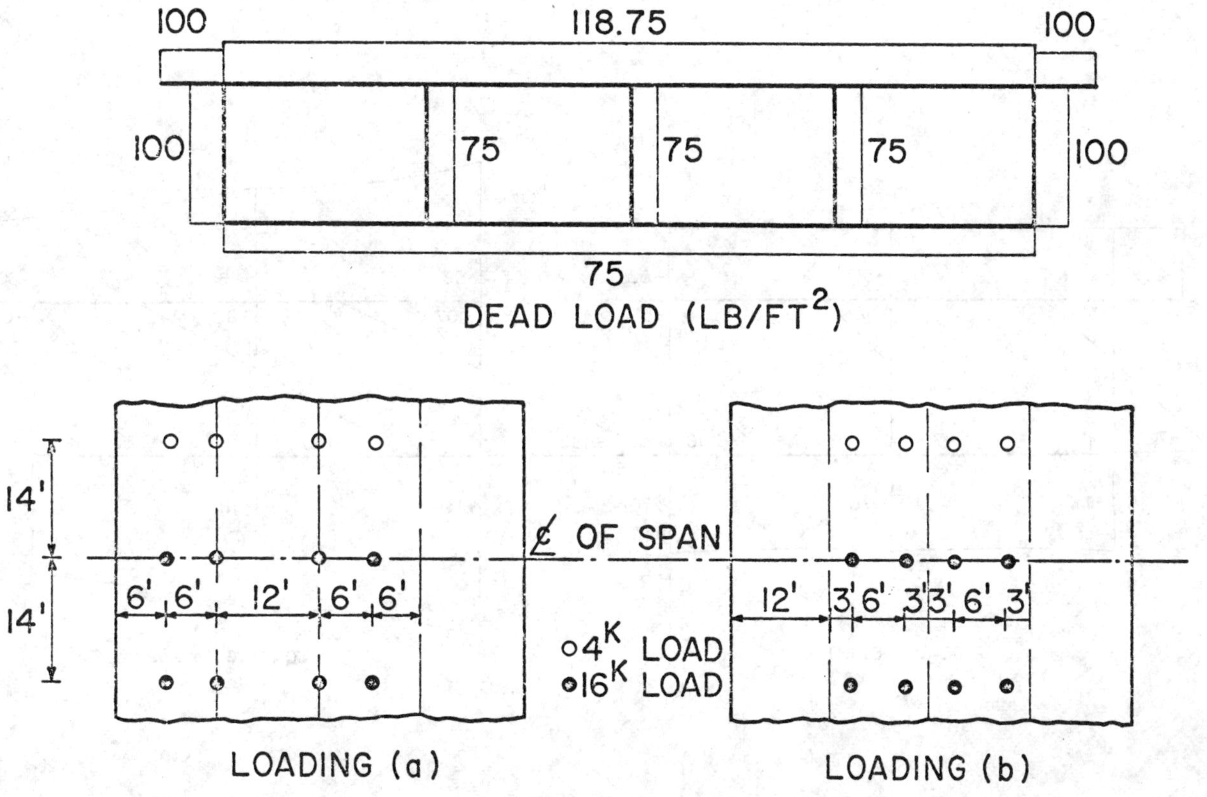

Fig. 6 Schemes of loadings.

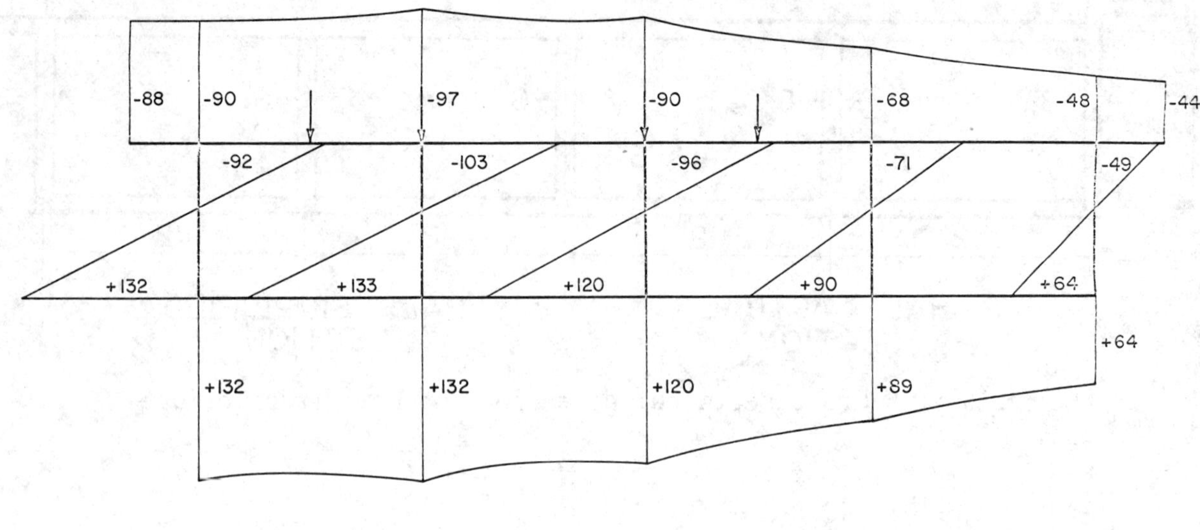

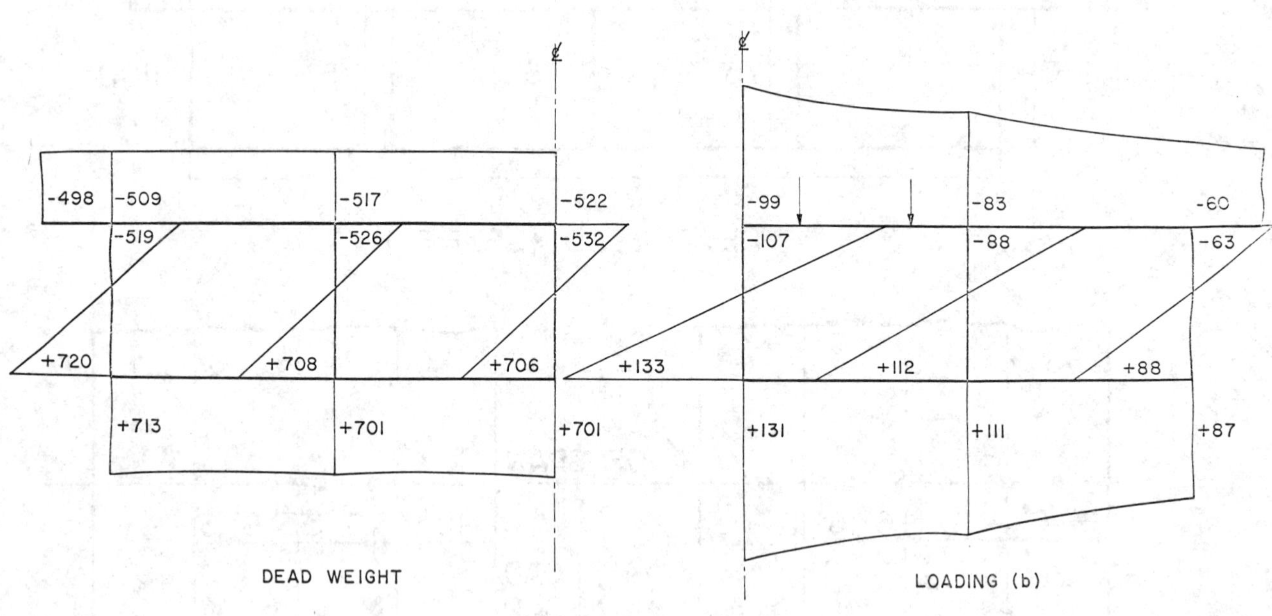

Fig. 7a)
Fig. 7b) Longitudinal stresses σ_y (in p.s.i.).

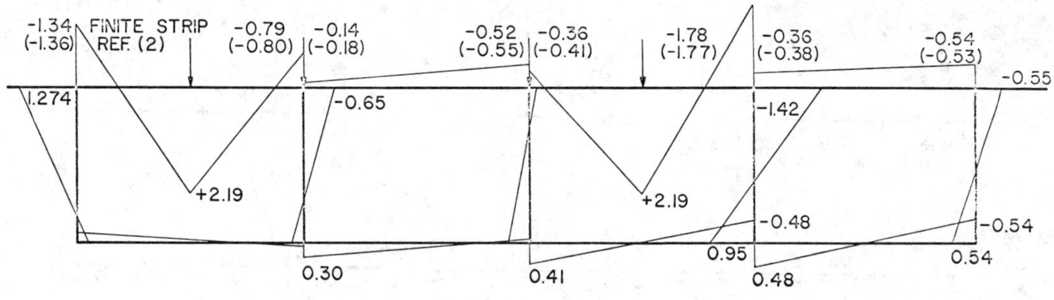

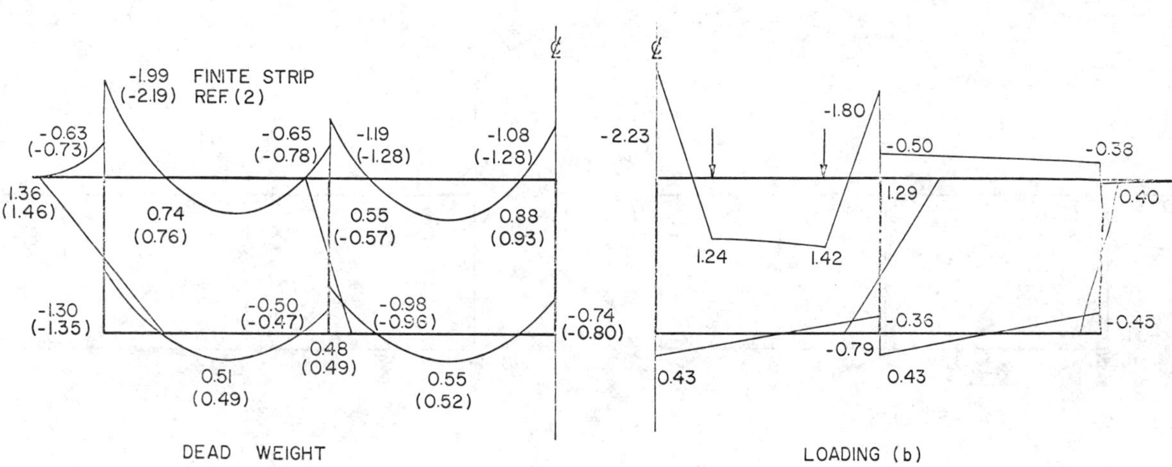

Fig. 8a)
Fig. 8b) Transverse moments M_x (in k-ft/ft).

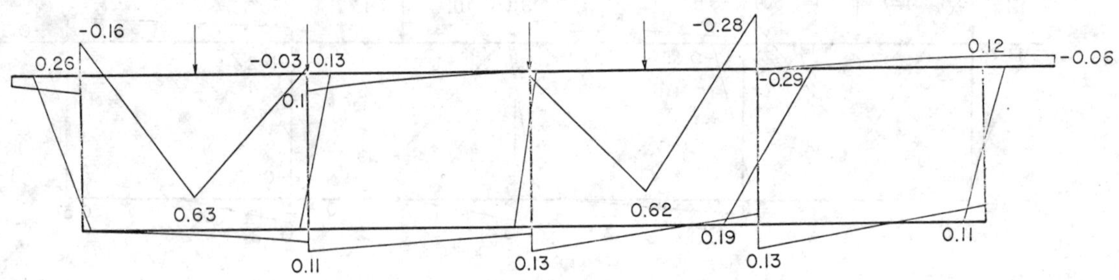

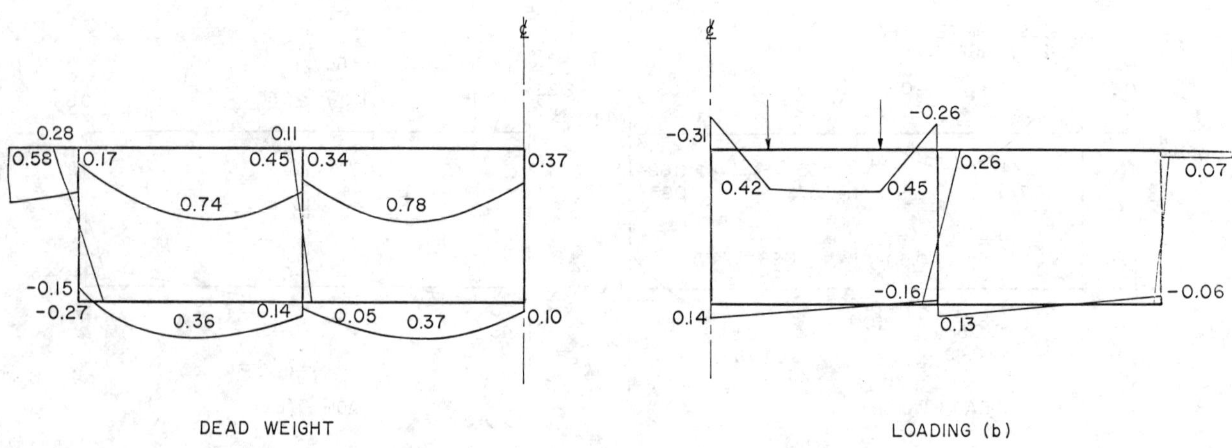

Fig. 9a)
Fig. 9b) Longitudinal moments M_y (in k-ft/ft).

EXPERIMENTAL AND ANALITICAL INVESTIGATION OF A HORIZONTALLY CURVED BOX-BEAM HIGHWAY BRIDGE MODEL

By I. ANEJA and F. ROLL

SYNOPSIS

Currently, a large number of concrete highway bridges having box-sections with cantilevered deck slabs are being constructed. This paper presents an investigation of horizontally curved box-beam bridges through model analysis and experimentation. A plastic model was constructed and tested under various loading conditions.

Keywords: box beams; bridges (structures); curved beams; finite element method; flexural tests; girder bridges; girders; models; prestressed concrete; reinforced concrete; research; strains; stresses; structural analysis.

ACI member, ISH ANEJA is a structural research engineer, Sun Shipbuilding & Dry Dock Company, Chester, Pennsylvania. He received his undergraduate engineering education in India. Before coming to the United States in September of 1961, he worked as an engineer with Central Public Works Department in India. He received MS and PhD degrees in civil engineering in 1962 and 1968 respectively, from the University of Pennsylvania. Prior to joining Sun Shipbuilding, from September 1966 to May 1968, he held a faculty position as an assistant professor of engineering, PMC Colleges, Chester, Pennsylvania.

ACI member, FREDERIC ROLL is professor of civil engineering at the University of Pennsylvania. Dr. Roll is vice-chairman and former chairman of ACI Committee 209, Creep and Volume Changes in Concrete; member of ACI Committee 426, Shear and Diagonal Tension, ACI Committee 435, Deflections, ACI Committee 115, Research and the ACI Ad Hoc Committee on Structural Models. He is also a member of ASTM and ASCE committees and is a member of several professional societies. He holds graduate degrees from Columbia University. As the recipient of a National Science Foundation Science Faculty Fellowship, Dr. Roll spent 6 months at the Cement and Concrete Assoc. in England and 8 months at the National Civil Engineering Laboratory in Portugal investigating the techniques of structural model analysis in 1963 to 1964. He is the author of scientific papers which have appeared in technical journals here and abroad.

INTRODUCTION

Currently, a large number of concrete highway bridges having box-sections with cantilevered deck slabs are being constructed. The cross-sections consist of a single cell, multiple adjacent cells, or multiple separate cells with vertical or inclined webs joined at the deck. These structures may be either cast-in-place or constructed by precasting short lengths of the box-section and then post-tensioning the segments together to form the required bridge structure.

Since these structures are frequently used for highway interchanges as well as multilevel or single level approaches of several highways from different directions to an existing bridge, they are frequently horizontally curved in plan. Due to the geometry of horizontally curved, elevated portions of the highways and the nature of the loads carried by them, and depending upon the support conditions and support locations, they are subjected to high torsional moments as well as flexural moments and shears. Box-sections, however, are particularly efficient in resisting torsion and flexure, and, therefore, these structures are becoming increasingly important.

Unfortunately, because of the complexity of the behavior of horizontally curved box-sections, no satisfactory simple analysis is available to determine the response of such a structure subjected to different loading conditions of practical significance, e.g. dead load, uniformly distributed load on top deck, lane loads or combinations of partial lane loads. Prior to this study, only a small amount of experimental and or theoretical work has been done to determine the response of such structures using models (3,8)* or prototype structures (6). Consequently, conservative methods must be used to design the components of the box-section.

The object of the research herein described was to investigate the structural response of a typical horizontally curved box-beam highway bridge (1) by fabricating a Plexiglas model, applying various typical loading conditions, and measuring the corresponding strains at the inner and outer surfaces of the top deck, bottom flange and inner and outer webs at selected cross-sections. These strains were then converted to tangential and radial stresses to determine the stress distribution across a transverse section due to the applied loading conditions.

A corresponding stress distribution was also found by means of an approximate analytical solution using the finite element Method of Analysis.

---

* Numerals in parentheses refer to corresponding items in Appendix I - References

A typical comparison of the experimental and theoretical stresses due to the simulated dead load and uniformly distributed load on the top deck have been plotted for top and bottom flanges, and inner and outer webs at the midspan cross-section. The experimental stresses at the midspan, quarter-span and support sections are tabulated.

A brief description of fabrication, preparation and instrumentation of the model members followed by supplementary tests, model tests, discussion of results and conclusions are given in the following pages. Detailed descriptions of the above are given elsewhere (1,7).

DESCRIPTION OF THE MODEL

The model material was Plexiglas 11-UVA, which has a minimum variation of dimensions or material properties. A commercial adhesive, PS-18, was used to fabricate the model.

Geometry. - The model represented to a linear scale factor of approximately 1/30 a bridge with circular curvature in plan having an angle of 60° between support sections and 6° overhangs at the supports. The radius of curvature to the center-line of the model was 34.4 inches. The model was 2.81 ins. deep and 43.23 ins. long along its center-line.

The dimensions and shape of the model are shown in Figure 1.

The bridge model was simply supported on pairs of Plexiglas columns, each column placed directly under a web. Each pair of columns lay on a radial transverse section as shown in Figure 1 so that the center-line span length was 36.0 ins. Under certain loading conditions, the curved bridge requires large downward reactions at the columns which was accomplished by prestressing the columns (1,7).

Details of the columns are shown in Figure 2.

Fabrication and Preparation. - Plexiglas II-UVA has a low modulus of elasticity permitting smaller test loads for measurable strain response. It is easy to form (4) at a reasonably low temperature which is advantageous in fabricating the curved webs. The Plexiglas sheets were rough cut to the required size and shape and these rough cut surfaces of the model members were then finished smooth by hand, to the required size.

The curved webs were formed in a small specially constructed oven using appropriately curved two-part wooden molds. The molds were constructed so that when clamped together, the annular space left between the two halves of the mold was equal to the desired final thickness and curvature of the mold. A temperature of 350°F maintained for 10 minutes softened the Plexiglas sufficiently so that, due to its own weight, it deflected to the shape of the lower mold. The lower mold and softened plastic were then removed from the oven, and the upper mold quickly clamped to the lower mold with the enclosed heated Plexiglas. The entire assembly was then permitted to cool to room temperature and, after 24 hours, the web was removed in its final desired shape. Detailed description of fabrication and preparation is given elsewhere (1,7).

For loading purposes, the top and bottom flanges were divided into 390 and 234 sectors respectively by inscribing 40 radial lines for top and bottom flanges and 11 and 7 circumferential lines for the top and bottom flanges respectively. All radial lines were equally spaced 1.875° apart between sections S-8 and S-8' and 1.50° apart in the overhangs. Holes of 0.036 inches diameter were drilled at the center of gravity of each of these sectors in both top and bottom flanges. Dacron fishing lines, used for loading the model, were later threaded through these holes.

Prior to assembly of the model, electric resistance strain gages were attached to the inside and outside surfaces of the top flange, bottom flange and webs as described later in the instrumentation section.

The inner and outer webs were cemented to the bottom flange first. Loading accessories consisting of soft neoprene washers and Plexiglas buttons of slightly larger diameter than the outside diameter of the washers were fixed at the load points to the inside surface of the bottom flange before cementing the webs to it. Before cementing the top flange to the webs, Dacron fishing lines of suitable length were threaded through each of the 390 loading point-holes on the top flange and 240 corresponding holes in the bottom flange. The top end of each fishing line was attached to the corresponding Plexiglas button by means of a small brad. To the lower end of each fishing line was attached a loading hook with a plastic bottle cap. These caps were later used to attach plastic bottles filled with the required amount of lead shot corresponding to the applied load.

An end view of the model showing the neoprene washers, the Plexiglas buttons and Dacron line is seen in Figure 3.

Instrumentation. - After the components of the model were prepared for final assembly but prior to assembly, electric resistance strain gage rosettes were attached to the model components. The rosettes were attached to the external, and internal surfaces of the top and bottom flanges and webs at the support, quarter-span and mid-span sections designated S-8', S-4' and S-O respectively. In all cases, one leg of the rosette was oriented in the radial direction.

The location of gages at a typical gage section is shown in Figure 4.

All gages were foil gages manufactured by the Budd Company and were temperature-compensated for plastic. At each gage section, a total of 40 rosette gages were used; 18 for the top flange (9 on each face), 10 for the bottom flange (5 on each face), and 6 for each web (3 on each face of each web). As a precautionary measure, rosette strain gages were also attached to the inside surfaces of the inner and outer webs at gage section S-4, the other quarter-span section.

In all there were 126 rosette gages and 16 uniaxial gages (4 on each column face as shown in Figure 2.) to be read for any loading condition.

TESTING

Supplementary Tests. - Because of the creep characteristics of Plexiglas and the heating effects of electric resistance gages applied to materials with poor heat diffusion properties (even though, "temperature compensated" gages or "dummy" gages are used for temperature compensation), well-defined values of modulus of elasticity and poisson's ratio are difficult to obtain. The creep effects in Plexiglas were minimized by maintaining low stresses and waiting until creep deformations had essentially ceased before recording strains. The temperature effects were minimized by using temperature-compensated foil gages and a low voltage strain indicator. Therefore, the instrumentation, order of magnitude of stresses and interval of time between application of load and strain measurement were kept the same, for the calibration tests (1) and the actual tests on the model.

The material properties of representative samples of each of the box-beam components were obtained by conducting flexure and tension tests. Longitudinal and transverse strains were measured by means of biaxial, electric resistance strain gages attached to the opposite surfaces of the specimens. The gages were attached to the specimens and the model components with Eastman 910 adhesive.

Test loads on the model had to be maintained while a large group of gages were read taking approximately 15 to 20 minutes for a complete set of gage readings. Therefore, while conducting the supplementary tests, incremental loads were maintained for several minutes before recording the strains. A typical strain vs. time graph (1) for a stress of 500 psi in flexure (estimated to be the maximum stress expected in the model), showed that creep is essentially negligible after 60 seconds of the application of the load or load increment. Since the model was primarily subjected to flexure, therefore, only the values of material properties obtained from flexure tests were used in converting the measured strains to stresses.

Based on the average values of strains obtained from loading and unloading curves for the flexure tests and three tests per specimen and two specimens of each component, the properties of the Plexiglas are shown in Table 1.

Table 1. - Material Properties

Component	Modulus of Elasticity psi	Poisson's Ratio
Top Flange	519,700	0.334
Bottom Flange	506,300	0.323
Web	498,400	0.353

The columns were calibrated by conducting compression tests on each column. Uniaxial electric resistance gages, temperature-compensated for plastic were attached to each face of the column. Average strains of three tests on each column were obtained for each uniaxial gage on all four faces of the column. Calibration curves of load vs. average strain for each column were drawn and these curves were used to determine the reaction on the column for any loading condition.

The effect of loading accessories (neoprene washers) on the material properties was investigated by conducting flexure tests on previously tested flexure specimens after cementing these accessories to them. Based on these tests it was concluded that they had no appreciable effect on the material properties.

Model Tests

Load No. 1. - For simulated dead load of the bridge, loads of 0.508 lb/cu in., proportional to the volumes of the flange sectors, were applied at their centroids. The simulated dead load of the webs was applied at 21 load points on each web, each load proportional to the volume of web between load points. The total applied load was 162.4 lbs.

The locations of typical load points are shown in Figure 5.

The loads were applied to the flanges by means of plastic bottles filled with the required amount of lead shots. These bottles were attached to caps at the end of the Dacron fishing line, one for each load point, emerging from the underside of the box-beam. To the other end of the fishing line passing through a hole in the flange were attached loading accessories previously discussed and shown in Figure 3. Initially all bottles filled with the required quantity of lead shot were supported on a plywood platform so that all Dacron lines were slack and the entire structure unloaded as shown in Figure 6. The load was applied to the structure by lowering the platform manually by means of a scissor jack until all the bottles were free from the platform. Load was removed from the bridge by raising the platform until all bottles rested on it.

The simulated web loads were applied to the tops of the webs at the load points by means of several sets of independent, load distributing beams and dead weights.

Load No. 2. - Simulated uniformly distributed live loads on the top flange of 0.494 lb/sq. in. were applied by filling the appropriate bottles associated with the top flange with the required amount of lead shot and removing those bottles associated with the bottom flange. A typical set up for loads is shown in Figure 6 with the load supported on the platform. The total applied load was 256.6 lbs.

An overall view of the test set-up is shown in Figure 7.

TEST RESULTS

With the help of a computer program the strain gage readings obtained for the two load conditions were converted into moments per unit length and normal forces per unit length in the tangential and radial directions, as well as radial (σ_r) and tangential (σ_θ) normal stresses at each gage location of each gage section. The experimental values of the radial and tangential stresses for exterior and interior surfaces of the model members at the respective gage locations for the simulated dead load and uniformly distributed live load on the top flange are given in Tables 2, 3 and 4. The exterior and interior surface identifications for the model members and the gage locations are shown in Figure 4.

TABLE 2 EXPERIMENTAL STRESSES* - SECTION S-O

PART OF BEAM	GAGE NO.	Load 1 - Dead Load				Load 2 - Uniform Deck Load			
		ER*	IR	ET	IT	ER	IR	ET	IT
TOP	1	8.1	4.6	-89.3	-65.5	6.0	9.2	-145.4	-98.6
FLANGE	2	25.1	-7.2	-89.7	-66.7	68.1	-40.2	-133.7	-121.3
	3	156.0	-139.1	-55.6	-106.9	278.2	-248.4	-78.9	-175.6
	4	78.2	-67.9	-67.8	-71.0	123.0	-98.6	-109.5	-108.5
	5	-1.4	11.9	-91.2	-43.7	-31.0	41.5	-158.3	-62.3
	6	-68.3	78.2	-101.8	-19.4	-110.1	128.5	-149.0	-38.5
	7	-109.5	106.6	-111.6	-12.4	-139.8	161.3	-155.7	-30.7
	8	15.9	-9.0	-70.6	-53.4	51.6	-41.5	-105.2	-88.5
	9	5.1	-0.4	-71.7	-60.4	9.0	-2.9	-111.1	-75.6
BOTTOM	10	-152.4	133.2	114.4	174.0	-173.6	134.3	199.0	258.8
FLANGE	11	-61.4	32.4	123.3	123.7	-104.4	56.1	187.7	200.2
	12	29.9	-36.2	159.7	90.1	-3.7	-13.8	215.7	153.0
	13	54.6	-63.3	125.0	76.8	66.1	-93.6	198.2	117.6
	14	46.1	-55.5	134.9	80.4	134.0	-162.4	225.1	89.6
OUTER	15	47.6	-44.4	-34.7	-51.1	46.1	-71.4	-14.8	-87.8
WEB	16	10.3	-14.1	42.0	37.7	38.0	-34.1	78.0	51.6
	17	-35.8	22.7	89.2	113.8	-45.0	15.1	138.0	171.3
INNER	18	-86.2	42.2	-47.9	-10.4	-73.2	67.3	-61.9	-25.2
	19	-26.8	24.9	25.8	36.7	-24.1	29.7	44.7	50.4
	20	-2.4	-12.6	82.0	77.3	14.4	-34.9	132.5	117.1

* Stress - psi; ER, IR - Exterior & Interior Radial; ET, IT - Exterior & Interior Tangential

TABLE 3 EXPERIMENTAL STRESSES* - SECTION S-4'

PART OF BEAM	GAGE NO.	Load 1 - Dead Load				Load 2 - Uniform Deck Load			
		ER*	IR	ET	IT	ER	IR	ET	IT
TOP	1	0.9	4.8	-75.2	-48.0	6.2	5.8	-113.8	-74.5
FLANGE	2	24.5	-12.0	-74.4	-57.7	67.0	-49.7	-99.8	-114.7
	3	178.5	-168.1	-35.0	-98.8	313.9	-302.9	-43.4	-171.0
	4	97.0	-77.2	-48.7	-57.0	134.6	-117.8	-84.1	-88.2
	5	-6.9	8.9	-75.3	-29.2	-26.4	46.2	-133.4	-32.7
	6	-82.7	94.9	-79.6	-0.7	-143.3	158.8	-128.8	-6.9
	7	-131.5	131.3	-99.5	5.6	-176.7	189.9	-141.7	5.2
	8	14.9	-6.4	-51.8	-34.7	45.2	-41.9	-68.6	-53.8
	9	1.9	-0.3	-53.4	-30.4	0.7	3.7	-81.9	-40.2
BOTTOM	10	-180.9	150.5	81.1	152.3	-208.2	191.6	137.4	232.4
FLANGE	11	-68.0	51.8	93.4	94.4	-117.7	81.3	141.7	152.7
	12	30.1	-36.9	115.0	48.8	-3.6	-16.6	162.7	89.5
	13	78.1	-76.7	89.5	39.8	92.8	-114.3	146.1	59.9
	14	61.1	-75.1	92.0	43.2	168.3	-197.0	175.9	51.4
OUTER	15	64.3	-65.7	-11.4	-51.9	103.2	-111.9	8.7	-86.8
WEB	16	26.8	-17.6	47.7	27.9	46.9	-39.9	79.4	39.4
	17	-39.5	27.1	77.5	100.8	-45.3	18.9	135.7	151.0
INNER	18	-100.3	72.6	-38.4	-1.8	-77.4	110.3	26.5	-8.1
WEB	19	-39.7	26.2	14.6	27.7	58.4	23.1	24.3	35.9
	20	0.0	-7.9	55.0	58.2	13.6	-40.8	86.5	73.7

* Stress - psi; ER, IR - Exterior & Interior Radial; ET, IT - Exterior & Interior Tangential

TABLE 4 EXPERIMENTAL STRESSES* - SECTION S-8'

PART OF BEAM	GAGE NO.	Load 1 - Dead Load				Load 2 - Uniform Deck Load			
		ER*	IR	ET	IT	ER	IR	ET	IT
TOP	1	0.1	-2.0	5.1	-18.3	0.1	6.9	3.5	-23.0
FLANGE	2	27.5	22.0	41.7	-12.1	65.7	-92.3	67.5	-21.1
	3	288.6	-300.9	112.5	-77.8	490.6	-531.4	177.4	-140.8
	4	145.8	-141.2	29.0	-43.0	226.0	-219.3	49.7	-29.4
	5	0.5	24.6	-31.2	-4.3	-28.2	-19.2	-59.7	104.5
	6	-151.7	165.6	-71.5	69.5	-235.7	271.3	-98.8	107.4
	7	-271.4	278.7	-93.8	86.0	-385.7	399.2	-129.3	115.3
	8	15.7	-7.3	-2.7	7.8	60.0	-42.4	8.6	5.4
	9	4.7	9.1	6.2	7.0	0.5	-4.8	-7.8	-2.0
BOTTOM	10	-335.2	271.5	-152.1	127.1	-457.8	378.5	-222.6	206.1
FLANGE	11	-135.1	99.0	-26.5	46.2	-195.2	168.5	-65.1	82.8
	12	-13.5	-33.5	36.5	-0.4	-27.0	-13.0	41.9	14.5
	13	-90.9	-126.2	22.8	-20.9	148.6	-195.3	71.3	-29.2
	14	201.3	-183.3	51.1	-45.6	351.4	-361.8	147.4	-95.0
OUTER	15	61.0	-138.6	58.6	-12.9	117.5	-232.0	102.8	-26.2
WEB	16	14.6	-102.7	59.8	4.1	30.3	-173.8	68.8	3.3
	17	-144.7	-204.9	-17.5	-46.7	-237.9	-339.7	-48.6	-79.8
INNER	18	-123.8	94.3	-37.4	35.6	-190.4	112.4	-60.7	51.4
WEB	19	-59.6	54.9	-10.7	24.2	-85.9	78.6	-9.1	33.4
	20	9.0	-18.1	5.8	12.4	43.4	-10.8	11.5	0.5

* Stress - psi; ER, IR - Exterior & Interior Radial; ET, IT - Exterior & Interior Tangential

The column reactions for the two loading conditions are shown in Table 5 together with the theoretical reactions.

Table 5 - Column Reactions

Column	Load No. 1 (Dead Load)		Load No. 2 (Live Deck Load)	
	Exper.	Theor.	Exper.	Theory
R_A	5.8	1.4	11.8	5.3
R_B	79.5	79.8	119.5	123.0
R_C	4.5	1.4	7.3	5.3
R_D	77.0	79.8	117.3	123.0
Total	166.8	162.4	255.9	256.6

All reactions are in pounds.

THEORETICAL ANALYSIS

The exact mathematical solution for a horizontally curved box-beam highway bridge would be impractical because the geometry of the structure would lead to prohibitive complexities in its equations of elasticity. Therefore, this model was analyzed by the finite element Method of Analysis.

For this purpose the model was divided into 240 panels for the flanges and webs. The flange elements were treated as flat plate elements with curved boundaries for determining their stiffness properties. Although the web elements are cylindrically curved plates, they are treated as flat rectangular elements because of the limitation of the available finite element computer program.

A finite element computer program based on the stiffness matrix method of analysis, developed by the Franklin Institute (9), was utilized to analyze the model.

The program allows only five degrees of freedom at the nodal points of elements for determining their stiffness properties.

For each loading condition the output of the computer program gave radial and tangential normal stresses at inner and outer surfaces at the middle points of the sides and at the center of each element. Thus these stresses were obtained theoretically at each gage section for the two loading conditions.

As a typical comparison between the experimental stresses and those obtained using the finite element method, stresses, for the inner and outer surfaces, have been plotted for top and bottom flanges, and inner and outer webs at gage section S-O for the two loading conditions. They are shown in Figures 8 to 13 for the dead load condition and in Figures 14 to 19 for uniformly distributed load on the top flange. Similar graphs can be drawn for gage sections S-4' and S-8'.

It may be noted from Figures 8 to 19 that the radial stresses obtained by the finite element method are in close agreement with those obtained experimentally. The tangential stresses, however, do not compare as well, but it should be noted that the shapes of the tangential stress plots obtained from experimental values and finite element method values are basically the same. In general the finite element values are always lower than the experimental ones.

This discrepancy in the theoretically obtained tangential stresses points out the need for detailed study of the various possible sources of errors (5) present in this method of analysis.

In this connection it may be noted that the stiffness properties of the element were obtained by using assumed polynomials (2) describing the displacement field of an element and thus approximating its actual displacement field. Furthermore, the total stiffness properties of an element were obtained basically by combining the extensional stiffness and pure bending stiffness of a flat rectangular plate element having the assumed displacement field. The curved elements of the web were approximated by flat elements which introduced discontinuities at each joint of curved elements and hence resulted in some inaccuracy in the theoretical results.

Further approximations were introduced in the theoretical results by allowing only five degrees of freedom at each nodal point of the element and neglecting the 6th degree of freedom, namely, the rotation of the element about a normal to its middle surface.

The accuracy of the experimental results was checked (1) by the following two checks.

1. The experimental column reactions obtained by using the calibration curves were compared with the reactions obtained theoretically and were found to have very good agreement for both loading conditions as seen in Table 5.
2. The applied bending moment at a gage section obtained by using the applied load and the theoretical reactions was compared with the resisting moment, obtained from the experimental tangential stress distribution at the section. The comparison showed a good agreement between the applied moment and the resisting moment at the sections.

CONCLUSIONS

Plastic models can be successfully used to investigate the structural response of curved, box-beam highway bridges when subjected to various loading conditions.

On the basis of the study described in this paper, it can be concluded that the finite element method of analysis can be used for obtaining radial stress distribution across the cross-section of a horizontally curved box-beam highway bridge structure. The tangential stresses, obtained by the finite element method were not good in magnitude, but were predicted well for distribution and sense. Therefore, there is a need to modify these tangential stresses so as to conform to the actual stresses obtained experimentally.

ACKNOWLEDGMENTS

This investigation is based on a thesis, submitted by I. Aneja, to the University of Pennsylvania, in 1968, in partial fulfillment of the requirements for the degree of Doctor of Philosophy. Thanks are due to Dr. Z. Zudan at the Franklin Institute Research Laboratories, Philadelphia, for making available the finite element computer program and computer time and also to the Computer Center of the University of Pennsylvania for making their facilities available.

APPENDIX I - REFERENCES

1. Aneja, I. "Experimental and Analytical Study of a Horizontally Curved Box-Beam Highway Bridge Model", Thesis presented to the University of Pennsylvania, Philadelphia, Pennsylvania, in 1968, in partial fulfillment of the requirements for the degree of Doctor of Philosophy (University Microfilms, Ann Arbor, Michigan).

2. Clough, R. W., "The Finite Element Method in Structural Mechanics", Stress Analysis. O. C. Zienkiewicz and G. S. Holister, Ed., John Wiley and Sons, Ltd., London, 1965.

3. Cutts, Charles E., "Horizontally Curved Box Beams" Proceedings Separate No. 128 of American Society of Civil Engineers, Published in May 1952.

4. "Fabrication of Plexiglas" Published by Rohn & Haas Company, Philadelphia, Pa. 19105, P. 5. Stress Limits, p. 13 Cementing Plexiglas.

5. Fulton, Robert E., Eppink, Richard T., Walz, Joseph E., "The Accuracy of Finite Element Methods in Continuing Problems" Presented at the Fifth U. S. National Congress of Applied Mechanics, Minneapolis, Minnesota, June 14-17, 1966.

6. Raymond E. Davis, John J. Kozak and Charles F. Shaffey, "Structural Behaviour of a Concrete Box-Girder Bridge" Published in Highway Research Record 76 Design - Bridges and Structures, June 1965 by the Highway Research Board, Washington, D. C.

7. Roll, F., Aneja, I. "Model Tests of Box-Beam Highway Bridges with Cantilevered Deck Slabs. Conference Preprint No. 395 American Society of Civil Engineers, Transportation Engineering Conference, Philadelphia, Pa., October 17-21, 1966.

8. Sommerville, G., Roll, F., and Cadwell, J.A.D., "Tests on a one-twelfth Scale Model of the Mancunian Way", Technical Report No. TRA/394, December 1965, Published by Cement and Concrete Association, Great Britain.

9. Zudan, Z. "Analysis of Asymmetric Stiffened Shell Type Structures by the Finite Element Method", The Franklin Institute Research Laboratories, Philadelphia, Pa. 19103. To be published later in the Journal of Nuclear Engineering and Design.

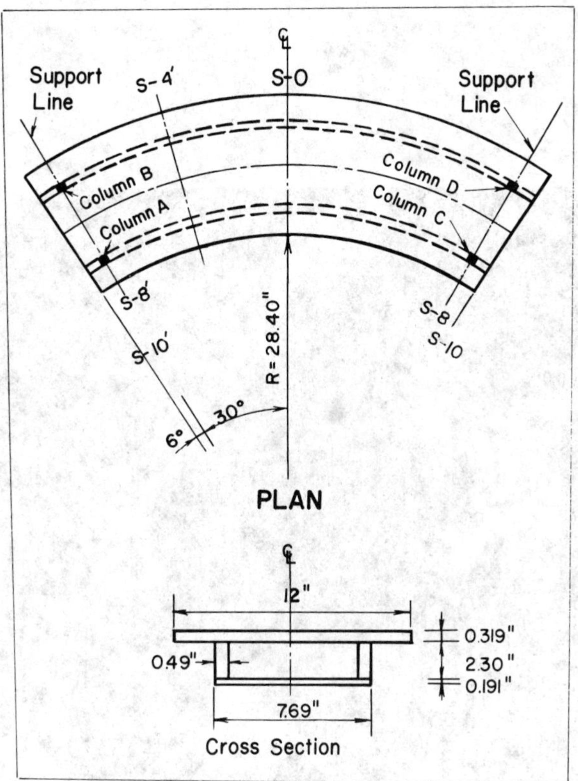

Fig. 1 - Dimensions of Model

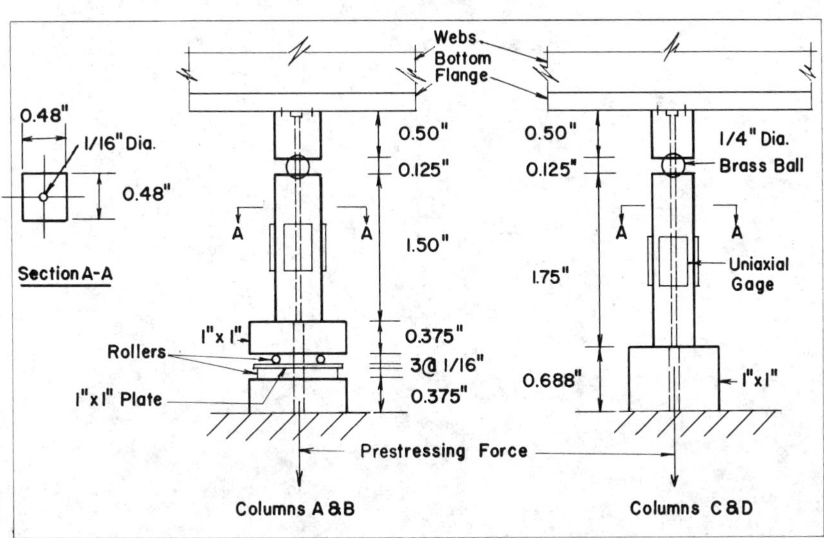

Fig. 2 - Column Details

Figure 3 End view of curved bridge model showing loading buttons and cord

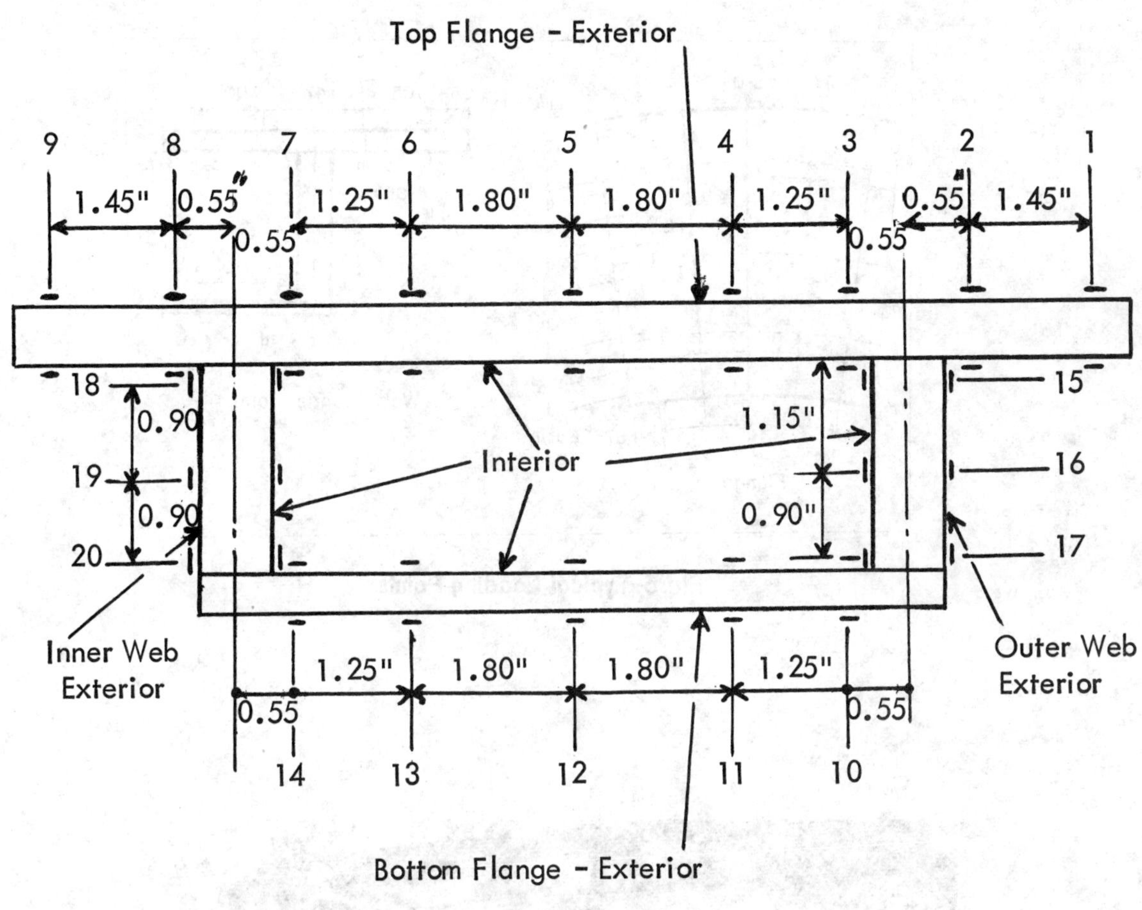

CROSS - SECTION

EXPERIMENTAL DATA IDENTIFICATIONS FOR

(a) Location of Gages at a Gage Section

(b) Model Member Surfaces

Figure 4

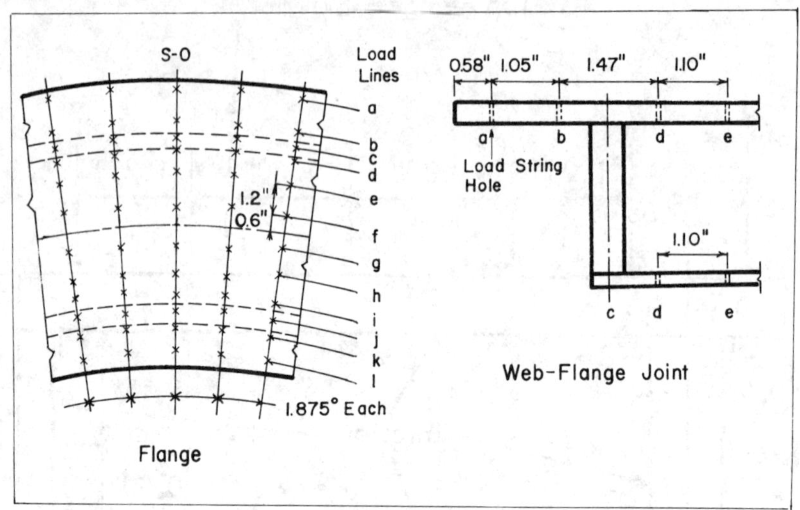

Fig. 5-Typical Loading Points

Figure 6 View of loading bottles supported on platform for curved bridge model

Figure 7 Overall view of curved bridge model

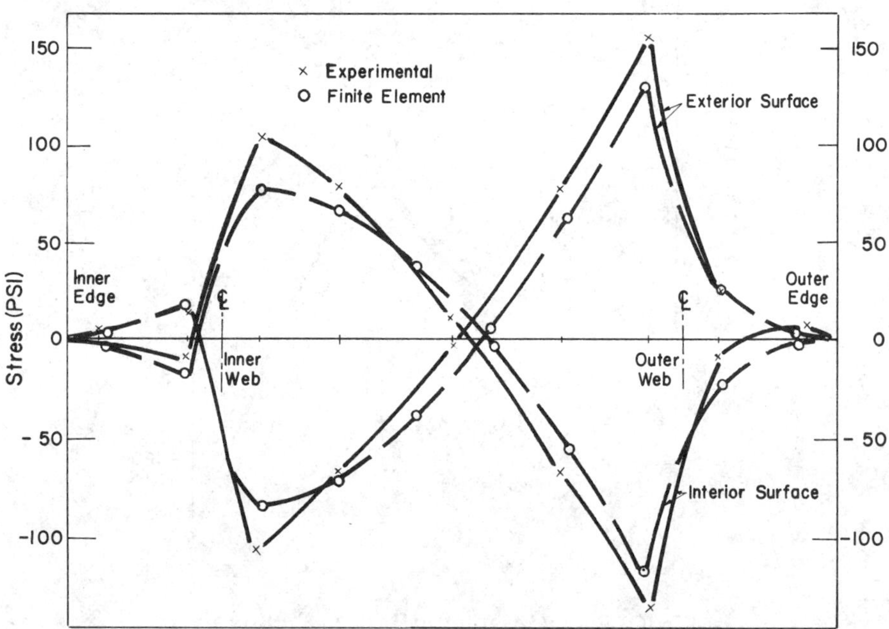

Fig.8–Radial Stresses In Top Flange (Load No.1, Section S–0)

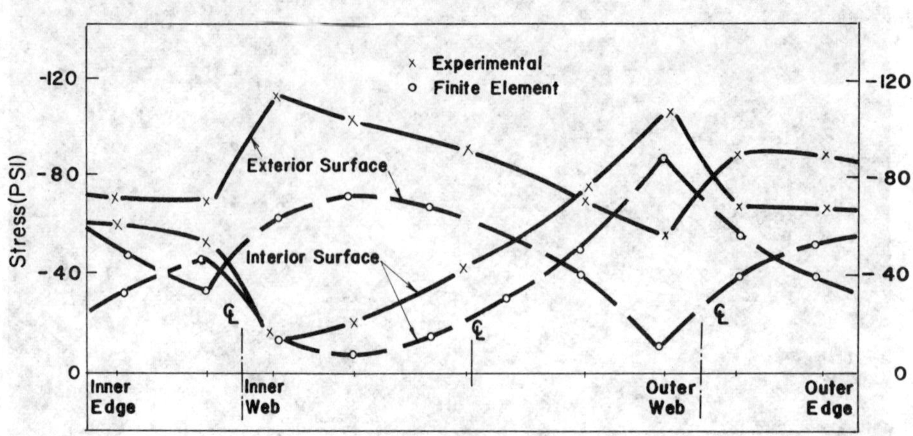

Fig. 9-Tangential Stresses In Top Flange (Load No. 1, Section S-0)

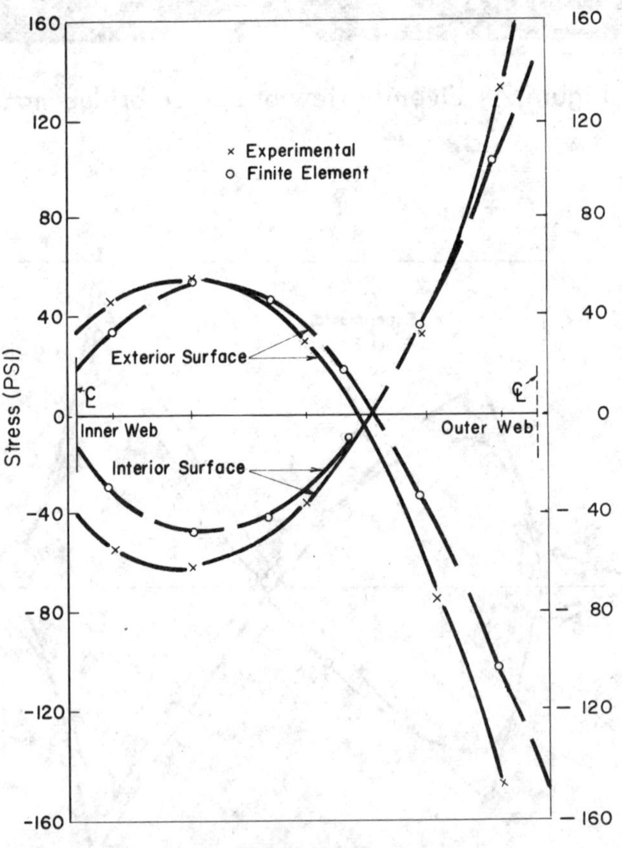

Fig. 10-Radial Stresses In Bottom Flange (Load No. 1, Section S-0)

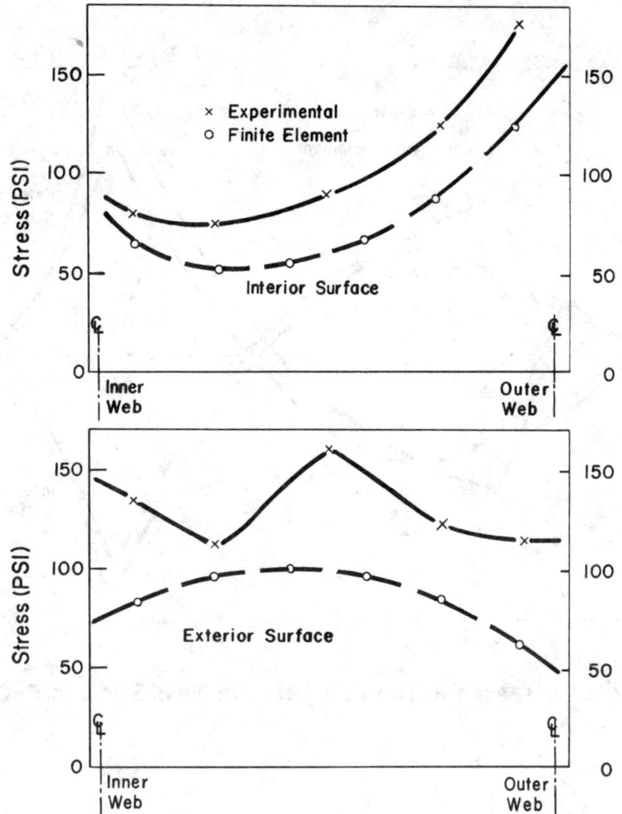

Fig.11-Tangential Stresses In Bottom Flange (Load No. 1, Section S-0)

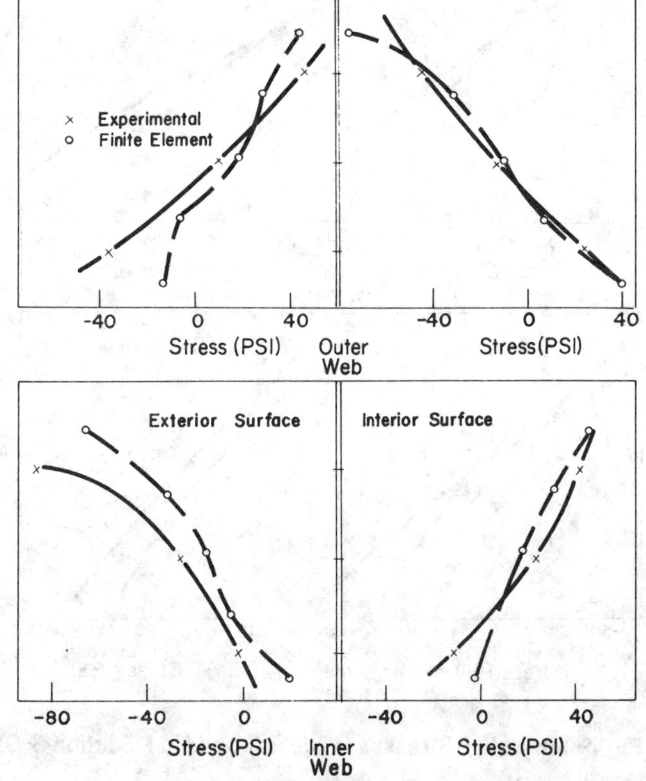

Fig.12-Radial Stresses In Webs(Load No.1, Section S-0)

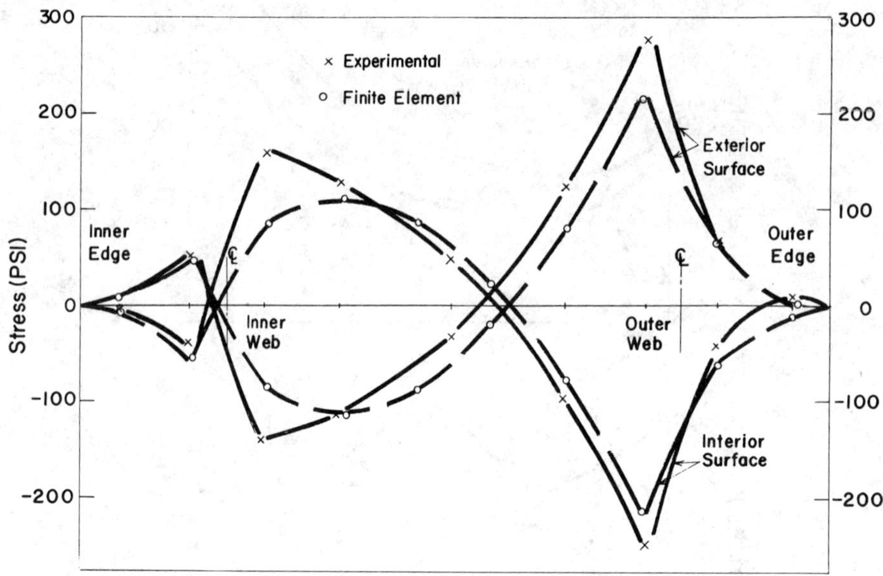

Fig.14-Radial Stresses In Top Flange (Load No.2, Section S-O)

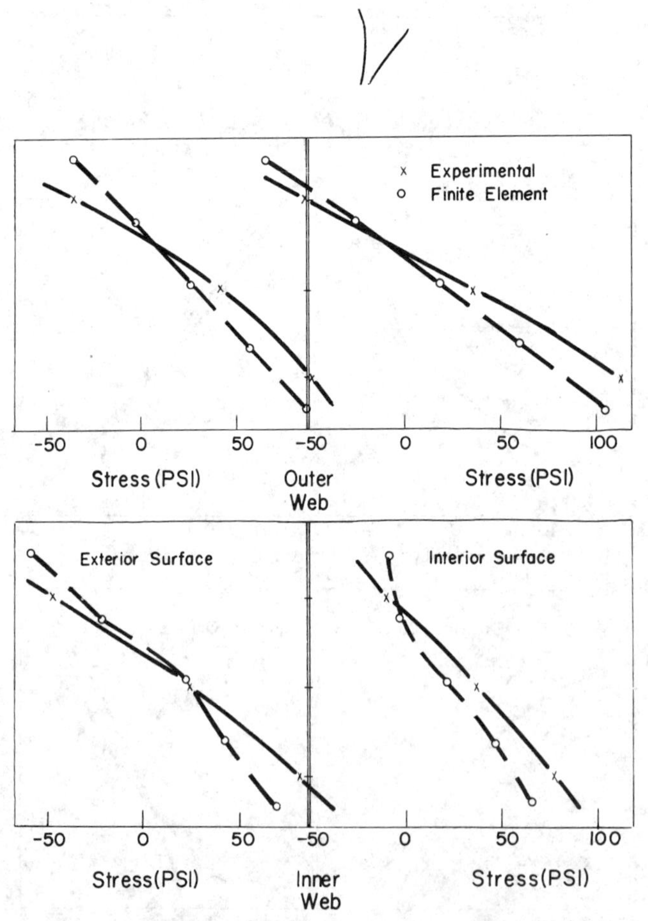

Fig.13-Tangential Stresses In Webs (Load No.1, Section S-O)

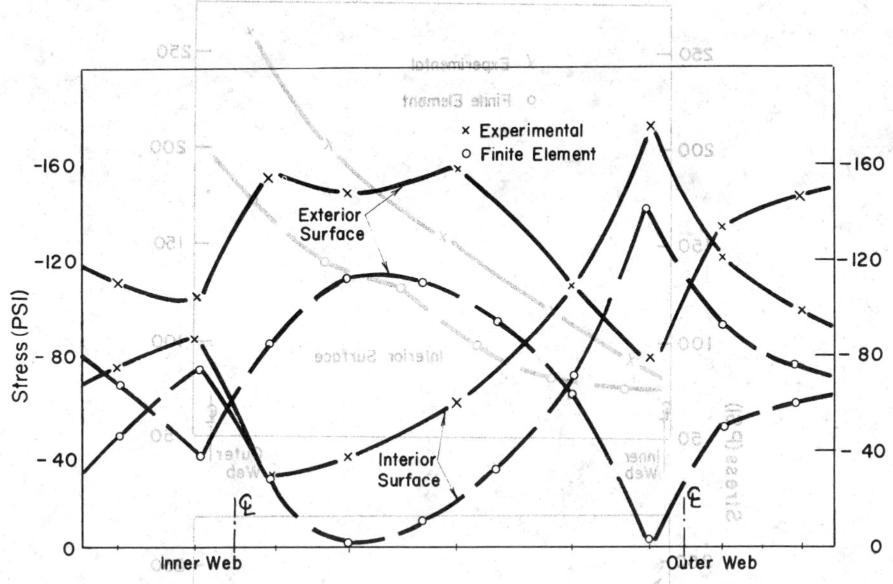

Fig.15-Tangential Stresses In Top Flange(Load No.2, Section S-O)

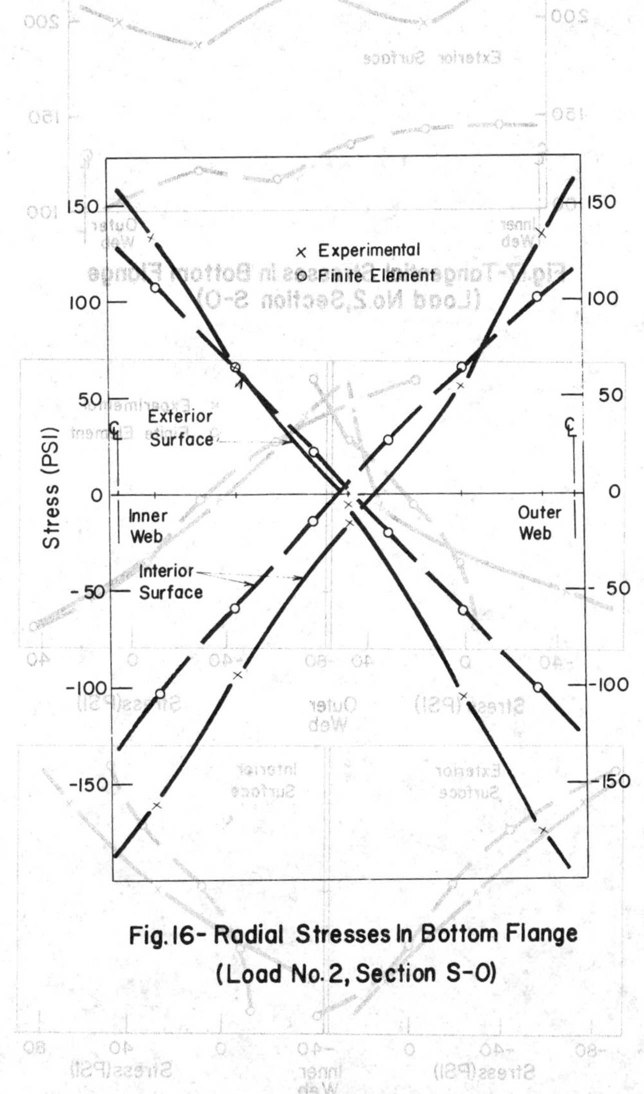

Fig.16- Radial Stresses In Bottom Flange (Load No.2, Section S-O)

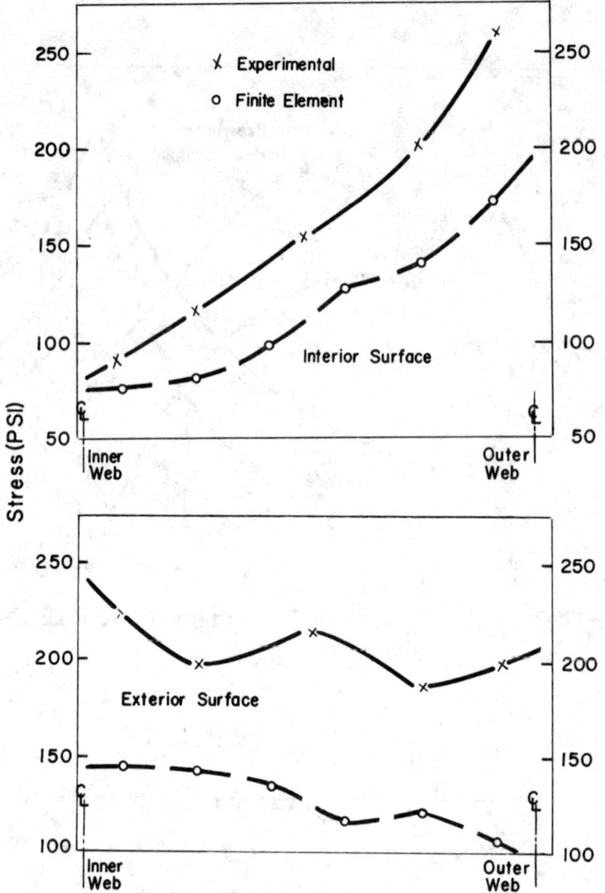

Fig.17-Tangential Stresses In Bottom Flange (Load No.2,Section S-0)

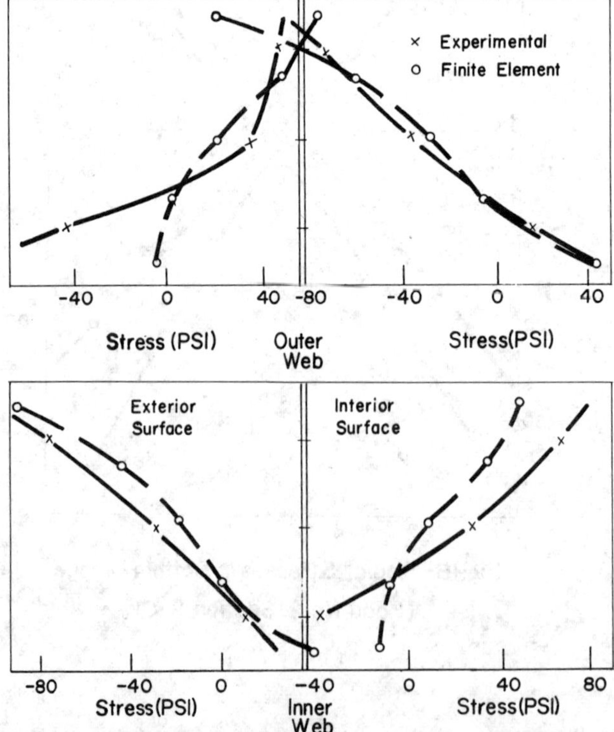

Fig.18-Radial Stresses In Webs (Load No.2,Section S-0)

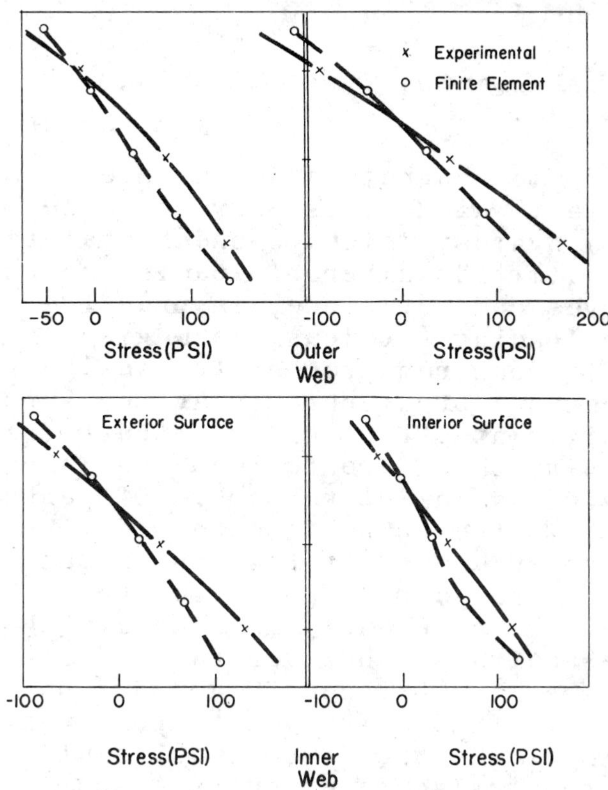

Fig.19–Tangential Stresses In Webs (Load No.2, Section S-0)

DISCUSSION

By R. E. ROWE and G. SOMERVILLE

ACI member, Director of Research and Development, The Cement and Concrete Association

ACI member, Structural Engineer, The Cement and Concrete Association

The authors are to be congratulated on an extremely competent model test which gives very valuable experimental data against which to check analytical approaches. The limited number of loading cases considered deserves comment since, in practice, actual vehicular loading (at least in England) will provide a more rigorous requirement for analysis. Similarly the presence of diaphragms at the supports will have a significant effect on the structural behaviour. However, these are refinements which will no doubt be considered in future work. Of perhaps greater interest, is the comparison between the results obtained and those predicted by the approximate finite element analysis. The authors point out that the radial stresses obtained are reasonably in accord with those predicted by the analysis; however the discrepancies in the peak stresses are between 20 and 30% on the analytical results. It is likely therefore that for concentrated point loads the discrepancies will be greater. The authors also point out that for the tangential stresses the comparison with the theoretical values is not good.

These points are not cited in criticism of the paper but to illustrate those aspects which require particular attention at the present time. In the field of elevated bridge structures of the hollow box spine type, there is a great need for experimental data on structure behaviour, not just in the elastic range but in the non-linear range of behaviour. Model tests must be carried out on practical forms of structure; these should consist of idealised models, such as that tested by the authors, to study elastic behaviour, realistic models in micro-concrete to study the effect of the non linear behaviour of the material, cracking, shear lag and stress diffusion (tests of this type have been carried out by the Association(1)(2)) and also on larger sections using normal concrete to assist in defining the parameters to be used in the structural analysis. In addition to this basic experimental study, a study of the various methods of analysis is required so that an assessment of accuracy can be made and perhaps more important, simplified, acceptable design procedures formulated. Work in these fields is being carried out by the Cement and Concrete Association, some of it sponsored by the Construction Industry Research and Information Association. We have reviewed some 300 papers dealing with the analysis and design of spine beam structures and have compared the results obtained from various analyses with those derived from model tests on the Mancunian Way and the Western Avenue Extension. Experimental work, both on perspex and micro-concrete models is planned to supplement the available experimental data. The aim of this work is to provide acceptable design techniques for these structures which deal with all the relevant limit states i.e. deflexion, cracking and ultimate load.

References:

(1) Tests on a one-twelfth scale model of the Mancunian Way. (Technical Report TRA/394 - December 1965) G SOMERVILLE, F ROLL & J A D CALDWELL. Published by Cement and Concrete Association, London)

(2) Tests on a prestressed micro-concrete model of a three cell box beam bridge. R A SWANN Paper presented to ACI Symposium on Model Testing, Spring Convention, 1968.

AUTHOR'S CLOSURE

The authors are grateful to Messrs. Rowe and Somerville for their interest and their comments regarding the quality and value of the experimental work.

The limitations on the loading conditions reported upon were imposed by editorial considerations restricting the length of the paper. In fact, five additional loading conditions were investigated consisting of lane loads and partial lane loads. One such loading condition of particular interest consisted of one-half of a lane loaded along the inner curve of the bridge and a diametrically opposite half-lane load along the outer curve thereby causing large torsional moments. The results of these tests will be reported in subsequent papers. The two loading conditions reported in the present paper, simulated dead load and uniform deck load, are of primary interest to the designer and were, therefore, selected for the Symposium. Cognizant of the importance of concentrated loads, the authors have already initiated a test program for this type of load.

The authors agree with the writers that the presence of diaphragms and additional longitudinal webs would have a significant effect on the structural behavior of the bridge and additional tests to investigate these effects are contemplated. It should be noted, however, that the authors deliberately selected such a simple cross-section to facilitate the comparison between analytical and experimental results. Considering the fact that no suitable method of analysis is yet available for such a simple shape, it seemed fruitless to start with a more complex cross-section. When a suitable theoretical analysis becomes available, it should be extrapolated for more complex shapes and compared with the results of tests on correspondingly complex models. The analyses and models referred to here are, of course, elastic models. Similar analyses and model tests should be carried out in the nonlinear range to determine the cracking and ultimate loads and the corresponding deflections. For this purpose, as pointed out by the writers, micro-concrete models will have to be used.

The authors also concur with the writers that the Finite Element analysis shown does not yield good comparison with the test data although the radial stresses are certainly in better agreement than the tangential stresses. In fact, one disturbing aspect of the tangential stresses is that they do not satisfy equilibrium requirements for moment indicating a serious discrepancy. The experimental tangential stresses, on the other hand, resulted in a maximum resisting moment which was 95% of the applied maximum moment lending confidence to the test data. It should be noted that the Finite Element method described in the report does not represent a method proposed or recommended by the authors. It was a method made available to them to check the validity of the method and it demonstrates one of the principle purposes of the research reported, namely to serve as a sounding board against which other theories can be checked. The authors welcome similar comparisonsand hope to be appraised of the success of such methods by their proponents.

A NEW APPROACH TO ULTIMATE STRENGTH OF REINFORCED CONCRETE BEAM IN INCLINED CRACKING AND REDUCTION OF WEB REINFORCEMENT IN BRIDGE GIRDERS

By ZENON A. ZIELINSKI

SYNOPSIS

On the basis of the author's research carried on since 1957, he defines strength limits of reinforced concrete beams, and strength in inclined cracking in particular. It appears that inclined cracking due to shear does not terminate the work of the beam. If some web reinforcement is provided and main tensile reinforcement is well anchored beyond the support, beams will be able to withstand further load increase until they reach the point of diagonal splitting strength limit due to arch behavior. Formulas are given for estimation of the arch strength limit and of necessary amount of web reinforcement. Apparently, the number of stirrups required for later arch work is much less than that required in traditional shear theory. Hence, it is proposed to revise code requirements in respect to shear strength and web reinforcement. This work appears to be important for the reinforced concrete bridge design practice, in cases where the main structure of bridge has beams subjected to high shear and moment.

Keywords: beams (supports); bending moments; bridges (structures); cracking (fracturing); diagonal tension; reinforced concrete; research; shear properties; strength; structural design; ultimate strength method; web reinforcement.

ACI member, ZENON A. ZIELINSKI received his MS degree in 1950, and PhD degree in 1957, both from Warsaw Technical University in Poland.

From 1950 to 1962, faculty member of this University, and also head of prototype precast structures design team in Industrial Building Research and Typical Design Office.

In 1962, went to United States as a visiting scholar, did research and lectured at the Universities of Illinois, California, North Carolina and Detroit.

Since 1965, Ford Foundation Consultant on Structural Design and Low Cost Housing.

Author of many prototype structures (precast buildings, bridges, girders, shells) research projects, and publications including books. ACI member since 1964.

INTRODUCTION

Adoption of the Ultimate Strength Design Method is a sign of farther progress and better knowledge of the working of reinforced concrete structure. However the Ultimate Design Method, as it is now presented in code requirements should be limited only to the interpretation of strength in bending. Interpretation of strength, as we used to call it, in bending and shear or in pure shear still remains controversial, in spite of the great amount of research work carried out in this field all over the world (see Reference).

Apparently, by utilising the Ultimate Strength Method it was possible to design for example, more economical open web reinforced concrete and eventually prestressed girders (13), (15), which have no reinforcement for shear at all and are one-half of the weight (Fig. 1 and 2), in contrast to comparable full-web-beams, which have more structural material and still require stirrups for "shear". Economical girders of $\ell \leqq 15$ h have been standardised for different spans of 30 to 180 ft., and adopted for factory production.

This paper is based on extensive research work designed with the purpose of studying the ultimate strength of a beam in inclined cracking, and determining the means of more rational reinforcement in the vicinity of support. Better knowledge of shear and inclined cracking strength is of great importance for reinforced concrete bridge design practice, because of the fact that the main structure of bridges is usually made of beams subjected to heavy, moving, concentrated loads, which produce combined moment and high shear.

Research work mentioned here was carried out since 1957 at the Warsaw Technical University, and later at the University of Illinois, University of California, and North Carolina State University, and consisted of 7 consecutive stages outlined below:

Stage 1 - basic - included tests on 92 beams of 46 types (2 samples for each type). All beams had constant width b=5.9 inches, length 1-78.7 inches, and main reinforcement of 2 bars of 0.71 inch diameter basically. The variables were: height of beam $h=0.1$, 0.2 or 0.5ℓ, bonded or unbonded reinforcement, loading scheme (1, 2 and 4 loads and loading in upside down position) and the shape of beam elevations changing according to loading scheme and bending moment diagram (Fig.3).

Stage 2 - included 29 samples representing special samples and support portions of beam subjected to diagonal compression (Figure 4).

Stage 3 - included 12 beams (of 6 types) of constant depth $h=0.2\ell$ with added support blocks, simulating joists monolithically connected to main girders (Figure 5) tested under one, two or four poiht loading.

Stage 4 - included 12 beams of constant depth of $h=0.1$ or 0.2ℓ with the same reinforcement of 0.71 inch diameter but with bond destroyed on different length segments (Figure 6). Test

Stages 1 - 4 were conducted at Warsaw Technical University, during 1957-1962.

Stage 5 - (conducted at the University of Illinois, in 1963) -- included photoelastic studies of 10 plexiglass models simulating concrete beam, reinforced concrete beam and beam with artificial cracks (Figure 7).

Stage 6 - (conducted at the University of Illinois, in 1963) -- included 3 beams of 6 x 16 inch cross section with stronger main reinforcement and defined higher strength against diagonal splitting at arch scheme (Figure 8).

Stage 7 - (conducted at the North Carolina State University, in 1965) -- included tests on 43 cement cubes subjected to different combined bi-directional compression and tension (Figure 9a, b and c) designed for defining of complex strength of concrete in beam zones under moment and shear [16].

The results of the above tests have been described in detail in a research bulletin now under publication at the Department of Engineering Research of the North Carolina State University at Raleigh, and partially in publications [14] and [16]. On the basis of these tests a better description of the strength limits of reinforced concrete beam will be attempted.

2. Strength of Reinforced Concrete Beams

2.1 General Concept

Strength limits of beams in general terms can be described by reaching limit deformation or by material failure. Reinforced concrete beams are made of two materials - steel, and concrete. Failure of the composing materials separately or simultaneously describes the strength of a beam. In the case of steel the failure is described by the yield (mild steels) or the rupture (high strength steels). The failure of concrete is described by cracking.

Basically, there are three main causes of cracking failure of concrete in a beam as presented in Figure 10 and defined as follows:

Cause I - Uni-axial tension and tearing crack, tangent to stress, valid for flexural tension zone.

Cause II - uni-axial compression, leading to loss of cohesion and splitting along the compression, valid for flexural compression zone of the beam, and,

Cause III - bi-directional tension and compression leading to cracking tangent to tension, valid for "shear" - or "moment + shear" loaded zones of the beam.

The knowledge of combined bi-directional strength of concrete is essential for proper evaluation of the cracking strength limits of beam.

On the basis of test results [12], [14], [17] with adequate accuracy for practical design purpose it seems possible to assume combined strength of concrete in bi-directional stress condition as a linear function presented in diagram Figure 11.

It is assumed that strength of concrete under equal bi-directional compression is about 25 per cent higher than uni-axial cylinder compression strength f'_c. It should be mentioned, however, that we do not yet have an adequate knowledge of the strength of concrete f_{to} under uni-axial tension. What we are measuring by splitting of the cylinder is a special case of bi-directional strength $f_{tc} = f'_t$ when cylinder is under compression f_c and simultaneous tension f'_t where $f_c = 3f'_t$ (if calculated on the Theory of Elasticity as it is practiced). Assuming linear function for f_{tc} as in the diagram of Figure 11, and $f_{to} \cong 0.1\ f'_c$ we have to define the pure tension strength of concrete as

$f_t' = 0.77f_{t_o}$

Similarly, so called shear strength f_{sc} will represent a special case of bi-directional loading when $f_c = -\ f_t$ and could be defined as $f_{sc} \cong 0.9\ f_{to}$.

In general we can name the following strength limits for a reinforced concrete beam:

Limit No.1 - First flexural cracking (equal to ultimate failure in case of concrete beam without or with very little tension reinforcement).

Limit No.2 - Inclined cracking under moment and shear due to beam work.

Limit No.3 - Inclined splitting due to arch work.

Limit No.4 - Ultimate flexural failure due to yield (or rupture) of tensile steel or crush of concrete in compression.

Limit No.5 - Excessive deformation of beam.

For economic reasons our aim should be to construct a beam with the maximum possible load carrying capacity defined by the ultimate flexural strength - Limit No 4, and to eliminate earlier failures which may be caused by any one of the cracking strength limits Nos 1, 2 and 3. Limit No.5, on excessive deformations, is less important and not often valid. The Ultimate Flexural Strength Limit No.4 is by now, quite well defined and verified by tests and we do not intend to discuss it here.

The cracking strength limits of a beam can be represented basically through three types of cracks as shown in Figure 12, for two-point loaded beam with bonded or unbonded reinforcement.

The first cracks to appear are usually the flexural cracks (cracking Cause 1 and reach of tensile strength f_{to}). Usually, there are few flexural cracks in the beams with unbonded reinforcement (crack F1) and a number of cracks (F2, F3) in bonded beams. Flexural cracks are developed vertically and define strength-Limit No.1.

Next to appear will be cracks of Group B in shear + moment loaded zones of beams (cracks B4 and B5). These cracks originally begin as vertical (up to main reinforcement level) but develop further as inclined (up to 45° in middle portion of the beam).

These cracks have been called shearing cracks, however they are appearing due to the bond and the bi-axial compression and tension stress conditions (cracking Cause III and reach of combined strength f_{sc}). There are no cracks of Group B in beams with unbonded reinforcement. Cracks of Group B appear due to beam action, when beams with unbonded reinforcement, from the first moment of the flexural cracking, work as tied arches.

Last cracks, which may appear only in beams under high shear, will be splitting cracks of Group S. These are diagonal cracks directed from the support to the loading point. They appear due to arch work and reach of f_{ct} ultimate combined strength of concrete under bi-directional compression and tension (cracking Cause III) or uni-axial compression strength f'_c (cracking Cause II). These cracks may appear in beams with unbonded reinforcement as well as in beams with bonded reinforcement. In a beam with bonded reinforcement, a diagonal splitting crack is usually connecting already existing cracks of Group B, but it also may intersect these cracks as shown in Figure 12 on the left side. A similar horizontal splitting crack may appear in the compression zone of beam, in its portion under pure moment loading.

We intend to discuss the cracking strength limits of beam in more detail.

2.2 Flexural Cracking - Strength Limit No.1

An experimental formula can be used for calculation of the flexural cracking moment M_{crf} as follows (compare Figure 13).

$$M_{crf} = u \, f_{to} \, \frac{I}{y_b} \tag{1}$$

Here "u" is an experimental stress increasing factor which can be defined on our tests as

$$u = 1.5 \, (1 + C \, \frac{p}{\phi} \, \frac{f_{to}}{y_b}) \tag{2}$$

where C is an another experimental factor describing the bond conditions and ϕ - diameter of tensile bars.

For unbonded reinforcement: C=0 and

$$u = \text{const.} = 1.5 \tag{2a}$$

For beams with bonded round bars: C=1.07 and

$$u = 1.5 \, (1 + 1.07 \, \frac{p}{\phi} \, \frac{f_{to}}{y_b}) \tag{2b}$$

The flexural cracking moment in practice is much lower than the ultimate moment, but usually higher than maximum working moment. For economical reasons, it has been agreed to accept the existence of flexural cracks, even in bridge design, under the condition that crack widths will be limited, for protection against corrosion.

Flexural cracking strength can be improved by prestressing, but, in any case, this has an almost negligible effect on ultimate flexural strength of beam. Flexural cracking strength is higher in beams with bonded reinforcement, and also in the case of reinforcement of smaller diameter bars.

2.3 Inclined cracking at beam scheme - Strength Limit No. 2.

Inclined cracking (compare cracks B3 and B4 in Figure 12) takes place because of the work, at so-called beam scheme and because of the bond between main reinforcement and immediately surrounding concrete.

What we used to call the shear stress v, is defined as (compare ACl-318-63):

$$v = \frac{V}{bjd} \tag{3}$$

depends on the bond stress

$$v_b = \frac{V}{jd\,\Omega} \tag{4}$$

Mainly the bond resistance $v_b \Omega\, dx$ (compare Figure 14) evokes in beam a bi-directional stress condition of

$$v_c = -v_t = \frac{v_b \Omega}{b} \tag{5}$$

Putting (4) into (5) we get known expression (3) for the shear stress

$$v = v_c = -v_t = \frac{V\Omega}{jd\Omega b} = \frac{V}{bjd}$$

The procedure followed to obtain this expression shows the dependence of shear stress v on bond resistance v_b. In case of beam with unbonded reinforcement there is no bond resistance, because of $v_b = 0$ also $v = v_c = -v_t = 0$ and inclined cracks cannot be expected at all. This is already a well known phenomenon confirmed by tests.

Non-existence of the bond and of the holding force $\Delta H = v_t \Omega \Delta x$ (compare Figure 14a) calls for transfer of the total tensile force H

further on up to the support and safe anchoraging there what is apparent to working at a tied arch scheme. Existence of the bond, on the contrary, evokes bi-directional inclined stress condition of $\mathcal{V}_c = -\mathcal{V}_t$ which are added to the flexural normal stress due to the moment. On the neutral axis where the flexural stress is equal to zero the strength of the beam is governed by the bi-directional equal stresses of $\mathcal{V}_c = -\mathcal{V}_t$. When these stresses reach their strength limit, defined in Figure 11 as $f_{sc} = \mathcal{V}_c = -\mathcal{V}_t \cong 0.9\ f_{to}$ the beam will be subjected to 45° inclined cracking described as strength Limit No. 2, (cracking Cause III according to Figure 10).

Determining the difference in behavior of beams with bonded and unbonded reinforcement was one of the first important study tasks in our research. In fact, all our test samples were repeated for bonded and unbonded reinforcement and had electric strain gauges placed along all bars.

Observation of the stress in the bar changes is summarised as in Figure 15. Beams with unbonded reinforcement from the very beginning work as tied arches (explained by parallel lines 1, 2, 3 etc). Also beams with bonded reinforcement, well anchoraged beyond the support, after any crack appearance carry the excess lead at the tied arch scheme. As it can be seen on the left side diagram of Figure 15 each next load-increase-line 3, 4 or 5 in cracked portions of the beam is in equal distance δ_1, δ_2 or δ_3, from the last line. Equal distances mean equal stress increases in the main reinforcement and the carrying of excess load at arch scheme.

If all main reinforcement is carried beyond the support and well anchored there, even beams with inclined cracks can remain in good working condition until they reach the diagonal splitting at arch scheme which will be defined next.

In any case, it appears here that inclined cracking could be admitted in the design practice same as flexural cracking. In fact, inclined cracking, since it appears much later than flexural cracking, could be treated more easily in code requirements.

As in the case of flexural cracking, it would be uneconomical to try to eliminate inclined cracks by mean of reinforcement. Tests show that at moment of cracking, limit strain in concrete may be of $\varepsilon = 0.0001$ to 0.00015 and the accompanying stress in steel only of $f = \varepsilon E = (0.0001 \text{ to } 0.00015) \times 30 \times 10^6 = 3000$ to 4500 psi.

For example, in a practical case of 1 per cent of stirrup reinforcement at f=3000 psi. and bi-directional strength of concrete of $f_{sc} = 300$ psi. the increase of cracking strength due to the web reinforcement would be only of the order of 10 percent (because $0.01 \frac{3000}{300} = 0.1$) which is very low.

Our task should be not only to accept the existence of inclined cracks but also to assure the additional load carrying capacity, beyond flexural and inclined cracking.

Apparently, even a quite small amount of the web reinforcement (smaller than that required on shear theory) can assure required additional load carrying capacity and the reaching of the higher strength Limit No.3 at arch scheme.

The limit strength in inclined cracking and beam work can be described by means of shearing force V_s as follows

for beam without web reinforcement:

$$V_s = v_c \, bjd = f_{sc} \, bjd \simeq 0.9 \, f_{to} \, bjd \qquad (6)$$

for beam with web reinforcement:

$$V_s = 0.9 \, f_{to} \, bjd \left(1 + p_s \frac{3000}{f_{to}} \cos\alpha_s\right) \qquad (7)$$

where α_s is an angle of inclination of stirrups from the vertical.

2.4 Diagonal splitting at arch scheme - Strength Limit No. 3

Three basic schemes of arch work can be identified for a beam with unbonded reinforcement as in Figure 16.

Scheme "a" relates to a beam loaded uniformly on its whole length. This scheme can be compared with an edge or wall corner. There are only radial compression stresses f_r in the vicinity of support, and no danger of diagonal splitting at all if main reinforcement has sufficient anchorage beyond the support and if an adequate bearing width (on bearing strength) is provided.

Scheme "b" relates to one- or two-point loaded beams. These beams are subject of diagonal splitting. Because of the geometry of support portion (between load and support) of the beam there will be curved streams of compression stresses f_{ct} , and simultaneous tangent tensile f_{tc} , which in limit stage may lead to diagonal splitting as indicated in Figure 16 with solid line.

Scheme "c" relates to a beam with three or more loading points situated in a distance of $c \geqslant h$ between each other. This scheme is composed of two superimposed "b" cases which can be considered separately.

Hence it will be enough to study only the case of Scheme "b". Our tests of Stage 2 were devoted to this case in particular. It appears possible for the design practice to assume a simplified rectangular stress block in the support segment of beam, as in Figure 17. This assumption may be compared with a similar, design practice in the assumption of a rectangular stress bloc for the flexural compression zone.

According to Figure 17, bi-directional stress condition depends on the geometry of support segment and can be defined as:

$$f_{ct} = \frac{S}{bh} \cos\alpha = \frac{H}{bh} \tag{8}$$

$$f_{tc} = \frac{S}{ab} \sin\alpha = \frac{V}{ab} \tag{9}$$

$$f_{ct}/f_{tc} = \frac{Ha}{Vh} = \frac{a^2}{h^2} \tag{10}$$

The diagonal splitting will occur when concrete in the middle portion of support segment reaches f_{tc} the limit strength in bi-directional tension and compression, which can be defined on the basis of proposed linear strength function as in Figure 11 and according to formula (10) as follows:

$$f_{tc} = \frac{f'_c}{\frac{f'_c}{f_{to}} + \frac{a^2}{h^2}} \tag{11}$$

Corresponding maximum load in terms of limit shearing force V can be described from (9) as

$$V_a = f_{tc}\, ab = \frac{f'_c\, ab}{\frac{f'_c}{f_{to}} + \frac{a^2}{h^2}} \tag{12}$$

or in case of present stirrup reinforcement of $p_s = \frac{A_s}{ab}$

$$V_{as} = f_{tc}\, ab\, (1 + p_s \frac{3000}{f_{tc}} \cos\alpha_s) \qquad (13)$$

Apparently, reaching of strength Limit No.3 as defined through formulae (8) - (13) will mean the termination of work ability only in the case of a beam with unbonded main reinforcement and none or very little web reinforcement.

In the case of sufficient web reinforcement, able to take over the whole splitting force V_a or V_{as} and to restrict the width of splitting crack the beam will be able to work further until it reaches ultimate flexural strength Limit No.4. In this case we will have a cracked support segment with the concrete able to work only for diagonal uni-axial compression and with no resistance against tangent tension and splitting action. Tangent splitting force will have to be carried totally by the web reinforcement.

In the same manner, beams with main reinforcement bonded can keep working beyond 45° inclined cracking strength Limit No.2 (due to beam work) through Limit No.3 (due to arch work) and further on until they reach flexural failure Limit No.4, if there is sufficient web reinforcement to restrict crack penetration and to carry the whole splitting force, calculated as for arch scheme, assuming that from the moment of 45° inclined cracking, concrete has no resistence in tangent tension.

3. Discussion of cracking strength limits

Hence, utilisation of maximum flexural strength limits is our primary task, a comparison of inclined cracking limits with the flexural limit will be of some interest.

Ultimate flexural strength, as defined by concrete, can be expressed on tests as moment

$$M_u \cong 0.35\ bh^2 f'_c \qquad (14)$$

Moment of the 45° inclined cracking (due to beam work and bond) for 2 point loaded beam (compare formula 6) can be expressed as

$$M_s = V_s\ a = 0.9\ f_{to}\ bjda \qquad (15)$$

It can be assumed that $f_{to} \cong 0.1\ f'_c$ and $jd = 0.67\ h$ than

$$M_s = 0.06\ abh\ f'_c \qquad (15a)$$

Comparison of (14) and (15a) gives a straight line function of (see Figure 18):

$$F_s = \frac{M_s}{M_u} = \frac{0.06\ abh\ f'_c}{0.35\ bh^2 f'_c} = 0.172\ a/h \qquad (16)$$

valid for $a/h < 5.8$

There is no danger of inclined cracking in beams without the web reinforcement for $a/h > 5.8$. No stirrup reinforcement will be required for one-point loaded beam of clear span $\ell \geq 11.6\ h \cong 12\ h$. Test results on beams without fully used flexural strength (due to concrete) will fall below the line F_s - in the Region 1. Those may be the beams without the 45° inclined cracks. Function F_s is well confirmed in the tests, and describes the lowest strength limit in inclined cracking for a bonded beam without web reinforcement. However test results on bonded beams with stirrups or on unbonded beams without stirrups will fall above the line F_s - in the Region 2.

Moment of diagonal splitting (at arch work) for 2-point loaded beam with unbonded main reinforcement and without web reinforcement can be similarly (compare formula 12) defined as:

$$M_a = V_a \cdot a = f_{tc}\, ba^2 = \frac{f'_c\, a^2 b}{\frac{f'_c}{f_{to}} + \frac{a^2}{h^2}} \simeq \frac{f'_c\, a^2 b}{10 + \frac{a^2}{h^2}} \qquad (17)$$

The comparison of (14) and (15) gives the function F_a as follows:

$$F_a = \frac{M_a}{M_u} = \frac{ba^2 f'_c}{\left(\frac{a^2}{h^2} + 10\right) 0.35\, bh^2 f'_c} = \frac{a^2}{h^2}\left(\frac{2.85}{\frac{a^2}{h^2} + 10}\right) \qquad (18)$$

valid for $a/h < 2.32$

There is no danger of inclined splitting due to arch work for beams with unbonded reinforcement when $a/h > 2.32$. There will be no stirrups required for a single-point loaded beam with unbonded tensile reinforcement of clear span $\ell \geq 4.64$ h. Again, the test results of unbonded beams with web reinforcement able to restrict crack width and taking over of the whole splitting force may fall above the line F_a - in the Region 3.

It is possible to construct a beam of $a/h = 2$ with bonded main reinforcement and with stirrups which will expose the 45° inclined cracks due to beam work and later also the diagonal splitting crack (eventually intersecting 45° inclined cracks). Test results for such a beam will be placed twice in Figure 18, mainly in points A and B. Similarly, it will be possible to construct a beam for which test results will be placed twice in points C and D or E and K. Double placement of test results have been demonstrated on several occasions during our research.

It would be interesting now, to compare the magnitudes of shearing forces V_a and V_s and required web reinforcement A_a and A_s as defined in the proposed arch theory and in traditional shear theory. Shearing forces are defined by formulas (6) and (12) and comparison gives as the function of:

$$F_3 = \frac{V_a}{V_s} = \frac{f_{tc}\ ab}{0.9\ f_{to}\ bjd} = \frac{f_{tc}}{0.9\ f_{to}}\ \frac{a}{jd} = \frac{f'_c}{0.9\ f_{to}}\ \frac{a}{jd}\ \frac{1}{\frac{f'_c}{f_{to}} + \frac{a^2}{h^2}} \qquad (19)$$

For $jd = 0.67\ h$ and $\frac{f'_c}{f_{to}} \simeq 10$

$$F_3 = \frac{V_a}{V_s} = \frac{a}{h}\ \frac{16.7}{10 + \frac{a^2}{h^2}} \qquad (19a)$$

Function F_3 has been plotted in Figure 19. As it can be seen, for cases of $1.5 < a/h < 6$ the shearing force V_a defined on ardh scheme is 2 to 2.6 higher than the V_s defined on beam work and 45° inclined cracking.

Similarly we can demonstrate (see Figure 20) a comparison of the required amount of web reinforcement A_s and A_a, necessary for taking over of the whole shearing forces V_s and V_a or the stresses of $f_{sc} = 0.9\ f_{to}$ and f_{tc}

$$F_4 = \frac{A_s}{A_a} = \frac{0.9\ f_{to}\ ab}{f_{tc}\ ab} = \frac{0.9\ f_{to}}{f_{tc}} \simeq 0.09\ (10 + \frac{a^2}{h^2}) \quad (20)$$

Again, the comparison shows that the amount of reinforcement estimated on arch theory is, for beams of $1.5 < a/h < 5.8$ much less than the amount estimated on traditional shear theory. It is true that the ACl 318-63 Building Code allows carrying by means of web reinforcement only reduced shearing stress $v = v_u - v_c$ (in excess of v_c) which the said concrete can carry by itself.

For ultimate strength theory it is assumed:

$$v_u = 10\phi\sqrt{f'_c} \text{ and } v_c = \phi\,(1.9\sqrt{f'_c} + 2500\ p_w \frac{Vd}{M})$$

where ϕ decreasing factor

In our case of concentrated loads and $M = V_a a$ can be assumed maximum value of $v_c = 3.5\phi\sqrt{f'_c}$ then difference to be carried by web reinforcement will be

$$v = 10\phi\sqrt{f'_c} - 3.5\phi\sqrt{f'_c} = 6.5\phi\sqrt{f'_c} \simeq 5.5\sqrt{f'_c}$$

The comparison of required web reinforcement A_{co} allowed on ACl with that required on arch theory gives

$$\frac{A_{co}}{A_a} = \frac{5.5\sqrt{f'_c}\ ba}{f_{tc}\ ab} = \frac{5.5\sqrt{f'_c}}{f'_c}\ (10 + \frac{a^2}{h^2}) \quad (21)$$

for the concrete of $f'_c = 3000$ psi it will be $\frac{A_{co}}{A_a} \simeq 0.1\ (10 + \frac{a^2}{h^2})$

and for the concrete of $f'_c = 4000$psi it will be $\frac{A_{co}}{A_a} \simeq 0.087\ (10 + \frac{a^2}{h^2})$

In other words, for concrete of f'_c = 3000 to 4000 psi the comparison of $\frac{A_{co}}{A_a}$ gives almost the same function as that presented in Figure 20. This means ACl-318-63 considers the amount of web reinforcement necessary as being much above what is actually required for provision of arch work. Such an excessive amount, as we already explained, is not at all necessary, especially in regions of $2.32 < a/h < 5.8$.

4. Analysis of web reinforcement requirement for bridge beam loaded with travelling single force P.

Let us study the case of a beam with clear span l with the balanced rectangular cross section of bh. The ultimate maximum flexural moment for such a beam can be assumed again as

$$M = 0.35\ bh^2 f'_c = \frac{P\ell}{4}$$

Hence maximum ultimate travelling force will be limited to

$$P = \frac{4x0.35\ bh^2 f'_c}{\ell} = \frac{1.4\ bh^2\ f'_c}{\ell}$$

then shear force (at P in distance "a" from left support) will be

$$= \frac{P\ (\ell - a)}{\ell} = \frac{1.4\ bh^2 f'_c\ (\ell - a)}{\ell^2}$$

To recognise the presence of the 45° inclined cracks due to beam work, and yet to provide load carrying ability beyond the arch strength limit, up to utilisation of maximum flexural limit, we will need web reinforcement, defined on the basis of arch theory, and able to take over the whole splitting force beginning from the 45° inclined cracking moment.

The total amount of web reinforcement for any distance "a" can be defined as:

$$A_a = \frac{V}{f_s} = \frac{1.4\ bh^2\ (\ell - a)}{\ell^2}\ \frac{f'_c}{f_s} \qquad (22)$$

In similar way the required reinforcement density will be

$$n_a = \frac{A_a}{a} = \frac{1.4\ bh^2\ (\ell - a)}{a\ell^2}\ \frac{f'_c}{f_s} \qquad (23)$$

In any case, web reinforcement will be required only for beams of $a/h < 5.8$ and $\ell/h < 11.6 = 12$.

Let us study as an example a case of beam of $\ell = 12$ h, $b = h/3$, $f'_c = 4000$ psi and $f_s = 30000$ psi. For such a beam

$$A_a = \frac{1.4\ h^3}{3x12\ h}\ \frac{4000}{30000}\ (1 - \frac{a}{\ell}) = 0.000435\ h^2\ (12 - \frac{a}{h})$$
$$= K\ (12 - \frac{a}{h}) \qquad (22a)$$

and $n_a = \frac{K}{a}\ (12 - \frac{a}{h})$ where $K = 0.000435\ h^2$ (23a)

Formulas 22a and 23a have been plotted in Figure 21, in solid lines.

The amount and the density of web reinforcement, required on ACl-318-63 could be estimated similarly as

$$A_s = \left(\frac{V}{jdb} - 3.5\phi\sqrt{f'_c}\right)\frac{ab}{f_s} = \frac{V_a}{jdf_s} - \frac{3.5\ \phi\ f'_c\ ab}{f_s}$$

For $jd = 0.67$ h and $\phi = 0.85$ and assumptions as before we will get

$$A_s = \frac{1.4\ bh^2\ (\ell - a)\ a}{\ell^2 .0.67\ h}\ \frac{f'_c}{f_s} - \frac{3\sqrt{f'_c}\ ab}{f_s} \quad \text{and}$$

$$A_s = K\left[1.5(12 - a/h)\ a/h - 4.8\ a/h\right] = K\ (13.2\ a/h - 1.5\ a^2/h^2) \qquad (24a)$$

and accordingly

$$\eta_s = \frac{A_s}{a} = \frac{K}{a}\ (13.2\ a/h - 1.5\ a^2/h^2) \qquad (25a)$$

Formulas 24a and 25a have been plotted in Figure 21, in dotted lines. The comparison of diagrams in Figure 21, shows that adoption of the suggested arch theory would permit significant reduction in web reinforcement requirement.

In the case of the given example, average density of web reinforcement could be reduced by more than half. We have to remember, however, that the arch scheme is possible only if the whole main reinforcement is carried and fully anchored beyond the support.

5. General conclusions

5.1 The tests show that all beams with unbonded reinforcement -- from the very beginning -- and beams with bonded main reinforcement -- from the moment of the first cracking -- work as in the arch scheme.

The arch scheme is more advantageous for web reinforcement but requires the whole main reinforcement to be carried beyond the support and fully anchored there, perhaps by means of welded plates or proper hooks (with eventual extra spirals placed around hooks).

In the case of concentrated loading, arch strength of beam depends also on the resistance of support segments (between support and loading points) against diagonal splitting, which may be a case in very deep beams with $a/h < 2.32$.

By provision of web reinforcement (stirrups recommended) in an amount enabling the assumption of more than whole splitting force due to arch scheme, it will be possible to construct a beam of "shear strength" higher than that defined by maximum flexural strength.

Apparently the amount of web reinforcement required for arch scheme is much lower than the amount required by ACl-318-63 on traditional shear theory.

The calculation of web reinforcement in the arch theory suggested here is very simple. For any shear span "a" we just have to provide web reinforcement in strength of shear force V, when in case of traditional shear theory we had to provide web reinforcement in strength of $V \times \frac{a}{jd}$ means $\frac{a}{jd}$ times more.

There is no need for web reinforcement in case of beam loaded uniformly if main reinforcement is fully anchored beyond the support. However if such a beam is subject of early 45° inclined cracking, it will be advisable to provide some web reinforcement, in order to restrict the penetration of inclined cracks and to make the arch scheme possible. A nominal amount of web reinforcement in the strength of single shear force V distributed on whole region of inclined cracking "a" (or in force of total load and distributed uniformly on whole beam span) will be sufficient.

5.2 Bond between main reinforcement and concrete is undesirable for inclined cracking of any beam. Bond existence is the main reason for the 45° inclined cracking which we used to call shear cracking. The best way of eliminating inclined cracking would be the complete destruction of bond. Most of our tests showed that even the ultimate flexural strength is higher in beams with unbonded reinforcement (if this reinforcement is anchoraged beyond the support).

It would be improper however to advise the complete elimination of bond. Presence of bond increases significantly the flexural cracking strength and increases the number of cracks but these cracks are reduced in width (good for corrosion protection). However, for beams subjected to very high shear, and mainly for short beams with steady loading points, it would be advantageous to eliminate bond on bar portions situated in shear zones. This would eliminate the inclined cracking and not injure the segments subjected to inclined splitting due to arch scheme. Such beams were demonstrated in our tests (example, beams of Test Stage 6). For improvement of both the flexural and the inclined cracking strength, it may be advisable to use tension reinforcement composed of a few, smaller diameter bars or wires having good bond strength and of big diameter round bars of high strength steel, with or without reduced bond strength, but with good end anchorages.

This would produce good flexural cracking strength of beam and would earlier impose the more beneficial arch work. In any case, it appears on our tests that previous tendency of using higher strength bars with improved bond strength (deformed bars) in case of beam under high shear could be revised in favor of rather smooth bars with extra anchorages at their ends.

5.3 The traditional shear theory is applicable only for bonded beam at early stage of elastic behavior up to the moment of 45° inclined cracking, but ceases to be applicable afterwards, when natural beam behavior and new arch work replaces previous beam work. If so, then checking of the shear stress beyond the moment of reach of the limit stress $v = v_c = - v_t = 0.9\, f_{to}$ has also no validity, and accordingly, there is no explanation for admissible or ultimate allowed shear stress concept still used in the code requirements. Recognition of an arch work should allow beams of much higher shear stress if checked traditionally. This was demonstrated on beam "c" of Test Stage 6 (constructed on basis of arch theory) which failed in flexure but after demonstrating the 45° inclined cracking and later also the diagonal splitting. Traditionally checked shear stress in this beam was $v = \frac{V}{bjd} = 1230$ psi. what at $f'_c = 3870$ psi gives $v = 20\sqrt{f'_c}$ which would not be allowed, under any circumstances, by AC1-318-63.

NOTATIONS

ℓ - clear beam span

a - shear span

b - width of the beam

h - depth of the beam

d - effective depth of the beam

jd - leveral arm

y_b - distance of the extreme tensile fibres from neutral axis

x - depth of the compression zone in flexure

$A = bh$ - area of the beam cross-section

A_s - area of the web reinforcement or amount of the web reinforcement required on shear theory

A_a - the amount of web reinforcement required on arch theory

A_o - area of main reinforcement

$p = \frac{A_o}{bh}$; $P_s = \frac{A_s}{bh}$

I - moment of inertia of beam section

Ω - perimeter of main reinforcement bars

ϕ - diameter of main reinforcement

f_c - compressive stress in concrete

f_t - tension stress in concrete

f'_c - cylinder compression strength of concrete

f_{to} - pure tension strength of concrete

f'_t - tension stress in concrete when tested by cylinder splitting

$f_{sc} = v_c = - v_t$ = shearing strength of concrete

f_{ct} - compression strength of concrete under combined bi-directional compression and tension

f_{tc} - tension strength of concrete under combined bi-directional tension and compression

f_{tt} - strength of concrete under combined bi-directional tension

f_{cc} - strength of concrete under combined bi-directional compression

f_{cr} - stress in extreme tension face of beam at flexural cracking

u - empirical stress increasing factor for flexural cracking strength of beam

f_s - stress in steel

f_y - yield strength of steel

ϑ_b - strength in bond between concrete and steel

ϑ_c - principal compression stress in shear

ϑ_t - principal tension stress in shear

$\vartheta = \frac{V}{bjd}$ - shearing stress

V - shearing force

V_a - shearing force at the moment of diagonal splitting (at arch work)

V_s - shearing force at the moment of 45° inclined cracking (beam work)

P - concentrated loading force

H - force in tension reinforcement

S - diagonal splitting force

n - ratio of steel to concrete moduluses of elasticity

M_u - ultimate flexural moment

M_{cr} - moment at the time of cracking in general

M_{crf} - first flexural cracking moment

M_s - moment of the time of 45° inclined cracking (shear cracking)

M_a - moment of the time of diagonal splitting (at arch work).

REFERENCES

1. Leonhardt, F., and Walter, R., - "Beiträge Zur Behandlung der Schubproblems im Stahlbetonbau" - Beton und Stahlbetonbau, Heft 12/1961, 2, 3, 6, 7/1962 (in German).

2. Mody, K.G., Viest L.M., Elstner, R.C., and Hognestad, E. - "Shear Strength of Reinforced Concrete Beams" - Journal of American Concrete Institute, December 1954, January, February, March 1955.

3. Taub, J., Neville, A.M. - "Resistance to Shear of Reinforced Concrete Beams" - Journal of ACI - August to December 1960.

4. Report of Joint ACI - "ASCE Committee on "Shear and Diagonal Tension", ACI Journal, January, February and March 1962.

5. Krefeld W.J., Thurston, C.W. "Studies on the Shear and Diagonal Tension Strength of Simply Supported Reinforced Concrete Beam", Columbia University Bulletin, June 1962.

6. Murashov, W.J. - "Treshchinoustoechivost, jostkost e prochnost jelezobetona" (Cracking Resistance and Strength of Reinforced Concrete), Mashstroesdat, Moskow, 1950. (in Russian).

7. Kani, G.N.J. "Riddle of Shear Failure and Its Solution," ACI Journal, April, 1964.

8. Kani, G.N.J. "Basic Facts Concerning Shear Failure," ACI Journal, Proceedings, Vol.63, No.6, June 1966, pp.675-692.

9. Kani, G.N.J., "How Safe Are Our Large Reinforced Beams" - ACI Journal, Vol.64, March 1967, and Discussion, Proceedings Vol.64, September 1967.

10. Bresler, B. and Scordelis, A.C. "Shear Strength of Reinforced Concrete Beams," ACI Journal, Proceedings, Vol.60, No.1 January 1963, pp.51-74.

11. Bresler, B. and MacGregor, J.G., "Review of Concrete Beams Failing in Shear," Preceedings, ASCE Vol.93, STI, February 1967, pp.343-372.

12. Glomb J. "Die Ausnutzbarkeit Zweiachsiger Druckfestigkeit des Betons in Flachentragwerken" (use of Bi-axial Compression Strength of Concrete for Surface Girders) Papers of Fédèration Intérnationale de la Précontrainte, 3rd ,ongress, Berlin, 1958 (in German).

13. Zielinski, Z.A., "Prefabrykowane Betonowe Dzwigary Sprezone" (Precast Prestressed Concrete Girders), Arkady, Warsaw, 1962 (in Polish).

14. Zielinski, Z.A., "Strength Limits for Reinforced Concrete Beam Subjected to Bending and High Shear," Journal of the Institution of Engineers (India), Vol.XLVIII, No.7, Part C14, March 1968.

15. Zielinski, Z.A. "Prestressed Concrete Typical Roofs in Poland" - Journal of Prestressed Concrete Institute, April 1963.

16. Zielinski, Z.A., and Browning J.S. "Badanie wytrzymalosci zaprawy cementowej w stanie dwukierunkowego sciskania i rozciagania" (Strength Investigation of Cement Mortar in Bi-directional Compression and Tension), Inzynieria i Budownictwo, No.3, Marzec 1967 (in Polish).

17. Polish Standards Committee "Konstrukcje z betonu-zasady obliczania i projektowania (Structures Made of Concrete - Calculation and Design Methods) Limit Design Code, Project 1963.

18. Zielinski, Z.A., "Research on Ultimate Strength in Shear of Bonded and Unbonded Reinforced Concrete Beams," International Symposium on Shear, Torsion and Bond in Reinforced and Prestressed Concrete, 14-17 January 1969, P.S.G. College of Technology, Coimbatore 4, India.

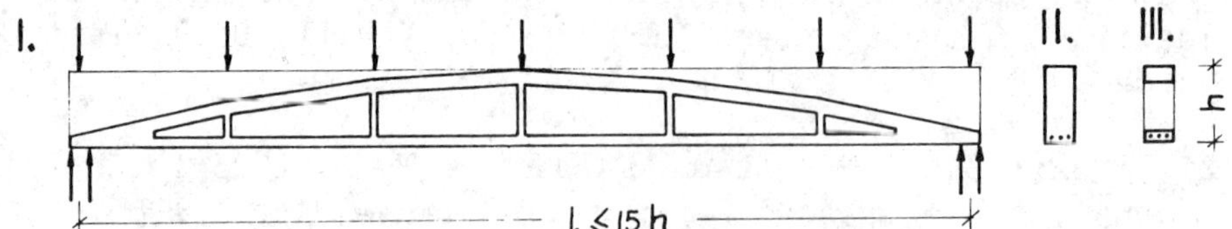

Figure 1 - Scheme of deriving of an open web economy girder out of reinforced concrete beam: i) elevation, ii) beam's section, iii) open web economy girder's section.

Figure 2a - Example of use of an economy roof girder of 60 ft. span and 4.5 feet high. Weight of this girder is 8,000 lbs.

Figure 2b - Factory produced standard economy girders of 60 to 100 ft. span.

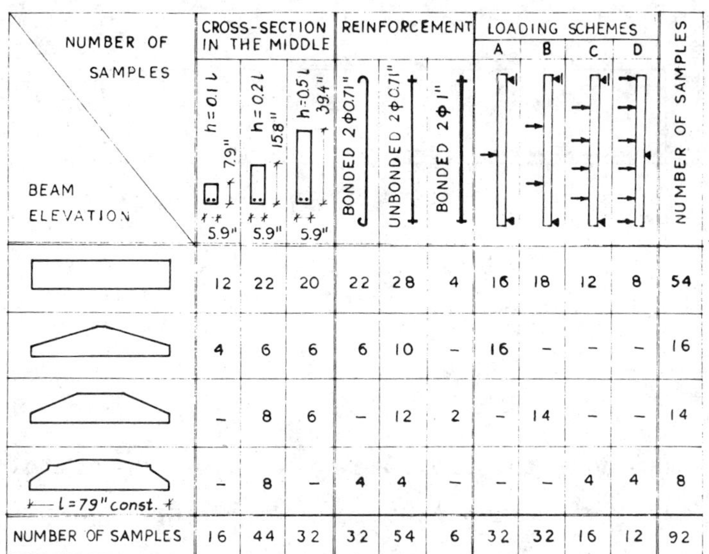

Number of samples / Beam elevation	Cross-section in the middle: h=0.1l 7.9" (5.9")	h=0.2l 15.8" (5.9")	h=0.5l 39.4" (5.9")	Reinforcement: Bonded $2\phi0.71"$	Unbonded $2\phi0.71"$	Bonded $2\phi1"$	Loading schemes: A	B	C	D	Number of samples
(rectangular)	12	22	20	22	28	4	16	18	12	8	54
(haunched)	4	6	6	6	10	–	16	–	–	–	16
(haunched)	–	8	6	–	12	2	–	14	–	–	14
(curved haunch) l=79" const.	–	8	–	4	4	–	–	–	4	4	8
NUMBER OF SAMPLES	16	44	32	32	54	6	32	32	16	12	92

Figure 3 - Beam samples of basic Test Stage 1.

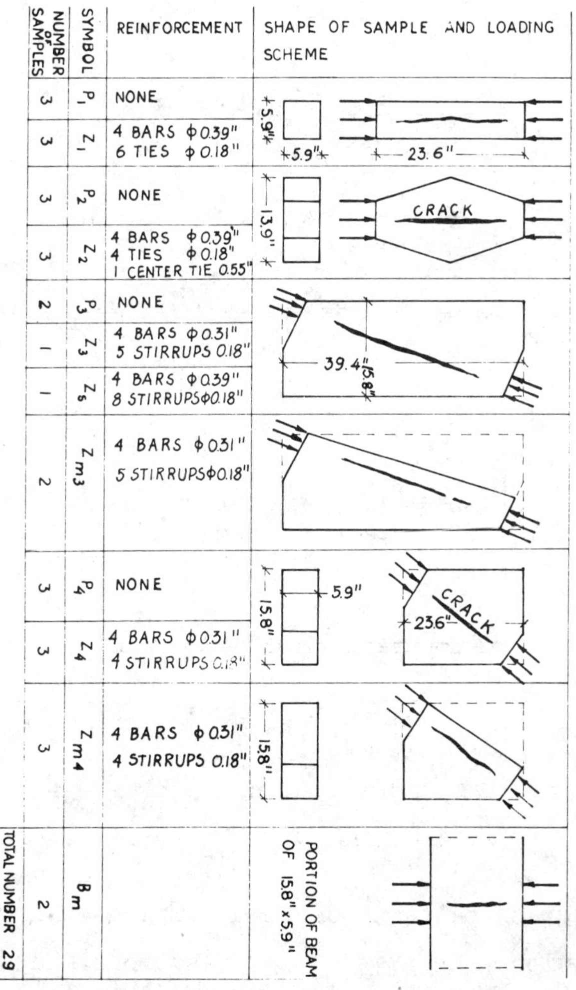

Number of samples	Symbol	Reinforcement	Shape of sample and loading scheme
3	P_1	NONE	5.9" × 5.9"; 23.6"
3	Z_1	4 BARS $\phi0.39"$ 6 TIES $\phi0.18"$	
3	P_2	NONE	13.9"; CRACK
3	Z_2	4 BARS $\phi0.39"$ 4 TIES $\phi0.18"$ 1 CENTER TIE 0.55"	
2	P_3	NONE	39.4"; 15.8"
1	Z_3	4 BARS $\phi0.31"$ 5 STIRRUPS 0.18"	
1	Z_6	4 BARS $\phi0.39"$ 8 STIRRUPS $\phi0.18"$	
2	Z_{m3}	4 BARS $\phi0.31"$ 5 STIRRUPS $\phi0.18"$	
3	P_4	NONE	15.8"; 5.9"; 23.6"; CRACK
3	Z_4	4 BARS $\phi0.31"$ 4 STIRRUPS 0.18"	
3	Z_{m4}	4 BARS $\phi0.31"$ 4 STIRRUPS 0.18"	15.8"
2	B_m		PORTION OF BEAM OF 15.8" x 5.9"
TOTAL NUMBER 29			

Figure 4 - Support portions of the beam and supplementary samples tested under diagonal compression - Test Stage 2.

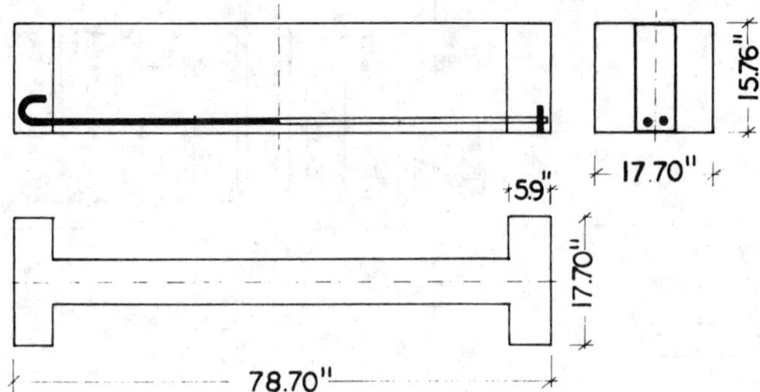

Figure 5 - Beam samples simulating the joists monolithically connected with main girders - Test Stage 3. Left portion relates to a beam with bonded reinforcement and right portion to a beam with unbonded reinforcement.

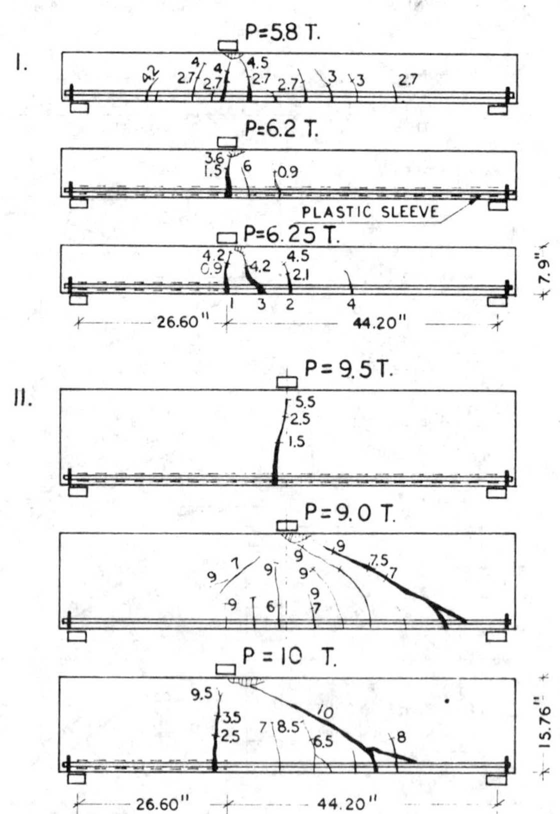

Figure 6 - Crack patterns on beam samples having reinforcement with partially destroyed bond - Test Stage 4.

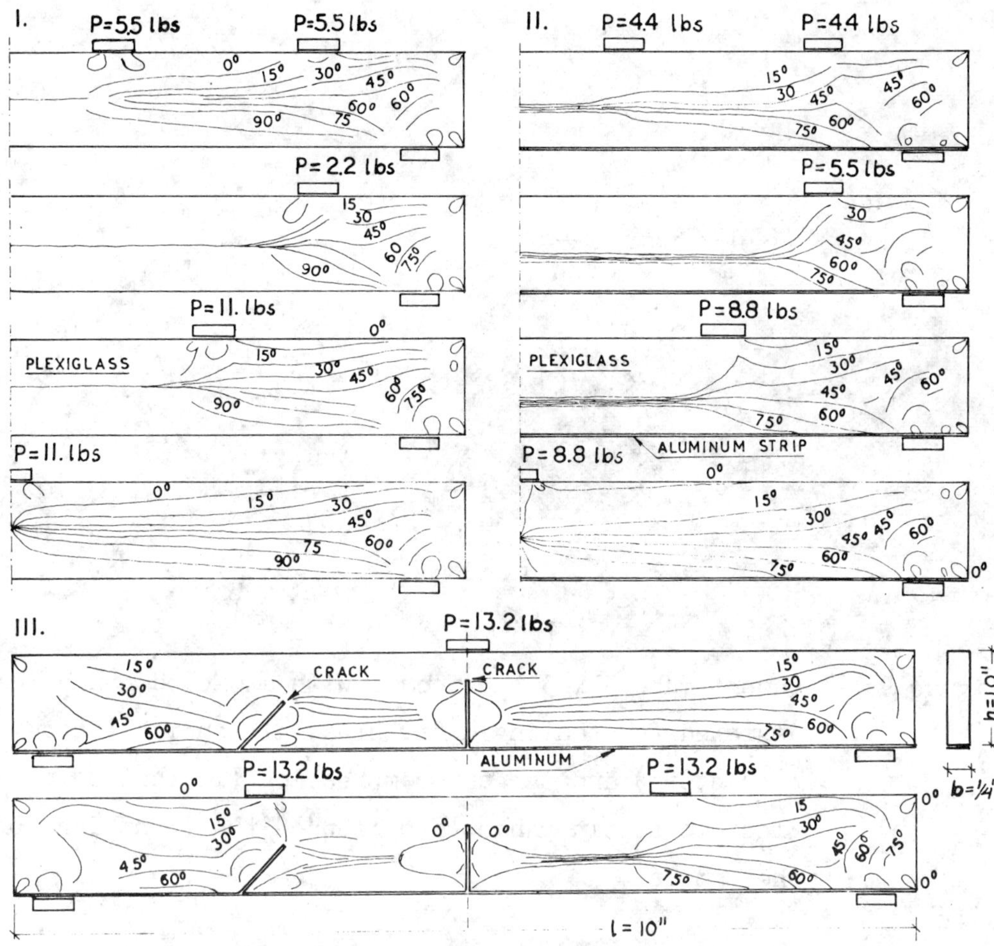

Figure 7 - Izoclinic lines, defined on photoelastic basis - Test State 5: i) concrete beam models, ii) reinforced concrete beam models, iii) as (ii) but with cut in cracks.

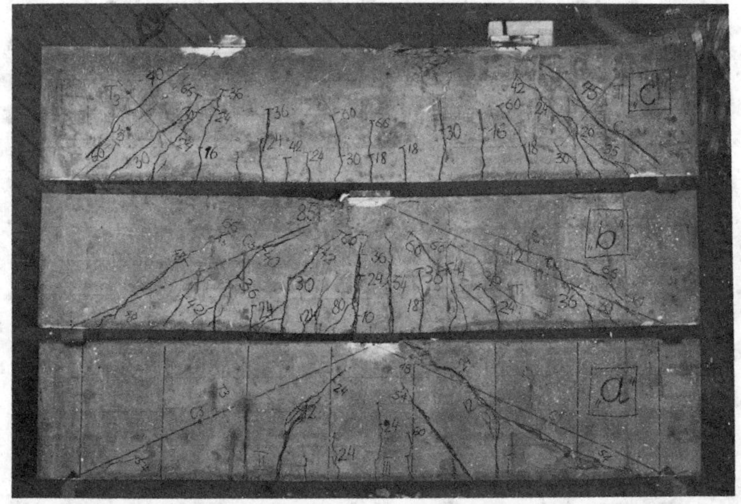

Figure 8 - Beam samples of Test Stage 6. All beams of 6" x 16" x 80" had 2 No.10 (1.27 dia) deformed bars of f_y=45,000 psi. Beams a and c had stirrups provided on arch theory.

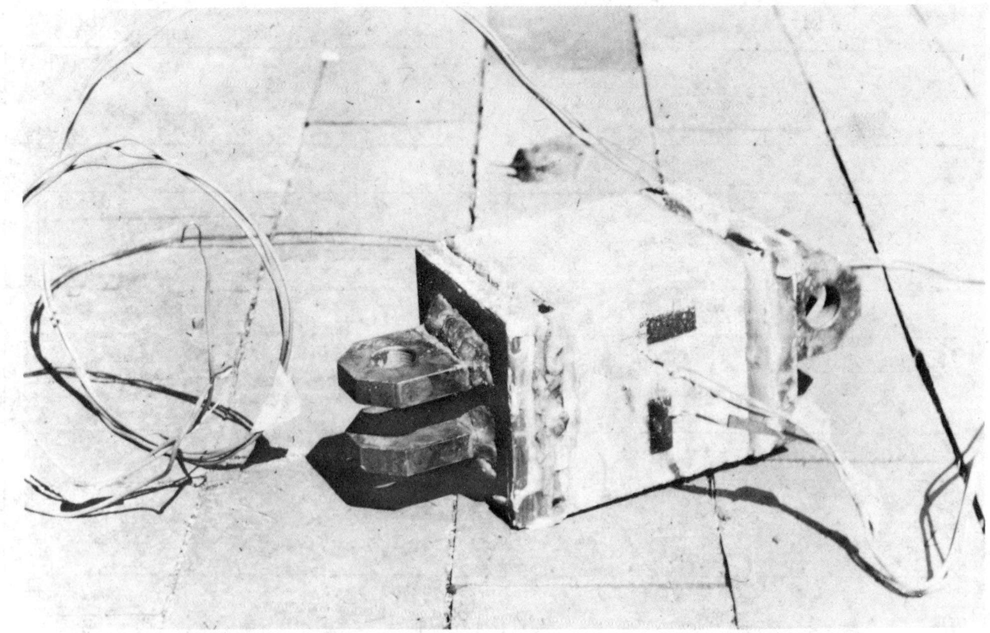

Figure 9a - Cement cube 3 x 3 x 3 inch., with attached connectors designed for testing under bi-axial tension (through connectors) and tangent compression (in testing machine). Electric strain gauges are seen on the front face of the sample.

Figure 9b - Tension frame for tests of cement cubes under bi-axial compression and tension. Test cube is placed in the frame.

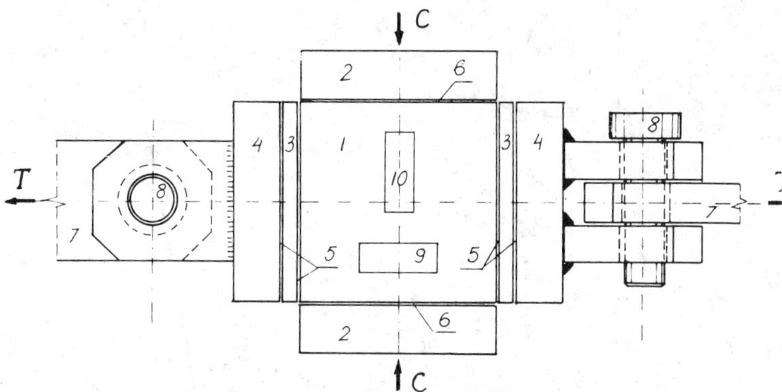

Figure 9c - Scheme of test sample and connectors: 1-- cube 3" x 3" x 3", 2 - steel plate, 3 - neoprene ¼", 4 - steel connector, 5 - apoxy, 6 - wax, 7 - tie, 8 - bolt, 9 and 10 - electric strain gauges.

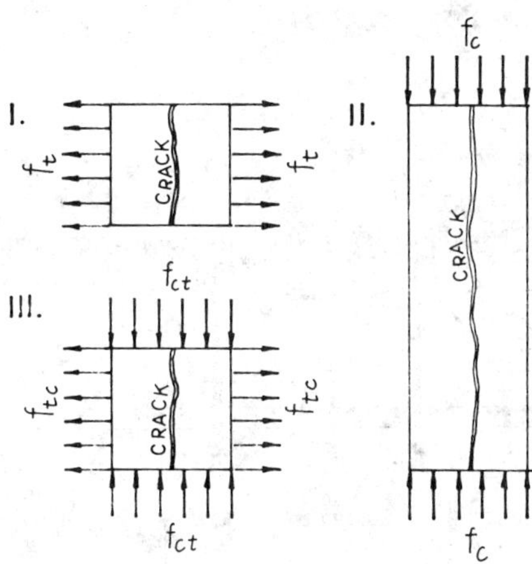

Figure 10 - Basic causes of the failure of concrete: i) uni-axial tension, ii) uni-axial compression, and iii) bi-axial tension and compression.

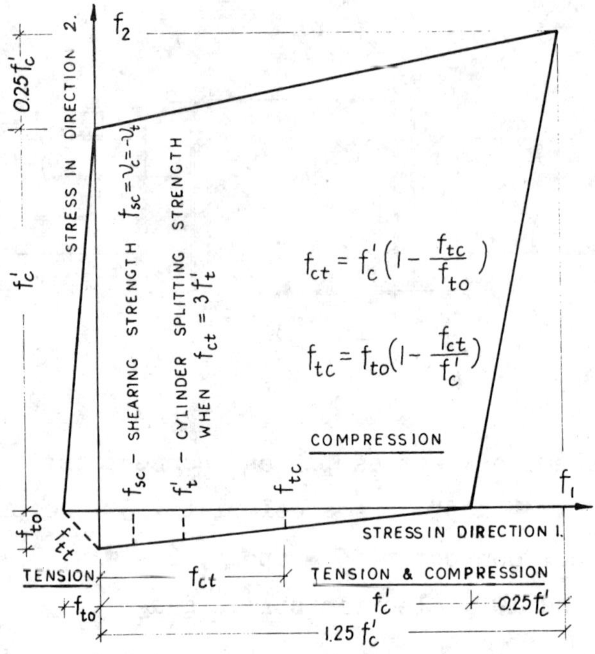

Figure 11 - Combined bi-directional strength of concrete (see notations for symbols).

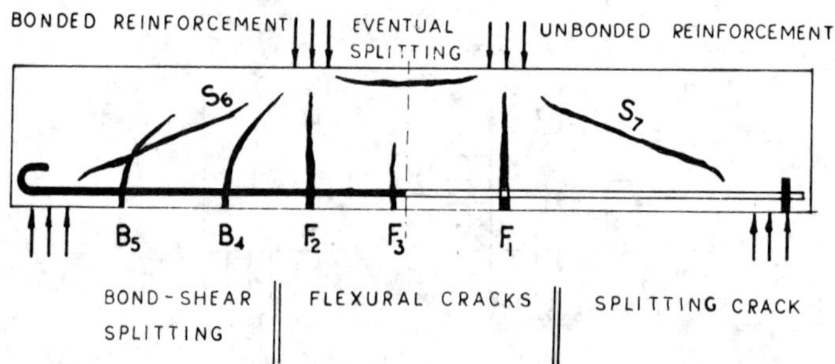

Figure 12 - Generalised crack propagation in the beam with bonded or unbonded reinforcement. F1-F3 - flexural vertical cracks, B4-B5 - inclined cracks due to the bond and beam work, "S6-S7 - splitting crack due to arch work". Numbers 1, 2, 3 etc., show the time order of cracking.

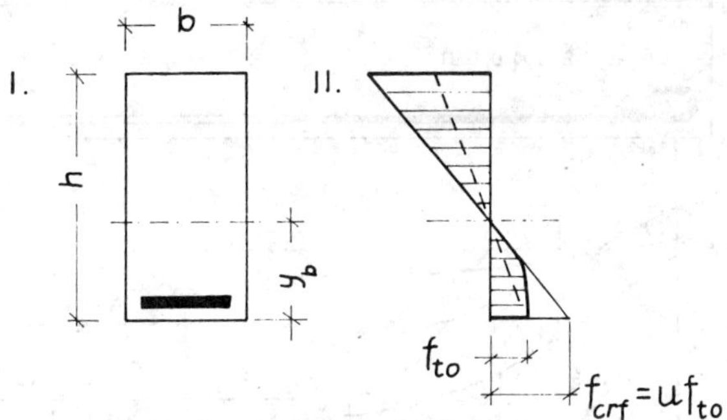

Figure 13 - Simplified stress diagram for empirical calculation of flexural cracking moment: i) cross section, ii) stress block.

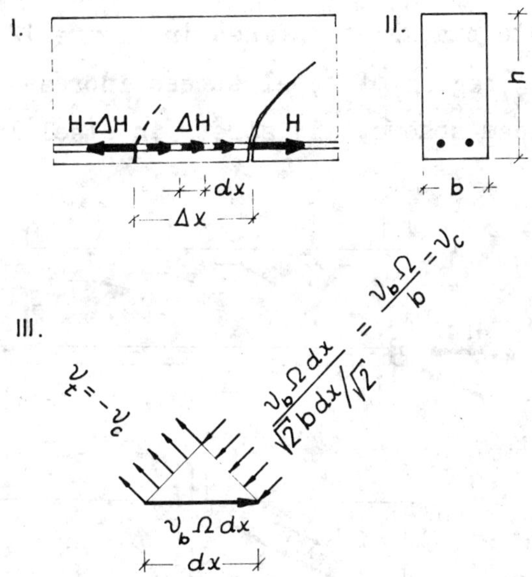

Figure 14 - Definition of bi-directional stress condition at inclined cracking of the beam caused by bond: i) segment of beam, ii) cross section, iii) stress in concrete due to bond.

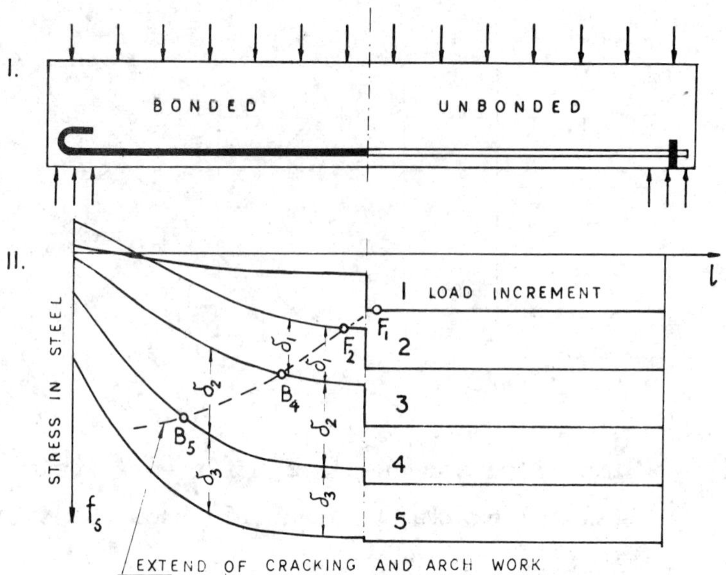

Figure 15 - Stress in steel increases along uniformly loaded beam with bonded or unbonded reinforcement. Letters F and B locate cracks as defined in Figure 12. Dotted line: shows region of equal stress increase and arch work: i) beam scheme, ii) stress in steel lines.

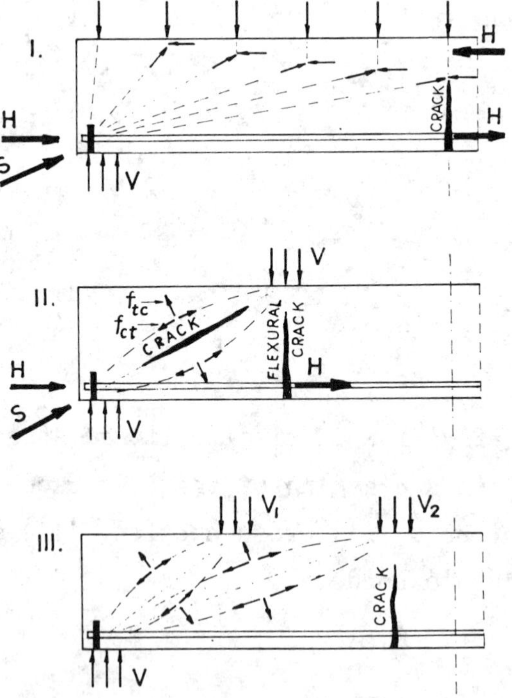

Figure 16 - Basic loading schemes describing arch strength of reinforced concrete beam with unbonded reinforcement: 1) uniformly loaded beam, ii) one- or two-point loaded beam - basic scheme, iii) three or more point loaded beam.

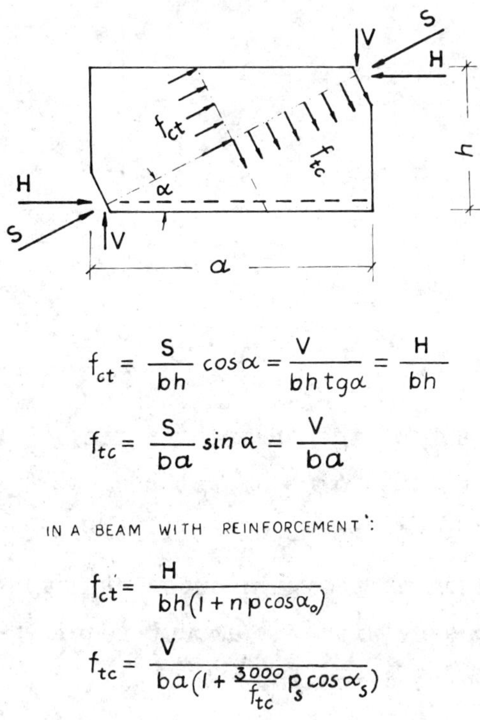

$$f_{ct} = \frac{S}{bh}\cos\alpha = \frac{V}{bh\,tg\alpha} = \frac{H}{bh}$$

$$f_{tc} = \frac{S}{ba}\sin\alpha = \frac{V}{ba}$$

IN A BEAM WITH REINFORCEMENT:

$$f_{ct} = \frac{H}{bh(1 + np\cos\alpha_o)}$$

$$f_{tc} = \frac{V}{ba(1 + \frac{3000}{f_{tc}} p_s \cos\alpha_s)}$$

Figure 17 - Simplified stress distribution in the support segment of beam under diagonal compression.

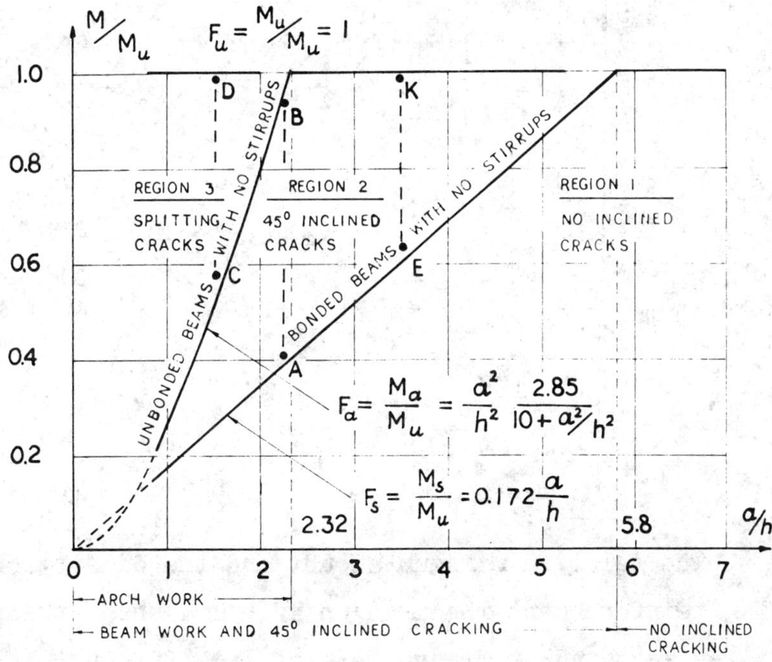

Figure 18 - Graphical illustration of the relative cracking strength limits for two-point loaded beam in relation to a/h.

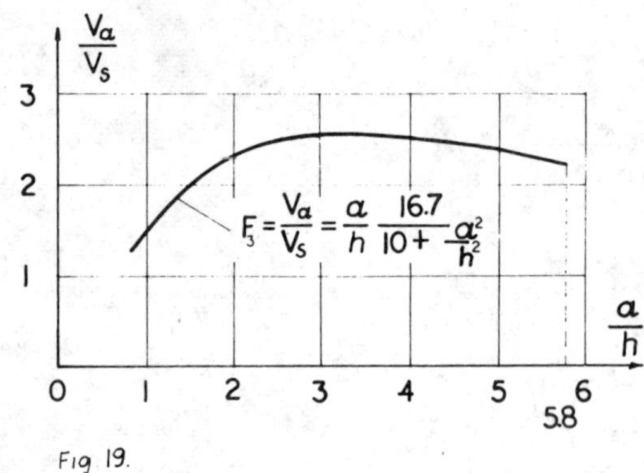

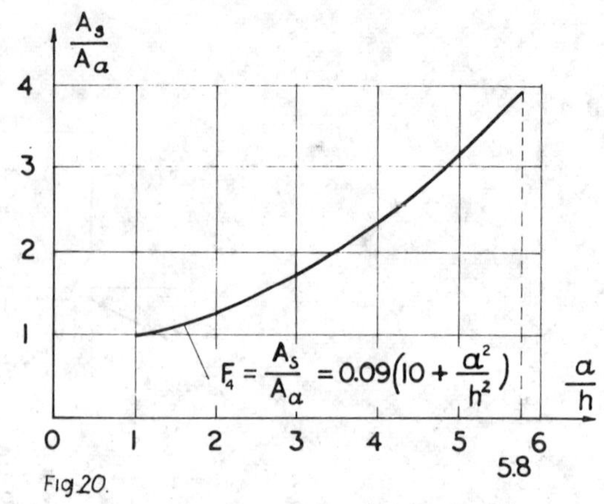

Figure 19 - Comparison of the shearing force V_a at arch work with the shearing force V_s at beam work and inclined cracking for beams without stirrups as related to a/h.

Figure 20 - Comparison of the reinforcement amount A_s required on shear theory with the amount required on arch theory A_a as related to a/h.

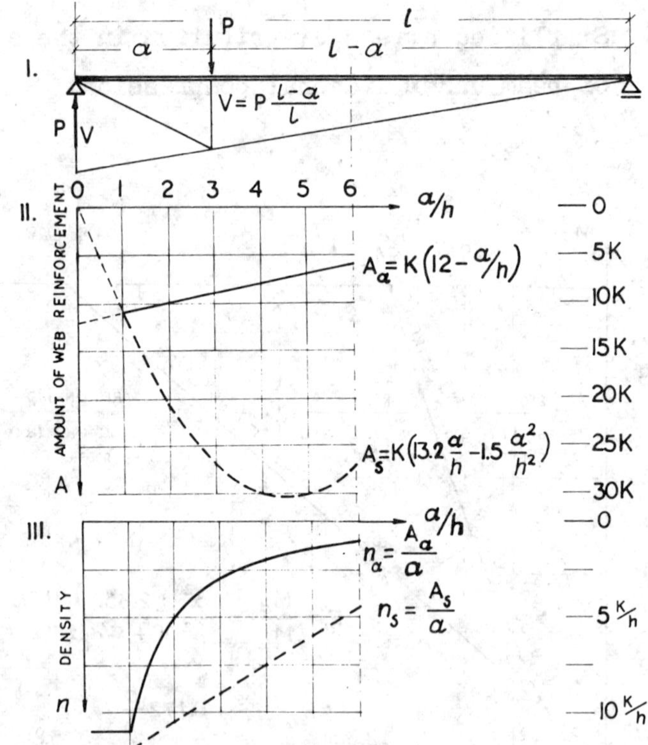

Figure 21 - The relative maximum amount and the density of web reinforcement required on arch and shear theory for a rectangular bridge beam of l = 12h; b = 1/3h; f'_c = 4000 psi; f_s = 30,000 psi loaded with a single travelling force P: i) loading scheme; ii) required amount of web reinforcement A_a on arch and A_s on shear theory, iii) required density of web reinforcement.

DISCUSSION

By G. T. SUTER

ACI member, Assistant Professor of Structural Engineering, Carleton University, Ottawa

The author's paper presents an interesting approach to defining and reaching the full flexural strength of beams containing unbonded main tensile reinforcement. While the writer is in general agreement with the author's overall description of various cracking and failure modes, he cannot support the general validity of some of the formulae which the author introduces. A critical review of these formulae follows.

The writer feels that equation (14) giving $M_u \simeq 0.35\ bh^2 f'_c$ is too approximate a relation to serve as a basis for determining the ultimate flexural strength. Its limitations can be readily verified by considering beams of identical cross-section but of varying amounts of main tensile reinforcement having also varying yield strengths [19]. Similarly, relation (15) for the author's shear cracking moment represents such a simplified approach to the complex diagonal failure problem in reinforced concrete beams, that its applicability appears doubtful to the writer. Thus it is evident that the writer also disagrees with the author's equation (16) and its graphical representation in Figure 18: while the author's relation $F_s = M_s/M_u \approx 0.172\ a/h$ essentially stipulates that the shear cracking moment is only a function of the a/h - (or a/d) ratio, extensive test data by Kani [8, 9] have shown conclusively that the diagonal tension failure or shear cracking moment is influenced also greatly by the amount of tensile reinforcement, p, and by the effective depth, d, of the member. Therefore the author's transition point between regions 1 and 2 cannot be fixed at a/h = 5.8, but must be considered a variable which is a function of p and d.

Further, the basis of derivation of the author's equation (17) is the assumption that the stresses f_{ct} and f_{tc} can be considered acting uniformly over their respective areas bh/cos α and ba/cos α (see Figure 17). Here the author neglects the regions of biaxial compression in the vicinity of the load points, although both Brock's work [20] and the analogy of a concrete cylinder under a split-tensile test [21] show that this cannot be considered a valid assumption and will lead to an overestimation of the diagonal splitting moment, M_a. This overestimation in M_a in turn leads to web reinforcement requirements when based on "traditional shear theory" which appear larger than would be required if the author had used a more realistic approach to his derivations for M_a and M_s.

The writer would also like to point out that in practice the utilization of the relatively high diagonal splitting strength of unbonded members may be very limited. Thus the author concludes himself already that for reasons of closer crack spacing, crack width control, and limitation of inclined cracking, "it will be advisable to provide some web reinforcement" and "it would be improper . . . . to advise the complete elimation of bond." Yet it should be emphasized that already by these minimum provisions of web reinforcement and bond the benefits of the arch scheme will be negated. This is so because even in an unbonded beam containing a very small amount of web reinforcement, the locations where web reinforcement and main tensile steel meet will in effect create regions of bond which will not permit the beam to function purely in the arch scheme [22]. As a result, in practice it would be uncertain just how much one could rely on arch behavior and in order to be safe such a member would still have to be reinforced for shear in the normal manner.

REFERENCES

19. Winter, G., Urquhart, L.C., O'Rourke, C.E., and Nilson, A.H., "Design of Concrete Structures", McGraw-Hill, 7th edition, pp. 49-52.

20. Brock, G., "Effect of Shear on Ultimate Strength of Rectangular Beams with Tensile Reinforcement", ACI Journal, Proceedings V.56, No. 7, January 1960, pp. 619-637.

21. Davies, J.D., and Bose, D.K., "Stress Distribution in Splitting Tests", ACI Journal, Proceedings V.65, No. 8, August 1968, pp. 662-669.

22. Kani, G.N.J., "A Rational Theory for the Function of Web Reinforcement", ACI Journal, Proceedings V.66, No. 3, March 1969.

AUTHOR'S CLOSURE

The author wishes to thank for discussion contributions. The contributions once again show that generalisation of the strength of reinforced concrete, depending on to many changing practical factors, is a very difficult problem, Nevertheless, for simplification of the design practice, we will have to continue using generalised and approximate concepts for a long time to come.

Dr. Suter gives his reservations to a few approximations adopted in the paper for discussion of cracking strength limits. It does not need to mention that the ultimate flexural strength of beam depends not only on the amount and yield strength of tensile reinforcement but also on the strength and type of concrete, compression reinforcement, ratio of a/h or ℓ/h, mode of loading and load application, etc.

The value of $M_u = 0.35\ bh^2 f'_c$ has been adopted in the paper on the basis of European experience as practical limit for flexural strength, defined by compression zone of beam, and eliminating failure of compression zone before reaching of yield or limit elongation of tensile reinforcement.

The European Concrete Committee (reference 30 p. 62) recommends for concrete of $f'_c \leq 200\ KG/cm^2$, a limit moment of $0.375\ bd^2 \sigma'^{*}_b$ what for an average beam of $h = 1.06\ d$ and $\sigma'^{*}_b = 0.85\ f'_c$ gives limit of $M_u = 0.35\ bh^2 f'_c$ as adopted in the paper.

The author finds the above definition of concrete strength limit of beam very convenient.

Given by the author relation (15) and (16) respectfully, defines particular strength limit of beam mainly the moment of 45% inclined cracking on neutral axis due to bi-directional equal compression and tension, caused by bond presence. This limit as it has been demonstrated in the paper, in most cases, does not define the diagonal failure of reinforced beam at all and certainly should not be considered as sufficient to described all cases of complex diagonal failure.

The author agrees with Dr. Suter that considering different practical factors the transition point between region 1 and 2 fixed at $a/h = 5.8$ in Figure 18 may be variable.

Available tests, however, (compare diagram of Figure 25, reference 14) show negligible variation of transition point and support well obtained by the author linear relation for $F_s = 0.172\ a/h$.

Dr. Suter quotes the latest results of Messrs Davies and Bose (21) theoretical computation of bi-directional stresses in cylinders and cubes under diagonal splitting which do not support the author's assumption of linear stress distribution in support blocks as described in Figure 17 and equation (17).

Unfortunately, valuable theoretical computations of Messrs Davies and Bose are based on linear elastic behavior of concrete and cannot be utilised for describing of final moment of diagonal splitting when concrete is subjected to plastic behavior and yield causing transformation of stresses similar to transformation in compression zone of beam at ultimate flexural failure or in tension zone at flexural cracking.

It appears that our test stage 2, on support portion of beams and comparable tests on beam which had utilised arch capacity and according diagonal splitting cracks (compare reference 14 Figures 20 and 21, reference 18 Figure 25 and evaluation of beams tested in Illinois and Table 1), verify the author's assumptions in this respect sufficiently well.

The author feels it necessary to apologise that having restricted space for this paper, he was not able to give a more detailed description of his concept. However, detailed description and discussion of test results mentioned in this paper will be available in Research Bulleting, now in print, by the Department of Experimental Research of the University of North Carolina at Raleigh.

In this bulletin is also included the definition of how much "one could rely on arch behavior" versus beam behavior. Apparently, as it have been demonstrated on specially designed beams, tested in the University of Illinois, that it is possible to provide beams only with limited amount of stirrups due to, suggested here, arch interpretation, and to treat earlier flexural and "shearing" cracking as not disqualifying intermediate work limits.

REFERENCES

[30] "Recommendations for an International Code of Practice for Reinforced Concrete", published by the American Concrete Institute and Cement and Concrete Association.

TABLE 1: Comparison of Splitting Tests on Support Segments with Relevent Beams with Diagonal Splitting Cracks

Item	Samples of Tests Stage 2	Psin α/f'_c		Beams of Stage 1		Splitting force V_a/f'_c		Ratio 4/8	REMARKS
		each kip	average kip	symbol	sigh	each kip	average kip		
1	2	3	4	5	6	7	8	9	10
1	Z_{m3}	6.35	6.35		$Z_2$02A	5.90	5.90	1.08	V_a = shear force at moment of diagonal splitting crack appearance
2	P_4	11.00	11.80		$P_1$05	12.70	11.60	1.01	
	Z_4	12.60			$P_2$05	9.30			
					$P_2$05AU	13.30			
					$P_2$02	9.80			
					$P_2$02BU	11.30			
					$P_2$02BUW	13.00			
3	Z_{m4}	12.70	12.70		$Z_1$05A	12.60	13.50	0.94	
					$Z_2$05A	13.30			
					$Z_2$05AU	16.70			
					$Z_2$02BU	11.90			
					$Z_2$02BUW	13.20			
4	B_m	P_{cr}/f'_c 19.40	19.40		$P_1$05	19.50	18.60	1.04	
					$P_2$05	15.50			
					$P_2$05BU	20.20			
					$Z_2$05BU	18.50			
					$P_1$05	18.30			
					$P_2$05	19.50			

ULTIMATE STRENGTH OF A REINFORCED CONCRETE SLAB WITH BOUNDARY FRAME SUBJECTED TO A CONCENTRATED LOAD

By YUZO AKATSUKA and HIROSHI SEKI

SYNOPSIS

This paper describes the test results of six reinforced concrete slabs with boundary frames and discussed the ultimate strength of reinforced concrete slabs. Slabs were 1.4^{m} square and 10^{cm} thick with an effective depth of 7.0^{cm}. They were subjected to a centrally located, concentrated load and were supported on the four corners. Variables were (1) rigidity of boundary frame and (2) ratio of reinforcement. From the types of cracking lines observed, the formula of calculation of ultimate flexural strength based on yield line theory was suggested by thinking of rotational capacity of plastic hinge and torsional rotation of boundary frames. Shear failure of slab was considered to be shear diagonal tension failure. It was found that ultimate strength of shear largely depended on the dowel action of reinforcement.

Keywords: concrete slabs; diagonal tension; failure; flexural strength; hinges (structural); reinforced concrete; research; rotation; shear properties; strength; structural analysis; yield line method.

ACI member YUZO AKATSUKA is chief, Materials Laboratory, Port and Harbour Research Institute, Ministry of Transport, Nagase, Yokosuka, Japan. In 1963 he obtained an MS degree in civil engineering from the University of Tokyo. Dr. Akatsuka is the author of two books on prepacked concrete and has had several other papers on reinforced concrete published. In May 1966 he was awarded the 1965 JSCE Yoshida Prize by the Japan Society of Civil Engineers for basic studies on quality control of prepacked concrete.

HIROSHI SEKI is junior research engineer, Port and Harbour Research Institute, Ministry of Transport, Nagase, Yokosuka, Japan. In 1965 he received a BS degree in civil engineering from Waseda University. Mr. Seki is the author of several papers dealing with the properties of admixtures, high strength reinforcing deformed bars, and impact of reinforced concrete. Currently, he is a member of the Japan Society of Civil Engineers and the Japan National Council on Concrete.

1. Introduction

The ultimate strength of a reinforced concrete slab largely depends on the type of slab failure, i.e. either flexural or shear failure. The yield line theory[1], which gives the ultimate flexural strength based on the assumed yield line pattern according to the shape of the slab and the manner in which lines of crackings are formed in the final condition, is considered applicable to their reinforced concrete slabs under clear support with such small amount of reinforcement that the strength of a slab is determined by yielding of the reinforcing bars. However, there is a limit to the range in which the theory can be applied as it is accompanied with difficulties in obtaining ultimate strength of slabs under more complicated conditions of loading, ratio of span and thickness, and peripheral restraint conditions.

The ultimate strength of a slab under concentrated load is often determined by shear failure load smaller than flexural failure load calculated by the yield line theory. It has been reported that flexural failure occurs on a simple slab and shear failure on a continuous slab[2]. The type of failure is thought to be influenced by various factors, such as, properties of materials, shape of slab, loading, peripheral restraint conditions, ratio of shearing force to bending moment, and so on. At present, even the mechanism of shear failure of a reinforced concrete beam remains unsolved. Theoretical analysis of shear strength of a reinforced concrete slab might be more difficult.

Formulus for estimating shear strength of rectangular slabs simply supported have been proposed by Elstner and Hognestad,[3] Moe,[4] Yitzhaki,[5] and Long and Bond,[6] based on numerous tests of a models. But such problems as stress distribution around loading point, development of diagonal tension cracks, and the relations between bending moment and shear failure have been left unsolved, and equations satisfying all conditions are not yet to be obtained.

This report describes the results of experiments of slabs with boundary frames. These slabs are imagined to be elastically supported on beams with larger rigidity than the slabs, with the four corners supported by beams on reinforced concrete pile columns or steel pile columns. The experiments consist of two series. In the first series, the rigidity of cross section of boundary frames was varied in three different ways. In the second series, the ratio of main reinforcement had three different values. In order to apply the yield line theory to slabs with complicated support conditions, rotational capacity at plastic hinge of slabs and torsional rotation of boundary frames were taken into consideration. It is of importance to accurately grasp the phenomenon of shear failure, but many difficulties are met in observation and measurement of points of occurrence and growth of diagonal tension cracks. These phenomena have been studied along with past test result and, in addition, the effects of dowel action have been examined and it has been found from the results of experiments that shear strength depends largely on dowel action.

2. Method of Test

2.1 Specimens

Reinforced concrete slabs 10^{cm} thick and 1.4^{m} square with boundary frames as shown in Fig.1 were used. The principal dimensions are shown in Table 1. The two series described below were tested.

Series I: The objective was to reveal effects of boundary frames on the elastoplastic behavior of reinforced concrete slabs. The ratio of reinforcement was maintained constant at about 1% as were the widths of the cross sections of the boundary frames at 40^{cm} , but the heights were varied at 30, 45 and 60^{cm}.

SeriesII: The aim was to find the influence of the ratio of reinforcement upon ultimate strength, especially upon shear failure. For this purpose, three values of the ratio of reinforcement at 1.13%, 1.30%, and 2.30% were tested, while the widths of cross section and heights were maintained constant at 40^{cm} and 45^{cm} respectively.

2.2 Test Method

Slabs were supported at four corners at a distance of 2^{m}. Load was applied at the center of the slab with a steel disc of 19^{cm} diameter. Strain was measured with wire strain gauges while deflexion and lateral displacement of boundary frame were measured with dial gauges. The width of cracks, cracking load and failure load were measured and crack lines were recorded. The loads were increased every 1 to 2 tons up to failure. The manner in which the tests were conducted is shown in Fig.2.

3. Failure of Reinforced Concrete Slab under Concentrated Load

3.1 Elastoplastic Behavior of Slab

The relationships between load at the ceter of slab and deflexion, and between the load and strain(reinforcement) are illustrated in Fig.3 and Fig.4. These results indicate that the relationship between load and deformation can be divided into 4 phases, (1) until cracking is produced at the reverse surface of the slab, (2) until cracking is produced at the center span of the boundary frame, (3) until the reinforcement at the center of slab reaches yield point, and (4) when the plastic range is spread over the entire surface of the slab. Slab 4CS-1 broke down after it reached the 4th phase. Failures of Slabs 4CS-2 and 4CS-5 took place at Phase 3, and failures of Slabs 4CS-3, 4CS-4 and 4CS-6 at Phase2. Fig.5 shows the measured and calculated data of deflexions at the centers of Slabs 4CS-1, 4CS-2 and 4CS-3. The calculated data were based on elastic theory for a slab simply supported along four edges and for a slab fixed along four edges.

3.2 Observation of Failure

Slab 4CS-1 broke down from shear failure of concrete as the loading disc sunk into the slab. After crack lines were fully developed, the reinforcement at the center of slab reached yield point and the plasticized was spread rapidly over the whole slab. Failure of slabs 4CS-2~4CS-6 suddenly took place from shear without crack lines beeing fully developed. The phenomenon occurred too rapidly for prediction of failure. Strain of reinforcement near concentrated load at failure was below $+1000\times10^{-6}$ cm/cm ~ $+1500\times10^{-6}$ cm/cm for Slabs 4CS-2~4CS-6. Compressive strain of concrete was -1500×10^{-6} cm/cm~-2000×10^{-6} cm/cm for every slab, and the stress distribution at the cross section of the compression zone of concrete was estimated to be linear. Initial cracking loads and failure loads are given in Table 2. Failure load was less than the calculated value of flexural failure, except in the case of Slab 4CS-1.

3.3 Application of Yield Line Theory

Crack line patterns at failure are shown in Fig.6. Although it is impossible to accurately discuss the applicability of the yield line theory on Slabs 4CS-2 ~ 4CS-6 because these slabs broke down before the mechanism was formed, ultimate flexural stregth of slabs with boundary frames can be estimated assuming plastic hinge as follows;

Negative plastic hinge is formed at the foot of a haunch where resistance moment is the smallest. The negative crack line, as shown in Fig.6, is closer to being circular rather than square as assumed by Johansen[1] and others. The slab reaches collapse when the members fulfill mechanism conditions and deformation proceeds **indefinitely.** Reinforced concrete on the other hand has a limit to its rotational capacity. It is necessary to take into consideration the torsional rotation of beams in order to evaluate effects of stiffness on the ultimate flexural strength. According to Ban[7], the rotational capacity of plastic hinge of rectangular beams with single reinforcement is as given bellow.

$$\varphi = \frac{1}{\left(1-\frac{\beta_s p}{2}\right)}\left\{\beta_s p+\frac{4(1-\beta_s p)(1-\frac{\beta_s p}{2})}{\beta_s p}\right\}\left(\frac{0.056}{\sqrt{\sigma_c}}-0.00014\sqrt{\sigma_c}\right)$$

where, $\beta_s = \sigma_y/\sigma_c$

σ_c : compressive strength of concrete

σ_y : yield point of reinforcing bar

p : ratio of reinforcement

Assuming that the distribution of shear force transfered to the boundary frame is triangular, elastic twisting rotation, j, at the center span is

$$j=\frac{11\ell p}{24f_1 G b^2}$$

where, ℓ : span length

p : total load carried by boundary frame

G : modulus of rigidity

b : width of boundary frame

f_1 : constant dependent on h/b

The calculated values of φ and j, and their measured values at load close to failure are shown in Table 3. These data indicate that rotation of boundary frames are so small that they are negligible compared with those of plastic hinge. Therefore, tested slabs can be considered to bear negative resistance moment, m, around the slab at flexural failure.

Positive crack lines are affected by generation of plastic hinge at the mid-span of boundary frames. The ultimate load for rectangular and circular yield line patterns as assumed in Fig.7 are obtained by the following;

$$P=16m/(1-r/a)$$
$$P=4\pi am/(a-c) \qquad (1)$$

When the ratio of diameter of loading disc to length of a side of the slab is below 0.3, P_c is smaller than P_r. The ultimate load is given by Eq.(1) independently of the number of radial crack lines for circular yield line patterns. Considering these facts, the flexural failure load of slabs in these tests can be estimated by the Eq.(1). The results are given in Table 2.

4. Ultimate Shear Strength of Reinforced Concrete Slab

4.1 Shear Failure of Slab

Shear failure of reinforced concrete slabs can be classified as follows:

punching shear failure

shear compression failure

diagonal tension failure

shear tension failure

Elastic and plastic analyses are required to clarify the mechanism of shear failure. Numerous explanations of this mechanism have been offered but the problem is as yet unsolved. Thus the conditions of such failure and their interdependence are not yet understood. At present, it would appear proper to study individual failure phenomena under various experimental conditions, to pinpoint decisive factors of failure and to obtain ultimate shear strength experimentally. Study of punching shear failure is not necessarily for concrete slabs in general as it is observable only under special experimental conditions.

In these experiments, the conical crushed part of the slab was removed after failure and the broken surface was observed. As shown in Fig.8(a), the failure line runs downward from the periphery of the loading plate at a constant angle and it is deflected near reinforcement with the angle becoming markedly obtuse. No tendencies of the concentrated load from the loading disc being remarkably shared by the compressed part of concrete was observed in these experiments. Diagonal tension failure seems to have occurred independently of bending crack.

Moe[(4)] carried out experiments on slabs with column stubs at the centers and supported simply at their sides. He observed development of crack and shear failure lines through a hole provided near column stub, and found that in many cases bending cracks were transformed into inclined cracks, but in several slabs noticed sudden generation of diagonal tension cracks independetly of bending cracks, which is similar to the results obtained here. The failure angle of Slab 4CS-5 was 27° and that of Slab H-10 in Moe's experiment was 28°. This suggests that the types of the failures in these experiments were almost identical. It can be concluded that the failure lines in our experiments were caused by diagonal tension failure and the concentrated load was resisted by shear of concrete and dowel action of the reinforcement. The calculated and experimental values of shear failure are given in Table 2. The following experimental formula proposed by Moe was used for the calculation.

$$P_{shear} = \frac{15\left(1-0.075\,\frac{r'}{d}\right) bd\sqrt{f_c'}}{1+5.25\,\frac{bd\sqrt{f_c'}}{P_{flex}}}$$

where, P_{shear} : load at shear failure (lb)

r' : length of a side of loading plate (assumed $r' = \pi r/4$)

d : effective depth of slab (in.)

b : circumference of loading plate (in.)

f_c' : compressive strenth of concrete (psi)

P_{flex} : flexural failure load obtained from the yield line theory (lb)

The difference between the two values is about 10 % for Slabs 4CS-4 and 4CS-6, and 20 % for Slabs 4CS-1, 4CS-2 and 4CS-5. The experimental value for 4CS-3 was 1.5 times larger than the calculated value. The above is assumed to be because the experimental formula was derived from a slab with a column stub, slabs were simply supported along four edges, ultimate flexural load, P_{flex}, obtained on the assumption that elastic range would be reached, was involved in order to examine the effect of bending though the slab did not actually reach the elastic range.

4.2 Shear Strength and Ratio of Reinforcement of Slab

The ultimate strength of Slabs 4CS-4 and 4CS-6 which are similar in their thickness and other conditions and different only in the ratio of reinforcement (p=2.30% and p=1.13%) are compared in Table 2. They are 15.0^t and 15.6^t. Since compression reinforcement almost completely does not share any shearing force of the slab(3), a difference of ratio of reinforcement as small as 1~2 % for equal nominal diameters may have no significant effect on the shear strength.

Tensile reinforcement is considered to share a part of shearing force by dowel action. As shown in Fig.8(b), shearing force, S_s, on the reinforcement is shared by concrete tensile resistance at the region, l_o, where concrete reaches in the state of plasticity. Putting the angle of diagonal tension cracking at about 30° accoding to 4.1 above, then

$$S_s = \sigma_t \pi l_o (r + 2\sqrt{3}d + l_o) \qquad (2)$$

where, S_s : share of shearing force due to dowel action

r : diameter of loading disc

d : effective depth of slab

l_o : range of dowel action

Test results showed that the length, l_o, was about 5^{cm}. Putting this value in Eq.(2), $S_s = 18.9^t$ is obtained. This is slightly over the measured value of failure load.

From the above, it is obvious that the shearing force is shared by shear resistance of the concrete itself to diagonal tension and by dowel action of the reinforcement, and that the latter effect is considerably great. But, the ratio of shearing force shared, the l_o region of dowel action, the deformation capabilities at final state of shear and tension, shear resistance zone of diagonal tension cracks, and stress distribution are left unsolved. No significant relation was found between the ratio of reinforcement and shear strength. But this does not mean that the ratio of reinforcement has no effect. In view of the dowel action it is also conceivable that diameter of reinforcing bar and bar spacing may significantly affect shear strength.

5. Conclusions

This experiment was carried out in order to obtain data for ultimate strength design of reinforced concrete slabs under large concentrated loads. Slabs had boundary frames along the edges and were supported at four points. Each slab was 1.4 m square, and the thickness was 10 cm. Variables were the rigidity of cross section of boundary frames and ratio of reinforcement. Within the scope of the experiments, the following may be stated:

(1) For a reinforced concrete slab under concentrated load, shear failure is dominant over flexural failure in many cases, and this tendency is higher as the rigidity of the boundary frame becomes higher.

(2) A 1~2 % difference in reinforcement ratio for equal nominal diameters of reinforcing bars has no significant effect on ultimate shear failure.

(3) Shear failure of the slab was caused by diagonal tension. Dowel action of the reinforcement seems to have had remarkable effects on ultimate stregth.

(4) The ultimate strength can be reasonably obtained on the assumption that the negative yield line patterns of a slab with boundary frame are circular.

Many problems are however left unsolved. For correct evaluation of ultimate strength of slabs, careful examination of the following problems should be required.

(1) Clarification of factors affecting the location and load at which diagonal tension cracks of slabs under concentrated load are formed and study of a method to obtain them correctly.

(2) Analysis of the effect of rigidity of a boundary frame upon the elastoplastic behavior of a slab, and study of a method for quantitative evaluation.

(3) Investigation of the ratio of load shared between diagonal tension crack and dowel action of reinforcement at failure.

(4) Finding of the relationship between flexural failure and shear failure of a slab.

(5) Clarification of the effects of membrane stress on the ultimate strength of a slab.

References

(1) Johansen, K.W., "Yield-line theory", Cement and Concrete Association, 181pp., 1962

(2) Okada, Kiyoshi, and Koyanagi, Wataru, "On the Flexural Strength of Structural Lightweight Aggregate Concrete Slabs", Materials, Vol.15, No.157, pp.716-723, 1966.10 (in Japanese)

(3) Elstner, Richart, C., and Hognestad, Eivind, "Shearing Strength of Reinforced Concrete Slabs", Journal of the A.C.I., Proc. Vol.53, pp.29-58, July, 1956

(4) Moe, Johanes, "Shearing Strength of Reinforced Concrete Slabs and Footings under Concentrated Loads", Portland Cement Association, Research and Development Laboratories, Development Department, Bulletin D47, 130pp., April, 1961

(5) Yitzhaki, David, "Punching Strength of Reinforced Concrete Slabs", Journal of the A.C.I., Proc. Vol.63, pp.527-542, May, 1966

(6) Long, Ardian, Ernest, and Bond, Douglas, "Punching Failure of Reinforced Concrete Slabs", Journal of the I.C.E., pp.109-135, May, 1967

(7) Ban, Shizuo, and Yamada, Minoru, "Rotational Capacity of Plastic Hinge at Reinforced Concrete", Transactions of the Architectural Institute of Japan, Vol,58, pp.42-48,1952.2 (in Japanese)

Tab. I Dimensions of slabs and properties of materials employed

Series	Slab number	Dimension (cm)		Steel ratio (%)		Concrete (kg/cm²)			Deformed bar (kg/mm²)		Ultimate moment
		Effective depth	Boundary frame width height	Tensile reinforce-ment	Compre-ssive reinforce-ment	σ_{28}	σ_{test}	E test ($\times 10^5$)	Yield point	Tensile strength	(kg·cm/cm)
I	4CS-1	7.4	40 × 30	0.96	—	310	341	2.3	41.6	58.1	2030
	4CS-2	7.8	40 × 45	0.91	—	317	364	2.5	41.6	58.1	2160
	4CS-3	7.1	40 × 60	1.00	—	291	345	2.6	41.6	58.1	1940
II	4CS-4	6.2	40 × 45	2.30	—	239	250	2.1	37.9	57.3	2660
	4CS-5	7.3	40 × 45	1.30	—	239	247	2.1	37.9	57.3	2310
	4CS-6	6.3	40 × 45	1.13	0.57	239	243	2.1	38.6	55.6	1550

Tab. 2 Initial cracking and failure loads

Series	Slab number	Cracking load (ton)			Measur-ed failure load	Ultimate flexural load ③		Ultimate shearing load	
		① Calcu-lated	② Calcu-lated	Measur-ed	P_{meas} (ton)	P_{flex} (ton)	$\frac{P_{meas}}{P_{flex}}$ (%)	P_{shear} ④ (ton)	$\frac{P_{meas}}{P_{shear}}$ (%)
I	4CS-1	4.6	5.8	6.0	17.0	29.5	58	19.8	86
	4CS-2	3.8	4.8	7.0	28.0	31.4	90	21.7	129
	4CS-3	4.4	5.5	6.0	28.0	28.2	99	19.0	147
II	4CS-4	2.7	3.4	4.0	15.0	38.7	39	15.8	95
	4CS-5	3.3	4.2	7.0	21.0	33.6	63	18.0	117
	4CS-6	2.6	3.3	6.0	15.6	22.5	69	14.1	111

① Calculated load for rectangular slabs simply supported along four edges

② Calculated load for rectangular slabs fixed along four edges

③ Calculated based on yield linc theory

④ Calculated based on Hoe's equation

Tab. 3 Rotational capacity at plastic hinge of slab and torsional rotation of boundary frame

Slab number	Rotational capacity* φ (radian)	Torsional rotation		$\frac{j_2}{\varphi}$ (%)
		Calculated j_1 (radian)	Measured j_2 (radian)	
4CS-1	0.0136	0.00012	0.004	31
4CS-2	0.0093	0.00010	0.000	0
4CS-3	0.0131	0.00005	0.000	0
4CS-5	0.0225	0.00011	0.000	0

* Rotational capacity at the negative plastic hinge of reinforced concrete slab

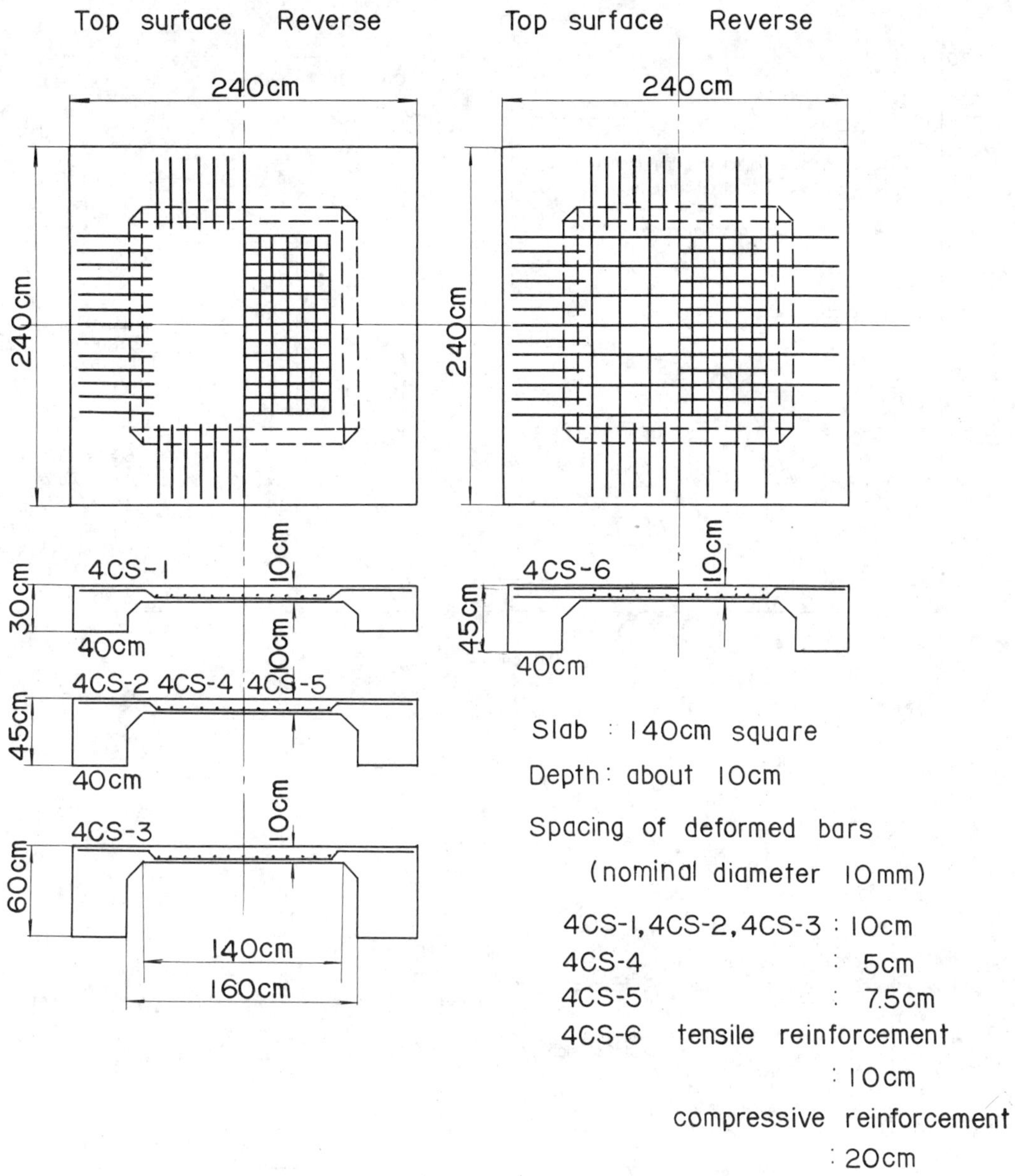

Top surface Reverse Top surface Reverse

240cm 240cm

240cm 240cm

4CS-1 10cm 30cm 40cm

4CS-6 10cm 45cm 40cm

4CS-2 4CS-4 4CS-5 10cm 45cm 40cm

4CS-3 10cm 60cm

140cm

160cm

Slab : 140cm square

Depth : about 10cm

Spacing of deformed bars

(nominal diameter 10mm)

4CS-1, 4CS-2, 4CS-3 : 10cm

4CS-4 : 5cm

4CS-5 : 7.5cm

4CS-6 tensile reinforcement : 10cm

compressive reinforcement : 20cm

Fig. 1 Test slabs

Fig. 2 Testing Arrangement

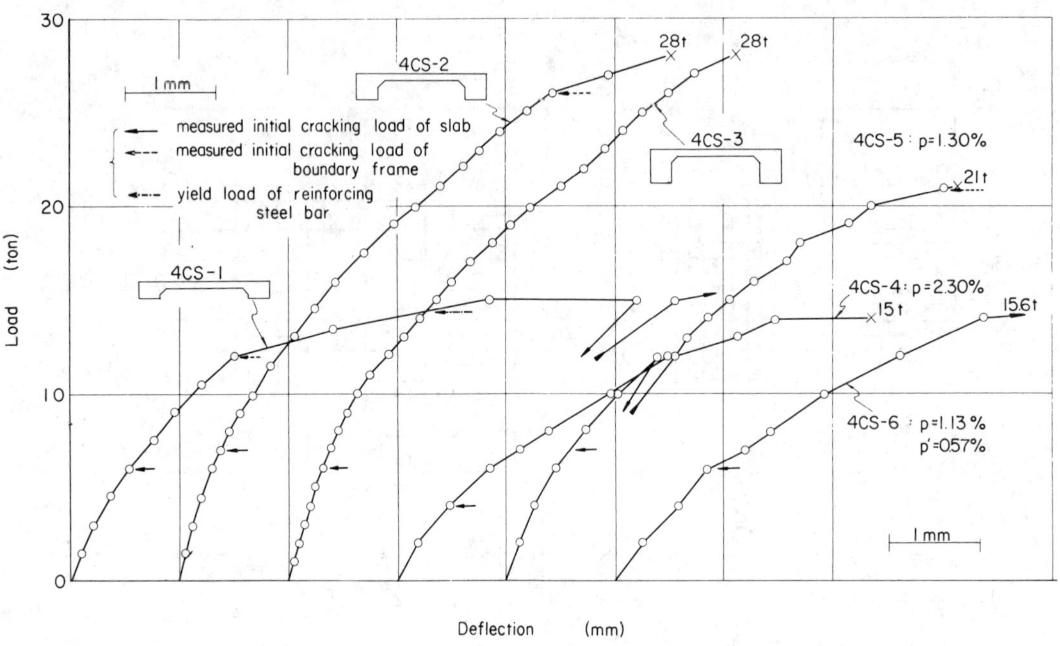

Fig. 3 Load ~ deflection curves at the center of slabs

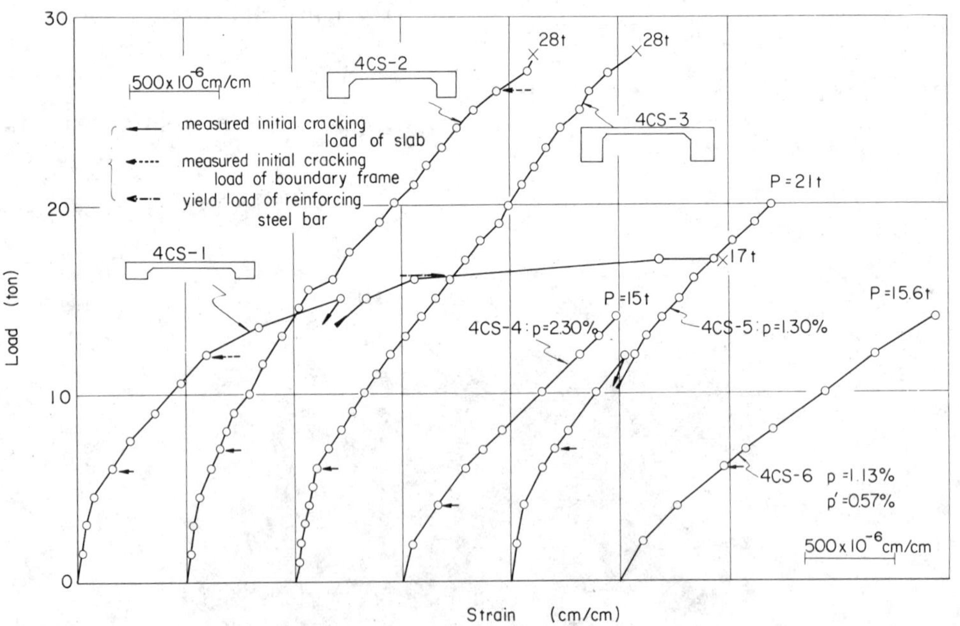

Fig. 4 Load ~ strain (reinforcing steel bar) curves at the center of slabs

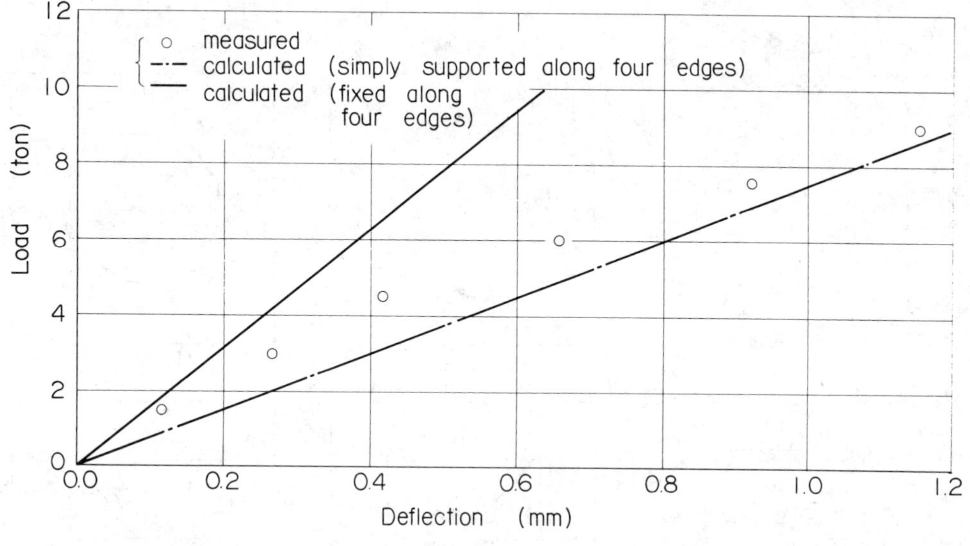

(a) 4CS - 1

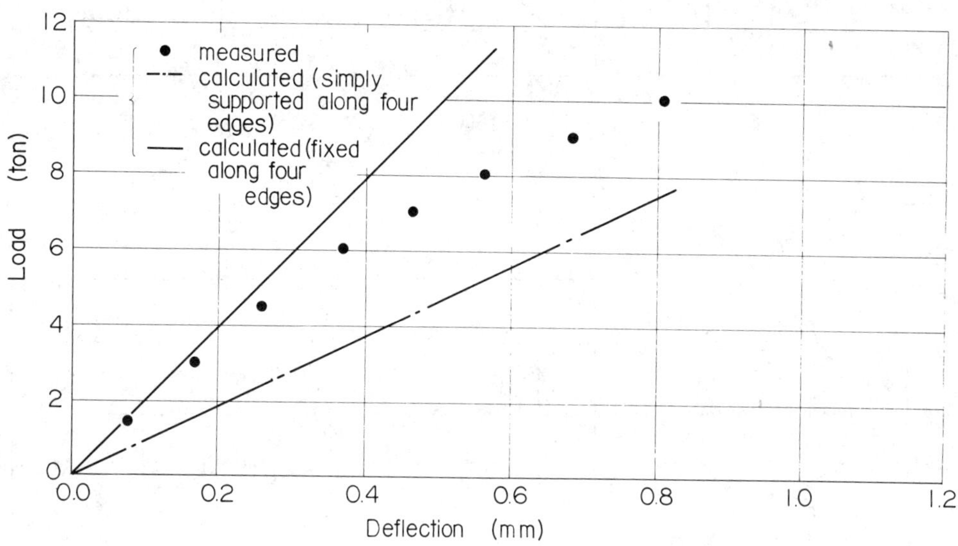

(b) 4CS-2

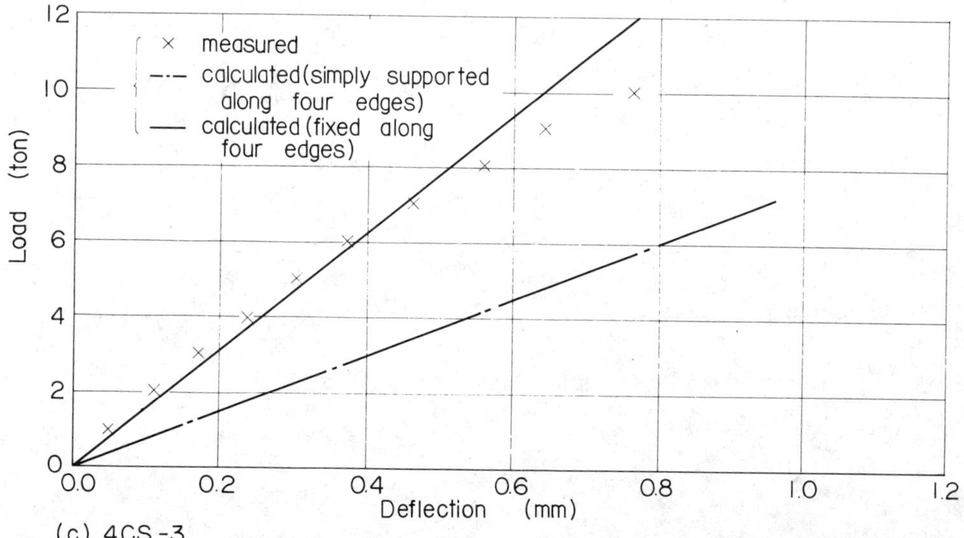

(c) 4CS -3

Fig. 5 Measured and calculated deflections at the center of slabs

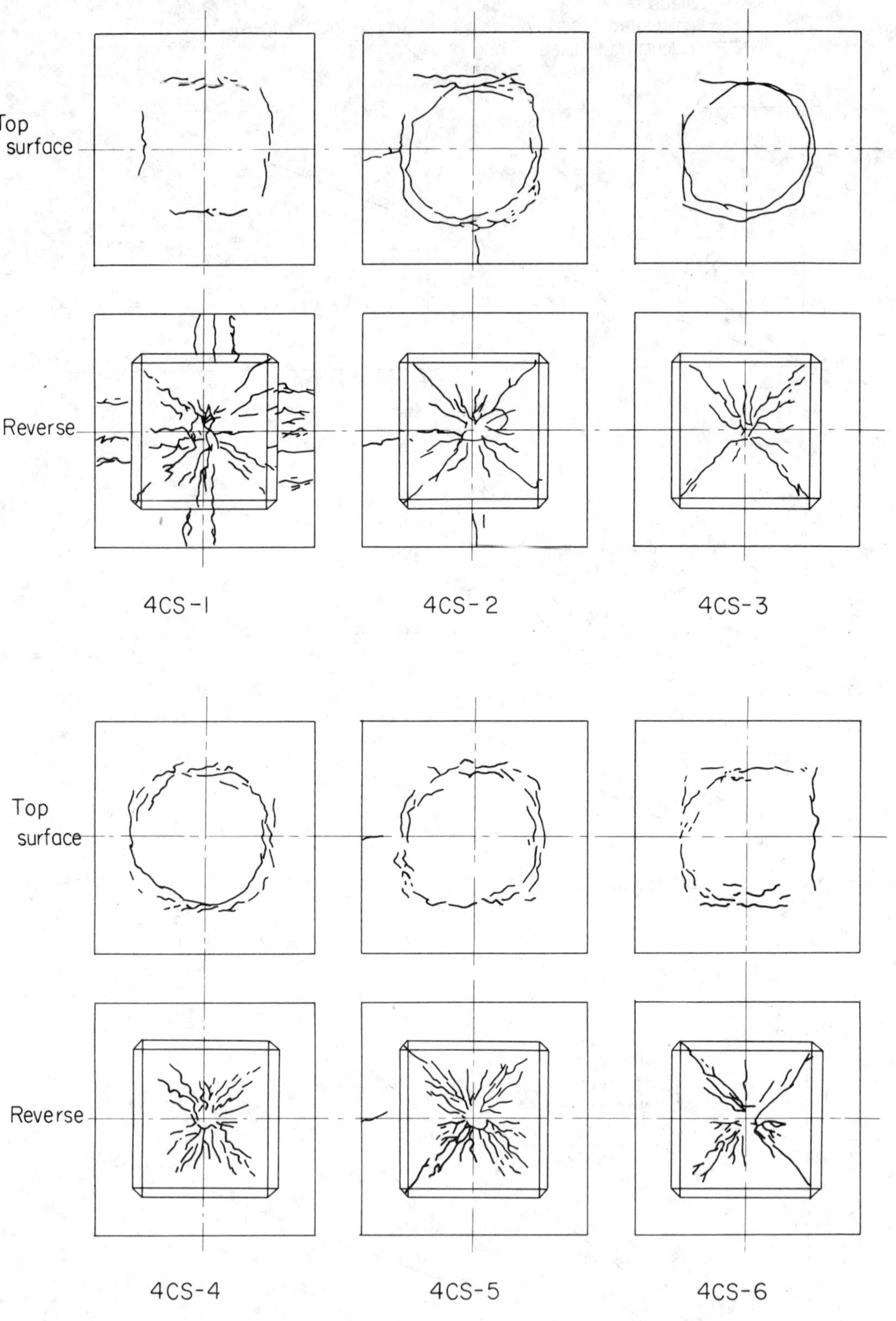

Fig.6 Crack formation of slabs at failure

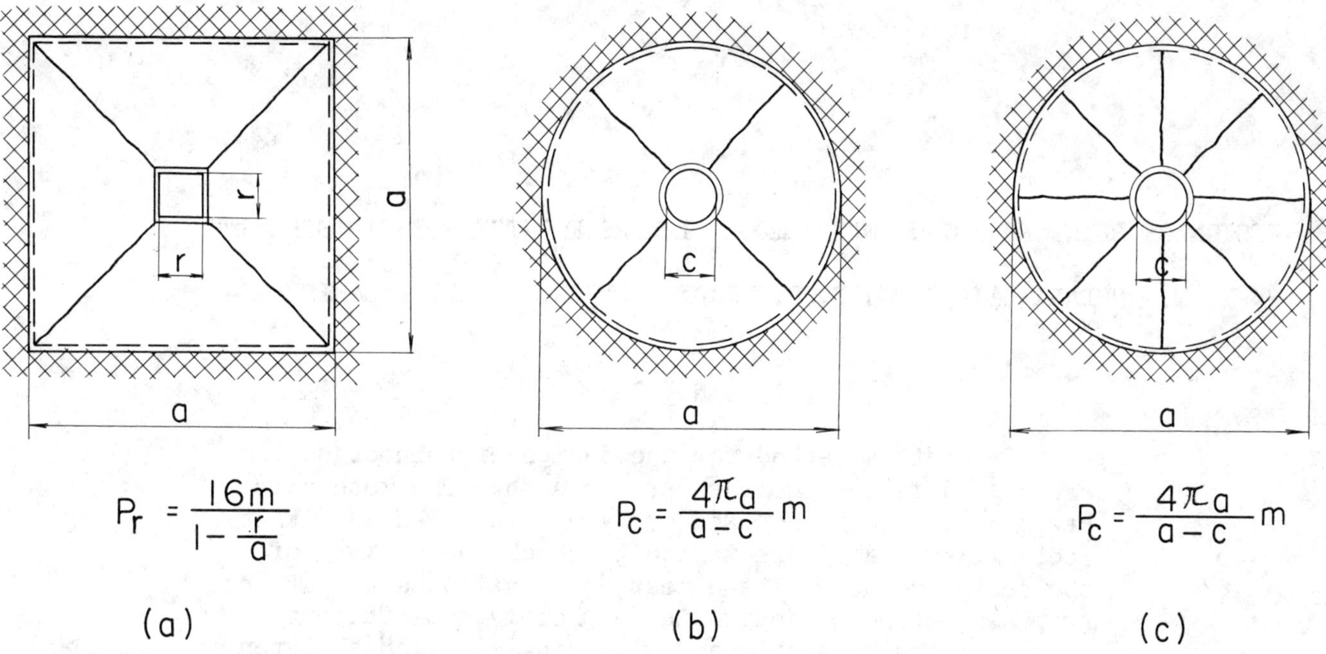

Fig. 7 Yield-line patterns

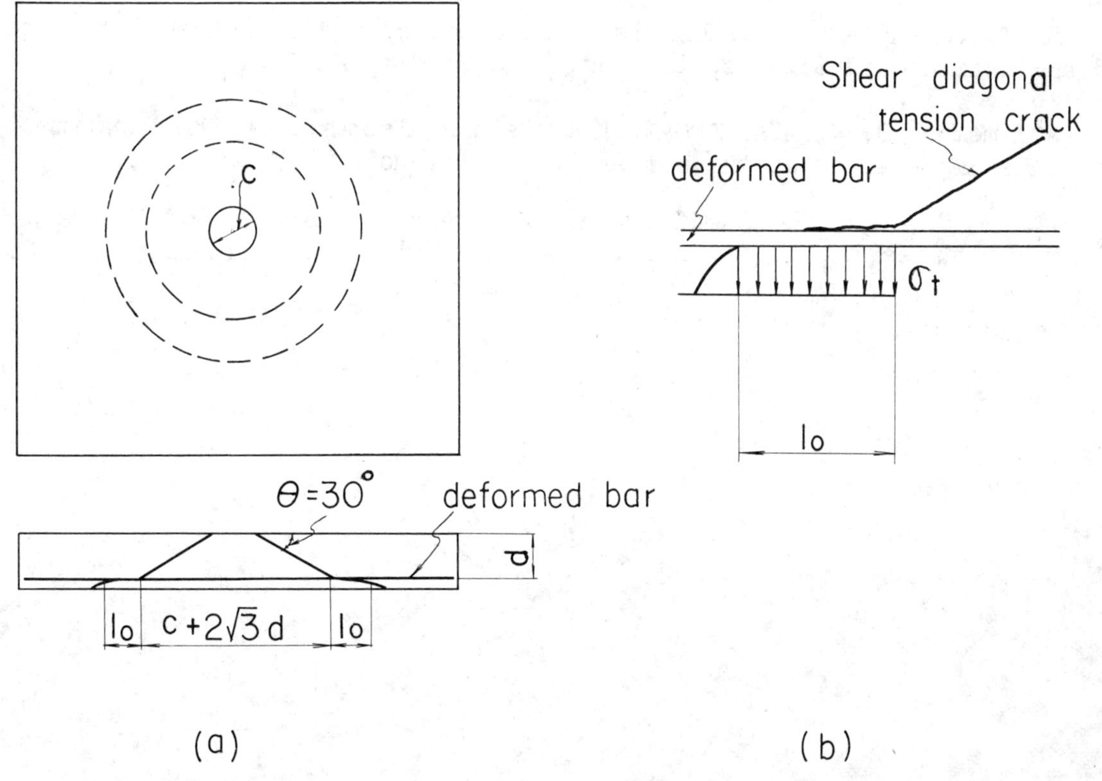

Fig. 8 Type of shear failure and dawel action

DESIGN OF REINFORCED CONCRETE BRIDGE GIRDERS FOR THEIR SHEAR STRENGTH

By K. T. SUNDARA RAJA IYENGAR, B. VIJAYA RANGAN, and R. PALANISWAMY

SYNOPSIS

Presents a method for the design of reinforced concrete girders for their shear strength. The method is based on a theory proposed by Iyengar and Rangan. Fifty rectangular beams were tested to check the working of the design method. These test results indicate that the proposed method of design is completely satisfactory except in the case of beams with single-legged skeleton stirrups.

Keywords: beams (supports); bending; bridges (structures); girders; reinforced concrete; research; shear properties; stirrups; structural design.

K. T. SUNDARA RAJA IYENGAR is a professor of civil engineering at the Indian Institute of Science, located in Bangalore, India.

ACI member B. VIJAYA RANGAN is a visiting lecturer in the Department of Materials Engineering at the University of Illinois.

ACI member R. PALANISWAMY is the CSIR Research Scholar of the Department of Civil Engineering at the Indian Institute of Science in Bangalore, India.

The problems relating to the shear strength of reinforced concrete members have received considerable attention from many investigators throughout the globe. A large number of investigation containing over one thousand beam tests have been reported in the literature. Based on these research data, in 1960, the ACI-ASCE Committee[1] 426 on shear and diagonal tension suggested the following equations for the design of reinforced concrete beams for their shear strength:

$$\frac{V_c}{bd} = [1.9\sqrt{f'_c} + 2500p\,\frac{Vd}{M}] \leq 3.5\sqrt{f'_c} \tag{1a}$$

$$V_s = A_w\, f_{yw}\,\frac{d}{s} \tag{1b}$$

and $$V_u = V_c + V_s \tag{1c}$$

These equations, later on, have been incorporated in the ACI Building Code 318-1963 with the inclusion of a capacity reduction factor, ϕ taken equal to 0.85. Eqs. (1) are based on the concept of nominal shear stress and the shear reinforcements are to be designed to take up the shear force along with the concrete so as to avoid shear failure and thus ensuring only flexure failure in an indirect way.

The research conducted in the recent years has indicated the limitations of Eqs. (1). A closer examination of Eq. (1a) would reveal that the term V_c/bd mostly depends on f'_c and that the term $2500p\,\frac{Vd}{M}$ is not a true representation of the influence of these parameters on the shear strength of beams. This has been pointed out by Kani in one of his papers[2]. Owing to these reasons, the necessity for a new design method becomes obvious. The prime purpose of this paper is an attempt to provide reasonably conservative design method which could account for the true influence of various parameters on the shear strength of beams.

USEFUL STRENGTH OF BEAMS IN COMBINED BENDING AND SHEAR:

Recently Sundara Raja Iyengar and Vijaya Rangan[3] proposed a rational theory for the shear strength of reinforced concrete beams. The theory has been based on two distinct mechanisms of failure of beams applicable for low and high Moment/Shear ratios. The resulting equations of the theory are of the following form which are very similar to Kani's[2] except for the value of α_{TR}.

$$\frac{M_u}{M_{f\ell}} = \frac{(2/k)}{\alpha + \sqrt{\alpha^2 + 2}} \quad \text{for} \quad \alpha \leq \alpha_m$$

$$= \frac{\alpha}{\alpha_{TR}} \quad \text{for} \quad \alpha \geq \alpha_m \qquad (2)$$

(Notations are listed in the Appendix)

The predictions of the theory have been compared with over one thousand test results available in the literature. From the comparison, a good agreement between the computed and test results have been found and the error made by the theory was normally on the conservative side in most of the cases[4].

The theoretical equations directly give the reduction in the flexural capacity of beams in combined bending and shear. According to the theory, maximum reduction in the flexural capacity of beams occurs at $\alpha = \alpha_m$.

On either side of α_m, the reduction in the flexural capacity of beams decreases uniformly and becomes zero at $\alpha = 1.0$ and at $\alpha = \alpha_{TR}$. Even though the beams with $\alpha < \alpha_m$ have enough reserve strength such that their flexural capacity increases with the decrease in the value of α, this increase in strength can only be obtained at the cost of excessive cracking of beams. So from practical view point it may be necessary to ignore this reserve strength of beams. Hence for all values of α less than α_m, the reduction in the flexural capacity of the beams can be taken as the one obtained at $\alpha = \alpha_m$. This will result in somewhat conservative results.

In Fig. 1, the above suggested method of estimating the useful shear strength of beams is compared with the ACI Code Equation (Eq. 1a) for a group of beams[2] whose results are also given in the same figure. From comparison it is evident that the ACI Code formula is very conservative in the case of low values of α.

DESIGN RECOMMENDATIONS:

Based on the useful strength beams, the following procedure is suggested for the design of beams under combined bending and shear:

(1) The beam is first designed for the ultimate bending moment calculated at different sections using the recommendations given in the codes for the design of beams under pure bending.

(2) From the properties of the beam, the quantity α_{TR} is calculated using the relation

$$\alpha_{TR} = 21\ p\ f_y/f'_c \quad (3)$$

(3) For sections with $M/Vd \geq \alpha_m$, the shear-moment capacity of the beam is increased to the flexural capacity by providing shear reinforcement in the form of vertical stirrups using the relation:

$$\frac{M}{Vd} = \frac{\alpha_{TR}}{\phi}\left(1 - \frac{A_w f_{yw} d}{sV}\right) \quad \ldots (4)$$

where α_{TR} is calculated from (2) and ϕ is the capacity reduction factor which can be taken equal to 0.85.

(4) For sections with $M/Vd \leq \alpha_m$, the M/Vd ratio for such sections is taken as equal to α_m and the shear reinforcement is calculated using the equation given (3) where α_m is given by

$$\alpha_m = \frac{(2/k)\ \alpha_{TR}}{\sqrt{\frac{4}{k}\alpha_{TR} + 2}} \quad \ldots (5)$$

and $k = 0.75$.

(5) If M/Vd is greater than or equal to α_{TR}/ϕ theoretically no shear reinforcement is required.

(6) For beams with I or T sections, if the position of neutral axis determined during the flexure analysis falls within the flange then the whole flange width is considered to be effictive in resisting the

shear force; otherwise the effective width of the beam can be taken as equal to the width of rib or web.

Limitations:

(i) If $M/Vd < 1.0$, the recommendations given above are not applicable.

(ii) The spacing of vertical stirrups is not to be more than ϕ times the effective depth of the beam where $\phi = 0.85$.

DESIGN EXAMPLE:

In order to illustrate the application of the design recommendations, the shear reinforcement requirements for a main beam of a reinforced concrete bridge will be determined. The beam has to be designed for the ultimate loads given in Table 1. The flexural analysis of the beam yielded the physical properties given in Table 1.

For the section $x/L = 0.21$,

$$\alpha_{TR} = \frac{21\ p\ f_y}{f'_c} = \frac{21 \times 0.0135 \times 50}{3} = 4.72$$

$$\alpha_m = \frac{(2/k)\ \alpha_{TR}}{\sqrt{\frac{4}{k}\ \alpha_{TR} + 2}} = 2.42$$

Since $\alpha > \alpha_m$, as per the recommendations,

$$2.48 = \frac{4.72}{0.85}\left(1 - \frac{A_w f_{yw} d}{sV}\right)$$

$$\text{or} \quad \frac{A_w}{bs} = 0.225\%$$

Similarly the shear reinforcement requirement can be calculated for other sections. For the same girder, the shear reinforcement requirements were calculated using the design formula given in ACI Building Code (318-63)[5]. The results are compared in Fig. 2. From Fig. 2 it can be seen that the ACI equation is over-conservative for the sections with low M/Vd ratios.

EXPERIMENTAL INVESTIGATION:

In order to know the actual working of the design recommendations, series of tests were conducted. The experimental work consisted of testing of fifty rectangular beams reinforced with different amounts of transverse stirrups. Both closed two-legged stirrups and skeleton single legged stirrups were used. Most of the beams were designed to fail in flexure using the recommendations given in this paper. Ordinary Portland cement and the aggregates obtained from local sources were used to yield a concrete having an average cylinder strength of 3500 psi. The reinforcing rods were plain round bars having a yield strength ranging between 45 to 50 ksi. The beams were moist cured and they were tested in an Universal testing machine with simply supported ends. One or two concentrated loads placed symmetrically on the beam caused the loading for the beams. Prisms of 6 in. x 12 in. size were used to know the compressive strength of concrete for each group of beams.

A summary of test results is given in Table 2. Table 2 also includes the values of $M_u/M_{f\ell}$ calculated using the design equation (excluding the coefficient ϕ) for the purpose of comparison. From the comparison of results the following conclusions can be drawn:

(i) Beams designed to fail in flexure, $(M_u/M_{f\ell})_{calc.} = 1.0$:

(a) All the beams with two-legged closed stirrups (except for Beam WE5) developed their full flexural capacity and failed in flexure.

(b) All the beams with single-legged skeleton stirrups failed in shear with or without developing their full flexural capacity. The maximum deviation was noticed in the case of Beam WE3. Even though Beam WE3 contained enough amount of A_w/bs to fail in flexure, it failed in shear developing only 67 percent of its flexural capacity.

(ii) Beams designed to fail in shear, $(M_u/M_{f\ell})_{calc} < 1.0$:

(a) Beams with two legged closed stirrups seem to offer conservative results, especially for the case of beams with $\alpha = 2$. This is due to the effect of neglecting the reserve strength possessed by the beams with the low values of α.

(b) In the case of beams with single-legged skeleton stirrups, the calculated values over-estimate the test results.

From these observations, it can be concluded that the single-legged skeleton stirrups are not efficient as shear reinforcements. This suggests that for the design method given here, only two-legged stirrups should be used.

CONCLUDING REMARKS:

Based on the results of a rational theory, a new method has been suggested ror the design of beams under combined bending and shear. Fifty rectangular beams with different amounts of stirrups were tested to know the working of the design method. Test results indicate that the working of the design method is completely satisfactory except in the case of beams with single-legged skeleton stirrups. The suggested method of design has been compared with the recommendations of ACI Building Code (ACI 318-63) and it has been found that the ACI equation is over-conservative for low values of α .

REFERENCES:

1. ACI-ASCE Committee 426(320), "Shear and Diagonal Tension," ACI Journal, Proceedings V. 59, March 1962, pp. 353-396.

2. Kani, G. N. J., "Basic Facts Concerning Shear Failure," ACI Journal, Proceedings V. 63, June 1966, pp. 675-690.

3. Sundara Raja Iyengar, K. T. and Vijaya Rangan, B., "A New Theory for the Shear Strength of Reinforced Concrete Beams," The Indian Concrete Journal, V. 41, March 1967, pp. 102-109.

4. Sundara Raja Iyengar, K. T., and Vijaya Rangan, B., "Shear Strength of Reinforced Concrete Beams," Annual Report, Civil and Hydraulic Engineering Department, Indian Institute of Science, Bangalore, 1966.

5. ACI Committee 318, "Building Code Requirements for Reinforced Concrete (ACI 318-63)," American Concrete Institute, Detroit, 1963, 144 pp.

NOTATION:

A_w - area of cross section of shear reinforcement.

b,d - breadth and effective depth of a cross section, respectively.

f'_c - compressive strength of concrete as given by a prism or a cylinder.

f_y, f_{yw} - yield strengths of longitudinal tension steel and shear reinforcing steel, respectively.

k - biaxial coefficient (Ref. 3), taken equal to 0.75.

M - bending moment at any section.

$M_u/M_{f\ell}$ - relative beam strength.

p - tensile reinforcement ratio.

s - spacing of stirrups.

V - shear force at any section.

V_c - shear carried by concrete.

V_s = shear carried by stirrups.

$V_u = V_c + V_s$

$\alpha = M/Vd$

$$\alpha_m = \frac{(2/k)\,\alpha_{TR}}{\sqrt{\frac{4}{k}\alpha_{TR} + 2}}$$

$$\alpha_{TR} = 21p\, f_y/f'_c$$

$$\alpha'_{TR} = \alpha_{TR}\left(1 - \frac{A_w f_{yw} d}{sV}\right)$$

ϕ = capacity reduction factor, equal to 0.85.

TABLE 1: Design of a Bridge Girder: Summary of Results

X/L	M_u (in-kips)	V_u (kips)	p %	α	$(A_w/bs)\%$ Authors	$(A_w/bs)\%$ ACI318-63
0.0825	17600	320	0.650	1.00	0.189	0.331
0.105	20400	313	0.750	1.19	0.206	0.320
0.210	36600	269	1.350	2.48	0.225	0.245
0.315	47800	211	1.700	4.12	0.131	0.150*
0.420	55000	169	2.000	5.92	0.072	0.150*
0.500	57000	110	2.100	9.42	Nominal	0.150*

Note: b x d = 24 in. x 55 in.; f'_c = 3 ksi; $f_y = f_{yw}$ = 50 ksi. The girder is a simply supported one and x is the distance of a section from the support.

*Minimum requirement

TABLE 2: Summary of Test Results

Beam Mark	bxd (in x in)	f'_c ksi	p %	$\frac{A_w}{bs}$	α	M_u (in-kips)	α'_{TR}	$M_u/Mf\ell$ Test	$M_u/Mf\ell$ Calc**	Ratio: Test/Calc.	Mode of Failure
(1)	(2)	(3)	(4)	(5)	(6)	(7)	(8)	(9)	(10)	(11)	(12)
WA1	4x6.75	3.40	2.18	0.612	2.22	191	2.22	1.00	1.00	1.00	F
2	4x6.75	3.40	2.18	0.448	2.66	213	3.10	1.00	0.93	1.08	F
*3	4x6.75	3.65	2.18	0.364	3.11	195	2.79	0.98	1.00	0.98	S
*4	4x6.75	3.65	2.18	0.276	3.55	226	3.60	1.13	0.99	1.14	S
WB1	4x6.75	3.40	2.18	0.612	2.22	191	2.22	1.00	1.00	1.00	F
2	4x6.75	3.40	2.18	0.448	2.66	196	2.75	1.00	1.00	1.00	F
*3	4x6.75	3.65	2.18	0.364	3.11	164	2.19	0.82	1.00	0.82	B
*4	4x6.75	3.65	2.18	0.276	3.55	188	3.12	0.94	1.00	0.94	S
WC1	4x6.75	4.07	2.18	0.612	2.22	222	2.30	1.00	1.00	1.00	F
2	4x6.75	4.07	2.18	0.448	2.66	215	2.62	1.00	1.00	1.00	F
*3	4x6.75	3.46	2.18	0.364	3.11	190	2.85	0.95	1.00	0.95	S
*4	4x6.75	3.46	2.18	0.276	3.55	188	3.29	0.94	1.00	0.94	S
WD1	4x6.75	3.82	2.18	0.426	2.66	184	2.46	1.00	1.00	1.00	F-S
2	4x6.75	3.82	2.18	0.445	2.51	181	2.46	1.00	1.00	1.00	F
A1	5x6.75	3.23	1.74	0.400	3.00	206	1.74	1.00	1.00	1.00	F
2	5x6.75	3.23	1.74	0.400	2.00	218	2.97	1.00	0.85	1.18	F
3	5x6.75	3.23	1.74	0.400	2.00	218	2.97	1.00	0.85	1.18	F
4	5x6.75	3.23	1.74	0.400	2.50	214	2.38	1.00	1.00	1.00	F
5	5x6.75	4.07	1.74	0.327	3.00	217	1.97	1.00	1.00	1.00	F
*6	5x6.75	4.07	1.74	0.245	3.00	185	2.22	0.86	1.00	0.86	S
*7	5x6.75	4.49	1.74	0.178	3.00	180	2.45	0.84	1.00	0.84	S
*8	5x6.75	4.49	1.74	0.151	3.00	194	2.71	0.91	1.00	0.91	S
B1	5x6.75	3.19	2.32	0.435	2.00	283	4.50	1.00	0.67	1.49	F-S
2	5x6.75	3.19	2.32	0.435	2.50	272	3.82	1.00	0.78	1.28	F
3	5x6.75	3.19	2.32	0.435	2.00	280	4.40	1.00	0.68	1.47	F-S
4	5x6.75	3.19	2.32	0.435	2.50	280	3.80	1.00	0.78	1.28	F
5	5x6.75	4.07	2.32	0.435	3.00	264	3.00	1.00	1.00	1.00	F
6	5x6.75	4.07	2.32	0.356	3.00	268	2.94	1.00	1.00	1.00	F
*7	5x6.75	4.49	2.32	0.280	3.00	225	2.81	0.85	1.00	0.85	S
*8	5x6.75	4.49	2.32	0.218	3.00	240	3.38	0.90	0.89	1.01	S-A
C1	5x6.35	4.02	3.09	0.490	2.00	267	4.40	0.86	0.69	1.24	S
2	5x6.35	4.02	3.09	0.490	2.50	298	4.00	1.00	0.76	1.31	F
3	5x6.35	4.02	3.09	0.490	2.00	300	4.50	0.97	0.67	1.44	S
4	5x6.35	4.02	3.09	0.490	2.50	317	4.15	1.00	0.74	1.35	F
5	5x6.35	2.84	3.09	0.490	3.00	247	2.64	1.00	1.00	1.00	F
6	5x6.35	2.84	3.09	0.490	3.00	269	4.20	1.00	1.00	1.00	F-S
7	5x6.35	2.84	3.09	0.400	3.00	258	5.00	1.00	1.00	1.00	F
8	5x6.35	2.84	3.09	0.302	3.00	266	6.30	1.00	1.00	1.00	F
*B9	5x6.75	4.49	2.32	0.178	3.00	247	3.68	0.88	0.82	1.07	S
*10	5x6.75	4.49	2.32	0.163	3.00	217	3.60	0.77	0.84	0.92	S
*11	5x6.75	4.49	2.32	0.151	3.00	218	3.75	0.78	0.80	0.97	S
WE0	4x6.75	3.90	2.91	0.000	3.55	137	7.05	0.53	0.50	1.06	S
*1	4x6.75	3.90	2.91	0.204	3.55	167	4.24	0.65	0.84	0.78	S
*2	4x6.75	4.40	2.91	0.258	3.55	181	3.80	0.70	0.93	0.76	S
*3	4x6.75	4.12	2.91	0.306	3.55	173	3.12	0.67	1.00	0.67	S
*4	4x6.75	3.92	2.91	0.350	3.55	207	3.18	0.80	1.00	0.80	S
5	4x6.75	3.92	2.91	0.392	3.55	236	3.24	0.91	1.00	0.91	S
6	4x6.75	4.21	2.91	0.445	3.55	281	3.42	1.00	1.00	1.00	F
7	4x6.75	4.21	2.91	0.515	3.55	277	2.82	1.00	1.00	1.00	F
8	4x6.75	3.98	2.91	0.576	3.55	250	1.87	1.00	1.00	1.00	F

Note: (i) $\alpha'_{TR} = \alpha_{TR}\left(1 - \frac{A_w f_{yw} d}{sV}\right)$

(ii) f_y = 45 ksi; f_{yw} = 50 ksi; f'_c - 6 in x 12 in prism strength.

(iii) F-Flexure; S-Shear; B-Dond, A-Anchorage.

(iv) *Beams with single-legged skeleton stirrups.

**Coefficient ϕ was not included in the calculated values.

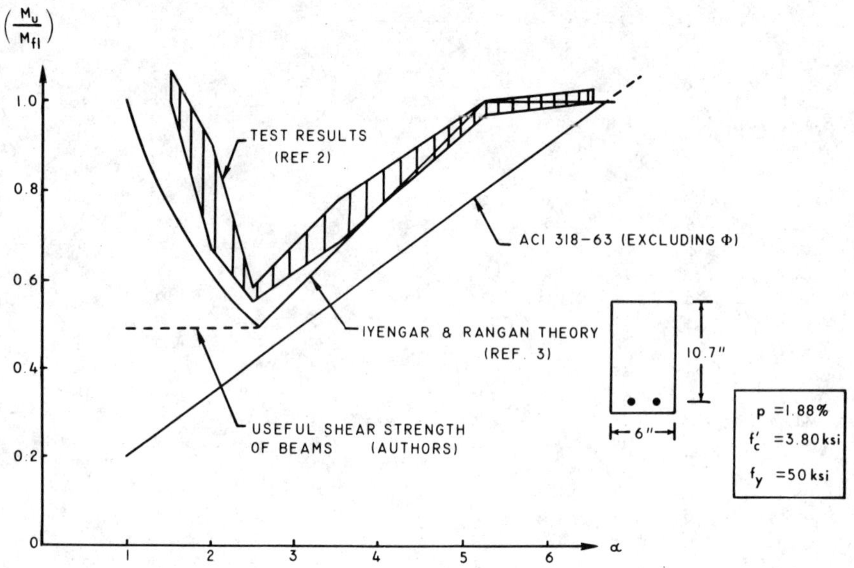

Fig. 1 - Comparison of Results: Useful shear strength of reinforced concrete beams.

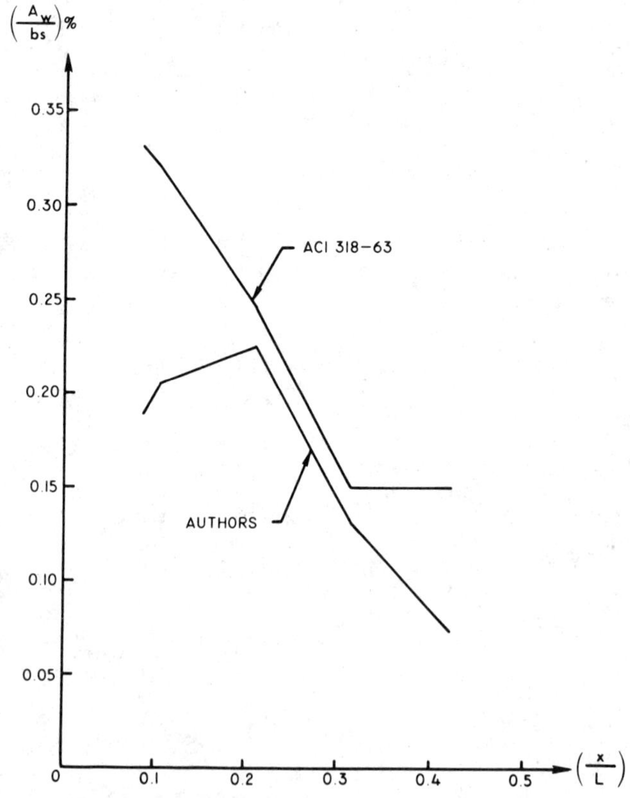

Fig. 2 - Design of Shear Reinforcement for a Bridge Girder: Comparison of Results.

DISCUSSION

By M. A. SHEIKH, H. A. R. DE PAIVA, and A. M. NEVILLE

Chief Engineer (Civil), West Pakistan Industrial Development Corporation, Karachi, Pakistan.

Professor of Civil Engineering, The University of Calgary, Calgary, Canada.

Department of Civil Engineering, University of Leeds, Leeds, England.

The authors' desire to derive a simple rational design formula is commendable, but the simplicity of their expressions is achieved at the expense of ignoring some real factors and the rationality is marred by somewhat arbitrary assumptions.

As the authors' design procedure is based on their earlier work,[1] some of the comments to follow will refer to those earlier derivations as well as to their use in the present paper. For instance, the expression for α_{TR} was obtained on the assumption that the ratio of compressive to tensile strength of concrete is 9. This ratio is known not to be constant,[2] and the assumption to the contrary is inadmissible. As a consequence, Eq. (3) cannot be accepted as being valid outside a narrow range of concrete strength.

There are further flaws in that equation. It suggests that $_{TR}$ is directly proportional to the percentage of longitudinal steel and inversely proportional to the compressive strength of concrete. Let us examine these two propositions in turn.

The first one requires that, for a given quality of concrete and of steel, the value of $_{TR}$ should increase in the same proportion as the steel area ratio increases. While some increase has been observed, it is smaller than would be required by Eq. (3), as shown by the following values derived from Kani's tests.[3] Here column 3 gives the actual value of $\alpha_{TR} = (\frac{a}{d})_{TR}$ (Eq. 11 in ref. 1), and column 4 gives the value that would satisfy Eq. (3), taking the value of α_{TR} at the lowest steel area ratio as a basis.

Steel area ratio, p	Compressive strength of concrete, f'_c psi	Actual α_{TR}	α_{TR} for Eq. (3)
0.0080	3800	3.2	3.2
0.0188	3800	5.2	7.5
0.0280	3800	6.5	11.2
0.0080	5000	2.9	2.9
0.0188	5000	5.0	6.8
0.0280	5000	6.5	10.2

This discrepancy throws considerable doubt on the validity of the authors' design equations but the situation is even more disquieting when we try to verify the proportionality of α_{TR} and f'_c in Eq. (3). We can use the same test results of Kani's.[3] As before, column 4 gives the value of α_{TR} that would satisfy Eq. (3), taking the value at the higher concrete strength as a basis.

Steel area ratio, p	Compressive strength of concrete, f'_c	Actual α_{TR}	α_{TR} for Eq. (3)
0.0280	5000	6.5	6.5
0.0280	3800	6.5	8.5
0.0188	5000	5.0	5.0
0.0188	3800	5.2	6.6
0.0080	5000	2.9	2.9
0.0080	3800	3.2	3.8

It seems thus that, contrary to Eq. (3), the influence of the compressive strength of concrete on the behavior of a beam in shear is very small. This was, indeed, suggested some time ago.[4]

Let us now turn to the influence of the a/d ratio on the behavior in shear. The authors do not take the effect of vertical compressive stress into proper account but only include a constant k in Eq. (5). A more rational approach has been recently suggested.[5]

The mechanism of failure of short beams, or of beams with loads near the supports, is quite different from that in beams with more usual a/d ratios:[6,7] it is sensitive to the method of load transfer to the beam and is also affected by the development of arch action. The effects of vertical stresses when load is applied through the beam surface have been established for some time,[8] and it is known that beams loaded through framed-in members fail at loads near the inclined cracking load.[9] The authors disregard the existence of inclined cracks[10] when estimating the strength of beams with low a/d ratios and, although there can be a large reserve of strength above inclined cracking, it cannot be relied upon. Moreover, the loss of serviceability on the development of inclined cracks should not be ignored. Thus the ACI Code is not as wasteful as the authors believe, and the design on the basis of the inclined cracking load should not be too hastily abandoned.

We should also note that the arch action is not developed in continuous beams,[11] so that the authors' recommendation that for $\alpha < \alpha_m$, the reduction in shear strength be taken as equal to the reduction at $\alpha = \alpha_m$ is valid for simply supported beams only. If the recommendation is applied to continuous beams it is not on the conservative side.

Eq. (5) can be further criticized on the grounds that it predicts the minimum relative beam strength at an a/d ratio between 1.8 and 3.7, while in fact the usual range is between 2.3 and 2.8. Had an average value of a/d = 2.5 been assumed, much of the work on the strength of beams with a small value of could have been avoided without adversely affecting the authors' approach.

Of more general interest is the question of design for uniformly distributed loading. The authors make no suggestions on this; guidance on the critical value of would be of interest.

A further criticism concerns the authors' disregard of the dowel action and the aggregate interlock which often accompanies it. The dowel action is far from negligible,[12] and a detailed analysis of the problem is available.[13] Indeed, the authors' test data can be interpreted to mean that dowel action is of importance; all their beams with single-legged skeleton stirrups failed in shear, and such beams do not develop dowel action. The necessity for support of the main reinforcement by stirrups was stressed in an earlier paper.[6] The same paper emphasized the importance of limited spacing of stirrups - a point mentioned by the authors as "Limitation (ii)", but seemingly unrelated to their analysis.

We may note in passing that by adjusting their strength of concrete and yield of steel to common values the authors report a flexural moment which is not the actual moment of the beam under test but only a comparative flexural strength. This procedure may not be justified in developing what is claimed to be a rational theory.

There is no doubt that the authors' approach is simple and easy to use in a design office. However, because they ignored real factors which may be important in some cases, their formulae are dangerous if used for beam proportions and load disposition departing from the usual.

REFERENCES

1. Iyengar Sundara Raja, K. T., and Rangan Vijaya, B., "A new Theory for the shear strength of Reinforced Concrete Beams," The Indian Concrete Journal, V. 41, March 1967, pp. 102-109.

2. Neville, A. M., "Properties of Concrete", John Wiley (New York) and Sir I. Pitman and Sons, (London) Ltd., 1963, pp. 532.

3. Kani, G. N. J., "Basic Facts Concerning Shear Failure", ACI Journal, Proceedings V.63, June 1966, pp. 675-690.

4. Neville, A. M., and Lord, E., "Some Factors in the Shear Strength of Reinforced Concrete Beams", The Structural Engineer", Vol. 38, No. 7, July 1960, pp. 213-223.

5. Sheikh, M. A., de Paiva, H. A. R., and Neville, A. M., "Calculation of flexure-shear strength of Prestressed Concrete Beams", PCI Journal, V. 13, No. 1, Feb. 1968, pp. 69-85.

6. Neville, A. M., and Taub, J., "Resistance to Shear of Reinforced Concrete Beams", ACI Journal, Proc. V. 57: No. 2, Aug. 1960, pp. 193-220; No. 3, Sept. 1960, pp. 315-336; No. 4, Oct. 1960, pp. 443-464; No. 5, Nov. 1960, pp. 517-532; and No. 6, Dec. 1960, pp. 715-730.

7. Bresler, B., and MacGregor, J. G., "Review of Concrete Beams failing in Shear", Journal of the Structural Division, ASCE, V. 93, No. ST 1, Feb. 1967, pp. 343-372.

8. Ferguson, P. M., "Some Implications of Recent Diagonal Tension Tests", ACI Journal, Proc. V. 53, No. 2, Aug. 1956, pp. 157-172.

9. Taub, J., and Neville, A. M., "Shear Strength of Reinforced Concrete Beams Loaded Through Framed-in Cross-Beams", International Association for Bridge and Structural Engineering, Sixth Congress, Stockholm, 1960, Preliminary Publication, pp. 77-84.

10. de Paiva, H. A. R., and Siess, C. P., "Strength and Behavior of Deep Beams in Shear", Journal of the Structural Division, ASCE, V. 91, No. ST5, Oct. 1965, pp. 19-41.

11. Sheikh, M. A., de Paiva, H. A. R., and Neville, A. M., "Strength and Behavior of Two-Span Continuous Pretensioned Concrete Beams", ACI Journal, Proc. V. 65, No. 1, Jan. 1968, pp. 37-48.

12. Krefeld, W. J., and Thurston, C. W., "Contribution of Longitudinal Steel to Shear Resistance of Reinforced Concrete Beams", ACI Journal, Proc. V.63, No. 3, March 1966, pp. 325-344.

13. Armishaw, J. W., Bunni, N. G. and Neville, A. M., "Distribution of Shear in Rectangular Beams" (in two parts), Concrete and Constructional Engineering (London), V. 41, No. 4, April 1966, pp. 119-130; No. 5, May 1966, pp. 157-161, 183.

AUTHOR'S CLOSURE

The authors are thankful to the writers for their valuable elaborate discussion. At first, it is heartening to note that they seem to approve the "relative strength concept" introduced by late Professor Kani in recent years.

After the submission of their paper in 1968, the authors had many second thoughts about their formulae. Even though the formula $\alpha_{TR} = 21\ p\ f_y/f'_c$ predicted over one thousand test results within an error of $\pm$ 15 percent for the usual ranges of the variables, it was not accurate for the ranges departing from the usual. Also, as pointed out by the writers as well as by the authors (see Figs. 5-9 of Reference A), the relative strength, in general, does not vary in the same proportion as p or f'_c . The reasons for these discrepancies are due to: (i) adoption of a constant value of 9 for f'_c/f'_t

and (ii) using a constant value of 0.833 for shear-moment lever-arm coefficient. Since these numbers are average values for the usual ranges of the variables, the predictions of the formula were sufficiently accurate for such cases.

Recently, one of the authors (Rangan) had overcome these discrepancies and derived a more accurate formula for diagonal cracking strength of reinforced concrete beams. Besides equilibrium equations, a simple strain-compatability is also used in the derivation of the formula. Detailed derivations and comparison of theoretical results with numerous test results are presented in a forthcoming publication(B). The final equations of this analysis are given below:

Relative Diagonal Cracking Strength, $M_{cr}/M_{fl} = \alpha/\alpha_{TR}$ .... (a)

where $\alpha = M/Vd$ (or a/d).

Two alternatives are given for the calculation of α_{TR} :

α_{TR} by 'accurate analysis' :

$$\alpha_{TR} = p\, f_y \,/\, 18\, K\sqrt{f'_c} \qquad \text{....... (b)}$$

where $K = (\sqrt{1 + 2\lambda}-1)/\lambda$ and $\lambda = 2.5\, f'_c/p$(ksi)

α_{TR} by 'approximate analysis' :

$$\alpha_{TR} = f_y \sqrt{p}\ /12\text{(ksi)} \qquad \text{....... (c)}$$

In formulae (b) and (c), α_{TR} , K and λ are dimensionless quantities derived from the analysis, p is tension steel area ratio in percent, f_y is yield stress of tension steel in ksi, f'_c is compressive strength of concrete in ksi, and $\sqrt{f'_c}$ is also in ksi.

Using Equations (b) and (c), α_{TR} values were recalculated and the results are compared with those derived from Kani's tests in Table A. (For beams with distributed load, $M/V = \ell/4$ as suggested by Kani). These results are encouraging.

Based on these new results, a design method has been formulated(C). In the modified version, Eq. 5 is abandoned and the cross-sectional area of vertical stirrups, A_v is given by

$$A_v = \frac{Vs}{f_{yw}d}\left(1-\frac{\alpha}{\alpha_{TR}}\right) \qquad \text{....... (d)}$$

where α/α_{TR} is the relative diagonal cracking strength as given by Eq. (b) or (c), V is the ultimate shear force at a section, s is the spacing of stirrups and f_{yw} is the yield stress of stirrup-wire ($\alpha = M/Vd > 1$).

Equation (d) is simple and easy to use in a design office and the parameter α_{TR} , as given by Eq. (b) or (c), takes into account the real factors influencing the diagonal cracking strength of reinforced concrete beams. The authors once again thank the writers for expending their time and energy in preparing an interesting discussion.

References

A. Iyengar, K.T.S., Rangan, B.V., and Swamy, R.P. "Some Factors Affecting the Shear Strength of Reinforced Concrete Beams", The Indian Concrete Journal, V.42, December 1968, pp. 499-505.

B. Rangan, B.V. "Diagonal Cracking Strength of Reinforced Concrete Beams", under publication.

C. Iyengar, K.T.S., and Rangan, B.V. "Recommendations to I.S. Code for the Design of Reinforced Concrete Members Under Torsion, Bending and Shear", under publication.

Table A. Comparison of Theoretical and Test Results.

p percent	f'_c ksi	α_{TR} from Kani's tests	Eq. (b)	Eq. (c)
2.80	5.0	6.5	7.2	7.0
	3.8	6.5	7.7	
2.05 (distributed load)	5.6	5.5	5.8	6.0
1.88	5.0	5.0	5.7	5.7
	3.8	5.2	5.8	
	2.5	5.6	6.4	
0.80	5.0	2.9	3.3	3.7
	3.8	3.2	3.4	
	2.5	-	3.6	
0.50	5.0	-	2.5	2.9
	3.8	2.5	2.6	
	2.5	-	2.7	

TORSIONAL STRENGTH OF RECTANGULAR CONCRETE BEAMS IN BRIDGE DESIGN

By MAHMOUD A. HELMY

SYNOPSIS

A rational analysis of the strength of rectangular concrete beams transversally reinforced with stirrups, subjected to torsion in combination with shear and bending is proposed. Pure torsion and cases of combined bending and torsion are considered special cases of the general analysis. Application of the analysis to design is discussed and a numerical design example is fully worked out.

Keywords: beams (supports); bending; bridges (structures); cracking (fracturing); girders; rectangular beams; reinforced concrete; shear properties; stirrups; structural analysis; structural design; torsion.

ACI member MAHMOUD A. HELMY is a lecturer in structural engineering at Alexandria University in the United Arab Republic. Dr. Helmy authored and co-authored several papers on torsion and on the strength of concrete under combined stresses.

INTRODUCTION

In bridge design the presence of torsion is inevitable. Torsional moments are induced due to unsymmetrical loading on the deck. Spandrel beams should be designed to allow for torsional moments. In practice, torsion is always accompanied with shear and bending.

So far no satisfactory method of design is available, this is due to the lack of information about the behavior of the beams subjected to such forces. A considerable quantity of experimental investigation in the problem has been conducted recently. The bulk of the experimental results deal with pure torsion or combined bending and torsion. The number of experiments designed to investigate the problem of strength under combined bending, shear and torsion is still small.

The analysis presented in this paper is based on the limited experimental results available. It treats the general problem and sets a conservative method of design.

BACKGROUND

The first widely applied method for the design of members subjected to torsion is due to E. Rausch[1]. The basic equation for rectangular beams reinforced transversally with closed vertical stirrups is

$$T = 2(A_v/S)\ f_v\ b'\ h' \qquad (1)$$

where T = applied torque

A_v = area of one leg of the stirrup

f_v = stress in the stirrup

S = spacing of the stirrups and

b',h'= breadth and depth of the concrete section enclosed within the stirrup.

In addition to the closed stirrups, longitudinal reinforcement is necessary to resist the longitudinal component of the stress. The total area of longitudinal reinforcement to be added to that required for bending is given by the equation

$$A_{sa} = \frac{T(b' + h')}{f_s b' h'} \qquad (2)$$

where A_{sa} = total area of additional longitudinal reinforcement,

and f_s = stress in the longitudinal reinforcement.

Rausch's method is widely applied to calculate the additional torsional reinforcement[2] in beams.

Recently, a theory was proposed by N. N. Lessig[3] to predict the ultimate strength of beams subjected to torsion combined with bending and shear. Experiments to support this theory were conducted by Yu. V. Chinenkov[4] and I. M. Lyalin[5]. Lessig assumed that all the reinforcing bars crossing a tension crack were yielding: such assumption failed to be valid in some cases. Limitations of Lessig's theory were pointed out by P. Zia[7].

The assumed yielding of all bars lead to the conclusion that the first failure mechanism, shown in Fig. 1, cannot form in the presence of shear. However, Lyalin reported that some of the beams tested in combined bending, shear and torsion[5] had a failure which "definitely followed the first mode of failure".

Modified methods, based on Lessig's failure mechanisms and keeping the assumption that all bars crossing a tension crack were yielding, were proposed by H. H. Evans and S. Sarkar[6] and M. P. Collins, P. F. Walsh, F. E. Archer, and A. S. Hall[8].

The ultimate strength of rectangular beams in combined bending and torsion was rigorously treated by the author in previous works[9,10]. In his analysis the author adopted Lessig's mechanism but the assumption that all the bars crossing a tension crack were yielding was unnecessary.

T. C. Hsu concluded from his research[11,12] that the ultimate strength of rectangular concrete beams in torsion is given by the equation

$$T_u = T_o + T_s \qquad (3)$$

where T_u = ultimate torque

T_o = intercept of the experimental strength line with the torque axis

T_s = contribution of steel reinforcement to the strength given by:

$$T_s = (0.66 \cdot m + 0.33\ h'/b')\ A_v/S\ f_{vy}\ b'\ h' \qquad (4)$$

where m = ratio of the volume of longitudinal bars to the volume of stirrups defined as

$$m = 0.5\ A_{sa} \cdot S \,/ \left[A_v\ (b' + h')\right]$$

A. H. Mattock[13] suggested a similar design equation based on the results of the same research.

The conclusion that the strength is the sum of the contribution of the concrete and steel had been suggested by others[14-18]. These conclusions were based on experimental results of beams tested in pure torsion. In such methods the steel contribution to the ultimate strength is less than that given by Rausch's equation.

CRACKING PATTERNS AND FORMATION OF FAILURE MECHANISMS

When a beam is subjected to shearing stresses, resulting from torsional moments or shearing forces, inclined cracks normal to the direction of the principal tensile stress takes place when the latter attains a critical value. If the beam is transversally unreinforced, it would fail at a load or torque equal to or just higher than the cracking load or torque. The pattern of the cracks is influenced by the concrete tensile strength, the normal bending stresses and the shear stresses resulting from the applied shearing forces and applied torsional moments. After cracking the transverse reinforcement comes into action and compensates the loss in strength. Further loading will reduce the strength of the concrete section and increase the share of resistance contributed by the reinforcement. Further cracking would occur then. The new cracks may have the inclination of the first cracks or new pattern may form if the relative bending-shear-torsion ratios are varied.

The shear stresses due to torsion do not have the same sign on the two opposite vertical sides of the beam, while those due to shearing forces have the same sign on both sides. An inclined crack is expected early on the side where the shear stresses due to the shearing force and the torsional moment are additive.

On the other side, where the shear stresses are subtractive, the cracks may appear as extensions to those on the additive side if the shearing force is small relative to the torsional moment. Mechanisms 1 and 2, Fig. 1, are likely to form under such conditions. Mechanism 1 has a compression zone on the upper side where the applied bending moment would produce compressive stresses. This is the normal case where large bending moments are acting. Unlike mechanism 1, the compression zone in mechanism 2 is located where the applied bending moment would cause tensile stresses. Such mechanisms form under low bending moments if the beam is insufficiently reinforced at the top. This mechanism has been reported, in the case of combined bending and torsion[8-10,19].

When the shearing force is relatively large the cracks on the subtractive side would be parallel to those on the additive side. Mechanism 4, Fig. 1, is likely to form under such conditions. Since the shear stresses due to the shearing force, which is the dominating action in this mechanism, are diminishing towards the top and the bottom of the beam, the cracks on the bottom side are perpendicular to the beam axis.

If the magnitudes of the shearing stresses on the subtractive side are equal or nearly equal no inclined cracking is expected on that side. It is reasonable to assume that the compression zone would form on this side, which is the case of mechanism 3, Fig. 1. Other conditions governing the formation of this mechanism are discussed later.

In all the above cases the magnitude of the bending moment, shearing force and the torsional moment are such that inclined cracks would occur. An interaction diagram to predict the strength of plain concrete beams without web reinforcement was suggested by T. C. Hsu[20]. Cracking strength may be determined following a similar procedure.

If the bending moment has a magnitude approaching the ultimate strength no inclined cracks are likely to form. A mechanism with vertical or nearly vertical cracks would form. The shearing force and the torsional moment that can be resisted by the beam in such case are very small.

EQUILIBRIUM EQUATIONS

The notation used in the derivation of equilibrium equations are defined in the Appendix.

Assumptions

The following assumptions are made in deriving the basic equations:

1. The cracks have constant inclination on the side of the beam.

2. The compression zone is plane and the resultant of the shear stresses in this zone passes through the point of action of the resultant compressive force.

3. The natural axis is parallel to the nearest side of the beam.

4. The transverse reinforcement is uniformly distributed over the cracked length of the beam under consideration.

5. Stresses in the stirrup parts in tension and perpendicular to the direction of the shearing force are equal to the difference between the maximum stress in the stirrup parts which are parallel to the shearing force and the stresses that would be induced in them if the shearing force was acting in their plane.

6. Concrete does not contribute to the strength.

7. The failure is initiated by the yielding of one set or both sets of reinforcement: longitudinal bars or stirrups.

8. The effect of the reinforcement in the compression zone is negligible.

If large bending stresses are acting, the first assumption is not strictly valid. However, the average inclination can always be considered in calculations. Although the resultants of both the compressive and the shear stresses may not be coincident, yet the difference the positions of the two resultants is small because the depth of the compression zone is small, and the error resulting from this difference in position is insignificant. The third assumption was proved in the case of symmetrical failure surface[3,9,10]. Although a compression with varying depth may be formed yet such assumption simplifies the basic equations, and the small depth of the compression zone reduces the possibility of large errors due to this assumption. The fourth assumption may lead to some error as only integer number of stirrups can cross a tension crack. When dealing with similar problems, G. S. Pandit and J. Warwaruk[18] considered only integer numbers of stirrup branches in the calculation of the ultimate strength; the errors resulting from this consideration may, in some cases, be more than those resulting from assuming uniform distribution of stirrups[9]. For design purposes an arbitrary factor may be introduced to make the error always on the safe side. Collins et al[8] used a factor of 0.8. If the stirrup spacing is small the error will be negligible. The fifth assumption is conservative. The stresses in the horizontal branches of the stirrups are diminishing according to this assumption. This provides a transition between the fourth mechanism and the other three mechanisms. When the longitudinal steel is of low lateral stiffness it bends and forces the cracks on the top or bottom surfaces to be perpendicular to the beam axis[12] thus the contribution of the horizontal branches of the stirrups is reduced. The fifth assumption cares for this reduction. The possible contribution of the concrete section to the torsional strength can be only due to the resistance provided by the compression zone. So far there is no precise measurement to support or contradict the sixth assumption. When the concrete strength was doubled in one of the author's experiments[9] with beams in combined bending and torsion no significant increase in the strength was observed. It must be noted that when the concrete was assumed to contribute to the strength, a reduction in the strength contributed by the reinforcement was always introduced by the investigator. The present analysis deals with under-reinforced beams, thus the failure may be initiated by the yielding of either the stirrups, or top or bottom longitudinal bars. In some cases however, both stirrups and the longitudinal bars yield simultaneously. The compression reinforcement may be ignored without any significant error.

Equilibrium Equations

Six equilibrium equations can be written for each failure mechanism, namely: the components of the internal and external forces in three perpendicular directions and the resultant moments of the internal forces and the external moments and forces about three non-planar axes should be equal to zero. Components of forces in the plane of the compression zone determine the resultant of the shear stresses in this plane. The magnitude and the direction of the resultant shearing force are not essential in the present analysis. Moments about the y-axis are significant only if the beam is failing according to mechanisms 1, 2 or 4.

The remaining equations can be reduced to the following:

1. An equation relating the resultant of the compression stresses and the stresses in the reinforcement. This equation is applied to estimate the depth of the compression zone.

2. Equation relating the internal forces to the moments of the external forces and couples about the x-axis for mechanisms 1, 2 and 4 or the y-axis in mechanism 3.

3. Equation relating the internal forces to the moments of the external forces and couples about the z-axis.

In the following the basic equations for each mechanism are derived.

Basic Equations

Mechanism 1

The forces acting within this mechanism are shown in Fig. 2. Considering the equilibrium of all forces in the y-direction on gets the equation:

$$f_v' = f_v - \frac{2V}{(A_v/S\ c_1(b'/b - w_1)} \qquad (a)$$

The consideration of all force components in the direction perpendicular to the plane of the compression zone, after the substitution for the stress f_v' from equation (a), yields the first basic equation which is:

$$f_c'\ x_1\ (b^2 + c_1^2) = A_s\ f_s\ b + (A_v/S)\ f_v\ w_1\ c_1^2\ b'/b - \frac{2V\ w_1\ c_1}{(1 - w_1\ b/b')} \qquad (5)$$

By considering the equilibrium of moments about the x-axis the second basic equation for this mechanism is obtained. Thus,

$$V\left((e_b - 0.25c_1(b'/b + w_1)\right) = A_s\ f_s\ (d - \beta x_1) - 0.25\ (A_v/S)\ f_v\ c_1^2(b'/b - w_1)\ (b'/b + w_1) \qquad (6)$$

The third basic equation for this mechanism is obtained by considering the equilibrium of moments of all force components about the z-axis. Thus

$$V\ (e_t \div 0.5\ b' + w_1\ \frac{h + h' - 2\beta x_1}{1 - w_1\ b/b'}) = 0.5(A_v/S)\ f_v\ w_1\ c_1\ (b'/b)\ (h \div h' - 2\beta x_1) + 0.5(A_v/S)\ f_v\ c_1\ b'\ (b'/b - w_1) \qquad (7)$$

Mechanism 2

This mechanism is similar to mechanism 1 with the compression zone located where the stresses resulting from the bending moment would be tensile. The basic equations for this mechanism are obtained from those of mechanism 1 by substituting $A_s'\ f_s'$ for $A_s\ F_s$ and writing the eccentricity e_b with a negative sign. The basic equations for this mechanism are:

$$\alpha f_c'\ x_2\ (b^2 + c_2^2) = A_s'\ f_s'\ b + (A_v/S)\ f_v w_2\ c_2^2\ b'/b - \frac{2V\ w_2\ c_2}{1 - w_2\ b/b'} \qquad (8)$$

$$V\ \left(e_b + 0.25\ c_2\ (b'/b + w_2) \quad + A_s'\ f_s'\ (d - \beta x_2)\right) = 0.25\ (A_v/S)\ f_v\ c_2^2\ (b'/b - w_2)\ (b'/b + w_2) \qquad (9)$$

$$V\ (e_t + 0.5\ b' + w_2\ \frac{h + h' - 2\beta x_2}{1 - w_2\ b/b'}) = 0.5(A_v/S)\ f_v\ w_2\ c_2\ (b'/b)(h + h' - 2\beta x_2) +$$

$$0.5(A_v/S)\ f_v\ c_2\ b'\ \ (b'/b - w_2\ ) \qquad (10)$$

Mechanism 3

In this mechanism the compression zone is on the vertical side of the beam as shown in Fig. 3. The stresses in the horizontal parts of the stirrups calculated applying the fifth assumption are given by the equation:

$$f'_v = f_v - \frac{V}{(A_v/S)\ (h'/h)\ w_3\ c_3} \qquad (b)$$

In the beam shown in Fig. 3 the longitudinal reinforcement consisted of two bars at top and bottom. In practice the longitudinal reinforcement is composed of more than two bars in the same row. The stresses in these bars vary according to their distance from the neutral axis. It is reasonable to assume that half the area of the longitudinal bars is stressed to the maximum and placed at the position of the extreme bar; such assumption is needed for simplicity.

By considering the equilibrium of all force components perpendicular to the compression zone, the first basic equation for this mechanism is obtained.

$$\alpha f'_c\ x_3(h^2 + c_3^2\ ) = 0.5(A_s\ f_s + A'_s\ f'_s\ )\ h + (A_v/S)\ f_v\ w_3\ c_3^3\ h'/h - V\ c_3 \qquad (11)$$

The second basic equation is obtained by considering the moment of all force components about the y-axis; thus:

$$A_s\ f_s + A'_s\ f'_s = (A_v/S)\ f_v\ e_3^2\ \frac{(h'/h - w_3\ )\ (1 + w_3)}{2(b + b' - 2\beta x_3)}$$

$$- V\ c_3\ (1/w_3\ - h/h')(1+w_3)/(2b') \qquad (12)$$

The third basic equation, which is obtained by considering the moments of all force components about the z-axis, is

$$V\left(e_t + (b/2 - \beta x3) + 0.5(h'/w3 - h)\right) = 0.5(A_V/S)\ f_V\ w3\ c3\ (h'/h)(b + b' - 2\beta x3) +$$

$$0.5(A_v/S)\ f_v\ c_3\ h'\ (h'/h - w_3) \qquad (13)$$

The equation obtained by considering the moments of all force components about the z-axis is of interest. This equation is written as follows:

$$V\,e_b = 0.5\,(A_s\,f_s - A_s'\,f_s')(d - d') \tag{14}$$

In the case of beams with equal reinforcement at the top and bottom, the right hand side of Eq. (14) will be equal to zero, as the stresses will be equal since the bars are at equal distance from the neutral axis. This leads to the conclusion that the third mechanism is likely to form only if the bending moment is equal to zero or has a small value.

Mechanism 4

It is clear that theequilibrium of the vertical components cannot be satisfied in mechanisms 1, 2,and 3 if e_t is smaller than b'/2. In such a case the failure may take place in a manner similar to that of shear failure, as shown in Fig. 4. The basic equations for this mechanism are given in the following. It should be noticed that the bending eccentricity is measured to plane of the compression zone.

$$\alpha f_c'\;b\,x_4 = A_s\,f_s \tag{15}$$

$$V\,(e_b - 0.5\,c_4) = A_s\,f_s\,(d - \beta x_4) \tag{16}$$

$$V\,(e_t + 0.5b') = (A_v/S)\,f_v\,c_4\,b' \tag{17}$$

EVALUATION OF THE PAREMETERS

In this analysis one set of the reinforcement is assumed at yield. Thus f_s or f_s' or f_v is known or assumed and the basic second equation is applied to determine the stresses in the other set. The stirrup stress is independent of the longitudinal bars stress in mechanism 4. In each set of equations the parameters c,w and the compression zone parameters f_c' , α and β are to be evaluated.

The length of the plastic hinge c depends on the cracking pattern, i.e., the inclination of the cracks on each side. Experiments showed that the inclination of the cracks under low bending moments is nearly constant while two distinct inclinations may be present under high bending moments[7,9]. Cracks inclined 45 deg to the beam axis are formed under high shear stresses resulting from a shearing force or a torsional moment, when accompanied with low bending stresses. For most practical cases an inclination of a 45 deg is reasonable. Thus the value of the length of the plastic hinge c is given by the following expressions for the different mechanisms.

$$c_{1,2} = 2h + b - 2x_{1,2} \qquad (18)$$

$$c_3 = h + 2b - 2x_3 \qquad (19)$$

$$c_4 = h - x_4 \qquad (20)$$

The length of the projection of the crack on the side opposite to the compression zone,w, is given by the following expressions, which are based on the assumption of continuous 45 deg cracks.

$$w_{1,2} = b/c_{1,2} \qquad (21)$$

$$w_3 = h/c_3 \qquad (22)$$

The magnitude of the shearing force acting in the compression zone can be determined by considering the equilibrium of force components parallel to the plane of compression zone. The strength of concrete is, then determined applying one of the failure theories under combined stresses.

Due to the small depth of the compression zone and the yielding of reinforcement, which initiate the failure rather than the crushing of the concrete, an accurate estimation of the compression zone parameters is not essential. It is sufficiently accurate to assume that:

$$\alpha f'_c = 0.85\, C_p = 0.85\, C_{cy} = 0.67\, C_{cu}$$

$$\beta = 0.5$$

SIMPLIFIED EQUATIONS

The basic equations of the first three mechanism can be largely simplified by introducing the simplifying assumption that the depth of the compression zone is such that the resultant compressive force coincides with the stirrup boundary.

By fixing the depth of the compression zone the first basic equation becomes unnecessary and the values of c and w are, as a result of fixing x, fixed. The iterative procedure is not required further and the basic operations are much simplified. The simplified basic equations are:

Mechanism 1

$$v\left(e_b - 0.5\,(b' + h')\right) = A_s f_s\, h' - (A_v/S)\, f_v h'(b' + h') \qquad (6\text{-a})$$

$$v\,(e_t + 1.5\, b') = 2(A_v/S)\, f_v b'h' \qquad (7\text{-a})$$

Mechanism 2

$$v\left(e_b - 0.5\,(b' + h')\right) + A_s' f_s' h' = (A_v/S)\, f_v h'\,(b' + h') \qquad (9\text{-a})$$

$$v(e_t + 1.5h') = 2\,(A_v/S)\, f_v b'h' \qquad (10\text{-a})$$

Mechanism 3

$$0.5\,(A_s f_s + A_s' f_s')h' = \left((A_v/S)\, f_v h' - v\right)(b' + h') \qquad (12\text{-a})$$

$$v\,(e_t + 1.5\, b') = 2\,(A_v/S)\, f_v b'h' \qquad (13\text{-a})$$

It can be seen that the simplified equations predicting the torsional strength are identical in the three mechanisms.

The simplified equations are most suitable for design.

INTERACTION DIAGRAM

Fig. 5 shows a typical interaction diagram drawn for beams b-8k, 1a, b-0-0, 1, 1a, b-8-0, 2, 2a, b-8-0, 4, 4a, tested by Lyalin[5]. The nominal cross section of the beams was 20x30 on (8 x 12 in.) and reinforced longitudinally by 4 bars of diameter 20 mm (3/4 in.) at the corners and with close stirrups of diameter 8 mm (5/16 in.) transversally. Other data for the beams are given in the appendix. An interaction diagram for beams subjected to combined bending, shear, and torsion is a surface composed of ordinates representing the torsional strength at different combinations of the shearing forces and the bending moments. The case of pure torsion is represented by the intersection of this surface with the T-axis. The trace of the surface on the T-M plane represents the special case of the combined bending and torsion. The trace of the surface on the T-V plane is characterized by a sudden change in slope at shearing force equal to one-half the ultimate shearing strength of the section. When the acting shearing force is higher than this value mechanism 4 is the only possible failure mechanism. The corner appearing on the T-M diagrams of mechanism 1 shows the moment at which both the stirrups and the longitudinal bars yield simultaneously. The inclined parts represent those cases when the longitudinal bars yield while the stirrups are still stressed below the yield point. Mechanism 1 and mechanism 3 result in equal torsional capacities at their common points. The nearly constant torsional moment in the diagrams of mechanism 1 represent failure initiated by the yield of the stirrups. A vertical line is drawn at the ultimate flexural strength since it is not likely that inclined cracks, and consequently any of the four mechanisms, would form when this moment is approached although the torsional resistance does not necessarily equal zero.

Failures initiated by the yielding of the top reinforcement, i.e., mechanism 2 did not appear on the present interaction diagram because the top and bottom reinforcements are equal. Such failure would not occur if the top reinforcement is equal to or more than

$$A_s' = \left((2M) + (b' + h')\ (V + T/b')\right)\ /\ (2\ f_y'\ h') \tag{23}$$

This equation is obtained by substituting the values of M and T in equations 9-a and 10-a. To provide the full efficiency for the stirrups the top bars should have an area not less than that given by the equation

$$A_{so} = \frac{T}{2_b' \; h' \; f_y'} \cdot (b' + h') \tag{24}$$

No top reinforcement is required to avoid the formation of mechanism 2 if

$$M \geqslant 0.5\,(b' + h')\,(V + T/b') \tag{25}$$

COMPARISON WITH EXPERIMENTAL RESULTS

So far the number of experiments on beams subjected to combined bending, shear, and torsion is small. The main sources of experimental results are the experiments conducted by Lyalin[5], Klus[21] and Goode[22]; Klus did not show the core dimensions of his beams. Goode's results are to be published. The beams tested under the effect of a concentrated load or group of concentrated loads with the shearing force being constant over a part of the beam. The relation between the moment and the shearing force is linear in the form

$$0 \leqslant M \leqslant A\,V$$

where A is the length of the part under constant shearing force measured from the point of zero moment. Thus under the same values of V and T a variable moment exists. It is then convenient to compare the results on the basis of torsion- shear relation. In drawing the T-V relation the V-M relation of the tested beam should be considered. The T-V relation is obtained by projecting the intersection of the interaction surface with the plane M= AV as shown in Fig. 5 and 6.

Fig. 7 represents the T-V relation thus obtained for Lyalin's beams. The present method predicts conservative values compared with the experimental results. Reasons for this deviation may be due to:

i) The theory neglects the effect of the resistance of the concrete and the dowel action of the longitudinal bars.

ii) The fifth assumption under estimates the contribution of the horizontal parts of the stirrups.

iii) Experiments showed that the inclination of the cracks where a moderate amount of bending is milder than 45 deg.

To evaluate these effects accurately more experimental results should be available.

APPLICATION TO DESIGN

The procedure in applying the present analysis to design may be summarized in the following:

1. The section is determined by considering the maximum bending moments, in the usual way of designing beams in flexure.

2. The shear stresses due to the shearing force is then determined applying the ACI Code equation:

$$v_u = V/bd \quad \text{or}$$

by applying the general form of this equation

$$v = V/j\,bd$$

3. The torsional stress is determined by applying the plastic theory for simplicity

$$T = 0.5\, b^2\, h\, \tau (1 - b/3h) \tag{27}$$

4. Web reinforcement, to resist the total shear stresses, should be provided if the sum of both stresses exceeds the cracking strength as given by the ACI Code[23]

$$v_u = 2\,\phi\sqrt{f'_c}$$

and the section should be increased if the sum of the stresses exceeds an upper limit[13] given by

$$v_u = 11\,\phi\sqrt{f'_c}$$

5. The area of stirrups is designed according to Eq. 7-2, 10-a, and 13-a

or Eq. 17 whichever mechanism is applicable.

6. The longitudinal steel should be checked applying the Eq. 6-a, 9-a, or 12-a whichever mechanism is applicable.

7. It is essential that the area of the top steel is adequate to prevent the premature failure according to mechanism 2. This can be checked by providing the minimum area as given by Eq. 23 and 24.

DESIGN EXAMPLE

A beam is simply supported over a span of 24 ft (7.2m). Provisions to prevent the twist are provided at the supports. The ultimate dead and live loads are given in Fig. 8 (after multiplying the working loads with the proper factors).

The possible combinations of the loads produce the sets of V, M, and T, diagrams of the various cases of loads in Fig. 8.

The concrete strength is 3000 psi (210 kg/cm^2) and the yield strength of steel is 50,000 psi (3500 kg/cm^2).

The cracking limit $= 2\ (0.85)\ \sqrt{3000} = 93$ psi (6.5 kg/cm^2)

The maximum capacity limit $= 2\ (0.85)\sqrt{3000} = 512$ psi (36.3 kg/cm^2)

From the consideration of the maximum bending moment on the beam, the cross section chosen is 12 x 24 in. (30 x 60 cm). The area of the longitudinal bars required for bending only = 3.1 in.^{2}.

$$v_u = \frac{20\ 000}{12^2 \times 22} = 114 \text{ psi } (8 \text{kg/cm}^2)$$

$$\tau = \frac{360\ 000}{12 \quad \times 24\ (1 - 12/\ .33 \times 24)\ /2} = 250 \text{ psi } (17.5 \text{ kg/cm}^2)$$

$$v_u + \tau = 364 \text{ psi } (25.5 \text{ kg/cm}^2)$$

The torsional shear stress is double the shear stress due to the shearing force and the difference between them exceeds the cracking limit, thus the cracking will follow the pattern of the first or second mechanisms of failure.

Calculations of the stirrups

$$e_t = 360\ 000\ /20\ 000 = 18 \text{ in. } (45 \text{ cm})$$

The core dimensions are 10 x 22 in. (25 x 55 cm)

Applying Eq. 7-a

$$20\ 000\ (18 + 15) = 2\ (A_v/S)\ 50\ 000 \times 10 \times 22$$

$$A_v/S = 0.0296 \text{ in}^2/\text{in.}$$

Closed stirrups, #4's at 6.5 in. on centers, will be sufficient (13 mm diameter, and 16.5 cm spacing).

Longitudinal bottom bars

$$e_b = 2880\ 000\ /\ 20\ 000 = 144 \text{ in. } (360 \text{ cm})$$

Applying Eq. 6-a

$$20\ 000 \left(144 - 0.5\ (10 + 22)\right) = A_s\ (50\ 000)\ (22) - \frac{0.196}{6.5}\ (50\ 000)(22)\ (10 + 22)$$

$$A_s = 3.3 \text{ in}^2 \quad (21.2 \text{ cm}^2)$$

Chosen 6-#7 (6 bars of diameter 22 mm)

Longitudinal top bars

Applying Eq. 23

$$A_s' = (10 + 22)\ (20\ 000 + 360\ 000/10)\ /\ (2 \times 22 \times 50\ 000) = 0.815 \text{ in}^2$$

$$(5.30 \text{ cm}^2)$$

Chosen 2 #6 of area 0.884 in^2 (2 bars of diameter 19 mm and area 5.7 cm^2).

No top reinforcement is needed if the moment is equal to or more than that given by Eq. 25

$$M = 0.5(10 + 22)\ (20\ 000 + 360\ 000/10) = 895000 \text{ in.-lb}$$

$$= (10350 \text{ m-kg})$$

This moment occurs at a distance 45 in. from the support.

If this check is done when the moment is minimum and the torsional moment is maximum, the moment as given by equation 25 is

$$M = 0.5(10 + 22)\ (10\ 000 + 360\ 000/10) = 735{,}000 \text{ in.-lb } (8500 \text{ m-kg})$$

This moment occurs at a distance 73.5 in. from the support.

Then the top bars should extend to a distance equal to 73.5 in. plus the anchorage length.

CONCLUSIONS

The present analysis is valuable in predicting the strength of the members subjected to combined bending, shear and torsion and having a rectangular reinforced concrete section. The analysis yields conservative estimates of the strength. Simplified design equation are suitable for the design of reinforced concrete members subjected to the combinations of forces and moments in any ratio.

REFERENCES

1. Rausch, E., "Design of Reinforced Concrete in Torsion". Dissertation presented to the Tecnishe Hocschule, Berlin for the degree of Dr. Ing. 1929

2. Fisher, G. P., and Zia, P., "Review of Code Requirements for Torsion Design," ACI JOURNAL, Jan. 1964, pp. 1-22.

3. Lessig, N. N., "Determination of the Load-Bearing Capacity of Reinforced Concrete Elements in Torsion," Trudy, No. 5 (Moscow), pp. 5-28. (English translation by Margaret Corbin as Foreign Literature Study No. 371, Portland Cement Association, Skokie, Ill.), 1959

4. Cinenkov, Yu. V., "Study of the Behavior of Reinforced Concrete Elements in Combined Flexure and Torsion," Trudy No. 5 (Moscow), pp. 29-53. (English translation as Foreign Literature Study No. 370, Portland Cement Association, Skokie, Ill.).

5. Lyalin, I. M., "Experimental Studies of the Behavior of Reinforced Concrete Beams with Rectangular Cross-Section Subjected to the Combined Action of Transverse Shear, Flexural, and Torsional Moments," Trudy, No. 5 (Moscow), 1959, pp. 54-77), (English translation as Foreign Literature Study No. 402, Portland Cement Association, Skokie, Ill.).

6. Evans, R. E., and Sarkar, S., "A Method of Ultimate Strength Design of Reinforced Concrete Beams in Combined Bending and Torsion," Structural Engineers, London, V. 43, No. 10, October 1965, pp. 337-344.

7. Zia, P., "Torsion Theories for Concrete Members," ACI Special Publications SP 18, Torsion of Structural Concrete, Detroit, 1968, pp. 103-132.

8. Collins, M. P., Walsh, P. F., Archer, F. E. and Hall, A. S., "The Design of Rectangular Reinforced Concrete Beams in Combined Torsion, Bending and Shear," Studies from the School of Civil Engineering, University of New South Wales, Australia, Report No. R-16, Aug. 1966, p. 33.

9. Helmy, M. A., "The Strength of Reinforced Concrete Rectangular Beams in Combined Bending and Torsion," Ph. D. Thesis, University of Manchester, March 1966, p. 207

10. Goode, C. D., and Helmy, M. A., "Ultimate Strength of Reinforced Concrete Beams in Combined Bending and Torsion," ACI Special Publication SP 18, Torsion of Structural Concrete, Detroit, 1968, pp. 357-377.

11. Hsu, T. C., "Torsion of Structural Concrete - Behavior of Reinforced Concrete Rectangular Members," ACI Special Publication SP 18, Torsion of Structural Concrete, Detroit, 1968, pp. 261-306.

12. Hsu, T. C., "Ultimate Torque of Reinforced Rectangular Beams," JOURNAL, the Structural Division, ASCE, Vol. 194, No. St. 2, Feb. 1968, pp. 485-510

13. Mattock, A. H., "How to Design for Torsion," ACI Special Publication SP 18, Torsion of Structural Concrete, Detroit, 1968, pp. 469-495.

14. Cowan, H. J., "An Elastic Theory for the Torsional Strength of Rectangular Reinforced Concrete Beams," Magazine of Concrete Research, V. 2, No. 4, July 1950, pp. 3-8

15. Anderson, P., "Rectangular Concrete Sections Under Torsion," ACI JOURNAL Sept.-Oct. 1937, pp. 1-11

16. Navaratnarajah, V., "A New Approach to the Ultimate Strength of Concrete in Pure Torsion," ACI JOURNAL, Feb. 1968, pp. 121-129

17. Sundara Raja Iyengar, K. T., and Rangan, B. Vijaya, "Strength and Stiffness of Reinforced Concrete Beams Under Combined and Torsion," ACI Special Publication SP 18, <u>Torsion of Structural Concrete</u>, Detroit, 1968, pp. 403-440

18. Pandit, G. S. and Warwaruk, J., "Reinforced Concrete Beams in Bending and Torsion," ACI Special Publication SP 18, <u>Torsion in Structural Concrete</u>, Detroit, 1968, pp. 133-163

19. Walsh, P. F., Collins, M. P., Archer, F. E. and Hall, A. S., "Experiments on the Strength of Concrete Beams in Combined Flexure and Torsion," Studies from the School of Civil Engineering, University of New South Wales, Report No. R-15, Feb. 1966, p. 29

20. Hsu, T. C., "Torsion of Structural Concrete, Interaction Surface for Combined Torsion, Shear, and Bending in Beams Without Stirrups," ACI JOURNAL, Jan. 1969, pp. 51-60

21. Klus, J. P., "Ultimate Strength of Reinforced Concrete Beams in Combined Torsion and Shear," ACI JOURNAL, Mar. 1968, pp. 210-215

22. Goode, C. D., private correspondence

23. ACI Committee 318, "Building Code Requirements for Reinforced Concrete, ACI 318-63," ACI, Detroit, 1963.

APPENDIX 1

b, h	breadth and depth of the concrete cross section
b', h'	breadth and depth of the concrete section enclosed within the
d, d'	depth measured from the extreme compression fiber of the concrete stirrups section to the top or bottom steel respectively
ℓ	length of the plastic hinge in mechanisms 1, 2, and 3 respectively
$c_1\ c_2, c_3, c_4$	length of the projection of the plastic hinge on the side of the beams in mechanisms 1, 2, 3, and 4 respectively
$x_1\ x_2, x_3, x_4$	The depth of the compression zone in mechanisms 1, 2, 3, and 4 respectively
A_s, A'_s	area of the longitudinal bars at the bottom and top of the beam respectively
A_{so}	minimum area of longitudinal bars at any side of the beam to secure the initiation of failure by the yield of the stirrups
A_{sa}	additional area of longitudinal bars in pure torsion according to Rausch
A_v	area of one leg of stirrup
S	spacing of the stirrups
e_b, e_t	eccentricities along and perpendicular to the beam axis of the shearing force
M, T, V	bending moment, shearing force and torsional moments applied on the beam
τ, v_u	ultimate shear stresses due to torque and direct shearing force respectively
f'_c	stress in concrete at failure
f_s, f'_s	stress in longitudinal bottom and top bars respectively
f_v, f'_v	stress in the vertical parts of the stirrup near to the shearing force
f'_v	stress in the vertical part of the stirrup further from the shearing force and in the horizontal parts of the stirrup
C_u, C_p, C_{cy}	strength of the concrete cube, prism or cylinder respectively

α, β coefficients for the average stress and position of the resultant compression in the compression zone

f_y, f'_y, f_{vy} yield stresses of the longitudinal bottom bars, the longitudinal top bars and the stirrups respectively

APPENDIX 2

Properties of beams in Fig. 7 tested by Lyalin[5]

Beam	Section	C_u		f_y, f'_y		f_{vy}	
		psi	kg/cm^2	ksi	kg/cm^2	ksi	kg/cm^2
b-8-k		1715	120	55	3840	76	5320
b-8-k		3050	211	55	3840	76	5320
b-8-0.1	All beams	2220	155	55	3850	66.9	4680
B-8-0.1a	20x31 cm 8 x 12 3/8 in.	2220	155	56.2	3940	77	5400
b-8-0.2		1930	135	56.5	3955	79.6	55.8
b-8-0.2a		2220	155	52.5	3670	75.6	5300
b-8-0.4		2170	152	56.6	3970	8290	5800
b-8-0.4a	20 x 30.5 cm 8 x 12.1/4 in.	2800	196	58.3	4070	84	5870

All beams were reinforced longitudinally with 4 bars of 20 mm diameter (25/32 in.) and
transversally with closed stirrups 8 mm (5/16 in.) spaced at 8 cm (3 1/8 in.).

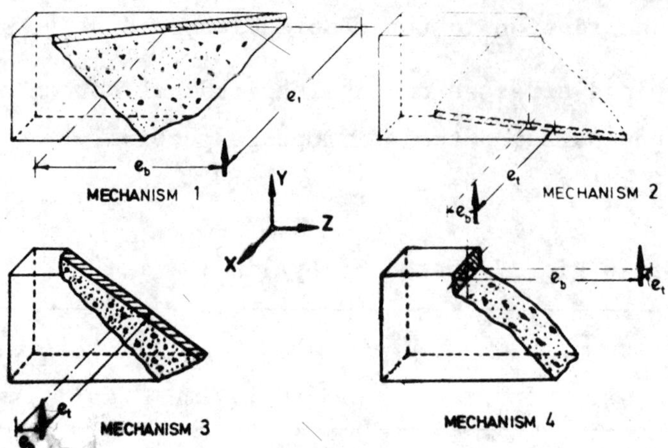

Fig. 1 Failure mechanisms

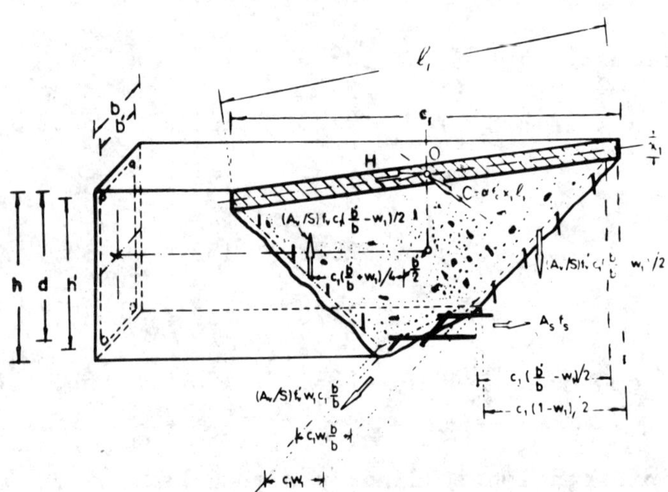

Fig. 2 Forces in Mechanism 1

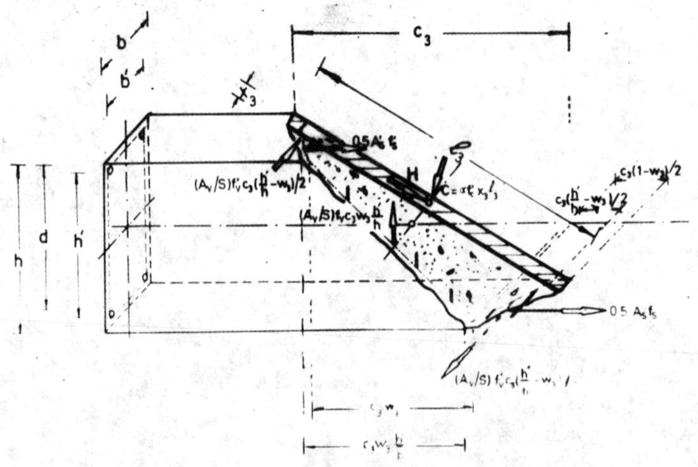

Fig. 3 Forces in Mechanism 3

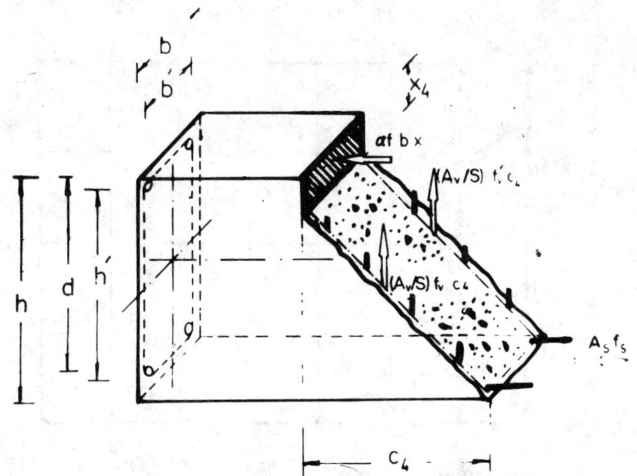

Fig. 4 Forces in Mechanism 4

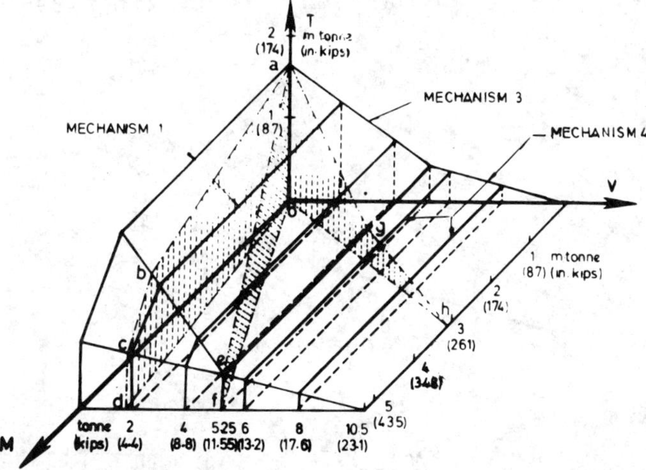

Fig. 5 Interaction Diagram

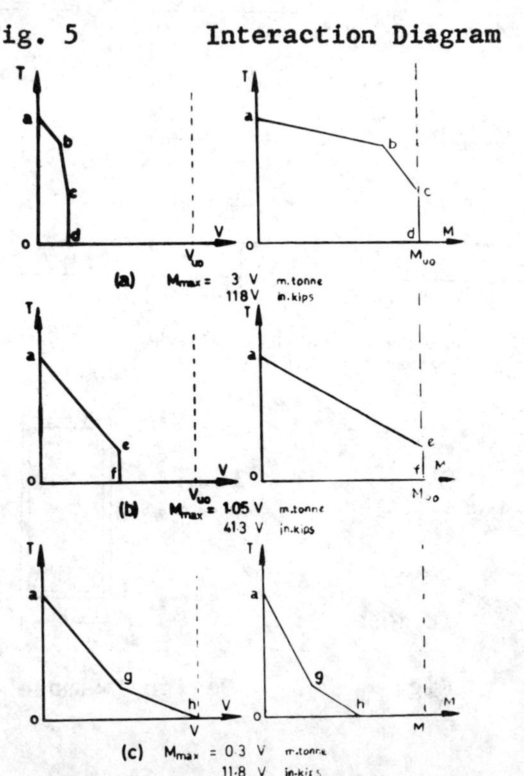

Fig. 6 Types of two dimensional interaction diagrams

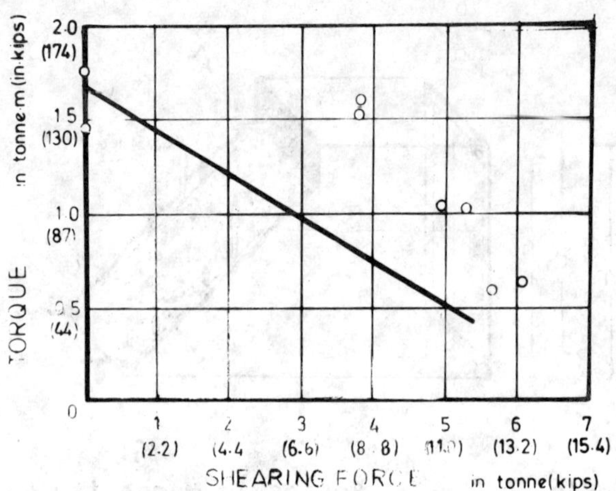

Fig. 7 Comparison with Lyalin's Beams[5]

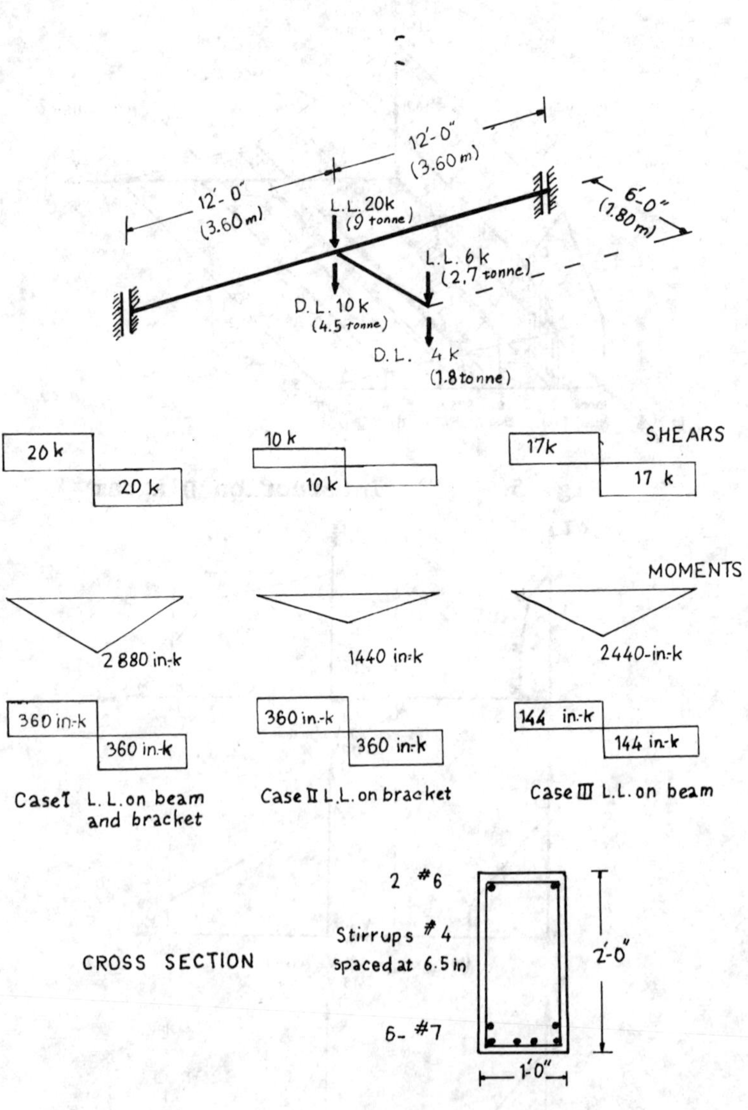

Fig. 8 Design Example

ULTIMATE SHEAR TESTS OF LARGE PRESTRESSED CONCRETE BRIDGE BEAMS

By JOHN M. HANSON and C. L. HULSBOS

SYNOPSIS

Nine ultimate strength tests on four 36-in. (91-cm) deep prestressed concrete I and box beams are reported. In several tests, the vertical web reinforcement in the shear spans was less than the minimum required by the ACI Building Code (ACI 318-63). Six tests ended with shear failures. The provisions of the ACI Building Code closely predicted the shear strength in these tests. Web shear crack widths were measured and found to be affected by the amount of web reinforcement in the beams.

Keywords: box beams; crack widths and spacing; deflections; flexural strength; I-beams; prestressed concrete; shear strength; structural analysis; ultimate strength method; web reinforcement.

ACI member JOHN M. HANSON is principal research engineer, Structural Research Section, Research and Development Division, Portland Cement Association, Skokie, Illinois. He is a member of ACI Committee 215, Fatigue of Concrete, and ACI-ASCE Committee 426, Shear and Diagonal Tension. Dr. Hanson did his undergraduate work at South Dakota State University, and has received graduate degrees from Iowa State University and Lehigh University. He has several years of experience with consulting engineering firms, and is a registered engineer in Colorado. He joined PCA in 1965.

ACI member C. L. HULSBOS is professor and chairman, Department of Civil Engineering, University of New Mexico, Albunquerque, N. M. Until September, 1965 he was research professor of civil engineering and chairman, Structural Concrete Division, Fritz Engineering Laboratory, Lehigh University, Bethlehem, Pa. Currently he is a member of ACI Committee 115, Research; 215, Fatigue of Concrete; and 437, Strength Evaluation of Existing Concrete Structures.

INTRODUCTION

Many design procedures are necessarily based on tests of relatively small-sized members. However, Kani[1] and MacGregor[2] have recently concluded that the ultimate shear strength of reinforced concrete beams is affected by the depth of the test specimen. Serviceability criteria pertaining to crack widths are also difficult to evaluate from tests on small-sized members.

According to the ACI Building Code Commentary (ACI 318-63),[3] the shear strength provisions of Section 2610 of the ACI Building Code[4] are

"...based upon a critical appraisal of 244 bonded prestressed beams which failed in shear, including both monolithic and composite sections up to 39 in. in width and $25^1/_2$ in. in depth." In metric units, this corresponds to 99 cm in width and 65 cm in depth. Many pretensioned prestressed concrete beams, particularly bridge beams, are considerably deeper than this. Standard AASHO-PCI bridge beams[5] range in depth from 28 to 54 in., (71 to 137 cm) and are designed for use with a composite deck slab. The Pennsylvania Department of Highways uses standard sections[6] which range up to 60 in. (152 cm) in depth. Sections up to 72 in. (183 cm) in depth have been used in some western states.

Furthermore, full-sized girders frequently differ significantly from test specimens in size and type of reinforcement. Perhaps more important, they often differ considerably in details. For example, web reinforcement in bridge beams is sometimes terminated in the tension flange without a hook or bend.

Scope

In this investigation, nine ultimate strength tests were carried out on four I and box beams having an overall depth of 36 in. (91 cm). These tests were conducted on shear span to effective depth ratios, a/d, ranging from 2.8 to 5.8. The vertical web reinforcement ratio in the shear spans varied from 0.07 to 0.20 percent.

The purpose of this investigation was to study the behavior and strength, particularly shear strength, of large beams. Comparisons are made to strengths predicted by the ACI Building Code.

TEST BEAMS

The test specimens consisted of two 47-ft. (14.3 m) and two 29-ft.

(8.8 m) prestressed concrete bridge beams. These beams had the nominal cross-sections shown in Fig. 1. They would normally be used with a composite slab, although they were tested non-compositely, so that the strength of the specimens alone would be known. Consequently, the test beams should be regarded as having "weak" compression flanges.

The beams were prestressed with straight $^7/_{16}$-in. (11 mm) diameter 270 ksi (19,000 kgf/cm^2) grade strand. The longitudinal reinforcement ratio in the I and box beams was 0.46 and 0.52 percent, respectively. Each strand was pretensioned to a nominal initial force of 21.7 kips (9840 kgf). Assuming losses of 5 percent at release, the computed stress in the top and bottom fibers is 550 psi (38 kgf/cm^2) tension and 1840 psi (129 kgf/cm^2) compression in the I-beams, and 550 psi (38 kgf/cm^2) tension and 2170 psi (152 kgf/cm^2) compression in the box beams. The strand in both sectionswere located so that if the member would fail in flexure, the strand strain would be greater than 1 percent and the neutral axis would be in the compression flange.

The size and location of the web reinforcement in the test beams are given in Fig. 2. The amount of web reinforcement in the different regions may be compared to the minimum web reinforcement required by Eq. (26-11) of the ACI Building Code (ACI 318-63),[4] which is rf_y equal to 77 psi (5.4 kgf/cm^2) for the I-beams and rf_y equal to 57 psi (4.0 kgf/cm^2) for the box beams.

The actual dimensions of the test beams varied somewhat from the nominal dimensions given in Fig. 1. The I-beams were up to $^1/_4$ in. (6 mm) wider and deeper than specified, and the strand were approximately $^1/_8$ in. (3 mm) high. The box beams were up to $^1/_4$ in. (6 mm) narrower than specified at the top, and within $^1/_8$ in. (3 mm) at the bottom. They were up to $^1/_2$ in. (13 mm) deeper than specified, and the strand were approximately $^1/_4$ in. (6 mm) high and $^1/_4$ in. (6 mm) eccentric. The web thickness of the box beams, which was measured after testing, varied by as much as $^7/_8$ in. (22 mm) from the nominal dimension of 5 in. (127 mm), but the total web thickness at any section was always close to 10 in. (254 mm). The thickness of the compression flange varied from 2.5 to 3.25 in. (64 to 83 mm).

Materials

The concrete mix contained 799 lb per cu.yd. (474 kg per cm) of Type III cement. Proportions by weight of the cement to sand to coarse aggregate were 1 to 1.5 to 2.4. Slump ranged between 1 and 2 in. (2.5 and 5 cm). An admixture was used to delay setting for a maximum period of 1 hour. The percentage of entrained air ranged from 4.5 to 7.2 percent.

The strength of the concrete at release and at test, as determined from tests on standard 6 by 12-in. (15 by 30-cm) cylinders cast in metal molds, is tabulated in Table 1. Each value given in Table 1 is an average of 3 or 6 tests.

Uncoated stress relieved strand meeting the requirements of ASTM A416-59 specifications was used for the prestressed steel. The load-strain curve shown in Fig. 3 is an average obtained from three strand tests. All three specimens failed in the grips, at an average load of 31.9 kips (14,500 kgf) and strain of 4.5 percent. Information from the manufacturer stated that the strand had an area of 0.1167 square in. (0.7529 cm^2).

Deformed No. 4, 5, and 6 bars were used as tensile reinforcement in the top flange or as end reinforcement in the beams. The web reinforcement was made from deformed No. 2, 3, and 5 bars. The specially obtained hot-rolled No. 2 bars had deformations comparable to the other mild steel reinforcement. At least 4 specimens of each size bar were tested, and the results of a typical test on each are shown in Fig. 4.. The values listed in the accompanying table are average values of all specimens tested.

TABLE 1 - PROPERTIES OF THE CONCRETE

Beam	At Release			At Test			
	Age (days)	f'_c (psi)*	E_c (ksi)**	Age (days)	f'_c (psi)*	E_c (ksi)**	f'_{sp} (psi)*
G-1	3	6820	5000	46	7920	5300	600
G-2	3	5910	4900	32	6660	4800	585
G-3	2	6570	4900	42	7930	5200	650
G-4	2	6200	4700	36	7580	·4800	625

*To convert to kgf/cm², multiply by .0703

**To convert to kgf/cm², multiply by 70.3

TABLE 2 - PRESTRESS FORCE

Beam	Prestress		
	Initial (kips)*	Loss (%)	At Test (kips)*
G-1	564	13	491
G-2	346	11	308
G-3	559	13	486
G-4	345	11	307

*To convert to kgf, multiply by 453.6

Fabrication

The beams were fabricated at a plant which regularly produces similar beams for the Pennsylvania Department of Highways. Standard fabrication procedures were followed except to install instrumentation or to obtain experimental readings.

The total prestress force given in Table 2 was estimated from 12 strand instrumented with load cells. The force in any instrumented strand was within 5 percent of the design force, except for strand which sustained single wire failures.

Five single wire failures occurred while stressing the strand. Three of these occurred in G-1, and the other two in G-2. One of the failures in G-1 occurred in the center region of the bed, and the strand containing this wire was replaced. The remaining failures occurred in the chucks, and these strand were not replaced. The load cells indicated that a strand lost approximately 10 percent of its force at the time of a single wire failure.

The beams and test cylinders were steam-cured in a tarpaulin covered enclosure in which the temperature was maintained at 140 ± 10 deg. F (60 ± 6 deg. C). The steam-curing began after a period of not less than 2 hours after casting, and continued for approximately 36 hours.

The prestress was released into the beams by torch cutting each strand simultaneously at both ends. Each strand was heated over a length of several inches before cutting.

The beams were stored in the prestressing plant for approximately three weeks, where the humidity was high. They were subsequently stored outdoors until they were shipped to the laboratory. Each beam was carefully examined after arrival at the laboratory. Tension cracks were found in the top flanges of the box beams. The cracks in G-1 were located approximately 10 in. (25 cm) apart in the end regions of the beam, and extended to a depth of about 10 in. (25 cm) near the junction of the void and end block. The only cracks observed in G-3 were at the junction of the void and end block, and extended to a depth of about 5 in. (13 cm).

A horizontal crack was found in both ends of G-4. These cracks occurred at the junction of the web and bottom flange and extended approximately 2 in. (5 cm) into the beam, to the location of the first stirrup. There were no cracks found in G-2.

Prestress

Deformation measurements from casting until approximately one day after release were made by readings on internal strain bars. Each strain bar consisted of a 1 in. (2.5 cm) and a 36 in. (91 cm) length of No. 4 bar with a waterproofed strain gage mounted at the center of the bar. Felt padding was wrapped around the short bar, and a rubber finger cot was placed over the felt before the short bar was attached to the center of the long bar. Thus, the short bar was not in contact with the concrete. Four such strain bars were embedded near the extremities of two different cross-sections of each beam. The bars were placed parallel to the strand. When readings were taken, it was assumed that the long bar gave the total strain change and the short bar gave the strain change due to change in temperature. Some difficulty was experienced with the strain bar readings, as the extreme dampness in the prestressing plant affected the reliability of the strain indicator.

Subsequent deformation measurements, until the time of test, were made with a Whittemore on targets cemented to the surface of the beams at the level of the center of gravity of the strand.

The loss in prestress force was calculated from these deformation measurements. A 5 percent allowance for stress relaxation was included, based upon the recommendations of Magura, Sozen, and Siess.(7) The estimated total percent loss and effective prestress are given in Table 2. It should be noted that this prestress is with the beam in a simply-supported position.

PROCEDURE AND PRINCIPAL TEST RESULTS

The tests were carried out in a 5 million lb. (2,300,000 kgf) Baldwin universal testing machine. Loads and reactions were transmitted through 2 by 8-in. (5 by-20 cm) steel plates and 8-in. (20-cm) diameter rollers. A thin layer of fast-setting gypsum plaster provided uniform bearing between the steel plates and the test specimen.

The load was applied in increments of approximately 5 percent of the predicted failure load. Experimental readings were taken after each load increment. These readings consisted mainly of measurements of deflections using Ames dial gages and level readings, strains in the compression flange using 6-in. (15-cm) electrical resistance gages, deformations at the level of the strand using a 5 and 10-in. (12.7 and 25.4-cm) Whittemore, and inclined crack widths using either a 5-in. (12.7-cm) Whittemore, laboratory-made extensometer, or a Gaertner microscope.

Nine tests were carried out on the four beams. In each test, a symmetrical one or two point loading was used. After the first test on each beam, the specimen was separated at the failure region. The remaining part of the beam was examined and reset under the testing machine. Second tests were conducted on all beams. A third test was conducted on only one beam, G-4. In three of the reloading tests, external reinforcement was used to strengthen the cracked shear span and to force the failure into the uncracked shear span. All test results were expressed in terms of applied load shear in the shear spans, including weight of testing apparatus.

The principal results of the I-beam tests are presented in Table 3. V_{cr} is applied load shear causing flexural cracking. The region of maximum moment in the second and third test on G-4 was not cracked during the first test, and so values of V_{cr} were also obtained for these tests. V_{ic} is the applied load shear causing inclined cracking. In the first test on G-2, inclined web shear cracking formed in both shear spans. Inclined flexure shear cracks formed in both shear spans of G-4 during the first test, but these cracks

Table 3 I-Beam Test Results

Beam	Test	Test Setup	$\frac{a}{d}$	V_{cr} * (kips)	V_{ic} * (kips)	V_f * (kips)	Failure
G-2	1	rf_y=114, P, rf_y=55; A C B; 9' 9' 9'	3.49	72	A End 104 B End 104	110	B End Shear
	2	P; A C; 9' 9'	3.49	–	–	118	Flexure
G-4	1	rf_y=91, P, rf_y=44; A C B; 15' 15' 15'	5.84	34	–	66	Flexure
	2	P; B; 7'-6" 7'-6"	2.92	76	110.5	114	Shear
	3	P; A; 7'-6" 7'-6"	2.92	76	119	136	Shear

*To convert to kgf, multiply by 453.6

Table 4 Box Beam Test Results

Beam	Test	Test Setup	$\frac{a}{d}$	V_{cr} (kips)*	V_{ic} (kips)*	V_f (kips)*	Failure
G-1	1	rf_y=105, P, rf_y=59; A C B; 9' 9' 9'	3.34	120	B end 136 A end 152 & 192	198.5	A End Shear
	2	P; C B; 9' 9'	3.34	–	B end 206.5	215.5	B End Shear
G-3	1	rf_y=70, P, rf_y=56; A C B; 15' 15' 15'	5.56	68		127.5	B End Shear
	2	P; A; 7'-6" 7'-6"	2.78	–	–	192	—

*To convert to kgf, multiply by 453.6

were not significant as far as the behavior of the member was concerned. Inclined web shear cracking formed in both the second and third test on G-4. V_f is the applied load shear causing failure. Two flexural failures and three shear failures were observed in these tests.

The principal results of the box beam tests are given in Table 4. During the first test on G-1, inclined web shear cracking occurred in the web on one side of Region B, then on the opposite side of the beam in Region A, and finally on the other side of Region A. Web shear cracking did not develop in the web on the other side of Region B until the second test. Inclined flexure shear cracking occurred in both shear spans during the first test on G-3. Except for the second test on G-3, these tests ended in shear failures. The second test on G-3 was influenced by damage sustained during the first test.

BEHAVIOR OF TEST BEAMS

The shear failure in the first test on G-1 occurred in the compression flange above and ahead of inclined cracking which had developed in the stronger shear span. Views of both sides of this shear span are shown in Fig. 5. In these photographs of the test beams, the vertical lines on the sides of the specimen mark the location of the stirrups. The crack patterns are marked so as to indicate extent of development for the indicated applied load shear.

The unusual appearance of the failure in G-1 reflects the twisting which apparently occurred when the inclined web shear cracking did not develop simultaneously in opposite webs. Some of the stirrups were pulled out of the concrete in the region where the inclined crack crossed the lapped splice, but there were no fractured stirrups. The shear failure in the second test on G-1 was also influenced by twisting.

The first indication of the shear failure in the first test on G-2 was spalling of the extreme compression fibers adjacent to the load point bearing plate. This was followed by the sudden extension of an inclined diagonal tension crack through the compression flange, intersecting the location of the spalling. The failure in the second test on G-4, shown in Fig. 6, was similar to this, except that there was no indication of spalling prior to the shearing of the compression flange. The failure in the third test on G-4 was also similar, but there was more general crushing of the compression flange adjacent to the load point. This failure is also shown in Fig. 6.

The shear failure that occurred in the first test on G-3 is shown in Fig. 7. The failure occurred very suddenly and resulted in complete collapse of the beam. It was caused by crushing in the compression flange above the inclined flexure shear cracking which had developed out to a distance of about 2.3d from the load point. Two stirrups were fractured on each side of the beam, but these were likely a consequence rather than a cause of the failure. This failure occurred at a load greater than the calculated flexural capacity of the member.

Flexural failures occurred in the second test on G-2 and the first test on G-4. In both cases these failures were due to crushing of the concrete in the compression zone. The failure in G-4 occurred at the center of the span and is shown in Fig. 8. Just before this failure occurred, cracks were observed which were parallel to the compressive stress in the failure region.

The flexure shear cracking which developed in the first test on G-4 adjacent to the load point in Region B is also shown in Fig. 8. This cracking had developed out to a distance of 1.8d from the load point. However, at no time did it appear that this cracking would cause a shear failure.

The mid-span deflection observed during the nine tests is shown in Fig. 9. The response was essentially linear to the load at which flexural cracking was observed. Beyond this load the deflections show the effect of the transition from an uncracked to a cracked section. The formation of inclined cracks seemed to have little influence on the deflection.

However, the formation of inclined web shear cracks had a very pronounced influence on strains measured on the compression flange of the test beams. Sudden changes in these strains resulted from the shift, up or down depending on the location of the cracking with respect to the section at which the strains were measured, of the resultant compressive thrust. The formation of inclined flexure shear cracks influenced the measured strains to a lesser degree.

Measurements of inclined crack widths in the web of the I-beams, just above the bottom flange, are shown in Fig. 10. In the first test on G-2, there were several inclined web shear cracks in both shear spans. The widths shown in Fig. 10a are for the widest crack in both shear spans, which in both cases was the crack closest to the load point. The initial readings were obtained at loads below the load at which the crack formed, since the loading valve on the testing machine was closed when the cracking occurred, and the load registered on the machine decreased. After failure in the B end in the first test, the crack in the A end had a residual width of 0.038 in. (.96 mm). Its subsequent growth during the second test on G-2 is also shown in Fig. 10a.

The maximum inclined crack widths measured during the first test on G-4 were 0.032 in. (.81 mm) and 0.027 in. (.69 mm) in Regions A and B, respectively. These measurements on flexure shear cracks were made at 97 percent of the failure load. Widths of the web shear cracks which occurred during the second and third tests on G-4 are shown in Fig. 10b.

In Fig. 10c, the growth in the inclined web shear cracks for the tests on both G-2 and G-4 is shown for applied load shear above the shear causing the inclined crack. This shear, $V - V_{ic}$, is generally assumed to be the shear carried by the stirrup reinforcement. The influence of the amount of web reinforcement, rf_y, on the width of the inclined web shear cracks is clearly evident in Fig. 10c. It also appears that the a/d ratio affected the width of these cracks.

Measurements of inclined crack widths near the center of gravity of the box beams are shown in Fig. 11. The inclined cracking in the first and second test on G-1 was of the web shear type. As previously noted, however, the cracking and failure in these two tests was influenced by twisting in the member. The inclined cracking in the first test on G-3 was of the flexure shear type. These measurements in both the A end and the B end of G-3 were obtained at a horizontal distance of about 30 in. from the load point. The widths of the flexure shear cracks seemed unaffected by the amount of web reinforcement.

The inclined cracks in both the I and box beams were very wide. Considerably more web reinforcement than that provided would be required to limit these crack widths, even when they first form, to commonly accepted values of 0.010 to 0.020 in. (0.25 to 0.51 mm).

STRENGTH CONSIDERATIONS

Predicted Strength

Previous research [8-10] has shown that significant inclined cracking must develop in a prestressed concrete beam before shear is critical. In a beam without web reinforcement, the shear causing significant inclined cracking is generally regarded as the ultimate shear strength. The addition of web reinforcement increases the shear strength, by an amount approximately equal to the shear carried by the stirrups crossed by the inclined cracking. Therefore an analysis of shear strength is closely related to inclined cracking strength.

Inclined cracking is caused by principal tension stresses in the web of the beam, or by flexural cracking that either turns and becomes inclined in the direction of increasing moment or precipitates inclined cracking above it. In the latter case the flexural cracking strength is important.

The provisions of Section 2610 of the ACI Building Code (ACI 318-63)[4] reflect both of these factors -- flexural cracking strength and inclined cracking strength -- in determining the shear capacity of a prestressed concrete beam. These provisions were used to calculate the strength of the test beams. The results were expressed in terms of applied load shear for the loading applied to each test beam, and are recorded in Table 5. Ratios of test to calculated strength are indicated for all of the test values listed in Tables 3 and 4. According to these provisions, web shear cracking should occur in the second test on G-3 and the second and third tests on G-4. Flexure shear cracking should occur in the remainder of the tests. However, except for the first tests on G-3 and G-4, the computed shear causing either web shear or flexure shear inclined cracking was nearly the same.

The ultimate flexural capacity of the test beams was calculated from a computer program based on the assumption of a linear strain distribution. Failure is assumed to occur when a strain of 0.003 is reached in the extreme fiber in compression. The program incremented the location of the neutral axis until the compressive force in the concrete and mild steel reinforcement above the neutral axis balanced the force in the strand below the neutral axis. The compressive force was determined by fitting a rectangular stress block to the part of the beam above the neutral axis, using procedures recommended by Mattock, Kriz, and Hognestad.[11] The strand forces were determined using analytical expressions to represent the load strain curve in Fig. 3. The applied load shear, V_{fu}, which would develop the calculated flexural

TABLE 5 - STRENGTH OF TEST BEAMS

		Flexural Cracking		Inclined Cracking		Flexural Capacity		Shear Capacity	
Beam	Test	Calc V_{cr} (kips)**	Test/Calc	Calc V_{ic} (kips)**	Test/Calc	Calc V_{fu} (kips)**	Test/Calc	Calc* V_{su} (kips)**	Test/Calc
G-1	1	126.0	0.95	166.5	0.82	222.5	0.89	200.7	0.99
	2	128.5	--	168.7	--	225.7	0.96	187.9	1.15
G-2	1	63.9	1.13	84.0	1.24	118.7	0.93	94.2	1.17
	2	66.2	--	86.4	--	121.0	0.98	107.6	1.10
G-3	1	68.0	1.00	93.4	--	126.6	1.01	111.6	1.14
	2	154.5	--	177.9	--	271.5	0.71	200.7	0.96
G-4	1	34.2	0.99	48.1	--	67.5	0.98	56.3	1.17
	2	81.2	0.94	97.5	1.13	147.7	0.77	105.7	1.08
	3	81.2	0.94	97.5	1.22	147.7	0.92	114.4	1.19

*When specimen failed in shear, V_{su} calculated for region where failure occurred.

**To convert to kgf, multiply by 453.6

capacity of the test beams is listed in Table 5 and compared to the ultimate shear the beam sustained.

It may be observed from Table 5 that the test to calculated ratios of flexural cracking strength are less than one for all except the first test on G-2 and G-3. The calculated strength assumes that flexural cracking occurs when the stress in the bottom fibers is equal to $6\sqrt{f'_c}$. These values are sensitive to the magnitude of prestress, and in view of the difficulties encountered in determining this prestress, it may be that the actual prestress was somewhat less than the measured prestress. If the maximum allowable value from the ACI Building Code of 0.6 f'_s is assumed for the prestress, it will be found that the test to calculated ratios of flexural cracking strength are all greater than one.

The test to calculated ratios of inclined cracking strength are greater than one for all except the first test on G-1. This was the test on the shorter box beam in which web shear cracking occurred first on one side in the weaker shear span, then on the opposite side of the stronger shear span, and finally on the same side in the stronger shear span, before the failure occurred in the stronger shear span. As previously described, the nature of this cracking indicated that it was influenced by twisting.

The predictions of ultimate flexural and shear capacity were extremely good. For the two tests ending in a flexural failure -- Test 2 on G-2 and Test 1 on G-4 -- the test to calculated ratio of flexural strength was in both cases equal to 0.98. For the remaining tests, except the second test on G-3, the average test to calculated ratio of shear strength was equal to 1.08.

Comparison to Previous Tests

In a previous investigation,[10] thirty-five shear tests on a doubly symmetric 18-in. (46-cm) deep prestressed concrete I-beam were reported. These beams were prestressed with six $^{7}/_{16}$-in. (11-mm) diameter strand containing varying amounts of vertical web reinforcement, and were made with concrete comparable to that of the 36-in. (91-cm) deep beams tested in this investigation. The strength of these 18-in. (46-cm) deep beams was also compared to the strength calculated according to the ACI Building Code (ACI 318-63).[4] The range of the reported test results is shown in Fig. 12.

The plotted points in Fig. 12 represent the results of the 36-in. deep beams tested in this investigation. It is evident that the test to calculated ratios of shear strength for the 36-in. deep beams were not as great as for the 18-in. (46-cm) deep beams. The comparison of the flexural and inclined cracking strength of the two sets of tests was similar.

The difference in shear strength of the 18-in. and 36-in. deep beams may be at least partly attributed to the different modes of failure. That is, the shear failures in the 36-in. deep beams occurred in the relatively weak compression flanges. In contrast, most of the shear failures in the 18-in. (46-cm) deep beams were due to web crushing at the junction of the web and compression flange. However, it is not as easy to attribute the similar decrease in inclined cracking strength to this difference in shape.

CONCLUDING REMARKS

Reference 12 contains a complete and detailed report on this investigation. The following conclusions are drawn from this work.

1. The shear strength of the 36-in. (91-cm) deep prestressed concrete I and box beams tested in this investigation was satisfactorily predicted by the provisions of Section 2610 of the ACI Building Code (ACI 318-63).

2. The ratio of test to calculated shear strength of these beams was not as great as for previously tested 18-in. (46-cm) deep prestressed concrete I-beams. Part of this difference is attributed to the relatively "weak" compression flanges of the 36-in. (91-cm) deep beams.

3. Inclined web shear crack widths were affected by the amount of web reinforcement in the test beams; flexure shear crack widths were not affected. Considerably more web reinforcement than the minimum required by the ACI Code (ACI 318-63) is needed if inclined cracking, when it first forms, is to be limited to commonly accepted values of 0.010 to 0.020 in.

4. Inclined web shear cracking did not form simultaneously in the opposite webs of the box beam. As a result, the strength and behavior of the member was adversely affected.

ACKNOWLEDGMENTS

This work was conducted in the Department of Civil Engineering at Fritz Engineering Laboratory, under the auspices of the Institute of Research of Lehigh University, as part of a research investigation sponsored by: the Pennsylvania Department of Highways; the U. S. Department of Commerce, Bureau of Public Roads; and the Reinforced Concrete Research Council.

Completion of this work was facilitated by the capable help of the Fritz Engineering Laboratory staff and technicians. The authors acknowledge with appreciation the work of Mr. Howard Brecht, former research assistant at Lehigh University, in carrying out these tests, which were the basis of his Master of Science thesis. The cooperation and assistance of Dr. D. A. VanHorn, Chairman of the Department of Civil Engineering at Lehigh University, and Mr. Joseph Nagle, President of Schuylkill Products, Inc., is gratefully acknowledged.

REFERENCES

1. Kani, G. N. J., "How Safe Are Our Large Reinforced Concrete Beams?", ACI Journal, Proceedings, V. 64, No. 3, March 1967, pp. 128-141.

2. MacGregor, J. G., "Discussion of Reference 1", ACI Journal, Proceedings, V. 64, No. 9, September 1967, pp. 603-604.

3. ACI Committee 318, "Commentary on Building Code Requirements for Reinforced Concrete (ACI 318-63)," American Concrete Institute, Detroit, 1965, 91 pp.

4. ACI Committee 318, "Building Code Requirements for Reinforced Concrete (ACI 318-63)," American Concrete Institute, Detroit, 1963, 144 pp.

5. Joint Committee of AASHO and PCI, "Standard Prestressed Concrete Beams for Highway Bridge Spans 30 feet to 100 feet," 1957.

6. Commonwealth of Pennsylvania, Department of Highways, Bridge Division, "Standards for Prestressed Concrete Bridges," Harrisburg, September 1960.

7. Magura, D. D., Sozen, M. A., and Seiss, C. P., "A Study of Stress Relaxation in Prestressing Reinforcement," Journal, Prestressed Concrete Institute, V. 9, No. 2, April 1964, pp. 13-57.

8. MacGregor, J. G., Sozen, M. A., and Siess, C. P., "Strength of Prestressed Concrete Beams with Web Reinforcement," ACI Journal, Proceedings, V. 62, No. 12, December 1965, pp. 1503-1519.

9. Mattock, A. H. and Kaar, P. H., "Precast-Prestressed Concrete Bridges. 4. Shear Tests of Continuous Girders," Journal, PCA Research and Development Laboratories, V. 3, No. 1, January 1961, pp. 19-46.

10. Hanson, J. M. and Hulsbos, C. L., "Ultimate Shear Tests of Prestressed Concrete I-Beams Under Concentrated and Uniform Loadings," Journal, Prestressed Concrete Institute, V. 9, No. 3, June 1964, pp. 15-28.

11. Mattock, A. H., Kriz, L. S., and Hognestad, E., "Rectangular Concrete Stress Distribution in Ultimate Strength Design," ACI Journal, Proceedings, V. 57, No. 8, February 1961, pp. 875-928.

12. Brecht, H. E., Hanson, J. M., and Hulsbos, C. L., "Ultimate Shear Tests of Full-Sized Prestressed Concrete Beams," Fritz Engineering Laboratory Report No. 223.28, Lehigh University, December 1965, 106 pp.

NOTATION

a = distance from simple support to nearest load point, i.e. shear span

d = distance from extreme fiber in compression to centroid of prestressing strand, i.e. effective depth

E_c = modulus of elasticity determined from tests on 6 by 12-in. cylinders

f'_c = compressive strength determined from tests on 6 by 12-in. cylinders

f'_{sp} = splitting tensile strength determined from tests on 6 by 12-in. cylinders

f_y = yield strength of non-prestressed steel

L = span length

r = web reinforcement ratio

s = horizontal spacing of web reinforcement

V = applied load shear

V_{cr} = V causing flexural cracking

V_f = V causing failure

V_{fu} = V required to develop computed flexural capacity of test beams

V_{ic} = V causing inclined cracking

V_{su} = V required to develop computed shear capacity of test beams

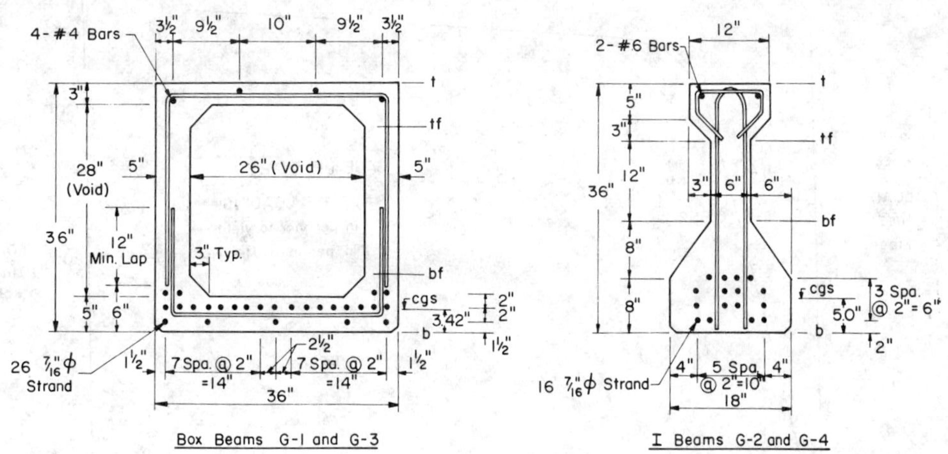

Note: To convert in. to cm, multiply by 2.54

FIG. 1 CROSS-SECTION OF TEST BEAMS

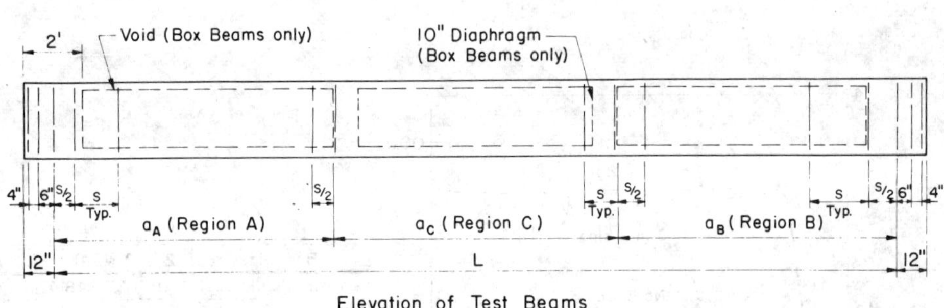

Elevation of Test Beams

Beam	Dimensions			Web Reinforcement								
				Region A			Region C			Region B		
	$a_A=a_B$ (ft)	a_C (ft)	L (ft)	Size (No.)	s (in.)	rf_y (psi)	Size (No.)	s (in.)	rf_y (psi)	Size (No.)	s (in.)	rf_y (psi)
G-1	9	9	27	3	12	105	5	12	247	3	21.6	59
G-2	9	9	27	3	18	114	5	12	412	2	18	55
G-3	15	15	45	3	18	70	5	12	247	3	22.5	56
G-4	15	15	45	3	22.5	91	5	12	412	2	22.5	44

Note: To convert ft. to m, multiply by 0.305
To convert in. to cm, multiply by 2.54
To convert psi to kgf/cm multiply by 0.0703

FIG. 2 WEB REINFORCEMENT IN TEST BEAMS

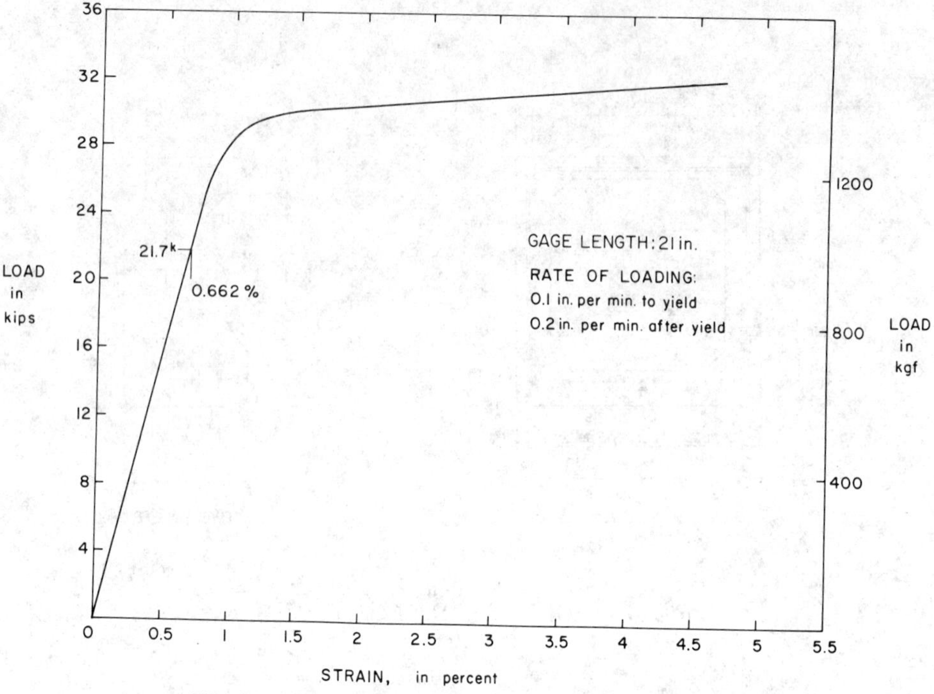

FIG. 3 LOAD-STRAIN CURVE FOR STRAND

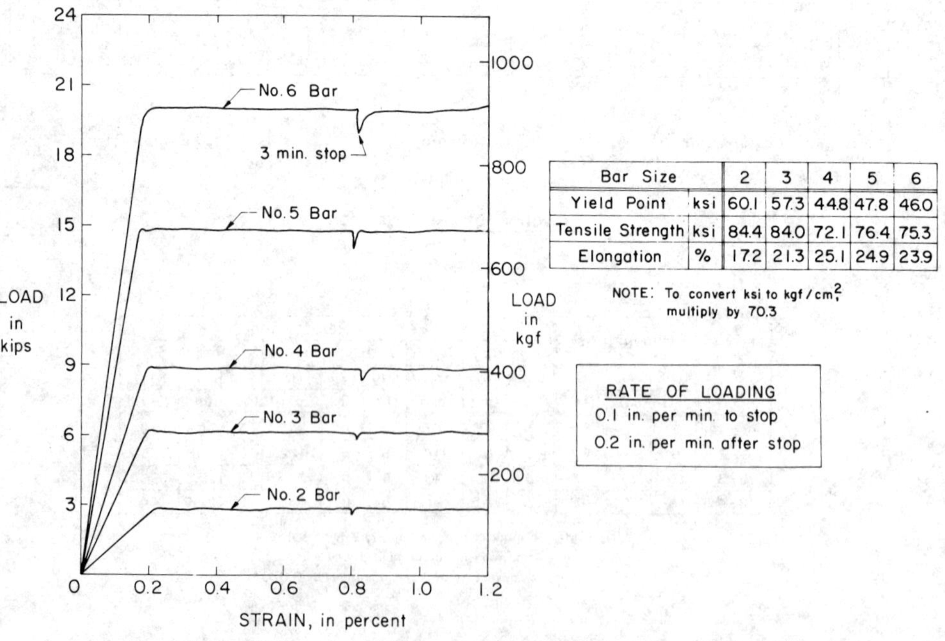

Bar Size		2	3	4	5	6
Yield Point	ksi	60.1	57.3	44.8	47.8	46.0
Tensile Strength	ksi	84.4	84.0	72.1	76.4	75.3
Elongation	%	17.2	21.3	25.1	24.9	23.9

FIG. 4 LOAD-STRAIN CURVES FOR REINFORCING BARS

Region A after failure

Opposite side of Region A after failure

Fig. 5 Views of G-1 after first test
Second test
Third test

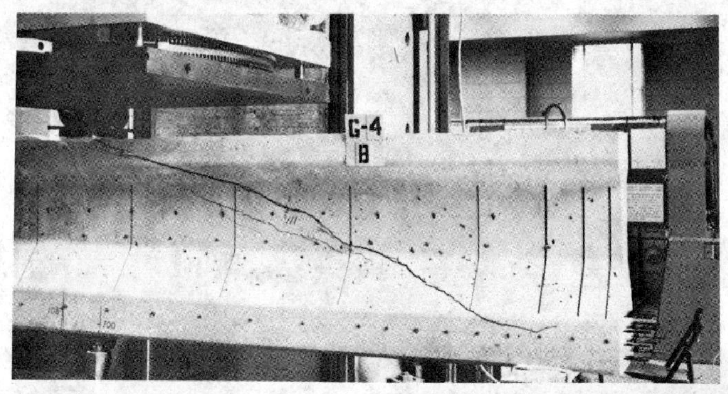

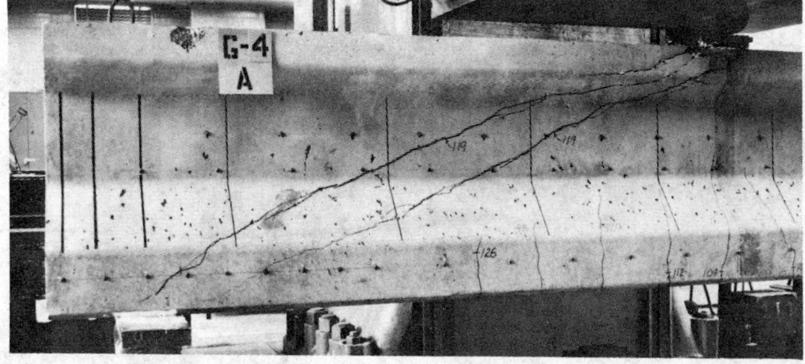

Fig. 6 Views of G-4 after second and third test

Region B near load point

Fig. 7 View of G-3 after first test

Failure region

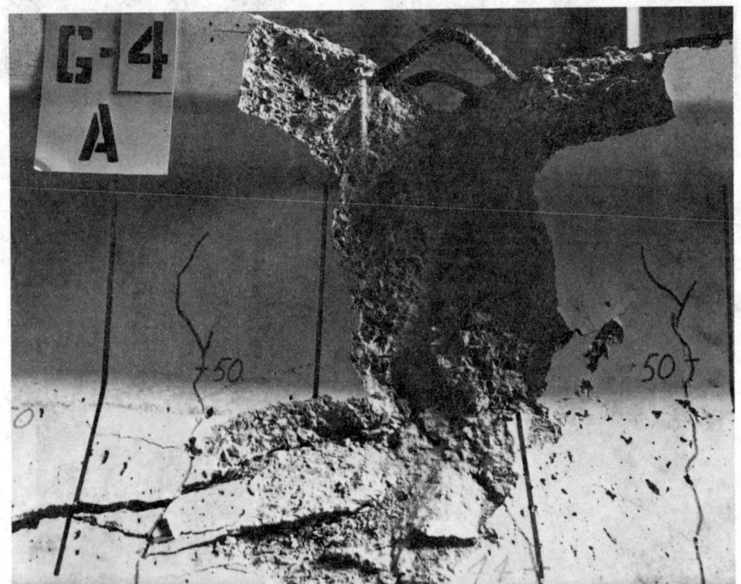

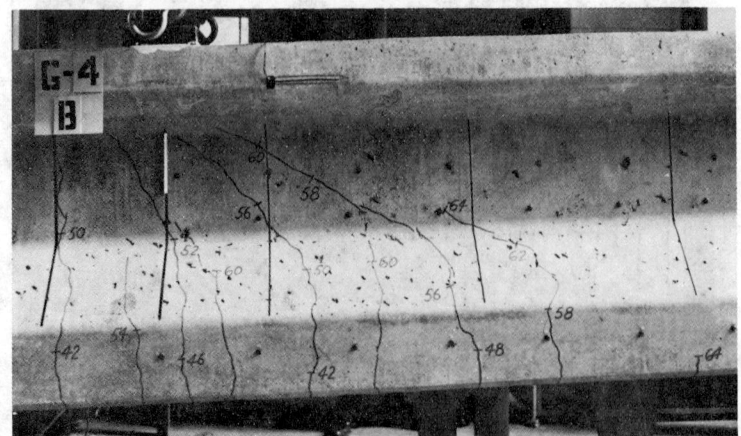

Fig. 8 Views of G-4 after first test

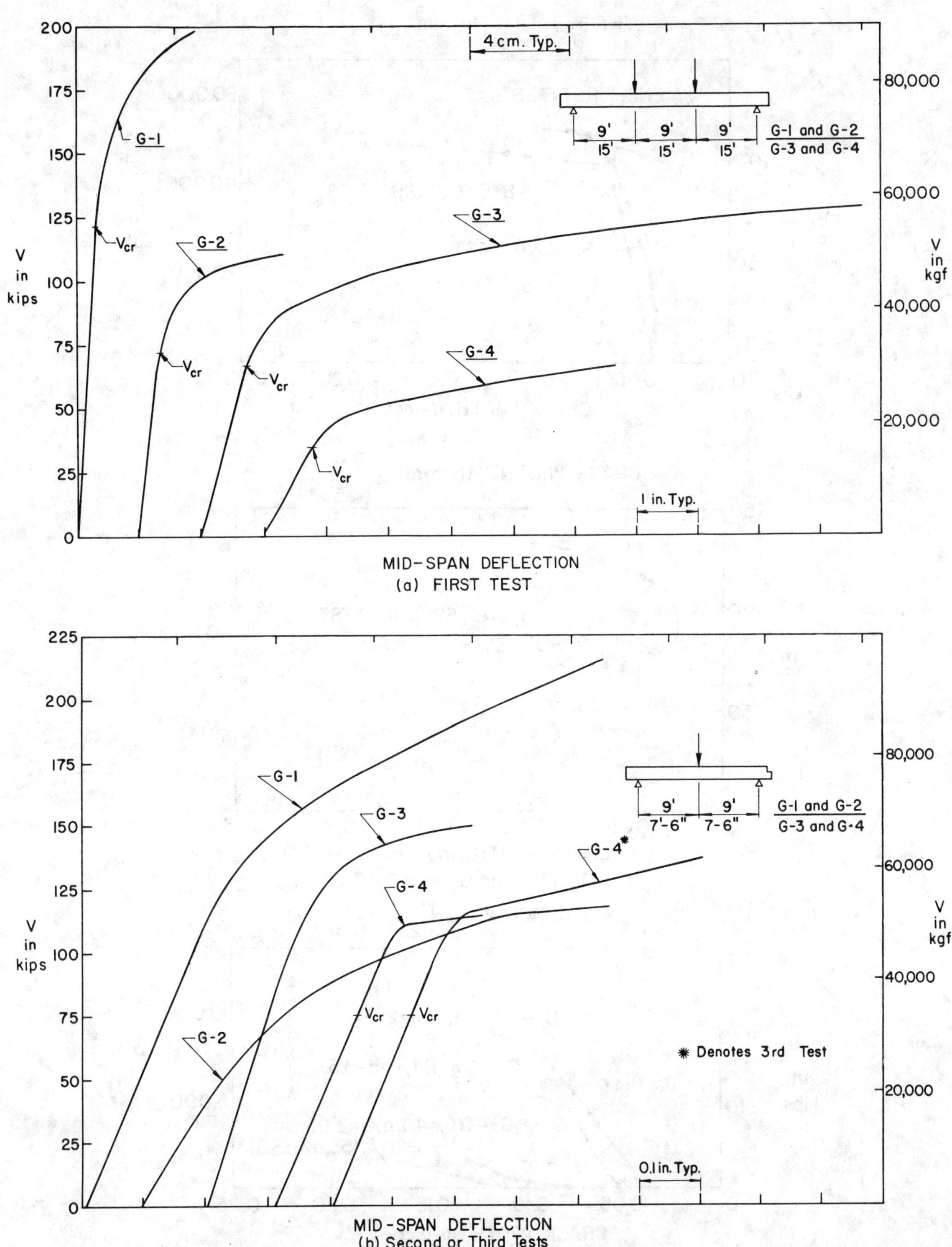

FIG. 9 DEFLECTION OF TEST BEAMS

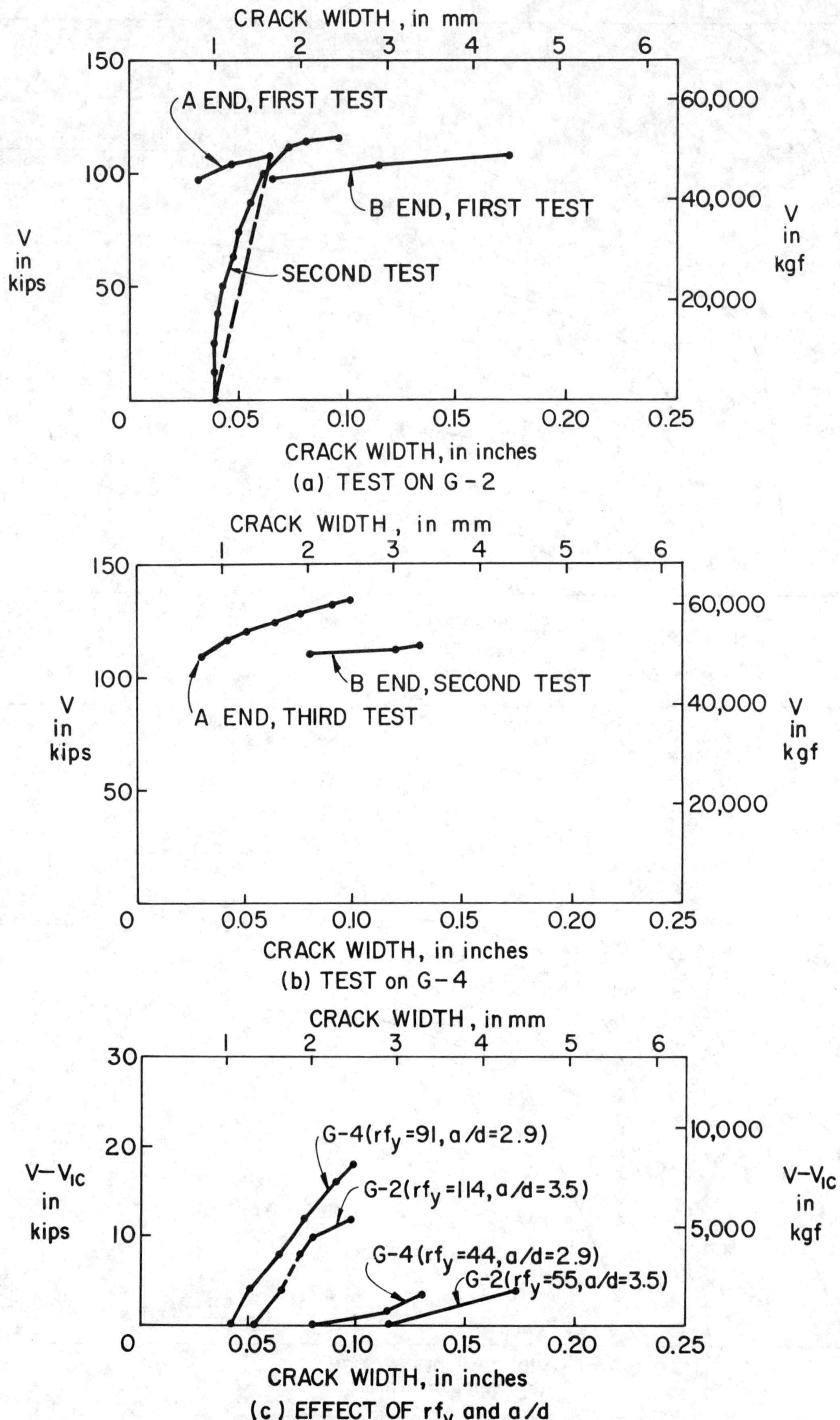

FIG. 10 INCLINED CRACK WIDTHS IN I-BEAMS

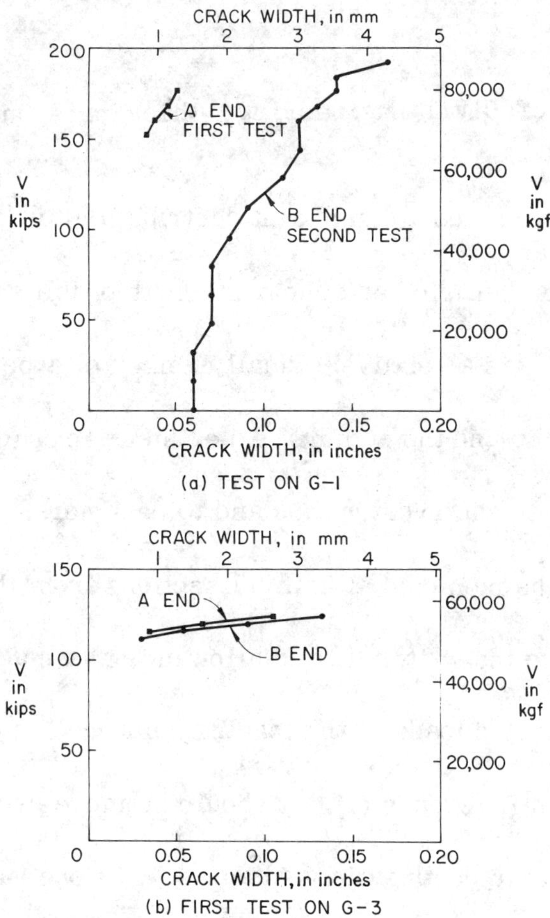

FIG. 11 INCLINED CRACK WIDTHS IN BOX BEAMS

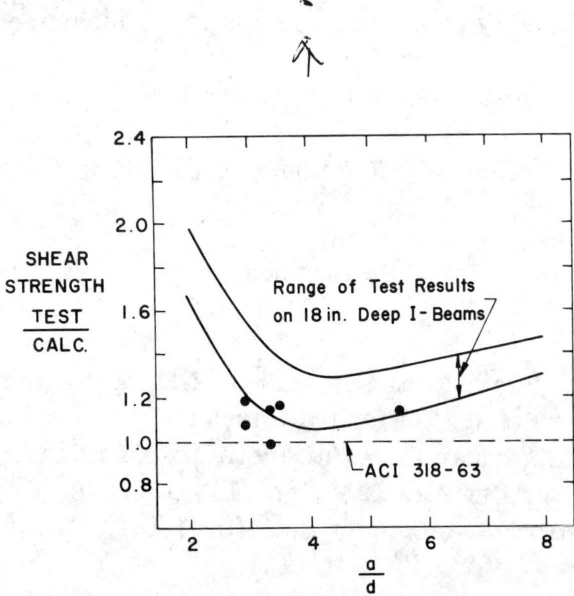

FIG. 12 COMPARISON OF TEST RESULTS WITH PREVIOUS TESTS

DISCUSSION

By A. BLSHARA

Associate Professor of Civil Engineering, Ohio State University

The authors have made a significant contribution to the understanding of the behavior and shear strength of full scale prestressed concrete beams. There is a relatively small number of experimental results available on large beams and the authors' experimental results would indeed prove very useful both to research investigators and to designers.

In calculating the moments at critical sections from the applied concentrated loads it seems to the writer that no allowance was made for the local distribution of concentrated loads at the loading points. The effect of such distribution was discussed in Reference (1). It should be more pronounced in beams with a small shear span to depth ratio. Also the ACI Code value of 0.003 adopted as the ultimate concrete compressive strain, which may be convenient for design purposes, seems to be very low if it is compared to measured experimental values reported under similar test conditions in References (1) and (2). It would be interesting to study the effect of such adjustments on the test results.

References

1. Mattock, Alan H., "Rotational Capacity of Hinging Regions in Reinforced Concrete Beams", Flexural Mechanics of Reinforced Concrete, SP-12, American Concrete Institute/American Society of Civil Engineers, Detroit, 1965, pp. 143-180; also Portland Cement Association Development Bulletin D-101.

2. Corley, W. G., "Rotational Capacity of Hinging Regions in Reinforced Concrete Beams", Proceedings, ASCE, V. 92, No. ST5, Oct. 1966, pp. 121-146; also PCA Development Bulletin D-108.

The authors thank Professor Bishara for his complimentary remarks about the paper.

Loads were applied to the test beams through 8-in. wide plates, as described in Reference (12). Calculated moments in the beams could be reduced only at sections within these bearing areas, and the maximum reduction for any loading arrangement would be 2 percent.

Calculated stresses in the extreme fibers or in reinforcement could be further reduced near load points if it is assumed that the applied load is distributed between 45 degree lines extending from the edges of the 8-in. wide plate to the neutral axis, as suggested in discusser's Reference (1). However, making this assumption would only affect calculations for tests with a single concentrated applied load, since the tests with two loads have a constant moment region. The resulting increase in computed flexural cracking strength or computed ultimate flexural capacity for any of the tests with a single load would be from 4 to 6 percent.

The authors do not regard a limiting concrete strain of 0.003 as low for these beams. In fact, G-4 carried its ultimate load for approximately 2 minutes before the failure shown in Fig. 8 occurred. During this time, the measured strain in the extreme fibers in compression, precisely at the section where this failure occurred, was 0.0023. It is the author's experience, however, that the computed flexural capacity of commonly-used prestressed beams is quite insensitive to the assumed value of limiting concrete strain.

LIMIT DESIGN FOR CONCRETE BRIDGES

By V. RAMAKRISHNAN, S. RAJASEKARAN, and R. KRISHNAMOORTHY

SYNOPSIS

The paper extends the application of A. L. L. Baker's ultimate load theory to the design of non-prismatic continuous girder and rigid frame bridges subjected to rolling loads. It deals mainly with two new aspects: (1) determination of influence lines for the rotation of 'plastic hinges' and (2) calculation of influence coefficients for non-prismatic members. To facilitate the calculation of the influence coefficients of non-prismatic structural members a volume integral table has been prepared. The procedure has been computerized by drawing up a list of Fortran instructions. An example is worked out to illustrate the application of this theory in the design of bridges.

Keywords: bridges (structures); computer programs; continuous beams; girders; hinges (structural); influence. lines; limit design method; moving loads; reinforced concrete; rigid frame bridges; rotation; structural analysis.

ACI member, DR. V. RAMAKRISHNAN is professor and head of the Department of Civil Engineering at P.S.G. College of Technology, Coimbatore, South India. Received his post-graduate education with special reference to Concrete Technology and Concrete Structures at the Imperial College and University College, London, where he was awarded the PhD degree in 1960. Engaged in teaching, research and consultation work, he is the co-author of a book on "Ultimate Strength Design for Structural Concrete" published by Pitman & Sons Ltd., London. He is also the editor of Proceedings of the first Indian Symposium on "Ultimate Load Design of Concrete Structures". He has published a number of technical papers and reports in the field of concrete technology and concrete structures.

S. RAJASEKARAN, lecturer in Civil Engineering Department, P.S.G. College of Technology, Coimbatore, received his BE and MSc (Engg.) degrees from the University of Madras. He has co-authored a few papers with Prof. V. Ramakrishnan. He is now pursuing advanced study and research at the University of Alberta, Edmonton, Canada.

R. KRISHNAMOORTHY, lecturer in Civil Engineering Department, P.S.G. College of Technology, Coimbatore, received his BE and MSc (Engg.) degrees from the University of Madras. He has co-authored a few papers with Prof. V. Ramakrishnan. He is currently engaged in his doctoral research work.

INTRODUCTION

Limit design procedures for the analysis and design of reinforced concrete indeterminate structures are drawing the attention of research workers and professional engineers because of their several advantages. Among the various limit design procedures Baker's limit design procedure has generally been considered eminently logical and adequately safe for the analysis and design of indeterminate structures subjected to stationary loads. In order that this theory may be used in the analysis and design of concrete bridge structures, the theory has to be extended to cover structures consisting of non-prismatic continuous members and structures subjected to moving loads. Although Baker's theory offers excellent possibility of such extension, this has not been attempted so far (1968). In this paper a procedure has been developed which allows the use of Baker's theory in the design of the above mentioned types of structures.

A.L.L.BAKER'S METHOD[1]

Baker's method is based on a set of general fundamental equations which are applicable to all types of statically indeterminate concrete structures. These equations are:

$$\delta_{10} + \bar{X}_1 \delta_{11} + \bar{X}_2 \delta_{12} + \bar{X}_3 \delta_{13} + \ldots + \bar{X}_N \delta_{1N} = -\theta_1$$

$$\delta_{20} + \bar{X}_1 \delta_{21} + \bar{X}_2 \delta_{22} + \bar{X}_3 \delta_{23} + \ldots + \bar{X}_N \delta_{2N} = -\theta_2$$

$$\vdots$$

$$\delta_{N0} + \bar{X}_1 \delta_{N1} + \bar{X}_2 \delta_{N2} + \bar{X}_3 \delta_{N3} + \ldots + \bar{X}_N \delta_{NN} = -\theta_N \qquad \ldots\ldots 1$$

In the above equations, 1, 2,..., N denote the individual plastic hinges. $\overline{X}_1, \overline{X}_2, \ldots, \overline{X}_N$ denote the magnitudes of the assumed plastic moments at these hinges. δ_{10}, $\delta_{20}, \ldots, \delta_{N0}$ are the rotations at hinges 1, 2,..., N due to externally applied loads when $\overline{X}_1, \overline{X}_2, \ldots, \overline{X}_N$ are zero. δ_{11}, δ_{12}, ... are the influence coefficients for hinge rotations, i.e., rotations due to unit moment applied at the hinge sections 1, 2.... N.. (For example, δ_{43} is the rotation of hinge '4' when unit moment is applied at hinge '3'.) 1, 2,...,N are the plastic hinge rotations. The influence coefficient is given by

$$\delta_{ik} = \sum \int_0^l \frac{M_i\, M_k\, ds}{EI} \quad \text{round the structure} \ldots\ldots \qquad (2)$$

where M_i = moment at any point in the structure when $\overline{X}_i = 1$ and all other $\overline{X}$'s are zero. M_k = moment at any point when $\overline{X}_k = 1$ and all other $\overline{X}$'s are zero.

$$\delta_{i0} = \sum \int_0^l \frac{M_i\, M_o\, ds}{EI} \quad \text{round the structure} \ldots\ldots \qquad (3)$$

where M_o = moment at any point in the structure due to applied loads when $\overline{X}_1, \overline{X}_2, \ldots, \overline{X}_N$ are zero.

The plastic hinge rotations θ_1, θ_2 etc. are calculated by plotting for each member of the structure separate diagrams of the moments due to applied load and due to unit equal and opposite moments acting at each hinge. The resultant rotation at any hinge when all loads act is the algebraic sum

sum of the rotations due to the moments caused by external loads (δ_{i0}) and the rotations due to the assumed internal plastic moments acting at each hinge ($\delta_{ik} \cdot \overline{X}_k$).

In this theory, it is assumed that a structure 'N' times statically indeterminate will develop 'N' hinges under increasing load prior to failure and that the plastic yield is concentrated at these hinges. The moments at the hinges are assumed to remain constant. Members between the points of yield are assumed to behave elastically having a linear moment curvature relationship. The flexural rigidity EI of the member between the plastic hinges is assumed to be constant (for prismatic members) and equal to the value at the idealized elastic limit. Thus, with the formation of 'N' hinges, the structure would become statically determinate. The structure will collapse (or in other words would have reached the ultimate load) when a very small additional increment of load would cause the formation of one or more additional hinges.

In the application of this theory, arbitrarily chosen values are assigned to the moments $\overline{X}_1$, $\overline{X}_2$.... $\overline{X}_N$ and the values necessary for full redistribution are evaluated. If the evaluated values of θ are positive and less than the permissible values, then the chosen values of $\overline{X}_1, \overline{X}_2, \ldots, \overline{X}_N$ can be used in the design. (Positive values of θ indicate that hinges have formed as assumed in the choice of values of $\overline{X}$.· Semi-empirical formulae based on exhaustive test results[2, 3, 4] have been recommended for calculating the permissible hinge rotations). Otherwise the values of $\overline{X}$ are adjusted until the calculated values of θ are positive and less than the permissible values. The nature of the equations suggests that $\overline{X}_p$ must be adjusted when θ_p is excessive.

Baker's equation can also be used to check the performance of the structure at working load. This is done easily by adjusting the arbitrarily selected values of $\overline{X}_1, \overline{X}_2, \ldots, \overline{X}_N$ until $\theta_1, \theta_2, \ldots, \theta_N$ values are zero (or very nearly so) in equation (1). Then these moments $\overline{X}_1, \overline{X}_2, \ldots, \overline{X}_N$ are the moments at the hinge sections according to the elastic theory. Working load stresses, based on the distribution of bending moment so obtained, can then be calculated and a check made to ensure the serviceability of the structure.

EXTENSION OF BAKER'S METHOD TO NON-PRISMATIC STRUCTURES SUBJECTED TO MOVING LOADS:

From the above outline, it is clear that the determination of the rotation of the hinges is the most important aspect of Baker's ultimate load theory. In the case of indeterminate structures with known loading patterns it is quite simple to calculate the rotations at critical positions as explained earlier. In the case of structures subjected to moving loads, the variability of load positions (and, consequently, the need to determine the load position causing maximum rotations), is an additional problem. The problem is tackled, in the elastic design methods, by drawing influence lines for the moment. A similar concept can be applied in the determination of hinge rotations also.

a) Determination of hinge rotations under moving loads:

Baker's continuity equation, for the elastic condition, takes the form

$$\delta_{io} + \sum_{k=1}^{N} X_k \, \delta_{ik} = 0 \qquad \ldots \quad \ldots \quad \ldots \quad (4)$$

Rearranging the above equation, we get

$$\delta_{io} = - \sum_{k=1}^{N} X_k \, \delta_{ik} \qquad \ldots \quad \ldots \quad \ldots \quad (5)$$

For example, for a structure having two degrees of indeterminacy, the continuity equations under elastic conditions are:

$$\delta_{10(e)} = - \delta_{11} X_1 - \delta_{12} X_2$$

$$\delta_{20(e)} = - \delta_{21} X_1 - \delta_{22} X_2 \quad \ldots \quad \ldots \quad (6)$$

where $\delta_{10(e)}$ and $\delta_{20(e)}$ are the rotations at the hinge locations 1 and 2 respectively under the working load. As the portions between the points of yield are assumed to behave elastically, the rotation $\delta_{10(p)}$ at the hinge location 1, at the instant when the structure has reached its ultimate load, may be expressed as

$$\delta_{10(p)} = \text{L.F.} \; \delta_{10(e)} \quad \ldots. \quad \ldots. \quad (7)$$

where L.F. is the load factor.

From equation (6)

$$\delta_{10(p)} = \text{L.F.} \left(- \delta_{11} X_1 - \delta_{12} X_2 \right) \ldots\ldots \quad (8)$$

The value of $\delta_{10(p)}$ obtained in this way can be used in the following Baker's equation for hinge rotation:

$$\delta_{10(p)} + \delta_{11} \bar{X}_1 + \delta_{12} \bar{X}_2 = - \Theta_1 \ldots\ldots \quad (9)$$

Hence

$$- \text{L.F.} \left(\delta_{11} X_1 + \delta_{12} X_2 \right) + \delta_{11} \bar{X}_1 + \delta_{12} \bar{X}_2 = - \Theta_1 \quad \ldots\ldots \quad (10)$$

If the sections are designed to resist the moments L.F. (X_1) and L.F. (X_2), then $\Theta_1 = 0$, and the design corresponds to the elastic case. If the sections are designed to resist moments $\bar{X}_1$ and $\bar{X}_2$ which are less than L.F. (X_1) and L.F. (X_2) then Θ_1 has a positive value and the sections undergo plastic rotation. The value of Θ_1 should be limited to the rotation capacity of the hinge.

In the equation (10) δ_{11} and δ_{12} are the influence coefficients which depend only on the geometry of the structure and $\overline{X}_1$ and $\overline{X}_2$ are the plastic moments of resistance of the sections and hence ($\delta_{11}\overline{X}_1 + \delta_{12}\overline{X}_2$) is a constant for the given structure. To get maximum rotation the expression L.F. (δ_{11} $X_1 + \delta_{12}X_2$) should be maximum in the equation (10). Hence, instead of drawing the influence line for rotation θ_1,it is sufficient to obtain the influence line for $\delta_{10(p)}$ itself (Equation 9). The appropriate load factors for dead and live load, and an impact factor to account for the dynamic effect of loading, should be applied in calculating the value of $\delta_{10(p)}$ according to Equation (8). The relative rotation θ_1 is obtained by substituting for $\delta_{10(p)}$ in the Equation (9). Similarly for any hinge i the influence line of $\delta_{io(p)}$ is drawn and θ_i value calculated. For the same assumed cross-sectional properties, various possible hinge patterns can be assumed and the one that gives the maximum value of $\delta_{io(p)}$ is selected as the critical hinge pattern. The hinge θ i is designed to have sufficient rotation capacity. With experience the worst possible hinge pattern can be selected by a few trials. A serviceability check should also be carried out in the usual manner to ensure safe working conditions.

b) Influence coefficients for a non-prismatic member:[5]

For the calculation of $\delta_{io(p)}$ the value of δ_{ik} (Equation 2) is necessary.

In equation (2) the function M_i/ EI is a non-linear function (as the rigidity function EI is a variable for a non-prismatic member) and the moment function M_k is linear. The product of the two functions equals the area of the curvilinear diagram of M_i/EI multiplied by the ordinate of the straight line diagram of M_k corresponding to the centre to gravity of the curvilinear diagram. The volume integrals for the usual diagrams of M_i/EI and of M_k in terms of the elastic parameters α, α' and β (which account for the non-prismatic nature of the structure) are presented in Table 1, Appendix 2. The above referred elastic parameters are available in standard tables and charts[6].

ILLUSTRATIVE EXAMPLE:

A typical example of a continuous girder bridge with parabolic haunches is worked out in Appendix 1 using the above method of analysis. The continuous beam considered is statically indeterminate to the second degree and hence two hinges are assumed to make the structure determinate, the hinge locations being so selected that no part of the structure forms a mechanism. To draw the influence line for $\delta_{10(p)}$ the influence coefficients δ_{11} and δ_{12} are calculated using the volume integral table. Assuming a unit load on the structure the values of X_1 and X_2 are determined for each load position and the influence lines for X_1 and X_2 are drawn (using the fixed point method). The influence line diagrams for $\delta_{10(e)}$ etc. are obtained by multiplying the ordinates of the influence line diagrams for moments X_1 and X_2 at the hinge sections by the respective values of the influence coefficients δ_{11} and δ_{12} etc. By applying the corresponding load factor for dead and live load the values of $\delta_{10(p)}$ and $\delta_{20(p)}$ are obtained. Sufficient rotation capacity is provided by suitable binders. Complete details of the solution of the problem are given in Appendix 1.

COMPUTER PROGRAM

The analysis and design by Baker's method of an indeterminate non-prismatic member subjected to moving loads can be conveniently divided into three steps.

The first step comprises the computation of plastic moments of resistance ($\bar{X}$ values) and EI values for the assumed sections of the various members.

The second step is the calculation of influence line ordinates for elastic bending moment at the assumed hinge sections. This analysis can be conveniently done by the 'fixed point method' which is particularly suitable for machine computations. This involves the calculation of the elastic parameters α, α' and β , and the determination of influence line ordinates for bending moments (X_i values).

The third step is the calculation of relative rotation of the hinges (θ_i values) which are checked with the permissible rotation capacity of the hinges. Corresponding to the above three steps computer programs can therefore be prepared so that they can be applied to the analysis and design of any type of problem.

The general computer flow charts for the above three steps are given in Fig. 4(a), (b) and (c) respectively. The programs were written in Fortran language and the results were obtained using IBM 1620 computer with a 40K storage unit. The computer program of flow chart 4(b) yields only the values of the elastic parameters and moment values (X_i). δ io(e) has to be calculated as explained earlier. An integrated flow chart for directly obtaining δ io(e) values has been suggested in Fig. 4(d).

CONCLUSION:

A.L.L. Baker's limit design procedure has been extended to solve problems of indeterminate prismatic and non-prismatic structure subjected to moving loads. The suggested procedure is simple and quick. The illustrative example given shows that the method is particularly suitable for the analysis of continuous girder bridges with varying cross-sections. The method is also suitable for machine computation.

ADKNOWLEDGMENT:

The authors are grateful to Professor G. R. Damodaran, Director, P.S.G. College of Technology, Coimbatore - 4, for his encouragement in the preparation of this paper. Sincere thanks are due to Professors Y. Ananthanarayana and A. N. Lakshmanan for their review and suggestions.

REFERENCE:

1. BAKER, A.L.L., Ultimate Load Theory Applied to the Design of Reinforced and Prestressed Concrete Frames, Concrete Publications Ltd., London, 1956.

2. RAMAKRISHNAN, V., and ARTHUR P. D., Ultimate Strength Design for Structural Concrete, by Pitman & Sons, London, 1968.

3. BAKER, A.L.L., and AMARAKONE, A.M.N., Inelastic Hyperstatic Frames Analysis, Flexural Mechanics of Reinforced Concrete, Proceedings of the International Symposium, Miami, Fla., Nov. 1964.

4. INSTITUTION RESEARCH COMMITTEE REPORT, Ultimate Load Design of Concrete Structures, Proceedings of the Institution of Civil Engineers, V. 21, Feb. 1962, pp. 399-442.

5. RAMAKRISHNAN, V., RAJASEKARAN, S., and KRISHNAMOORTHY, R., Influence Coefficient Method for Non-prismatic Structures (submitted for publication).

6. TAYLOR, THOMPSON and SMULSKI, Reinforced Concrete Bridges, John Wiley & Sons, 1958.

NOTATIONS:

Unless otherwise defined in the text, the following notation applies:

X_k - Unknown elastic bending moment acting at the hinge k.

$\overline{X}_k$ - Plastic moment of resistance acting at the hinge k.

σ_{cu} - Cube strength of concrete

σ_e - the compressive stress in concrete in the extreme fiber

σ_{sy} - Yield stress in steel

ϵ_c - The compressive strain in concrete at the extreme fiber

ϵ_{sy} - Yield strain in steel

A_t - Area of tensile reinforcement

b - breadth of the section

n_1d - depth of the neutral axis

$\alpha_1, \alpha_1', \beta_1$ - Elastic parameters for the first span

α'' - the shape factor for stress block

EI - Flexural rigidity of the section

I_c - The moment of inertia at the center of the span (minimum value along the length)

ℓ - span length

APPENDIX 1

EXAMPLE:

The general arrangement of the bridge to be designed is shown in Fig. 1. The bridge will be designed for the Indian Roads Congress Class A loading. Load factors will be assumed according to Indian Standards. The sectional and material properties are given in Fig. 1c and 1d.

I - DETERMINATION OF THE FLEXURAL RIGIDITY EI:

Assuming a linear strain distribution and a value of 0.00045 for the concrete strain (at the instant of yield of steel) the neutral axis depth for mid span section is

$$n_1 d = \frac{37.25}{\left(1+\frac{0.0012}{0.00045}\right)} = 10.18''$$

The compressive stress σ_c in the concrete at the top fiber of the flange (assuming a parabolic stress strain curve for concrete) is

$$\sigma_c = \frac{4 \times 0.85 \times 3000 \times 0.00045}{(0.004)^2} (0.004-0.00045) = 1019 \text{ psi}$$

Using the linear strain distribution, the compressive stresses at the middle and bottom fibers of the flange can be similarly calculated as 698 psi and 346 psi respectively. The compressive force contributed by the outstanding portions of the flange can thus be obtained as 285,000 lbs.

Taking the value of α'' as 2/3, the compressive force contributed by the rib portion is

$$\alpha'' \sigma_c b\, n_1 d = 2/3 \times 1019 \times 18 \times 10.18 = 125{,}500 \text{ lbs.}$$

The total compressive force at mid section = 419,500 lbs.

The total tensile force at mid section $= A_t \sigma_{sy} = 405{,}400$ lbs.

As the equilibrium condition is thus nearly satisfied, the assumed concrete strain is satisfactory. The plastic moment of resistance of all mid span sections is the same and equal to 133.9 x 10^5 lb-in.

The flexural rigidity $EI = \frac{M\, n_1 d}{\epsilon_c} = \frac{133.9 \times 10^5 \times 10.18}{0.00045}$

$= 30.2 \times 10^{10}$ lb-inch^2.

Similarly for the support sections (Fig. 1d) we obtain

$$\epsilon_c = 0.0009$$

Plastic moment of resistance = 707 x 10^5 lb-inch

$EI = 260 \times 10^{10}$ lb-inch^2.

II - DETERMINATION OF THE ELASTIC PARAMETERS:

Using the computer program the values for the elastic parameters α, α', and β are obtained as:

$\alpha_1 = 0.993$ $\alpha_2 = \alpha_2' = 0.651$ $\alpha_3 = 0.658$

$\alpha_1' = 0.658$ $\beta_2 = 0.854$ $\alpha_3' = 0.993$

$\beta_1 = 0.927$ $\beta_3 = 0.927$

III - CALCULATION OF INFLUENCE COEFFICIENTS:

The continuous beam shown in Fig. 1 is statically indeterminate to the second degree. Therefore two hinges are to be assumed. Five possible hinge patterns are shown in Fig. 2. For the first pattern the following influence coefficient values are obtained by using Table 1.

$$\delta_{11} = 4\left[\frac{\alpha_1\ \ell_1}{3\ EI_c} + \frac{\alpha_2\ \ell_2}{3\ \ EI_c}\right] = 122.7/\ EI_c$$

$$\delta_{12} = \delta_{21} = \frac{\beta_2\ell_{bc}}{6\ EI_c} = 31.88/\ EI_c$$

$$\delta_{22} = \frac{4}{3EI_c}(\alpha_3 + \alpha_3') = 122.7/\ EI_c$$

IV - CALCULATION OF ROTATIONS AT HINGE SECTIONS DUE TO MOVING LOADS:

(i) Influence line for $\delta_{10(e)}$:

Each span is divided into four parts. Considering unit moving load, influence lines are drawn for X_1 and X_2 (Fig. 3). Using these influence lines and the values of δ_{11} and δ_{12}, the influence line for $\delta_{10(e)}$ can be easily drawn (Fig. 3).

(ii) Determination of $\delta_{10(p)}$:

Using a load factor of 1.5 for dead load (I.S. 456-1964)

$$\delta_{10(p)} \text{ due to dead load } = -\frac{796.5 \times 10^5}{EI_c}$$

For the calculation of the hinge rotation due to live load the following factors are used:

Load factor = 2.2 (as per I.S. Code)

Impact factor = 1.1975 (as per I.R.C. Section 2)

Reaction factor = 1.11 (obtained by calculation)

Placing 2 trains of I.R.C. Class A loading (Fig. 3) along the span, the value of $\delta_{10(p)}$ due to live load is

$$- \frac{1130 \times 10^5}{EI_c}$$

Total $\delta_{10(p)}$ for dead and live load $= - \frac{1926.5 \times 10^5}{EI_c}$

For this hinge pattern the value of $\delta_{20(p)}$ is equal to $\delta_{10(p)}$.

V - CALCULATION OF PLASTIC ROTATION:

Using equation (9) $\theta_1 = \theta_2 = 0.0093$ radians.

VI - CALCULATION OF THE ROTATION CAPACITY OF THE HINGES:

Using the formulae suggested by Baker[3] the rotation capacity of the section, when 3/8" dia 2 legged binders at 30cm spacing are provided works out to 0.0208 radians. Thus the design is satisfactory.

CHECK FOR SERVICEABILITY:

Check for serviceability is carried out as usual.

For other hinge patterns, analysis is done on similar lines and the design is made for the worst condition.

APPENDIX 2

INFLUENCE COEFFICIENTS OF NON-PRISMATIC MEMBERS:

Let $M_i / EI_x = f(x)$

and $M_k = mx + o$

Then the influence coefficient δ_{ik} is given by

$$\delta_{ik} = \int_0^l \frac{M_i M_k \, dx}{EI_x} = \int_0^l f(x) \quad (mx + c) \quad dx = A \, (m\bar{x} + c) \quad \ldots\ldots \quad (11)$$

where A = Area of the M_i/EI_x diagram

$m\bar{x} + c$ = Ordinate of the M_k diagram corresponding to the position of centroid of the M_i/EI_x diagram.

To facilitate further calculations, the values of certain basic integral functions are obtained in terms of the elastic parameters[6] α, α' and β . For the member shown in Fig. 5a, we obtain

$$\alpha = 3 \int_0^l \frac{I_c}{I_x} \left(1 - \frac{x}{l}\right)^2 d\left(\frac{x}{l}\right)$$

$$\alpha' = 3 \int_0^l \frac{I_c}{I_x} \left(\frac{x}{l}\right)^2 d\left(\frac{x}{l}\right)$$

$$\beta = 6 \int_0^l \frac{I_c}{I_x} \left(\frac{l - x}{l}\right) \left(\frac{x}{l}\right) d\left(\frac{x}{l}\right)$$

$$\int_0^l \frac{dx}{EI_x} = \frac{l}{3 \, EI_c} = (\alpha + \alpha' + \beta)$$

$$\int_0^l \frac{x dx}{EI_x} = \frac{l^2}{6^x EI_c} (2 \alpha' + \beta)$$

$$\int_0^{l} \frac{x^2 dx}{EI_x} = \frac{\alpha' l^3}{3\ EI_c}$$

$$\int_0^{l} \frac{x\ (1 - x)\ dx}{EI_x} = \frac{l^3 \beta}{3EI_c}$$

To illustrate the method of computation, let us consider the case in which M_i diagram is a rectangle having an ordinate 'a' and M_k diagram is a trapezium. (Figs. 5b and 5c).

Then the area of the $\frac{M_i}{EI_x}$ diagram is

$$\int_0^{l} \frac{M_i}{EI_x} dx = \frac{al}{3EI_c} (\alpha + \alpha' + \beta)$$

The distance of the centroid of the M_i/EI_x diagram from A is

$$\bar{x} = \frac{\int_0^{l} \frac{M_i\ x\ dx}{EI_x}}{\int_0^{l} \frac{M_i}{EI_x} dx} = \frac{(2\alpha' + \beta)}{(\alpha + \alpha' + \beta)} \frac{l}{2}$$

The ordinate at a distance $\bar{x}$ from A in the M_k diagram is.

$$\frac{\bar{x}\ d + (l - \bar{x})\ c}{} = \frac{(2\alpha' + \beta)\ d + (2\alpha + \beta)\ c}{2\ (\alpha + \alpha' + \beta)}$$

The value of the product integral from equation (11) is

$$\delta_{ik} = \int_0^{l} \frac{M_i M_k\ dx}{EI_x} = \frac{al}{6EI_c} (2\alpha' + \beta)\ d + (2\alpha + \beta)\ c$$

By adopting a similar procedure other values of the product integrals shown in Table 1 are obtained. The product integral table for prismatic members is a particular case of Table 1.

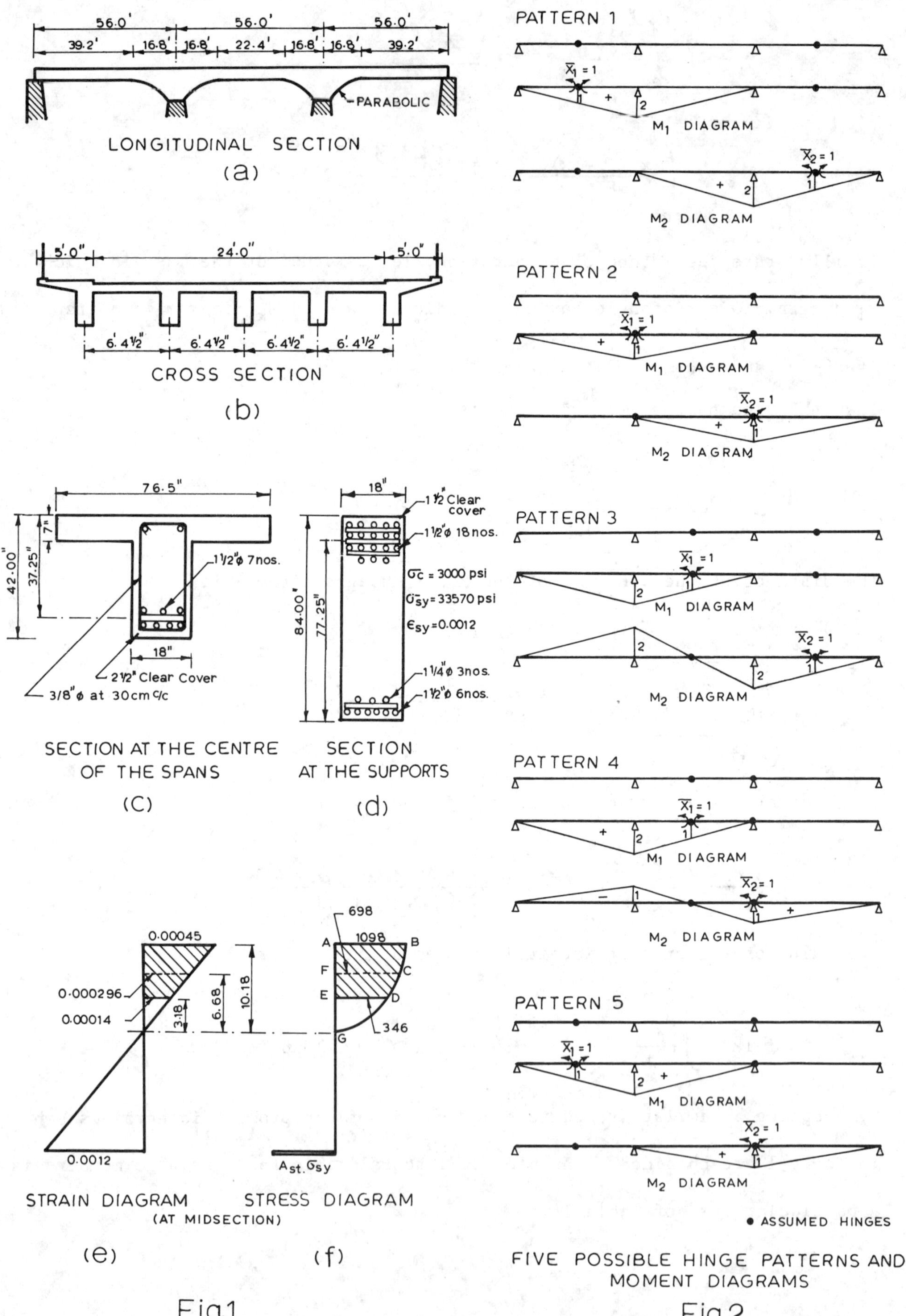

Fig.1

FIVE POSSIBLE HINGE PATTERNS AND MOMENT DIAGRAMS

Fig.2

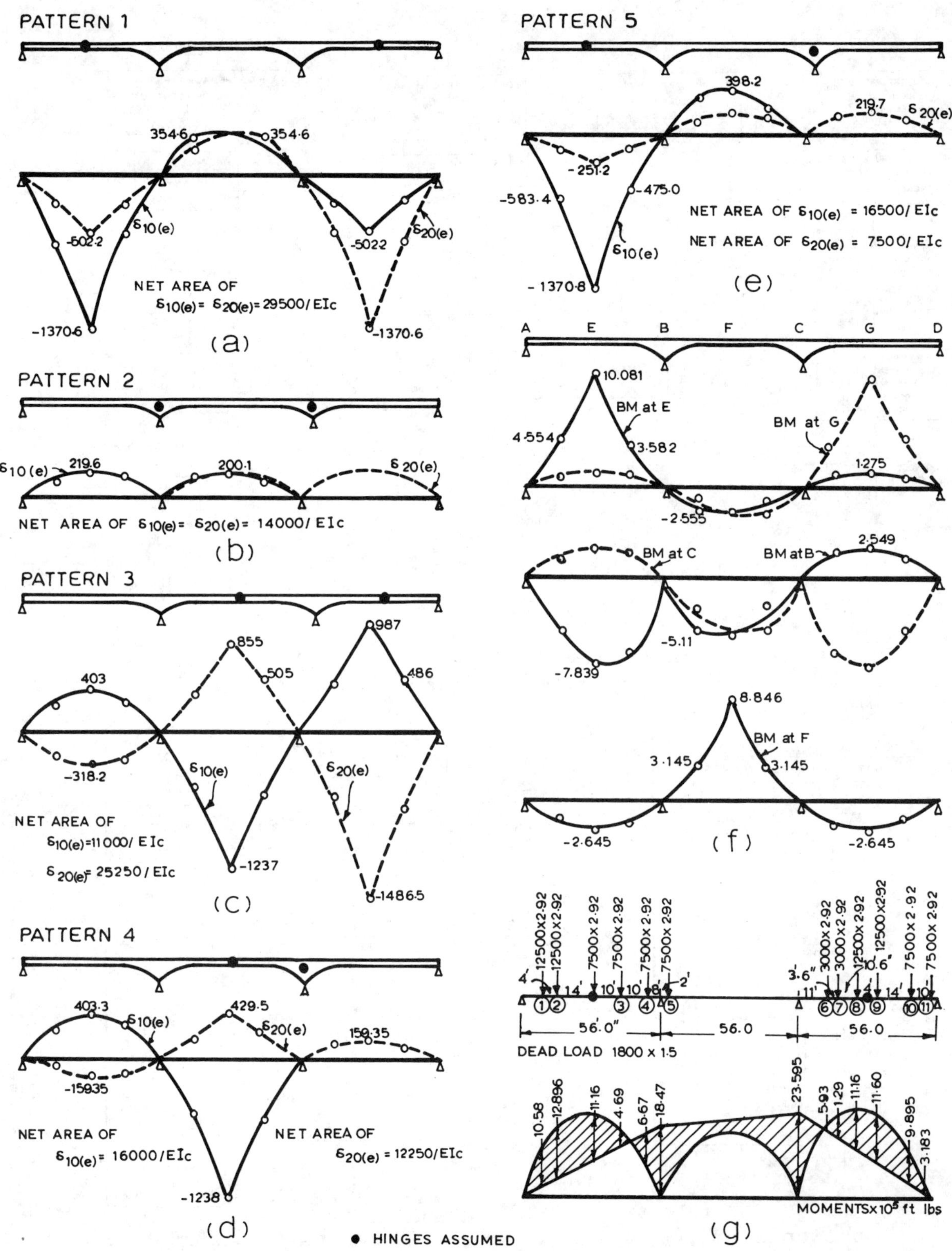

Fig. (a) to (e) – INFLUENCE LINES FOR $\delta_{10(e)}$ & $\delta_{20(e)}$

Fig. (f) – INFLUENCE LINES FOR BM AT THE HINGE SECTIONS

Fig. (g) – PLASTIC BENDING MOMENT DISTRIBUTION

Fig. 3

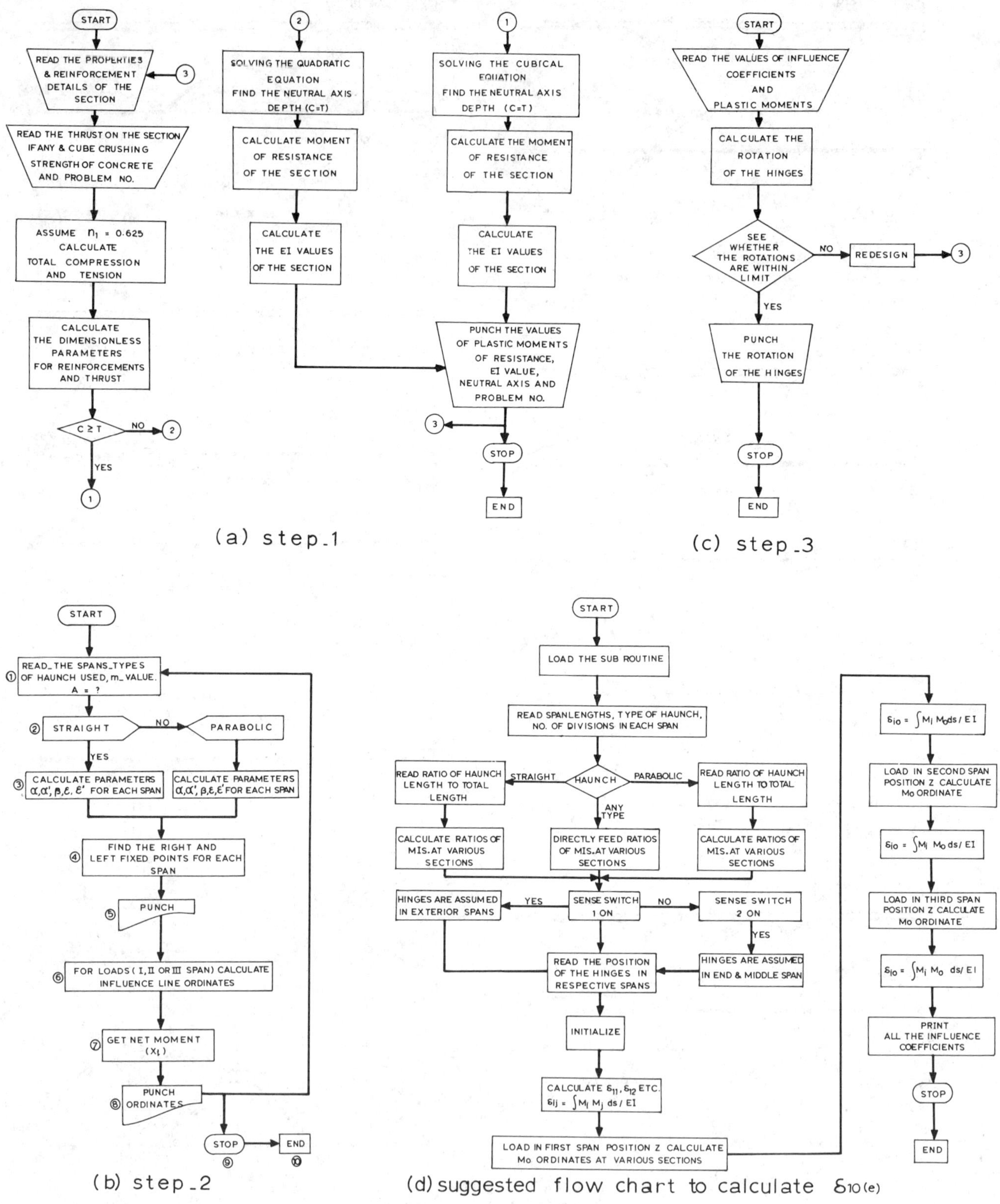

Fig. 4 COMPUTER FLOW CHARTS

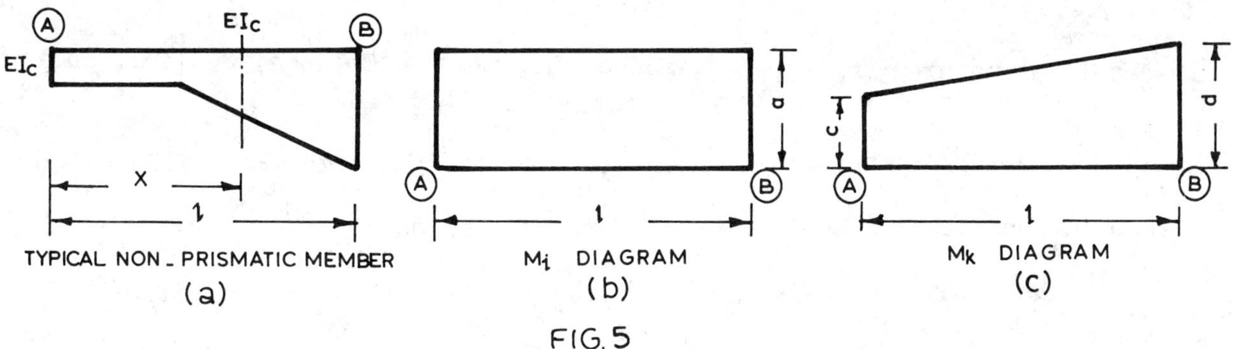

FIG. 5

TABLE 1 _ VOLUME INTEGRALS FOR NON _ PRISMATIC MEMBER $\int \frac{M_i M_k}{EI_x} dx$ VALUES

M_k DIAGRAM / M_i DIAGRAM	c, l	l, d	c, l	c, l, d
a, l	$\frac{lac}{3EI_c}(\alpha + \alpha' + \beta)$	$\frac{lad}{6EI_c}(2\alpha' + \beta)$	$\frac{lac\,(2\alpha + \beta)}{6EI_c}$	$\frac{la}{6EI_c}$ $(2\alpha' + \beta)d + (2\alpha + \beta)c$
b, l	$\frac{(2\alpha' + \beta)\,lbc}{6EI_c}$	$\frac{\alpha' lbd}{3EI_c}$	$\frac{\beta lbc}{6EI_c}$	$\frac{lb\,(2\alpha' d + \beta c)}{6EI_c}$
a, l	$\frac{(2\alpha + \beta)\,lac}{6EI_c}$	$\frac{\beta lad}{6EI_c}$	$\frac{\alpha lac}{3EI_c}$	$\frac{la\,(2\alpha c + \beta d)}{3EI_c}$
a, b, l	$\frac{lc}{6EI_c}$ $(2\,[(a\alpha + \beta\alpha') + \beta(a+b)]$	$\frac{ld}{6EI_c}(a\beta + 2b\alpha')$	$\frac{lc}{6EI_c}(\beta b + 2\alpha a)$	$\frac{l}{6EI_c}$ $[(a\beta + 2b\alpha')d + (b\beta + 2a\alpha)c]$

DISCUSSION

By R. NAGARAJA

Reader in Structural Engineering, Madhar Engineering College, Gwalior, India

The authors have to be congratulated for the extension of Baker's method to nonprismatic continuous girder frame bridges.

The method suggested by the authors is essentially applicable to only single beams rather than a system of interconnected beams. With the increasing need for accommodating the occasional abnormal load on the bridge the method would have been very useful had it considered several interconnected girders and different positions of load. The structural interaction between the longitudinal beams, transverse beams and the slab would influence the ultimate load capacity of the system considerably.

Considerable emphasis has been put in the paper on the rotational capacity of the plastic hinges. The rotational capacity of a plastic hinge in reinforced concrete, while dependent on the percentage of reinforcement in the section, could be influenced by the limiting concrete strains, the generally assumed value of which is 0.003. However, in sections containing transverse reinforcement Baker(1) has observed ultimate concrete strains of up to 0.01. In tests on models of beam and slab bridges at Queen's University at Kingston, the author(2) found limiting concrete strains around 0.008. Reinforced concrete sections proportioned as per the requirements of the ACI 318-63 Code have reasonably large rotational capacities. The recent Bureau of Public Roads(3) recommendation of reinforcement percentages less than 0.5 times the balanced area of steel would considerably enhance the rotational capacity of reinforced concrete sections. Thus the calculation of the rotational capacities of critical sections involved in the mechanisms of failure seems to be rather unnecessary.

References:

(1) Baker, A.L.L., "Ultimate Load Theory Applied to the Design of Reinforced and Prestressed Concrete Frames", 1st Edition, London, Concrete Publications Ltd, 1956.

(2) Nagaraja, R., "Ultimate Strength of Two and Four-Beam Highway Bridges" Ph.D. Thesis, Queen's University at Kingston, February 1969.

(3) "Strength and Serviceability Criteria - Reinforced Concrete Bridge Members - Ultimate Strength Design" Bureau of Public Roads U.S. Dept. of Commerce, August, 1966.

By C. W. YU

Senior Lecturer on Concrete Structures and Technology, Imperial College, London

The development of Baker's ultimate load theory to the design of non-prismatic continuous bridge girder as discussed in the paper is interesting. The validity of the development depends on the EI values used in the equations. The permissible rotations in Bakers' method depends on the EI values used in the calculations. All experimental verifications in this respect were carried out on uniform rectangular sections[1,2]. Perhaps the authors would explain what experimental work has been carried out to justify the use of similar expression for permissible rotations in the case of non prismatic members with haunches.

Reference:

1. Baker A.L.L. & Amarakone, A.M.N. - Inelastic Hyperstatic Frame Analysis, Flexural Mechanics of Reinforced Concrete Proceedings of the International Symposium, Miami, Flo. Nov. 1964.
2. Amarakone, A.M.N. & Yu, C.W. - Flexural Stiffness of R.C. members for ultimate Load Design. Civil Engineering and Public Works Review, Nov. 1965. pp 1637-1641.

By E. G. NAWY

Professor of Civil Engineering, Rutgers University, New Brunswick

The authors are to be congratulated on their valuable contribution to the field of limit behavior of continuous concrete bridges, particularly non-prismatic members subject to moving load. Their simplified extension of A.L.L. Baker's theory for application to moving loads and use of computers for determining compatibility of rotation and of the plastic moments do present the design engineer with proceedures that would have been too rigorous only few years ago.

The writer, however, feels that simplification can be introduced to reduce the possible number of collapse mechanisms shown in Figs. 2 and 3 of the paper. Such simplification can be achieved by imposing the location of the developing hinges at the supports only for instance. Choosing reinforcement along the span in such a manner that the span would remain understressed while the supports' reinforcement yields would force the plastic hinges to develop at the support only. Such procedure would not only be possible in reinforced but in prestressed continuous girders. In the case of continuous prestressed girders, prestressing can be confined to the span while continuity at the support can be achieved through normal reinforcement which would resist live load and impact only.[1]

Work done by the writer[2,3,4] demonstrates that the rotation capability of plastic hinges both for reinforced and prestressed bonded and non-bonded beams can be increased considerably (ten to twenty times in certain cases) through the use of spiral binders. The confining effect of these binders would render the plasticity zones exceedingly ductile, thereby permitting the safe use of limit design procedures in continuous concrete structural systems including continuous bridges.

References

1 - Lin, T.Y. "Design of Prestressed Concrete Structures," Text Book, 614 p.

2 - Nawy, E.G. and Salek, F., "Moment-Rotation Relationships of Non-Bonded Post-Tensioned I - and T-Beams - Proc. Journal of the Prestressed Concrete Institute, Vol. 13, #4, August 1968, pp. 40-55.

3. Nawy, E.G., Danesi, R.F., and Grosko, J.J., "Rectangular Spiral Binders Effect on Plastic Hinge Rotation Capacity in Reinforced Concrete Beams," - Proc. Journal of the American Concrete Institute, Vol. 65 #12, December 1968, pp. 1001-1010. Also"Discussion and Author's Closure" - Proc. Journal of ACI, Vol. 66 #6, June 1969.

4. Nawy, E.G. and Potyondy, J.G., "Moment-Rotation Relationships and Cracking of Spirally Bound Pretensioned Prestressed Concrete Beams" - Rutgers University, Bureau of Engineering Research Report #49, to be published.

AUTHOR'S CLOSURE

AUTHORS' REPLY TO THE DISCUSSION BY DR. NAGARAJA

The authors are thankful to Dr. Nagaraja for his discussion. The ultimate load analysis of the bridge deck considering the structural interaction between the longitudinal and transverse systems is a three dimensional problem. In this case bending and torsion hinges can be assumed in the bridge grillage. The analysis of a single continuous girder of a bridge is a two dimensional problem. While extending Baker's theory to the above two problems both pose the same basic difficulties such as the assumption of probable hinge positions due to a system of moving loads and the calculation of influence coefficients for the non-prismatic girder. Hence, to start with, the analysis of a single longitudinal continuous girder is considered in this paper, as the same approach can be extended easily to the analysis of bridge grillage also.

Reinforced concrete members designed as per any code will have a minimum quantity of shear stirrups which incidentally serves the purpose of binders to increase the maximum concrete strain more than 0.0035. In addition to the binder reinforcement, the percentage of longitudinal reinforcement, concrete strength, axial force, shear and torsion are also influencing the maximum concrete strain. Hence, there is a wide variation in the observed values of the limiting concrete strain from 0.002 to 0.03. Allowing for the variation of the measured concrete strains, based on a statistical treatment of the scattered results Baker has suggested a value of 0.0035 for unbound concrete and 0.012 for well bound concrete. Formulae have also been suggested by the various investigators[3,7,8] for the maximum concrete strain.

In the case of indeterminate structures with less number of redundancies it may not be necessary to check up the rotation capacity. But in the case of highly redundant frames and bridge grillages it becomes quite essential to provide maximum rotation capacity by means of special binders to prevent the exhaustion of rotational capacities of the first formed hinges and to allow the formation of further required hinges.

\- - -

AUTHORS' REPLY TO THE DISCUSSION BY DR. C. W. YU

The authors are thankful to Dr. Yu for his valuable discussion. One of the important aspects in the development of Baker's ultimate load theory to the design of non-prismatic continuous structures is the usage of modified EI value for the non-prismatic member. In this design procedure it is suggested to obtain modified EI value in terms of the EI value for the smallest cross section of the member (considering prismatic) and the elastic parameters. Experimental verification has been done by conducting tests on single bay single story portal frames of varying cross-section[9] (Fig. 1) to find out the validity of the suggested procedure.

The rotation calculated using the suggested values of EI are in close agreement with the permissible rotation (Table 1). A typical moment rotation diagram of the hinging section in the beam portion is shown in Fig. 2. The idealized diagram O L_1 L_2 is also plotted. The overall agreement of the idealized diagram with the actual diagram is quite close and is on the safer side.

REFERENCES

7) CORLEY, GENE W., "Rotational Capacity of Reinforced Concrete Beams," Proceedings of the ASCE, Oct. 1966, V. 92, No. ST 6, pp. 121-146

8) RAMAKRISHNAN, V. and KRISHNAMOORTHY, R., "Influence of Shear on the Rotation Capacity of the Plastic Hinges in Reinforced Concrete Frames," (To be published)

9) GURUSWAMY, P., "Ultimate Load Analysis of Two Pinned Reinforced Concrete Portal Frames of Varying Moment of Inertia," M. Sc. Thesis, 1966, P.S.G. College of Technology, Madras University.

AUTHORS' REPLY TO THE DISCUSSION BY DR. E. G. NAWY

The authors wish to thank Dr. Edward G. Nawy for his interesting comments.

The collapse mechanisms in Fig. 2 and 3 are shown to illustrate the application of the proposed method for any general possible number of collapse mechanisms. The authors are aware of Dr. Nawy's commendable work regarding the rotation capability of plastic hinges and agree that it is possible to force the hinges to occur at desired loactions by choosing the reinforcement. In all cases it may not always be economical by imposing the location of the developing hinges at the supports particularly in cases of nonprismatic continuous structures. The location of the hinge at a location other than supports may prove to be economical and hence the choice of the hinge locations is left to the designer.

The proposed limit design method has one more advantage compared to the present methods because the design is directly based on the maximum permissible deformations of the structure whereas the present methods are based on the moment capacities of the various sections. It is easy for the designer to visualize the magnitude of the rotations and the overall physcial behavior of the structure at various stages of the loading.

TABLE - I

S. No.	Portal Frame Mark	Permissible Beam Hinge Rotations Using e_{cu} = 0.0035	Rotations Calculated Using Suggested EI Value	$\frac{\text{Permissible Rotation}}{\text{Calculated Rotation}}$
1	P_2	0.0162	0.0184	0.8800
2	P_3	0.0150	0.0156	0.9620
3	P_4	0.0158	0.0180	0.8780
4	P_5	0.0184	0.0228	0.8070
5	P_6	0.0176	0.0232	0.7590
6	P_7	0.0150	0.0158	0.9490
7	P_8	0.0146	0.0158	0.9240

Note: Rotations are calculated for the beam hinge.

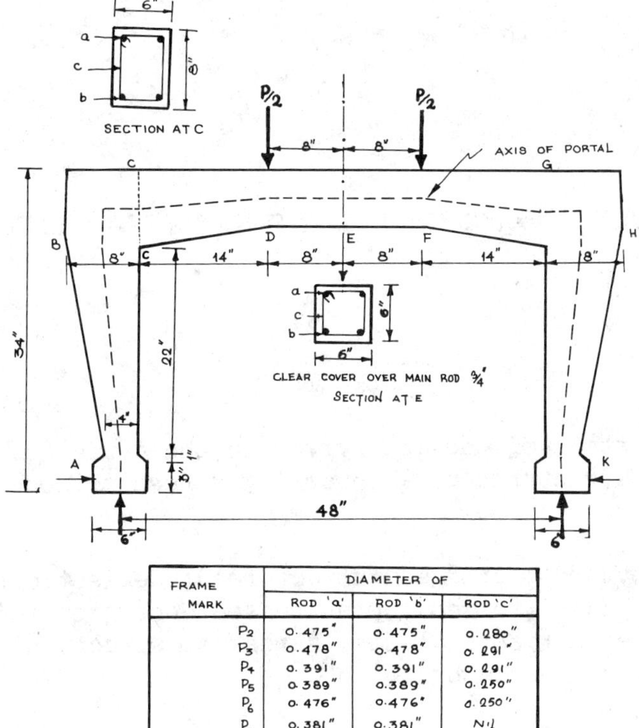

FRAME MARK	DIAMETER OF ROD 'a'	ROD 'b'	ROD 'c'
P_2	0.475"	0.475"	0.280"
P_3	0.478"	0.478"	0.291"
P_4	0.391"	0.391"	0.291"
P_5	0.389"	0.389"	0.250"
P_6	0.476"	0.476"	0.250"
P_7	0.381"	0.381"	Nil
P_8	0.476"	0.476"	Nil

Fig 1. FRAME DIMENSIONS AND LOADING

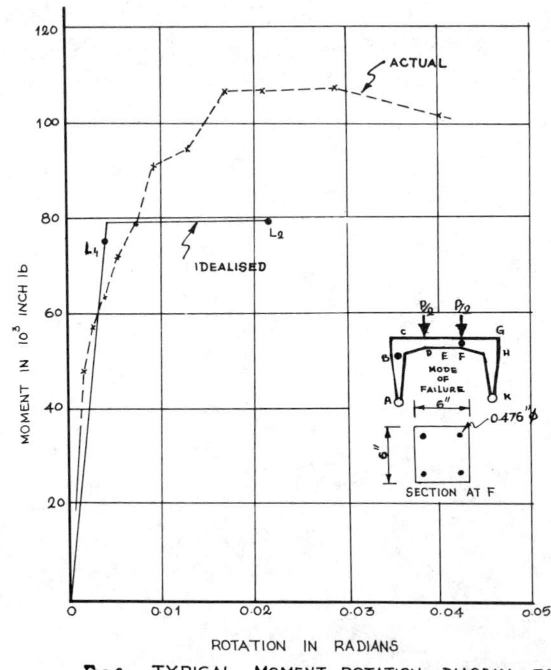

Fig 2 TYPICAL MOMENT ROTATION DIAGRAM FOR THE HINGE AT F

WORKING STRESS DESIGN OF CONCRETE BRIDGE STRUCTURES--A STATE-OF-THE-ART SURVEY

By V. RAMAKRISHNAN

SYNOPSIS

A state-of-the-art survey on the design of concrete bridge structures by the working stress method is presented.

Keywords: bridges (structures); deflections; dynamic loads; loads (forces); prestressed concrete; reinforced concrete; stress analysis; stresses; structural design; working stress method.

ACI member, DR. V. RAMAKRISHNAN is professor and head of the Department of Civil Engineering at P.S.G. College of Technology, Coimbatore, South India. Received his post-graduate education with special reference to Concrete Technology and Concrete Structures at the Imperial College and University College, London, where he was awarded the PhD degree in 1960. Engaged in teaching, research and consultation work, he is the co-author of a book on "Ultimate Strength Design for Structural Concrete" published by Pitman & Sons Ltd., London. He is also the editor of Proceedings of the first Indian Symposium on "Ultimate Load Design of Concrete Structures". He has published a number of technical papers and reports in the field of concrete technology and concrete structures.

INTRODUCTION:

Since the introduction of reinforced concrete into bridge practice some 80 years ago, research and experience have helped in evolving the basic principles of concrete bridge design. The object of this paper is to highlight only certain salient aspects of the art of designing and checking the performance of concrete bridge structures for purposes of initiating the discussion in this session and to indicate problems which stand further research in this important area of structural engineering.

The evolution of concrete bridge structures began with the discovery of the art of building reinforced concrete structures. The capacity of concrete to provide any desired form needed to impart aesthetic beauty to bridge structures, the high durability characteristics of concrete when exposed to normal environmental conditions, and the low cost of maintenance of concrete structures made the construction of short and medium span concrete bridges popular and economical. However, for very long spans conventional reinforced concrete bridge construction could not compete with steel construction. The relatively high specific weight of concrete still stands in the way of its use in long span bridge construction. This has prompted a search for ways of minimising the dead load in these long spans. Some of the notable solutions so far obtained to overcome this defect are:

i) Use of cellular deck construction (using precast units).
ii) Use of continuous hollow multiple box girder elements in bridges.
iii) Application of prestressing techniques.
iv) Double cantilever type of bridge construction
v) Use of light-weight concrete in bridge structures.[1]

Several combinations of the above solutions have also been successfully used. In modern times, prestressed box section has become a standard structural member for all slender long-span concrete bridge structures. These box-type members, because of their considerable torsional strength, allow themselves to be used in skew bridges and curved bridges which are of increasingly frequent occurrence in modern bridge practice. With the object of increasing the stiffness of these thin-walled box members, diaphragms are often used. The number and size of diaphragms in a hollow girder section should be limited to the minimum required for structural safety, as these diaphragms in addition to adding to the dead load, materially increase constructional difficulties. The criterion for spacing diaphragms in concrete box girders is yet to be evolved on a rational basis. When thin-walled box members are used, an additional check on the stability of the member also should be made.

It is to be mentioned that there is a minimum span length dependent upon the allowable stresses and other factors at which the thickness of sections of hollow girders becomes too thin for economical practical application.

Design data and design requirements:

Materials: In the course of time the technology of concrete making has developed so much as to make the concrete of today an almost different material from concrete of a few years ago. The technology has shown the way of producing concrete having a very high compressive strength. In the last ten years, progress in the manufacture of high-strength steel has created a fresh thinking in the design philosophy of concrete structures. Working stress design methods virtually prevent the efficient use of high strength steel in concrete structures. This is probably one of the reasons for the wider use of prestressed concrete structures, where such a use is possible even within the fold of working stress design concepts. This progress achieved in the production of quality bridge materials has created a necessity for a revision in the maximum values of admissible stresses for concretes and steel of different qualities and grades with a due eye on the factor of safety.

The bond characteristics between steel and concrete have also been improved by the introduction of deformed bars. However, a quantitative measurement of the bond efficiency is still a matter of research.

Load standards: Each country has stipulated certain load standards for the design of bridge structures. The prescribed load standards are now known to vary considerably from country to country. For example, the AASHO load standards are one of the lightest, while the Indian load standards - one of exceptionally heaviest. With the increase in traffic in modern times the load standards in certain countries may need an upward revision. Leonhardt[2] has recently compared the load standards of American, German, French and Indian practice and has expressed a need for rationalizing and unifying the load standards for recommending for International use. In this connection it is to be mentioned that as far as possible the prescribed load standards should be simple for use and should take into consideration:

i) Continuity of structure
ii) Span length of structure and
iii) Number of lanes carried by the structure.

As many countries are in the process of changeover to metric units, the occasion may be beneficially made use of in giving due thought to the revision of load standards.

Range of applicability of working stress design: Recently ultimate strength design and limit state design methods have started dominating the field of concrete structural design as they are more simpler and appear more rational than conventional working stress design methods. Inevitably ultimate strength and limit state design methods would be increasingly used in the design of concrete bridge structures as well. However, these methods have not been fully developed at present to the extent required for complete changeover in bridge design.

For instance there is no generally acceptable ultimate strength design method which takes into account the influence of shear and torsion adequately. In view of the increasing use of prestressed box section and the complexity of modern bridge structures (by the use of skew and curved alignments), this lack of knowledge limits the application of limit state design to only conventional types of structures.

Again for predicting the performance of bridge structures under working loads or service loads, it always becomes necessary to take recourse to service load analysis even when the ultimate strength procedures are used for proportioning the size of members.

The major difficulty is perhaps in the limit state of serviceability in which deflection is a most important criterion. The problem of structural flexibility is one in which experiences of past successes and failures alone serve as main evidence to guide a designer starting from first principles. It may be objected that the arbitrary deflection to span, and span to depth ratios used in working stress design procedure are crude. It is certainly a matter of regret that no satisfactory simple treatment of flexibility is available. However, it will be possible to exploit fully the concept of limit state design only when the criteria of serviceability are more clearly understood. In this connection, adequate deformation, creep and crack-width studies are called for.

There is little information available on the strength of orthotropically reinforced rectangular slabs subjected to concentrated loads. Hence working stress design methods are still needed for checking slab designs for wheel loads.

Plastic design methods are insufficiently developed when the action of live loads is important as in bridge structures. In addition to the above inadequacy in the development of limit state design methods, full philosophy of limit state design has also not been grasped by all people concerned with the building industry. This needs some time. Thus in the present context, working stress design procedures are necessary for continued use, at least as a supplement to predict service load performance.

<u>Serviceability conditions</u>: The major serviceability requirements to be satisfied in any bridge design are:

i) The stress range in concrete and in reinforcement must be within acceptable limits.
ii) The deflections due to dead load and live load should not be noticeable.
iii) The bridge must be dynamically sound.
iv) The structural materials are adequately protected against deterioration or corrosion.

Stress range: The amount of information available on the fatigue properties of reinforced concrete beams is limited; but it indicates that the possibility of fatigue failure in normal service is remote since the stress range is likely to be well below the endurance limits for both steel and concrete. Some tests conducted at PCA laboratories however indicate a need for further study when high-strength steels are to be used. On a tentative basis it may be said that fatigue will not be a factor in normal concrete bridge design.[3] The favorable behavior of prestressed concrete with regard to dynamic loading and its freedom from harmful cracks make it a highly desirable bridge material.

In many countries, full prestressing is specified regardless of the magnitude of the specified regardless of the magnitude of the specified live loads and safety factors. This means under service-loads, the concrete is under heavy compression permanently leading to considerable creep deformations. This in addition to altering the stress gradient, on short spans interferes with the riding qualities. Leonhardt[2] suggests that the magnitude of the prestress should be so chosen in relation to span length and load standards that for service load conditions, no tensile stress occurs in the extreme fibre, no limit being prescribed for the magnitude of tensile stress or tensile strain occurring under rare abnormal loads envisaged in many regulations.

While thus it is important to induce correct prestress in the concrete, when curved cables are used it is not easy to control the prestressing force at the center of the girder within a few percent of error. When the dead load to live load ratio becomes large as in long span bridges, a small percentage of prestressing error can cause appreciable error in concrete. Variation in section area of cable, variation of Young's modulus of cable, variation of friction loss, variation of stress distribution along the cable along with the errors in the measurement of elongation and in the reading of pressure gauge all collectively can cause a respectable error. Hence this aspect should be adequately considered both during design and construction.

Deflections: Deflections caused by live loads are unlikely to be a problem if vibrations caused by such loads are not objectionable. Hence it is suggested that deflection be controlled by limiting natural frequencies.

The visual effects of dead load deflections can be largely eliminated by the provision of adequate camber and it therefore appears to be unnecessary to place limits on calculated dead load deflections. If relatively large span to thickness ratios are used, from the standpoint of strength, then it may be desirable to place suitable limits on deflection or slab thickness. At present, such restrictions seem unnecessary. The introduction of limit state design, however, certainly calls for a check on the loss of stiffness resulting from creep, shrinkage, plasticity and cracking. In addition, a check on local damage may also become necessary.

<u>Design for dynamic effects</u>: Since the dynamic response of bridge loaded with a moving vehicle is of great importance to bridge design, studies to evaluate the magnitude of the dynamic amplification factors are to be carried out. The analytical methods so far used seem to be based on either the direct solution of the fundamental differential equation of transverse vibration of beam or energy procedure by means of Lagrangian equation. Though these analytical methods are available for the case where the moving load is idealized as a constant force or as a single mass upon an idealized simple beam; other cases like continuous beam and grillage girder bridge carrying a moving load composed of several masses and connected by a spring with non-linear elements still await solution. Concrete bridge structures, although they cannot yet be designed to extend over such great spans as modern steel suspension bridges, have not entered the region where aerodynamic forces can be important or can perhaps even dominate the design. Analytical procedures for calculating the natural frequency of unloaded bridges have already been developed for simple types of structures. Limits on the vibration characteristics of bridges are to be placed on the basis of estimates of human sensitivity and tolerance. In this connection it is known that both amplitude and frequency need to be limited. However, it is generally assumed that it is sufficient for practical purposes to set limits to frequency only. There is a lack of consensus as to what such frequencies should be. Various values ranging from 2 to 6.5 cps are being suggested. For predicting the performance of complicated bridge structures model analysis has also been successfully tried.

<u>Stress analysis</u>: The aspect of bridge design which has recorded the highest progress is in the field of stress analysis. Modern bridge analysis is becoming more and more precise and refined. The trend is towards accounting for all hitherto known secondary influences.

For the determination of stresses in bridge decks, two major distribution theories viz. orthotropic plate theory and grid network analysis have been developed. Controversy still exists as to the relative superiority of the above two methods. To facilitate the application of orthotropic plate theory, several ready-made influence surfaces, charts and tables have already been made available. However, the use of orthotropic plate theory presents some problems especially when stress-free edges, concentrated loads and slabs of unusual shapes are encountered. Grid net work analysis allows the use of matrix methods and hence the use of computers for obtaining quick solution for the problem. Other methods generally considered in connection with bridge deck analysis are: folded plate theory, finite difference method, finite element method, model analysis and moire fringe method. Three dimensional stress analysis procedures have been developed for continuous curved girder bridges taking into account both flexure and torsion. Detailed analysis of thin-walled box girders of rectangular and trapezoidal cross section is now made available. Analysis based on orthotropic plate theory is also found effective for the determination of dynamic characteristics of very wide bridges. Several procedures are now available for determining the stress distribution in skew slab bridge decks.

GENERAL REMARKS:

Design: Methods of design must be kept under constant review and attention should be paid to the broad philosophy and concepts of design as well as to the details. The rapid developments of modern times and the increasing number, size, scale and scope of the works will make bridge design much more complex than at present; and it will be necessary in future to design more precisely taking into consideration secondary, side and cross effects.

Use of computers: The value of computers in bridge analysis merits special attention. They have potential value not only in extending the possibility of making and of cheapening the calculations that feature in complicated bridge design, but also in organizing the bridge construction.

Prefabrication and standardization: Prefabrication of bridge deck components has helped in reducing the dead load by making the cellular deck construction possible economically. Standardization of bridge components is now known to lead to considerable economy. However, any tendency for standardization which inhibits development should be continuously checked. Also proper attention to span, skews, widths and loadings should be given while standardizing bridge components.

Field investigation: The value of knowledge gained through actual field experience cannot be over-estimated. Such a knowledge is basic for establishing serviceability conditions of bridge structures. However, development of instrumentation applicable to field investigation of bridge structures is not being given adequate attention at present.

Future research: Further work in the following areas will be fruitful in modernizing the design of concrete bridge structures.

1. Dynamic design aspects of bridge structures.
2. Field investigation of serviceability characteristics; Development of instrumentation applicable for field investigation.
3. Greater use of advanced aids such as computers, and finite element techniques.
4. Rationalization of load standards.
5. Development of light-weight concrete for use in bridge structures.
6. Detailed study of curved and skew bridges.
7. Temperature and shrinkage stresses in bridge structures.

REFERENCES:

1. "The Dyckerhoff Bridge in Wiesbaden, Germany", Indian Concrete Journal, Vol. 42, No. 12, Dec. 1968, pp. 494-498
2. LEONHARDT, F., "New trends in design and construction of long span bridges and viaducts", IABSE, Preliminary publication, 8th Congress, Sept. 1968.
3. LASH, S.D., "Rational design of beam and slab highway bridges", Engineering Journal, Vol. 51, No. 9, Sept. 1968.
4. "Civil Engineering in Japan", 1964.

ON EVALUATION OF THE CONCRETE CODE RESISTANCES BY COMPRESSION WHILE CALCULATING REINFORCED CONCRETE BRIDGES

By O. JA. BERG

SYNOPSIS

The development of the theoretic interpretation of strength and deformation nature permits to outline two parameter points (stress levels), besides limit of strength. These objective criteria can be used while designing concrete and reinforced bridge constructions, as they influence many properties of concrete. The allowable stresses in compression in the American Standard Specifications for Highway Bridges are compared with those in the Soviet Codes for Bridge Design, where they were brought in correspondence with the criteria mentioned. For practical aims a simple evaluation method of concrete nonlinear creep deformations for bridge calculating is given.

The contents of the article have direct bearing on the following subjects of the Symposium: Materials and Working Stress Design.

Keywords: bridges (structures); creep properties; reinforced concrete; standards; stress-strain relationships; structural design; working stress method.

OLEG Ja. BERG is professor and head, Department of Building Materials. and Concrete Constructions, All-Union Research Institute on Transport Constructions, Moscow, USSR. He graduated in 1938 from the Institute of Railway Engineers in Leningrad as bridge engineer and was engaged in bridge design and construction.

Since 1946 he has been working at the Research Institute mentioned above. He received his MS and PhD degrees in 1950 and 1958, respectively. He has devoted much of his time to carrying out and heading investigations in the field of concrete and reinforced concrete strength, deformation and techniques, preparing codes and practical methods for concrete bridge calculation.

The methods of elasticity theory are being used at present for the evaluation of the stress state of bridge constructions reinforced concrete members. The calculated stress values are compared with the code resistances (allowable stresses) of the material, which form some part of the unit ultimate strength determined by the adopted safety factor.

The development of the theoretic interpretation of strength and deformation nature [1,2,3,4] permits outlining some objective criteria for the evaluation of concrete state approach influenced by load factors. These criteria can be used while designing concrete and reinforced bridge constructions.

The concrete stress state under longtime acting forces of the prestressed reinforcement is the most characteristic feature of prestressed members. In accordance with the main idea of prestressed concrete, the increase of concrete stress intensity from prestressed reinforcement increases the cracking load for transversal cracks. But the excessive rise of concrete prestressing leads to such intolerable phenomena as the development of longitudinal cracks (in the direction of acting compressive forces) occurring during bridge maintenance. It creates the danger of destruction in the case of multiple repeated load acting with a large stress change amplitude ($\rho = \frac{\sigma_{min}}{\sigma_{max}} \rightarrow 0$). Besides nonlinear creep deformations begin to develop under high concrete stresses the value of which is necessary to calculate while designing a bridge construction.

The theoretical bases of the phenomena mentioned are connected with the process of disintegration and development of microcracks in concrete.

Attention has been paid to the investigation of the development of microcrack processes in concrete at different time in various countries. Of interest is the analysis of relationship between established processes of microcrack development in strength and deformation concrete theory and various properties which are important in service. Such a relationship is considered in this article, for it can be used while evaluating code resistances in the bridge design codes in the cases of multiple repeated and longtime loading and of nonlinear creep influence on member deformations. The author relies on the results of investigations carried out under his leadership in the All Union Research Institute on Transport Construction (Moscow, USSR).

It is necessary to begin with introducing a generalized indication for the process of concrete microcracking. For engineering calculations the compression diagram of concrete (Fig. 1a) characterizing the relationship stress versus strain $\sigma = f(\varepsilon)$ is widely being used. The investigation in the field of concrete strength and deformation theory has shown that it is necessary to introduce the diagram of concrete states under loading [2,4,5] along with the compression diagram. The diagram of states reflects the concrete structure change during loading process. For example, it can be expressed in the form of a relationship of concrete volume increment change or of concrete ultrasonic characteristics change versus compression stress data.

The concrete structure change with the alteration of the stress state on the concrete volume increment change ΔQ curve (Fig. 1b) is characterized as follows. At first the decrease of member volume takes place and then the process slows down. The increase of volume occurs then on each next stage of member loading. These phenomena are connected with the primary condensation of the structure and then with the development of the processes of disintegration and structure failure by means of micro-rupture formation changing then to microcracks and large destruction surfaces. On the ultrasonic diagram of states (Fig. 1c) the decrease of ultrasonic pulse propagation time on the given base of measurement, slowing down of this process and the increase of ultrasonic pulse propagation time at further loading growth on the member is being observed respectively.

The process of discondensation connected with the disintegration and further microdestruction begins at the stress level R^{o}_{cr} when the decrease of external member volume increment occurs on the curve of ΔQ (Fig. 1b). The shortest time of ultrasonic pulse propagation through the member corresponds to the microdestruction level R^{o}_{cr} on the ultrasonic curve (Fig. 1c).

The second parameter point R^{v}_{cr} corresponds to the largest reduction of member volume, i.e. to $\Delta Q = 0$. From this stress level one can observe through a light microscope the microcracks formed. The transition from concrete structure loosening to microdestruction and microcracks is taking place during the stress interval considered. The stress level R^{v}_{cr} characterizes the upper conditional microcracks level. Of interest also is the stress level R_{cr}.

The basic principle of concrete strength and deformation theory is that the passing of parameter points on the loading curve is associated with the development of new features.

Of greatest significance is the range from R^{o}_{cr} to R^{v}_{cr}. If one does not take account of the destruction from chemical corrosion, then the area of stress state down to R^{o}_{cr} is one securing safety maintenance of the structure. Down to R^{o}_{cr} the concrete deformations consist, on the whole, of elastic and linear creep deformations. The stress level R^{o}_{cr} determines the nonlinear creep origin arising from superposition of deformations associated with the concrete structure disintegration by loading on the deformation of creep proper. From this level one can observe the strength decrease because of the fatigue phenomena under multiple repeated loading, the longitudinal cracks can be developed under longtime loading. The latter circumstance is especially noticeable (on account of the constraint shrinkage superposition) at heavy reinforcement usually taking place in bridge constructions.

The excess of level R^{v}_{cr} is connected with the origin of deformations making progress in time and with overcoming of long-time strength. Practically the stress state beyond R^{v}_{cr} is intolerable during normal maintenance.

The relative values of code resistance (allowable stresses) are shown on Fig. 2 for two basic forms of concrete resistance; one is at the stage of transferring the prestressed forces from reinforcement to concrete and the other one is for the stage of maintenance. In American Standard Specifications for Highway Bridges [7] the constant level of stresses is (0.54 - 0.58)R_c and 0.39R_c for both cases respectively. The values of allowable stresses are given according to the classes of concrete (cube strength). In this connection the American code resistances depending on the cylinder strength were recounted to the Soviet Codes resistance R_c which is close to cylinder strength. The code strength R_c when calculating bridge constructions is equal to 0.875R, where R is cube strength. The cylinder strength is taken equal to 0.85R.

The code resistances of Soviet Codes [8,9] constitute a variable part prism strength. Besides the code resistance for the maintenance stage change within a wide range in relationship of the dead load stresses and the upper stress limit of load.

This peculiarity of code resistances is used in railway bridge fatigue calculation under multiple repeated loading. In highway bridge design the value of code resistance for design load is about equal the upper limit of this range. The variable value of code resistances in Soviet Codes is caused by bringing them in correspondence with the upper conditional microcracks level R^v_{cr} and the level R_{cr}.

The microdestruction levels assumed are affected by structure parameters, which are determined by characteristics of concrete mix components, means of molding and following working. But on the average relationship of these values against strength are observed, which can be given as follows:

$$\eta_o = \frac{R^o_{cr}}{R_c} = 0.35 \log R_c -- 0.5; \quad \eta_{cr} = \frac{R^v_{cr}}{R_c} = 0.35 \log R_c - 0.18,$$

where R_c is concrete code strength.

The equations given are attributed to dense concrete mixes with the aggregates from heavy rocks. The much higher homogeneity of sand concrete without coarse aggregate leads to parameter points rise. The same rise can be observed for aggregates with better cohesion with cement stone. Direct experiments have shown that concrete with lightweight aggregates (for example, agloporit) has a higher level of R^o_{cr} and R^v_{cr}.

The association of fatigue phenomena under multiple repeated loading and the microdestruction level R^o_{cr} is, for example, determined for concrete with cube strength more than 400 kg/cm^2 and the number of repeated loadings to 34 million [10].

It is necessary to take into account the nonlinear creep in the area R^o_{cr} - R^v_{cr}. The generalization of nonlinear creep data gave the opportunity to offer recommendations on additional increase of deformations depending on how much the level R^o_{cr} [11] is exceeded. The specific concrete creep strain (per unit of existing stresses) must be increased in this case by the factor $K(\eta_\sigma, \eta_o)$, which depends on the difference of relative levels of given stresses, for which the nonlinear creep influence must be taken into consideration, and the level R^o_{cr}.

Thus for practical aims it is possible to write with sufficient approach the equation for the specific concrete nonlinear creep strain C_N as follows:

$$C_N = C(t,\tau)\left[1 + K(\eta_\sigma, \eta_o)\right],$$

where $C(t,\tau)$ is specific linear creep strain depending on the concrete age at the time of loading τ and on the given time t,

$\eta_\sigma = \frac{\sigma}{Rc}$ the relative level of stresses.

For the specific linear creep strain the code data, which were proposed by E. Scerbakov and the author [12,13], can be used.

The factor $K(\eta_\sigma, \eta_o)$ is determined from the curve in Fig. 3 by the value $(\eta_\sigma - \eta_o)$. The curve on Fig. 3 is in agreement with experimental data, which were analyzed while plotting this curve.

The accumulation of concrete microdestructions and microcracks level data will enable to design more reliable bridge constructions for complicated effects connected with maintenance conditions, as many properties of concrete are influenced by these levels. The problem of construction reliability should make use, to a greater extent, of the investigation results on concrete strength and deformation theory.

REFERENCES

1. Proceedings of the All Union Research Institute on Transport Constructions. Moscow, Vol. 19, 1956.
2. O. Ja. Berg. The Physical Bases of Concrete and Reinforced Concrete Strength Theory. Stroijizdat, Moscow, 1960-61.
3. Proceedings of the All Union Research Institute on Transport Constructions. Moscow, Vol. 60, 1966.
4. Proceedings of the Fifth Congress of the FIP. Paris, 1966. Discussion on Session IV. Contribution by O. Ja. Berg.
5. O. Ja. Berg. Some Aspects on Concrete Deformation and Strength Theory. "Stroitelstvo i Arkhitectira" N 10, 1967.
6. O. Ja. Berg. Die Hauptentwicklungsrichtungen der Theorie der Festigkeit und Verformungen des Betons. Wissenschaftliche Zeitschrift der Technischen Universitat Dresden. Band 17 (1968), Heft 6.
7. Standard Specifications for Highway Bridges, Washington, 1961.

8. Technical Specifications for Railway and Highway Bridge Design SN 200-62. Moscow, 1962.

9. Design Instructions for Concrete Railway and Highway Bridges SN 365-67. Moscow, 1967.

10. T. S. Karanfilov, U. S. Wolkov. The Fatigue and Deformation of Concrete under multiple repeated loading. Trudy Gydroproekta, Sb. N 14, Moscow, 1966.

11. O. Ja. Berg, A. I. Rozhkov. On taking account of the Nonlinear Creep of Concrete. "Beton i Zhelezobeton", N 9, 1967, Moscow.

12. E. N. Scerbakov. Development of practical methods of allowing for Concrete Creep and Shrinkage in designing reinforced concrete members. "Beton i Zhelezobeton", N 8, 1967, Moscow.

13. O. Ja. Berg, E. N. Scerbakov. The Evaluation of the Creep of Concrete in the Design of Structures. Proceedings of the Symposium "Design Philosophy and its Application to Precast Concrete Structures". London, 1967.

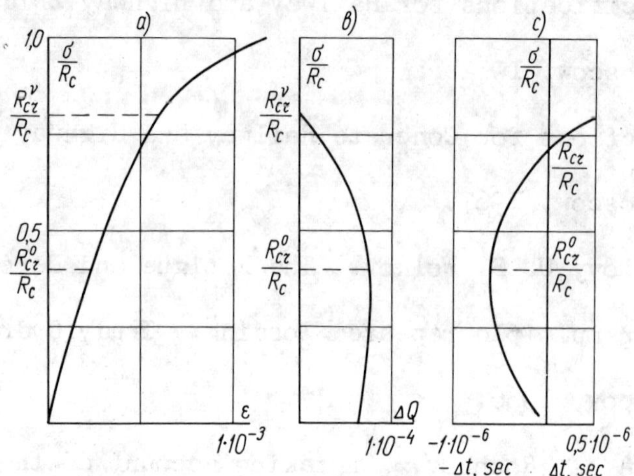

Fig. 1

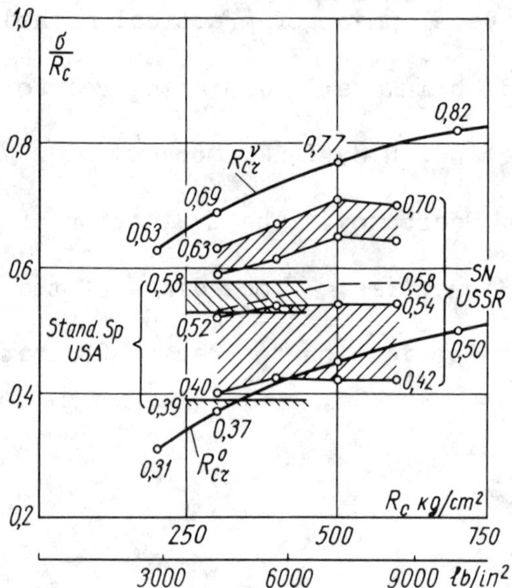

Fig. 2

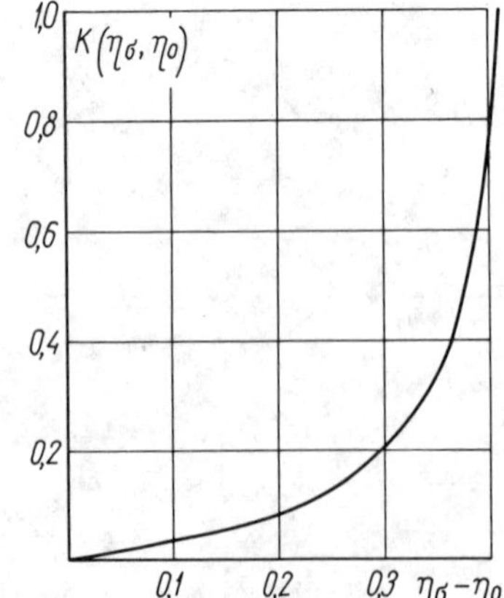

Fig. 3

A LOAD DISTRIBUTION METHOD OF ANALYZING STATICALLY INDETERMINATE CONCRETE BRIDGE DECKS

By R. P. PAMA and A. R. CUSENS

SYNOPSIS

The paper presents the analysis of statically indeterminate orthotropic bridge decks due to rectangular patch loads. Decks are classified into three main categories depending on relative rigidities in flexure and torsion. The analysis employs a series solution originally derived for statically determinate bridge decks. Three typical examples are discussed: column-supported, continuous and propped-cantilever decks.

Keywords: bridge decks, bridges (structures); computer programs; continuity (structural); flexural strength; loads (forces); concrete; statically indeterminate structures; structural analysis; torsion.

ACI member RICARDO P. PAMA is research fellow and honorary lecturer in civil engineering, University of Dundee, Scotland. He obtained his BS degree at Mapua Institute of Technology, Manila, in 1961, and his ME degree in structural engineering in 1964 at the SEATO Graduate School of Engineering (now Asian Institute of Technology), Bangkok, Thailand. He was awarded a PhD by the University of St. Andrews in 1968 for his work on orthotropic bridge decks.

ACI member ANTHONY R. CUSENS is professor and head, Civil Engineering Department, University of Dundee, Scotland. He is currently leader of a research team in Dundee engaged in the experimental investigation of load distribution in concrete bridge decks under a contract with the Construction Industry Research and Information Association, London. Professor Cusens is the author of numerous technical articles in the fields of concrete technology and concrete structures.

INTRODUCTION

In recent years traffic congestion on urban highways has led to a considerable increase in the construction of elevated highways and complex intersections in and around the major cities of the world. The bridges involved in such construction are often statically indeterminate and thus the attention of bridge designers has been drawn to the general problem of indeterminacy. This problem may be rendered more difficult by the nature of support conditions, e.g. systems of discrete columns, and also by anisotropy of the bridge deck.

The idealization of an actual bridge structure of different bending and torsional rigidities in two orthogonal directions into an equivalent orthotropic plate governed by the familiar equation

$$D_x \frac{\partial^4 w}{\partial x^4} + 2H \frac{\partial^4 w}{\partial x^2 \partial y^2} + D_y \frac{\partial^4 w}{\partial y^4} = p(x,y) \qquad (1)$$

is well known due to the work of Huber[1]. Its application to statically determinate right bridge decks with negligible torsional rigidity ($H = 0$) was first introduced by Guyon[2]. This was later extended by Massonnet[3] to cover cases falling between the torsionless and isotropic case (i.e. $H^2 \leq D_x D_y$). The case of articulated bridge decks ($D_y = 0$) has been formulated by Spindel[4]. The authors[5] have analyzed the case of torsionally stiff-flexurally soft bridge decks ($H^2 \geq D_x D_y$) and have presented a revised form of load distribution analysis to cover all practical cases of simply supported right orthotropic bridge deck. All these analyses apply to simply supported rectangular bridge decks only and use a load distribution approach based on Levy's method. Other mathematical techniques such as perturbation solutions, finite difference and finite element approximations, and line-solution techniques may also be used.

In 1962 Rowe[8] pointed out that no analytical procedure based on load distribution theory had been derived for assessing the load distribution characteristics of statically indeterminate bridge decks other than a solution derived by Hendry and Jaeger[9] for the torsionless case using Inglis'[7] basic functions. Its application is very limited since most highway bridges possess some degree of torsional rigidity and it is important to include this as a parameter in the general method of analysis.

A limited amount of theoretical work has been published on the problem of indeterminacy imposed by the presence of discrete column supports. The work of Leray[10] is based on a numerically determined biharmonic Green's function for an infinitely long plate. Morley[11] has given a solution for column-supported plates based on an iterative process which also starts with an infinite plate. However, these two methods treat the columns as point supports which does not hold true for the majority of cases encountered in practice, especially if wide columns are used to support narrow decks.

The method presented in this paper is based on the simple concept of removing the statically indeterminate reactive forces or moments and allowing the deck to deform elastically under load; the statically indeterminate forces are then applied one after the other and the compatibility of deformation is satisfied. Matrix analysis is used in finding the statically indeterminate forces. In this paper three types of indeterminacy will be discussed:

a. column-supported decks,

b. continuous decks, and

c. propped-cantilever decks.

THEORETICAL ANALYSIS

Considering an orthotropic bridge deck of flexural rigidity D_x and D_y in the x and y directions respectively, with torsional rigidity 2H given by

$$2H = (D_{xy} + D_{yx} + D_1 + D_2) \quad (2)$$

In eq. 2 D_{xy} is the longitudinal torsional rigidity, D_{yx} is the transverse torsional rigidity and D_1 and D_2 are the contributions of bending to the torsional rigidity of the deck. The deflection function obtained using the Levy type solution may be classified into three cases of bridge decks depending on relative flexural and torsional rigidities. These are as follows:

Case 1. Torsionally stiff, flexurally soft ; $H^2 \geq D_x D_y$

Case 2. Isotropic ; $H^2 = D_x D_y$

Case 3. Torsionally soft, flexurally stiff; $H^2 \leq D_x D_y$

It has been shown[2,3,4,5,6] that for a point load P acting at a distance C from the support, the deflection at any point distance x from the support is given by the expression

$$\omega = \frac{2PL^3}{\pi^4 D_x 2b} \cdot \sum_{n=1}^{\infty} \frac{1}{n^4} \sin \alpha_n C \sin \alpha_n x \cdot K \tag{3}$$

where $\alpha_n = \frac{n\pi}{L}$ (4)

and K is the load distribution coefficient appropriate for each case. In general, K is a function of the flexural and torsional rigidities of the deck, the aspect ratio of the deck, the rigidities of the edge beams (if present), and the transverse position of the load. Consider now a load P uniformly distributed over a rectangular area 2U x 2V as shown in Fig. 1. The deflection function due to this finite rectangular load is obtained by integrating Eq. 3 from (C – U) to (C + U) along the x-axis and from -V to +V along the y-axis. The equation then becomes

$$\omega = \frac{2PL^3}{2U \times 2V \times \pi^4 \cdot D_x} \cdot \sum_{n=1}^{\infty} \frac{1}{n^4} \sin \alpha_n x \cdot \int_{C-U}^{C+U} \sin \alpha_n \xi \, d\xi \cdot \frac{1}{2b} \int_{-V}^{V} K \cdot d\eta \tag{5}$$

Setting $$\frac{1}{2b}\int_{-v}^{v} K \, d\eta = K^{*} \tag{6}$$

the equation for deflection w reduces to

$$\omega = \frac{PL^4}{UV\pi^5 D_x} \sum_{n=1}^{\infty} \frac{1}{n^5} \sin\alpha_n U \sin\alpha_n C \sin\alpha_n x \cdot K^{*} \tag{7}$$

where K^{*} is a dimensionless load distribution coefficient for deflection at any point on the deck due to a finite rectangular patch load. The expressions for K^{*} are shown in the Appendix for cases 1 and 3 only; the isotropic case could be obtained from either case by studying the limits of K^{*} as D_x approaches D_y and H. This is conveniently obtained by digital computer from case 1 by setting $D_x = D_y$ and $H = 0.9999\ D_x$ or from case 3 by assuming $H = 1.0001\ D_x$ and $D_x = D_y$. With the general expression for deflection of determinate bridge decks known, the analysis of statically indeterminate bridge decks follows.

Analysis of Column-Supported Bridge Decks

Motorway bridges are sometimes provided with intermediate supports of discrete columns dictated by the width requirement of the motorway and economic and aesthetic considerations. It is always cheaper and more pleasing to the eye to provide slender columns than to build a massive intermediate support.

Column-supported bridge decks are statically indeterminate and the number of redundants if the end supports are simple ones is determined by the number of isolated columns supporting it. Fig. 2 shows the plan of a column-supported deck. The wheel load and column reactions are assumed uniformly distributed over a finite rectangular area in order to utilize Eq. 7 in the analysis. The redundant column reactions are removed and the bridge is allowed to deflect due to the load. The column supports will be replaced one at a time causing deflection at each of the points of column support 1 to m. For a point i distance L_i from the support, the deflection due to a uniformly distributed unit load acting at j which is located at a distance L_j from the support may be written as

$$\omega_{ij} = \frac{L^4}{U_j V_j \pi^5 D_x} \sum_{n=1}^{\infty} \frac{1}{n^5} \sin \alpha_n U_j \sin \alpha_n L_i \sin \alpha_n L_j \; K^*_{ij} \tag{8}$$

where K^*_{ij} is a general notation to denote the coefficient K^* from Eq. 7 for point i due to a load acting at j. At point i, the algebraic sum of all deflections due to the external load and all column reaction must be equated to the elastic deformation of column i plus the foundation settlement Δ_{is} at i. The elastic deformation of column i due to a unit load is obtained from the simple expression

$$\delta_{ii} = \frac{h_i}{A_i E_i} \tag{9}$$

where the subscripts h, A and E refer to the effective height, area and modulus of elasticity of the column. If the redundant column reactions are R_1, R_2 .... R_m for columns 1 to m respectively, then the equation of deflection compatibility for point i may be written as

$$P \cdot \omega_{ip} - (R_1 \omega_{i1} + R_2 \omega_{i2} + \dots R_i \omega_{ii} + \dots R_m \omega_{im}) = \delta_{ii} R_i + \Delta_{is} \quad (10)$$

Similar equations may be written for points 1 to m resulting in m simultaneous equations and this may be expressed in matrix form as shown

$$\begin{bmatrix} (\omega_{11}+\delta_{11}) & \omega_{12} & \cdots & \omega_{1i} & \cdots & \omega_{1m} \\ \omega_{21} & (\omega_{22}+\delta_{22}) & \cdots & \omega_{2i} & \cdots & \omega_{2m} \\ \vdots & \vdots & & \vdots & & \vdots \\ \omega_{i1} & \omega_{i2} & \cdots & (\omega_{ii}+\delta_{ii}) & \cdots & \omega_{im} \\ \vdots & \vdots & & \vdots & & \vdots \\ \omega_{m1} & \omega_{m2} & \cdots & \omega_{mi} & \cdots & (\omega_{mm}+\delta_{mm}) \end{bmatrix} \begin{bmatrix} R_1 \\ R_2 \\ \vdots \\ R_i \\ \vdots \\ R_m \end{bmatrix} = P \begin{bmatrix} \omega_{1p} \\ \omega_{2p} \\ \vdots \\ \omega_{ip} \\ \vdots \\ \omega_{mp} \end{bmatrix} - \begin{bmatrix} \Delta_{1s} \\ \Delta_{2s} \\ \vdots \\ \Delta_{is} \\ \vdots \\ \Delta_{ms} \end{bmatrix} \quad (11)$$

The problem reduces to the determination of the redundant column reactions R_1 to R_m. With these reactions known, the deflection of a point distance x from the support may be obtained by superposition, thus

$$\omega_x = \frac{PL^4}{UV\pi^5 D_x} \sum_{n=1}^{\infty} \frac{1}{n^5} \sin\alpha_n U \sin\alpha_n C \sin\alpha_n x \cdot K_{xp}^{*}$$

$$- \sum_{i=1}^{m} \left(R_i \frac{L^4}{U_i V_i \pi^5 D_x} \sum_{n=1}^{\infty} \frac{1}{n^5} \sin\alpha_n U_i \sin\alpha_n L_i \sin\alpha_n x \cdot K_{xi}^{*} \right) \quad (12)$$

If the elastic deformations of the columns are neglected then the terms δ along the diagonal of the matrix are set to zero. Similarly, if there is no settlement of supports, then the terms Δ_s may be omitted in Eq. 11.

With the redundant reactions known, the bending, twisting, shearing and reactive forces at any point x may be obtained by successive differentiation of Eq. 12. The column reactions are treated as loads and the net effect is obtained by superposition.

The relevant deflection-stress resultant relationships for orthotropic plates are summarized as follows:

$$M_x = -\left(D_x \frac{\partial^2 \omega}{\partial x^2} + D_1 \frac{\partial^2 \omega}{\partial y^2} \right)$$

$$M_y = -\left(D_y \frac{\partial^2 \omega}{\partial y^2} + D_2 \frac{\partial^2 \omega}{\partial x^2} \right)$$

$$
\begin{aligned}
M_{xy} &= D_{xy}\frac{\partial^2 \omega}{\partial x \partial y} \\
M_{yx} &= -D_{yx}\frac{\partial^2 \omega}{\partial x \partial y} \\
V_x &= -\left[D_x \frac{\partial^3 \omega}{\partial x^3} + (D_1 + D_{yx})\frac{\partial^3 \omega}{\partial x \partial y^2}\right] \\
V_y &= -\left[D_y \frac{\partial^2 \omega}{\partial y^3} + (D_2 + D_{xy})\frac{\partial^3 \omega}{\partial x^2 \partial y}\right] \\
R_x &= -\left[D_x \frac{\partial^3 \omega}{\partial x^3} + (D_1 + D_{xy} + D_{yx})\frac{\partial^3 \omega}{\partial x \partial y^2}\right] \\
R_y &= -\left[D_y \frac{\partial^3 \omega}{\partial y^3} + (D_2 + D_{xy} + D_{yx})\frac{\partial^3 \omega}{\partial x^2 \partial y}\right]
\end{aligned}
\qquad (13)
$$

These are conveniently evaluated with the aid of a digital computer since Eq. 13 entails the use of four different coefficients derived from K^* by successive differentiation as for statically determinate bridge decks[6].

In this analysis the column dimensions are considered which means that the analysis could be used to determine the effects of these dimensions on load distribution. In the case of small columns supporting wide bridge decks the columns may be idealized as point loads.

The analysis of the column-supported bridge deck as presented is not restricted to the simple case of a deck with a single row of columns.

The analysis could be used to cover the analysis of bridge decks with random column supports.

The only limitation of the analysis is in the actual shape of the columns. The analysis was developed for rectangular columns; for circular columns an approximation may be made by substitution of square sections with sides of 0.88 times the diameter of the circular column.

The wheel loads acting on the deck are also assumed to be rectangular and for the British Ministry of Transport HB loading 2U = 3 in., 2V = 15 in. For AASHO H20-S16 loading the width 2V = 20 in. The problem of concentrated wheel loads poses no difficulty since the dimensions U and V of the load may be made very small and the results check with those for concentrated loads.

The analysis incorporates the effect of edge stiffening beams since the flexural and torsional rigidities EI and GJ respectively are included as parameters in the coefficient K^* as shown in the Appendix. Using these edge beam rigidities, the analysis may also be extended to cover the analysis of orthotropic floor slabs with random intermediate supports.

The use of rectangular patch loads instead of concentrated loads has the main advantage of speeding the convergence of the series. For example, the convergence of the deflection series (Eq. 7) is controlled by $\frac{1}{n^5}$ as compared with $\frac{1}{n^3}$ for concentrated loads. By successive differentiation the convergence of the series for bending and twisting moments of the deck will be a function of $\frac{1}{n^3}$ and for shear and reactive forces it will be a function of $\frac{1}{n^2}$ and with this improved convergence the stresses of the deck may be evaluated using a few harmonics only saving considerable computer time.

Analysis of Continuous Bridge Decks

The analysis of bridge decks with intermediate line supports may be obtained as a special case of the column-supported deck. The reactive force induced at the intermediate support is replaced by step functions R_1, R_2, R_3 .... R_m uniformly distributed over a small area $2U_i \times 2V_i$. These reactive forces are treated as separate columns laid side by side extending across the entire width of the deck.

Referring to Fig. 3, the deflection at point i distance L_i from the support due to a unit load at distance C is

$$\omega_{ip} = \frac{L^4}{UV\pi^5 D_x} \sum_{n=1}^{\infty} \frac{1}{n^5} \operatorname{Sin}\alpha_n U \operatorname{Sin}\alpha_n C \operatorname{Sin}\alpha_n L_i \cdot K_{ip}^{*} \tag{14}$$

and for a unit reactive force at j, the deflection at point i may be written as

$$\omega_{ij} = \frac{L^4}{U_j V_j \pi^5 D_x} \sum_{n=1}^{\infty} \frac{1}{n^5} \operatorname{Sin}\alpha_n U_j \operatorname{Sin}^2\alpha_n L_j \cdot K_{ij}^{*} \tag{15}$$

which is a special case of Eq. 8 if $L_i = L_j$.

If there is no uneven settlement of foundation and elastic shortening is neglected, the equation of deflection compatibility at point i, due to the load P and m reactive forces may be written as follows:

$$R_1 \omega_{i1} + R_2 \omega_{i2} + R_3 \omega_{i3} + \cdots R_i \omega_{ii} + \cdots R_m \omega_{im} = P \cdot \omega_{ip} \tag{16}$$

Similar equations may be written for points 1 to m resulting in m equations which may be expressed in matrix form as

$$\begin{bmatrix} \omega_{11} & \omega_{12} & \omega_{13} & \cdots & \omega_{1i} & \cdots & \omega_{1m} \\ \omega_{21} & \omega_{22} & \omega_{23} & \cdots & \omega_{2i} & \cdots & \omega_{2m} \\ \omega_{31} & \omega_{32} & \omega_{33} & \cdots & \omega_{3i} & \cdots & \omega_{3m} \\ \vdots & \vdots & \vdots & & \vdots & & \vdots \\ \omega_{i1} & \omega_{i2} & \omega_{i3} & \cdots & \omega_{ii} & \cdots & \omega_{im} \\ \vdots & \vdots & \vdots & & \vdots & & \vdots \\ \omega_{m1} & \omega_{m2} & \omega_{m3} & \cdots & \omega_{mi} & \cdots & \omega_{mm} \end{bmatrix} \begin{bmatrix} R_1 \\ R_2 \\ R_3 \\ \vdots \\ R_i \\ \vdots \\ R_m \end{bmatrix} = P \begin{bmatrix} \omega_{1p} \\ \omega_{2p} \\ \omega_{3p} \\ \vdots \\ \omega_{ip} \\ \vdots \\ \omega_{mp} \end{bmatrix} \quad (17)$$

which is recognized as a special case of Eq. 11 if the δ's and Δ's are omitted.

With the reactive forces R_1 to R_m known, the deflection at any point on the deck may be obtained by superposition as shown in Eq. 12 and the bending and twisting moments, shearing and reactive forces may be evaluated by successive differentiation of the deflection function following Eq. 13.

Analysis of Propped-Cantilever Bridge Decks

The fixing moment at the built-in support of a propped cantilever bridge deck due to a load P is assumed to vary as shown in Fig. 4. The width of the bridge is divided into m strips and for each strip the actual fixing moment is replaced by average uniformly distributed moments M_1, M_2, M_3 .... M_i .... M_m for strips 1,2,3 ....i .... m respectively. These fixing moments M_1 to M_m are removed and the deck is allowed to rotate at the support due to the load P. For any point i at the support, the rotation due to this load is obtained by differentiating the deflection w with respect to x. Thus from Eq. 7

$$\left(\frac{\partial w}{\partial x}\right)_{x=0} = \frac{PL^3}{UV\pi^4 D_x} \sum_{n=1}^{\infty} \frac{1}{n^4} \sin\alpha_n U \sin\alpha_n C \cdot K^* \tag{18}$$

where K^* represents the appropriate load distribution coefficient for the orthotropic bridge deck classified according to relative rigidities. It is evident from Eq. 18 that the slope consists of a constant term multiplied by a distribution coefficient which is a function of the various rigidities of the bridge, aspect ratio of the deck and the transverse position of the load. To make a general analysis, replace the coefficient K^* by K^*_{ip} to represent the slope coefficient for i due to a load P. The slope at i may then be written as

$$\left(\frac{\partial w}{\partial x}\right)_{ip} = P \cdot S_{ip} \tag{19}$$

where

$$S_{ip} = \frac{L^3}{UV\pi^4 D_x} \sum_{n=1}^{\infty} \frac{1}{n^4} \sin \alpha_n U \sin \alpha_n C \; K^*_{ip} \tag{20}$$

The general expression for deflection due to a fixing moment at the support may be obtained from Eq. 7 by studying the limit of w as U and C approaches zero, thus

$$w = \lim_{\substack{U \to 0 \\ C \to 0}} \frac{PL^4}{UV\pi^5 D_x} \sum_{n=1}^{\infty} \frac{1}{n^5} \sin \alpha_n U \sin \alpha_n C \sin \alpha_n x \cdot K^* \tag{21}$$

or

$$w = \frac{PC L^2}{V\pi^3 D_x} \sum_{n=1}^{\infty} \frac{1}{n^3} \sin \alpha_n x \cdot K^* \tag{22}$$

Since PC = M, the equation may be written as

$$w = \frac{ML^2}{V\pi^3 D_x} \sum_{n=1}^{\infty} \frac{1}{n^3} \sin \alpha_n x \cdot K^* \tag{23}$$

Thus, the fixing moment M at the support may be treated as a large force P acting at a very small distance C from the support.

The slope at the support may be obtained by differentiating w with respect to x, hence

$$\left(\frac{\partial w}{\partial x}\right)_{x=0} = \frac{ML}{V\pi^2 D_x} \sum_{n=1}^{\infty} \frac{1}{n^2} \cdot K^* \tag{24}$$

In general, therefore, the slope at point i due to a unit moment acting at j may be written as

$$\phi_{ij} = \frac{L}{V_j \pi^2 D_x} \sum_{n=1}^{\infty} \frac{1}{n^2} K_{ij}^* \tag{25}$$

This moment at j produces slopes at all points from 1 to m and so with all other moments when applied at their proper locations. For point i, the algebraic sum of all slopes due to the load and due to moments M_1 to M_m must be equated to zero to satisfy the condition of full fixity at the built-in support. Thus, the equation of slope compatibility at i may be expressed as

$$M_1 \phi_{i1} + M_2 \phi_{i2} + M_3 \phi_{i3} + \cdots M_i \phi_{ii} + \cdots M_m \phi_{im} = P \cdot S_{ip} \tag{26}$$

If written for points 1 to m, the m simultaneous equations may be expressed in matrix form as follows:

$$\begin{bmatrix} \phi_{11} & \phi_{12} & \phi_{13} \cdots & \phi_{1i} \cdots & \phi_{1m} \\ \phi_{21} & \phi_{22} & \phi_{23} \cdots & \phi_{2i} \cdots & \phi_{2m} \\ \phi_{31} & \phi_{32} & \phi_{33} \cdots & \phi_{3i} \cdots & \phi_{3m} \\ \vdots & \vdots & \vdots & \vdots & \vdots \\ \phi_{i1} & \phi_{i2} & \phi_{i3} \cdots & \phi_{ii} \cdots & \phi_{im} \\ \vdots & \vdots & \vdots & \vdots & \vdots \\ \phi_{m1} & \phi_{m2} & \phi_{m3} \cdots & \phi_{mi} \cdots & \phi_{mm} \end{bmatrix} \begin{bmatrix} M_1 \\ M_2 \\ M_3 \\ \vdots \\ M_i \\ \vdots \\ M_m \end{bmatrix} = P \begin{bmatrix} S_{1p} \\ S_{2p} \\ S_{3p} \\ \vdots \\ S_{ip} \\ \vdots \\ S_{mp} \end{bmatrix} \tag{27}$$

The solution of Eq. 27 entails the inversion of an m x m matrix and the fixing moments M_1 to M_m are determined. The deflection of any point distance x from the support may be obtained by superposition as follows,

$$\omega_x = \frac{PL^4}{UV\pi^5 D_x} \sum_{n=1}^{\infty} \frac{1}{\eta^5} \sin\alpha_n U \sin\alpha_n C \sin\alpha_n x \cdot K^*_{xp} - \sum_{i=1}^{m} \left(M_i \frac{L^2}{V_i \cdot \pi^3 D_x} \sum_{n=1}^{\infty} \frac{1}{\eta^3} \sin\alpha_n x \cdot K^*_{xi} \right) \qquad (28)$$

Again, the bending and twisting moments, shearing and reactive forces are obtained following Eq. 13.

EXPERIMENTAL RESULTS

Experimental work to test validity of the foregoing analyses has so far been limited to tests on an isotropic slab of asbestos-cement. This slab was ½ in. thick and measured 16 in. by 34 in. in plan. It was made up into a column-supported deck as shown in Fig. 5. Four columns 14½ in. long and 3/8 in. square in cross-section were glued to the underside of the deck at midspan at points corresponding to the reference stations $-{}^3/_4 b$, $-{}^b/_4$, ${}^b/_4$ and ${}^3/_4 b$. The feet of the columns were glued to the web of a supporting rig. Electrical resistance strain gauges were attached on two opposite sides at midheight of the columns. Loads were applied at equal increments using a simple lever system and a data logger was employed to record the out-of-balance voltages which were converted to strain values and eventually to reactive forces of the columns. The applied loads were situated at the line of column supports in order to give maximum values of column reactive forces. These were significant enough to be recorded accurately by the data logger.

The results of three tests made under different eccentricities of load are shown in Table 1. A plan of the bridge deck showing the relative positions of the columns and the point of application of the loads is shown in Fig. 6. Good correlation between theory and experiment was obtained especially for the reactive forces of the more heavily stressed columns. At times one or more of the columns was observed to be in tension but the magnitudes of these tensile forces were well below 7% of the applied load and confirmed theoretical values. The theoretical results were obtained by digital computer which involves inverting a square matrix as described in the theoretical analysis.

CONCLUSIONS

A load distribution method based on orthotropic plate theory has been developed for the analysis of statically indeterminate orthotropic bridge decks. The analysis covers the whole range of orthotropic bridge decks from the torsionless case ($H = 0$) to the articulated deck ($D_y = 0$). The method was derived for loads distributed over a finite rectangular area but may be extended to cover the case of concentrated loads acting on the deck. Three typical examples are presented and the validity of the theory has been partially verified by test on a small asbestos cement model. Good correlation was achieved between theory and experiment but further experimental investigation using different types of bridge decks is highly desirable.

Table 1 Comparison of theoretical and experimental reactive forces due to a unit load on the deck.

Load Position	R_1		R_2		R_3		R_4	
	Theory	Expt.	Theory	Expt.	Theory	Expt.	Theory	Expt.
$b/8$	-0.0651	-0.0328	0.8407	0.8140	0.2624	0.3910	-0.0381	-0.0317
$3/8b$	0.1697	0.1557	0.9286	0.9220	-0.1173	-0.141	0.0171	0.0205
$5/8b$	0.7341	0.6580	0.2890	0.4100	-0.0267	-0.0451	0.0014	0.0164

REFERENCES

1. Huber, M.T., " Die Theorie der Kreuzweise bewehren Eisenbetonplatte nebst Anwendungen auf mehrere bautechnisch wichtige Aufgaben uber Rechteckplatten" , Der Bauingenieur, Berlin, 1923.
2. Guyon, Y., " Calcul des Ponts larges a Poutres Multiples Solidarisees par des Entretoises" , Annales des Ponts et Chaussees, Paris, No. 24, September-October, 1946, pp. 553-612.
3. Massonnet, C., " Methode de calcul des Ponts a Poutres Multiples Terant Compte de Leur Resistance a La Torsion" , Publications, International Association for Bridge and Structural Engineering, Vol. 10, Zurich, 1950, pp. 147-182.
4. Spindel, J.E., " A study of Bridge Slabs Having No Transverse Flexural Stiffness" , Thesis presented to the University of London, in 1961, in partial fulfilment of the requirements for the degree Doctor of Philosophy.
5. Pama, R.P. and Cusens, A.R., " Load Distribution in Multibeam Concrete Bridges" , Paper presented to the International Symposium on Concrete Bridge Design held at Toronto, Canada, April 1967.
6. Cusens, A.R. and Pama, R.P., " The Distribution of Concentrated Loads on Orthotropic Bridge Decks" , The Structural Engineer (to be published).
7. Inglis, C.E., " The Determination of Critical Speeds, Natural Frequencies and Modes of Vibration by Means of Basic Functions" . Transactions of the North East Coast Institution of Engineers and Shipbuilders, England, 1944.

8. Rowe, R.E., " Concrete Bridge Design" , C.R. Books, Ltd. 1962.

9. Hendry, A.W. and Jaeger, L.G., " The Analysis of Grid Frameworks and Related Structures" , Chatto and Windus, London, 1958.

10. Leray, Jean, " Calcul, par reflexions, des fonctions M-harmoniques dans une bande plane verifiant aux bords M conditions differentielles, a coefficients constants" , Arch. Mech. Strs. 16, 1964.

11. Morley, L.S.D., " The Analysis of Column Supported Plates with Special Application to Bridges" , Publications, International Association for Bridge and Structural Engineering, Vol. 27, 1967, pp. 95-138.

APPENDIX

Case 1: Torsionally Stiff-Flexurally Soft Bridge Decks ($H^2 \geq D_x D_y$)

The distribution coefficients K^* for this particular type of bridge deck is defined as follows:

$$K^* = \frac{D_x}{2D_y(r_1^2 - r_2^2)} \left[\frac{1}{r_2^2} \left(e^{-\beta_2(\xi_1 - \psi)} - e^{-\beta_2(\xi_1 + \psi)} \right) - \frac{1}{r_1^2} \left(e^{-\beta_1(\xi_1 - \psi)} - e^{-\beta_2(\xi_1 + \psi)} \right) \right.$$

$$\left. + A_n \operatorname{Cosh} \beta_1 \xi_0 + B_n \operatorname{Cosh} \beta_2 \xi_0 + C_n \operatorname{Sinh} \beta_1 \xi_0 + D_n \operatorname{Sinh} \beta_2 \xi_0 \right] \quad \text{For } \xi_1 \geq \psi$$

or

$$K^* = \frac{D_x}{2D_y(r_1^2 - r_2^2)} \left[\frac{2}{r_2^2} \left(1 - e^{-\beta_2 \psi} \right) - \frac{2}{r_1^2} \left(1 - e^{-\beta_1 \psi} \right) \right.$$

$$\left. + A_n \operatorname{Cosh} \beta_1 \xi_0 + B_n \operatorname{Cosh} \beta_2 \xi_0 + C_n \operatorname{Sinh} \beta_1 \xi_0 + D_n \operatorname{Sinh} \beta_2 \xi_0 \right] \quad \text{For } \xi_1 = 0$$

where

$$r_1 = \sqrt{\frac{H}{D_y} + \sqrt{\left(\frac{H}{D_y}\right)^2 - \frac{D_x}{D_y}}}$$

$$r_2 = \sqrt{\frac{H}{D_y} - \sqrt{\left(\frac{H}{D_y}\right)^2 - \frac{D_x}{D_y}}}$$

$$\beta_1 = \alpha_n b r_1 = \frac{n\pi b r_1}{L}$$

$$\beta_2 = \alpha_n b r_2 = \frac{n\pi b r_2}{L}$$

The constants are defined as follows:

$$A_n = \frac{(S_{31} - S_{41})\, b_{11} - (S_{11} + S_{21})\, b_{31}}{2(a_{31} b_{11} - a_{11} b_{31})}$$

$$B_n = \frac{(S_{11} + S_{21})\,a_{31} - (S_{31} - S_{41})\,a_{11}}{2(a_{31}\,b_{11} - a_{11}\,b_{31})}$$

$$C_n = \frac{(S_{31} + S_{41})\,d_{11} - (S_{11} - S_{21})\,d_{31}}{2(c_{31}\,d_{11} - c_{11}\,d_{31})}$$

$$D_n = \frac{(S_{11} - S_{21})\,c_{31} - (S_{31} + S_{41})\,c_{11}}{2(c_{31}\,d_{11} - c_{11}\,d_{31})}$$

where

$$S_{11} = \frac{1}{r_1}\left[GJ\alpha_n + (D_y r_1^2 - D_2)\frac{1}{r_1}\right]\left[e^{-\beta_1(\eta_1-\psi)} - e^{-\beta_1(\eta_1+\psi)}\right]$$

$$-\frac{1}{r_2}\left[GJ\alpha_n + (D_y r_2^2 - D_2)\frac{1}{r_2}\right]\left[e^{-\beta_2(\eta_1-\psi)} - e^{-\beta_2(\eta_1+\psi)}\right]$$

$$S_{21} = \frac{1}{r_1}\left[GJ\alpha_n + (D_y r_1^2 - D_2)\frac{1}{r_1}\right]\left[e^{-\beta_1(\eta_2-\psi)} - e^{-\beta_1(\eta_2+\psi)}\right]$$

$$-\frac{1}{r_2}\left[GJ\alpha_n + (D_y r_2^2 - D_2)\frac{1}{r_2}\right]\left[e^{-\beta_2(\eta_2-\psi)} - e^{-\beta_2(\eta_2+\psi)}\right]$$

$$S_{31} = \frac{1}{r_1^2}\left[EI\alpha_n + (D_y r_1^2 - D_2 - D_{xy} - D_{yx})\,r_1\right]\left[e^{-\beta_1(\eta_1-\psi)} - e^{-\beta_1(\eta_1+\psi)}\right]$$

$$-\frac{1}{r_2^2}\left[EI\alpha_n + (D_y r_2^2 - D_2 - D_{xy} - D_{yx})\,r_2\right]\left[e^{-\beta_2(\eta_1-\psi)} - e^{-\beta_2(\eta_1+\psi)}\right]$$

$$S_{41} = -\frac{1}{r_1^2}\left[EI\alpha_n + (D_y r_1^2 - D_2 - D_{xy} - D_{yx}) r_1\right]\left[e^{-\beta_1(\eta_2 - \psi)} - e^{-\beta_1(\eta_2 + \psi)}\right]$$

$$+ \frac{1}{r_2^2}\left[EI\alpha_n + (D_y r_2^2 - D_2 - D_{xy} - D_{yx}) r_2\right]\left[e^{-\beta_2(\eta_2 - \psi)} - e^{-\beta_2(\eta_2 + \psi)}\right]$$

and the terms a_{11}, b_{11} .... d_{31} are as follows:

$$a_{11} = (D_y r_1^2 - D_2) \, Cosh\beta_1 - GJ\alpha_n r_1 \, Sinh\beta_1$$

$$b_{11} = (D_y r_2^2 - D_2) \, Cosh\beta_2 - GJ\alpha_n r_2 \, Sinh\beta_2$$

$$c_{11} = (D_y r_1^2 - D_2) \, Sinh\beta_1 - GJ\alpha_n r_1 \, Cosh\beta_1$$

$$d_{11} = (D_y r_2^2 - D_2) \, Sinh\beta_2 - GJ\alpha_n r_2 \, Cosh\beta_2$$

$$a_{31} = EI\alpha_n \, Cosh\beta_1 - r_1 (D_y r_1^2 - D_2 - D_{xy} - D_{yx}) \, Sinh\beta_1$$

$$b_{31} = EI\alpha_n \, Cosh\beta_2 - r_2 (D_y r_2^2 - D_2 - D_{xy} - D_{yx}) \, Sinh\beta_2$$

$$c_{31} = EI\alpha_n \, Sinh\beta_1 - r_1 (D_y r_1^2 - D_2 - D_{xy} - D_{yx}) \, Cosh\beta_1$$

$$d_{31} = EI\alpha_n \, Sinh\beta_2 - r_2 (D_y r_2^2 - D_2 - D_{xy} - D_{yx}) \, Cosh\beta_2$$

Referring to Fig. 1, the location of the station relative to the centre of the bridge and load respectively are given by

$$\xi_0 = \frac{y_0}{b}$$

$$\xi_1 = Abs.\left[\frac{y_1}{b}\right] = Abs.\left[1 + \xi_0 - \eta_2\right]$$

and the parameter ψ is the ratio of the width of the load to the bridge, thus

$$\psi = \frac{v}{b}$$

Case 3: Torsionally Soft-Flexurally Stiff Bridge Decks ($H^2 \leq D_x D_y$)

The distribution coefficient K^* for this particular case is expressed as

$$K^* = \frac{D_x}{4 D_y r_3 r_4}\Bigg[\frac{1}{(r_3^2+r_4^2)}\Big\{\big[2r_3 r_4 \cos\beta_4(\xi_{\varphi_1}-\psi) + (r_3^2-r_4^2)\sin\beta_4(\xi_1-\psi)\big]e^{-\beta_3(\xi_1-\psi)}$$

$$-\big[2r_3 r_4 \cos\beta_4(\xi_1+\psi) + (r_3^2-r_4^2)\sin\beta_4(\xi_{\varphi_1}+\psi)\big]e^{-\beta_3(\xi_1+\psi)}\Big\}$$

$$+A_m \cosh\beta_3\xi_{\varphi_0}\cos\beta_4\xi_{\varphi_0} + B_m\cosh\beta_3\xi_{\varphi_0}\sin\beta_4\xi_{\varphi_0}$$

$$+C_m\sinh\beta_3\xi_{\varphi_0}\cos\beta_4\xi_{\varphi_0} + D_m\sinh\beta_3\xi_{\varphi_0}\sin\beta_4\xi_{\varphi_0}\Bigg] \quad \text{For } \xi_{\varphi_1} \geq \psi$$

or

$$K^* = \frac{D_x}{4 D_y r_3 r_4}\Bigg[\frac{2}{(r_3^2+r_4^2)^2}\Big\{2r_3 r_4 - \big[2r_3 r_4\cos\beta_4\psi + (r_3^2-r_4^2)\sin\beta_4\psi\big]e^{-\beta_3\psi}\Big\}$$

$$+A_m\cosh\beta_3\xi_{\varphi_0}\cos\beta_4\xi_{\varphi_0} + B_m\cosh\beta_3\xi_{\varphi_0}\sin\beta_4\xi_{\varphi_0}$$

$$+C_m\sinh\beta_3\xi_{\varphi_0}\cos\beta_4\xi_{\varphi_0} + D_m\sinh\beta_3\xi_{\varphi_0}\sin\beta_4\xi_{\varphi_0}\Bigg] \quad \text{For } \xi_{\varphi_1} = 0$$

with

$$r_3 = \sqrt{\frac{\sqrt{\frac{D_x}{D_y}} + \frac{H}{D_y}}{2}}$$

$$r_4 = \sqrt{\frac{\sqrt{\frac{D_x}{D_y}} - \frac{H}{D_y}}{2}}$$

$$\beta_3 = \alpha_n b r_3 = \frac{n\pi b r_3}{L}$$

$$\beta_4 = \alpha_n b r_4 = \frac{n\pi b r_4}{L}$$

The constants are defined as follows

$$A_m = \frac{(S_{13} + S_{23})\, d_{33} - (S_{33} - S_{43})\, d_{13}}{2(a_{13}\, d_{33} - a_{33}\, d_{13})}$$

$$B_m = \frac{(S_{13} - S_{23})\, c_{33} - (S_{33} + S_{43})\, c_{13}}{2(b_{13}\, c_{33} - c_{13}\, b_{33})}$$

$$C_m = \frac{(S_{33} + S_{43})\, b_{13} - (S_{13} - S_{23})\, b_{33}}{2(b_{13}\, c_{33} - c_{13}\, b_{33})}$$

$$D_m = \frac{(S_{33} - S_{43})\, a_{13} - (S_{13} + S_{23})\, a_{33}}{2(a_{13}\, d_{33} - a_{33}\, d_{13})}$$

where

$$S_{13} = \frac{1}{(r_3^2 + r_4^2)}\left[\left\{ GJ\alpha_n - \frac{r_3\,[D_2 - D_y(r_3^2 + r_4^2)]}{(r_3^2 + r_4^2)} \right\} \times\right.$$

$$\left\{ [r_3 \sin\beta_4(\eta_1 - \psi) + r_4 \cos\beta_4(\eta_1 - \psi)]\, e^{-\beta_3(\eta_1 - \psi)}\right.$$

$$\left. - [r_3 \sin\beta_4(\eta_1 + \psi) + r_4 \cos\beta_4(\eta_1 + \psi)]\, e^{-\beta_3(\eta_1 + \psi)} \right\}$$

$$-\left\{\frac{r_4\left[D_2 + D_y(r_3^2 + r_4^2)\right]}{(r_3^2 + r_4^2)}\right\} \times$$

$$\left\{\left[r_3 \cos\beta_4(\eta_1 - \psi) - r_4 \sin\beta_4(\eta_1 - \psi)\right] e^{-\beta_3(\eta_1 - \psi)}\right.$$

$$\left.\left. - \left[r_3 \cos\beta_4(\eta_1 + \psi) - r_4 \sin\beta_4(\eta_1 + \psi)\right] e^{-\beta_3(\eta_1 + \psi)}\right\}\right]$$

$$S_{23} = \frac{1}{(r_3^2 + r_4^2)}\left[\left\{GJ\alpha_n - \frac{r_3\left[D_2 - D_y(r_3^2 + r_4^2)\right]}{(r_3^2 + r_4^2)}\right\} \times\right.$$

$$\left\{\left[r_3 \sin\beta_4(\eta_2 - \psi) + r_4 \cos\beta_4(\eta_2 - \psi)\right] e^{-\beta_3(\eta_2 - \psi)}\right.$$

$$\left. - \left[r_3 \sin\beta_4(\eta_2 + \psi) + r_4 \cos\beta_4(\eta_2 + \psi)\right] e^{-\beta_3(\eta_2 + \psi)}\right\}$$

$$-\left\{\frac{r_4\left(D_2 + D_y(r_3^2 + r_4^2)\right)}{(r_3^2 + r_4^2)}\right\} \times$$

$$\left\{\left[r_3 \cos\beta_4(\eta_2 - \psi) - r_4 \sin\beta_4(\eta_2 - \psi)\right] e^{-\beta_3(\eta_2 - \psi)}\right.$$

$$\left.\left. - \left[r_3 \cos\beta_4(\eta_2 + \psi) - r_4 \sin\beta_4(\eta_2 + \psi)\right] e^{-\beta_3(\eta_2 + \psi)}\right\}\right]$$

$$S_{33} = \frac{1}{(r_3^2 + r_4^2)^2}\left[\left\{\left[D_y(r_4^2 - r_3^2) + D_2 + D_{xy} + D_{yx}\right](r_3^2 + r_4^2) - EI\alpha_n r_3\right\} \times\right.$$

$$\left\{\left[r_3 \sin\beta_4(\eta_1 - \psi) + r_4 \cos\beta_4(\eta_1 - \psi)\right] e^{-\beta_3(\eta_1 - \psi)}\right.$$

$$\left. - \left[r_3 \sin\beta_4(\eta_1 + \psi) + r_4 \cos\beta_4(\eta_1 + \psi)\right] e^{-\beta_3(\eta_1 + \psi)}\right\}$$

$$+ \left\{ 2D_y r_3 r_4 (r_3^2 + r_4^2) - EI\alpha_n r_4 \right\} \times$$

$$\left\{ \left[r_3 \cos\beta_4(\eta_1 - \psi) - r_4 \sin\beta_4(\eta_1 - \psi) \right] e^{-\beta_3(\eta_1 - \psi)} \right.$$

$$\left. - \left[r_3 \cos\beta_4(\eta_1 + \psi) - r_4 \sin\beta_4(\eta_1 + \psi) \right] e^{-\beta_3(\eta_1 + \psi)} \right\} \Bigg]$$

$$S_{43} = \frac{1}{(r_3^2 + r_4^2)^2} \Bigg[\left\{ EI\alpha_n r_4 - 2D_y r_3 r_4 (r_3^2 + r_4^2) \right\} \times$$

$$\left\{ \left[r_3 \cos\beta_4(\eta_2 - \psi) - r_4 \sin\beta_4(\eta_2 - \psi) \right] e^{-\beta_3(\eta_2 - \psi)} \right.$$

$$\left. - \left[r_3 \cos\beta_4(\eta_2 + \psi) - r_4 \sin\beta_4(\eta_2 + \psi) \right] e^{-\beta_3(\eta_2 + \psi)} \right\}$$

$$+ \left\{ EI\alpha_n r_3 - (r_3^2 + r_4^2)\left[D_y (r_4^2 - r_3^2) + D_2 + D_{xy} + D_{yx} \right] \right\} \times$$

$$\left\{ \left[r_3 \sin\beta_4(\eta_2 - \psi) + r_4 \cos\beta_4(\eta_2 - \psi) \right] e^{-\beta_3(\eta_2 - \psi)} \right.$$

$$\left. - \left[r_3 \sin\beta_4(\eta_2 + \psi) + r_4 \cos\beta_4(\eta_2 + \psi) \right] e^{-\beta_3(\eta_2 + \psi)} \right\} \Bigg]$$

The constants a_{13}, b_{13} .... d_{33} are defined as

$$a_{13} = \left[D_2 - D_y (r_3^2 - r_4^2) \right] \cosh\beta_3 \cos\beta_4 + 2D_y r_3 r_4 \sinh\beta_3 \sin\beta_4$$

$$+ GJ\alpha_n (r_3 \sinh\beta_3 \cos\beta_4 - r_4 \cosh\beta_3 \sin\beta_4)$$

$$b_{13} = [D_2 - D_y(r_3^2 - r_4^2)] \operatorname{Cosh}\beta_3 \operatorname{Sin}\beta_4 - 2D_y r_3 r_4 \operatorname{Sinh}\beta_3 \operatorname{Sin}\beta_4$$
$$+ GJ\alpha_n(r_3 \operatorname{Sinh}\beta_3 \operatorname{Sin}\beta_4 + r_4 \operatorname{Cosh}\beta_3 \operatorname{Cos}\beta_4)$$

$$c_{13} = [D_2 - D_y(r_3^2 - r_4^2)] \operatorname{Sinh}\beta_3 \operatorname{Cos}\beta_4 + 2D_y r_3 r_4 \operatorname{Cosh}\beta_3 \operatorname{Sin}\beta_4$$
$$+ GJ\alpha_n(r_3 \operatorname{Cosh}\beta_3 \operatorname{Cos}\beta_4 - r_4 \operatorname{Sinh}\beta_3 \operatorname{Sin}\beta_4)$$

$$d_{13} = [D_2 - D_y(r_3^2 - r_4^2)] \operatorname{Sinh}\beta_3 \operatorname{Sin}\beta_4 - 2D_y r_3 r_4 \operatorname{Cosh}\beta_3 \operatorname{Cos}\beta_4$$
$$+ GJ\alpha_n(r_3 \operatorname{Cosh}\beta_3 \operatorname{Sin}\beta_4 + r_4 \operatorname{Sinh}\beta_3 \operatorname{Cos}\beta_4)$$

$$a_{33} = [r_3(D_2 + D_{xy} + D_{yx}) - D_y(r_3^3 - 3r_3 r_4^2)] \operatorname{Sinh}\beta_3 \operatorname{Cos}\beta_4$$
$$- [r_4(D_2 + D_{xy} + D_{yx}) + D_y(r_4^3 - 3r_4 r_3^2)] \operatorname{Cosh}\beta_3 \operatorname{Sin}\beta_4$$
$$+ EI\alpha_n \operatorname{Cosh}\beta_3 \operatorname{Cos}\beta_4$$

$$b_{33} = [r_3(D_2 + D_{xy} + D_{yx}) - D_y(r_3^3 - 3r_3 r_4^2)] \operatorname{Sinh}\beta_3 \operatorname{Sin}\beta_4$$
$$+ [r_4(D_2 + D_{xy} + D_{yx}) + D_y(r_4^3 - 3r_4 r_3^2)] \operatorname{Cosh}\beta_3 \operatorname{Cos}\beta_4$$
$$+ EI\alpha_n \operatorname{Cosh}\beta_3 \operatorname{Sin}\beta_4$$

$$c_{33} = [r_3(D_2 + D_{xy} + D_{yx}) - D_y(r_3^3 - 3r_3 r_4^2)] \operatorname{Cosh}\beta_3 \operatorname{Cos}\beta_4$$
$$- [r_4(D_2 + D_{xy} + D_{yx}) + D_y(r_4^3 - 3r_4 r_3^2)] \operatorname{Sinh}\beta_3 \operatorname{Sin}\beta_4$$
$$+ EI\alpha_n \operatorname{Sinh}\beta_3 \operatorname{Cos}\beta_4$$

$$d_{33} = \left[r_3\,(D_2 + D_{xy} + D_{yx}) - D_y\,(r_3^{\,3} - 3r_3 r_4^{\,2})\right] \cosh\beta_3 \sin\beta_4$$
$$+ \left[r_4 (D_2 + D_{xy} + D_{yx}) + D_y\,(r_4^{\,3} - 3r_4 r_3^{\,2})\right] \sinh\beta_3 \cos\beta_4$$
$$+ \; EI\,\alpha_n \sinh\beta_3 \sin\beta_4$$

The parameters ψ, ξ_0 and ξ_1 are the same as in case 1.

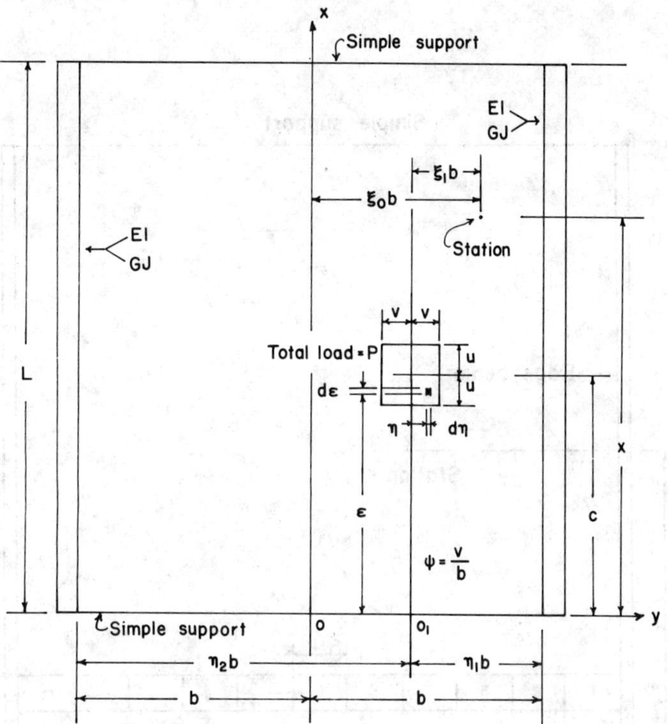

Fig. 1 Coordinate Axes used for bridge deck under uniformly distributed patch load

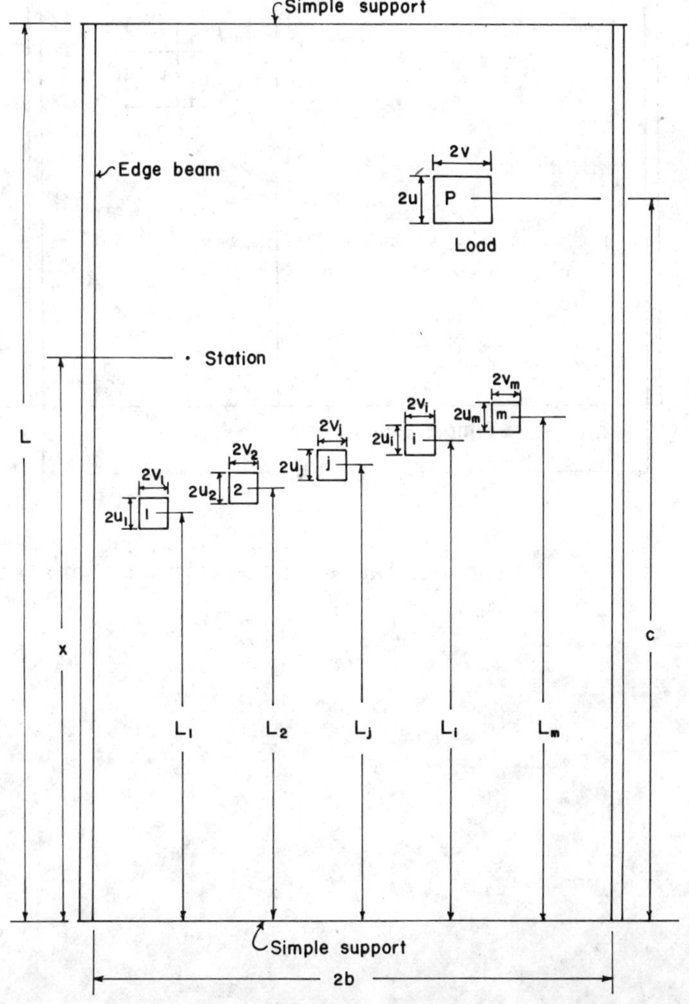

Fig. 2 Plan of Column-Supported bridge deck

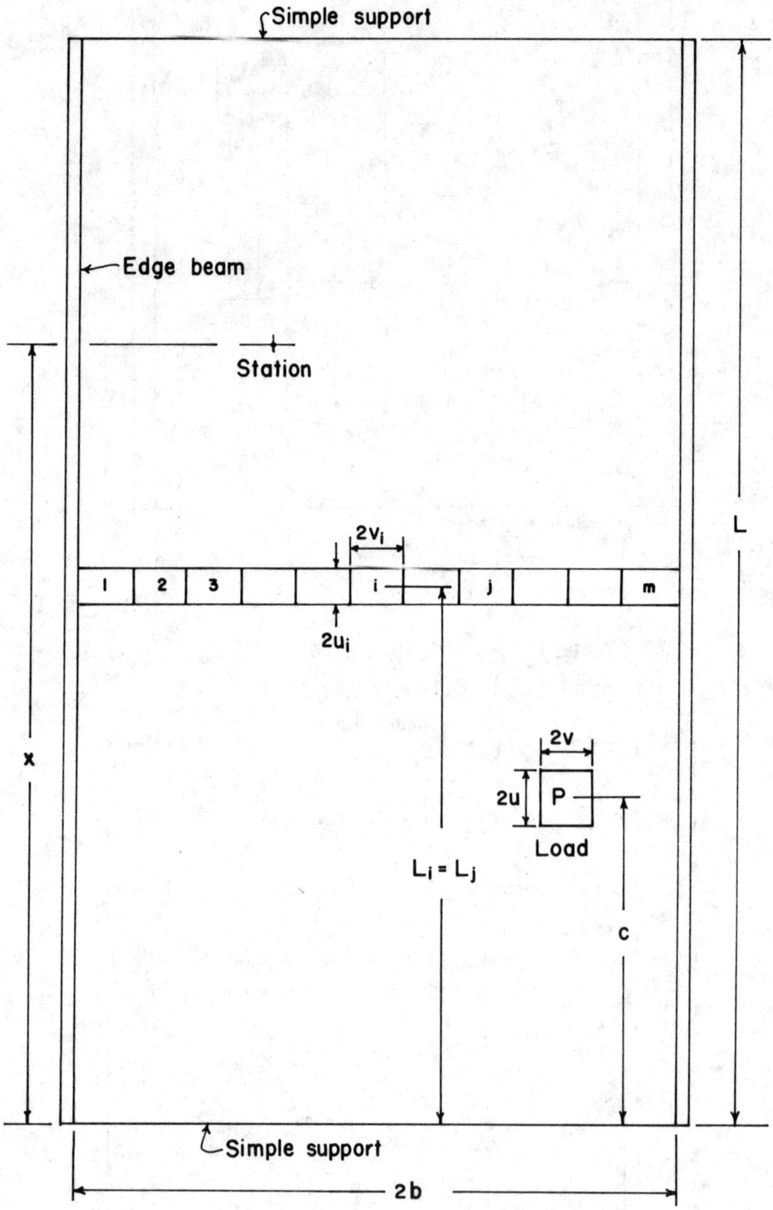

Fig. 3 Plan of two-span continuous bridge deck

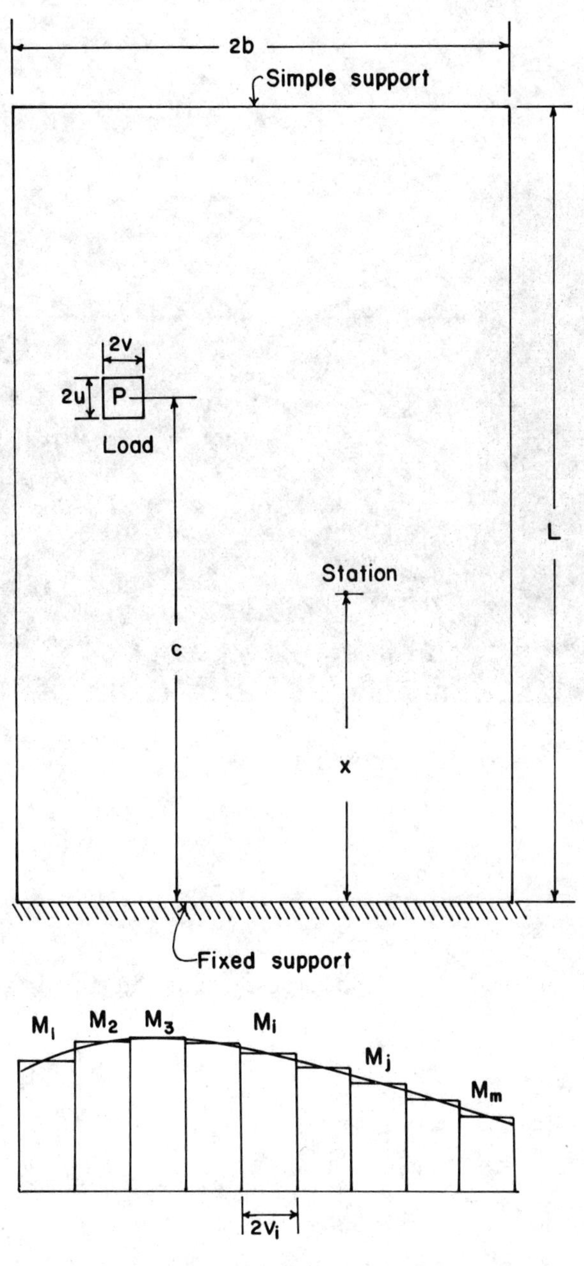

Fig. 4 Plan of propped-cantilever bridge deck

Fig. 5 Column-supported bridge deck

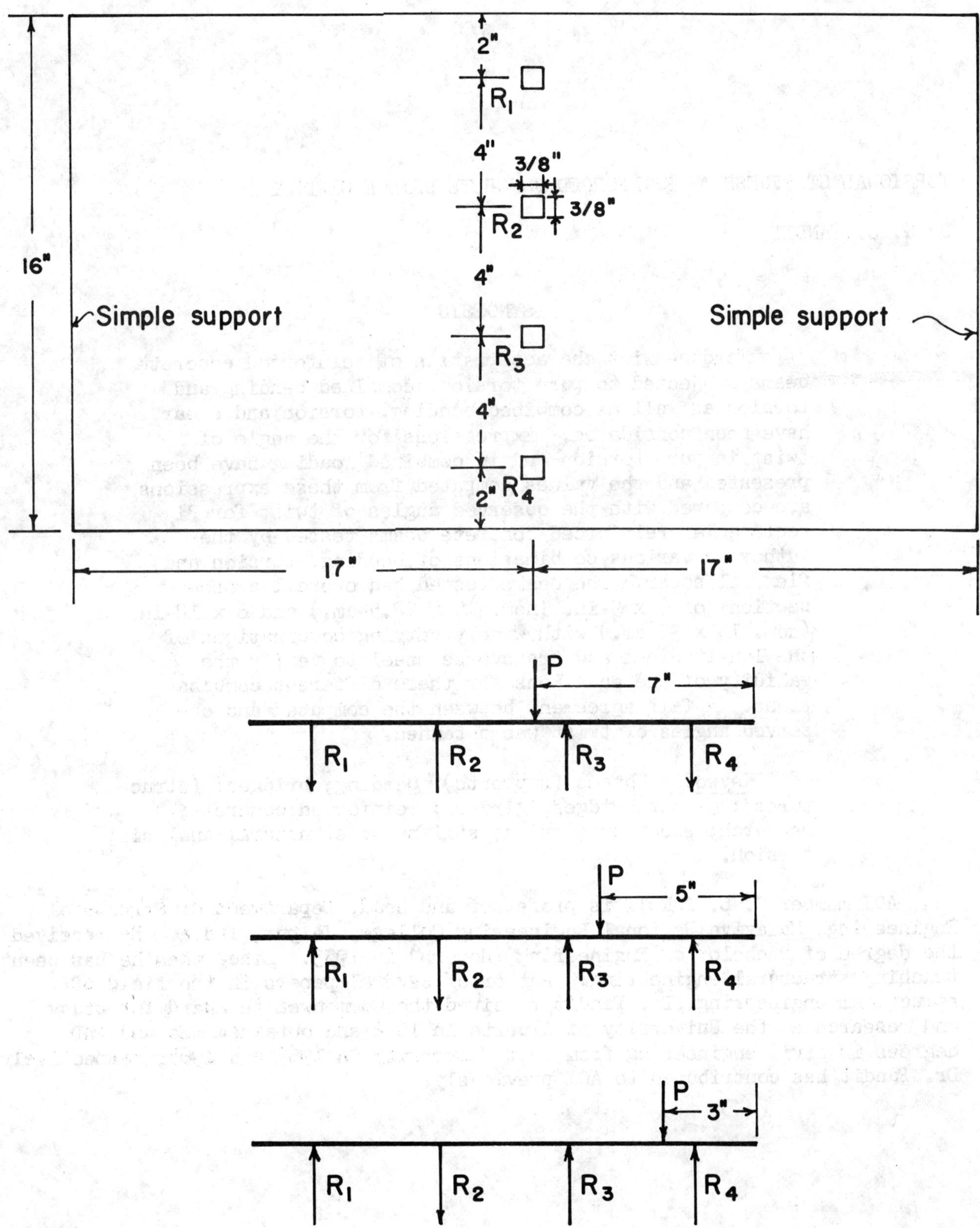

Fig. 6 Reactive forces on column-supported bridge deck

TORSIONAL STIFFNESS OF REINFORCED CONCRETE BRIDGE GIRDERS

By G. S. PANDIT

SYNOPSIS

Torque-twist characteristics of reinforced concrete beams subjected to pure torsion, combined bending and torsion as well as combined bending, torsion and shear have been considered. Expressions for the angle of twist in pure torsion and in combined loading have been presented and the values computed from these expressions are compared with the observed angles of twist for 31 rectangular reinforced concrete beams tested by the author in various combinations of bending, torsion and flexural shear. The beams tested had overall cross-sections of 6 x 9-in. (nom. 15 x 22.5-cm.) and 6 x 12-in. (nom. 15 x 30-cm.) with widely varying combinations of the longitudinal and transverse steel to verify the validity of the equations for these different combinations. A fair agreement between the computed and observed angles of twist was obtained.

Keywords: beams (supports); bending; bridges; (structures); girder bridges; girders; reinforced concrete; research; shear properties; stiffness; structural analysis; torsion.

ACI member G. S. PANDIT is professor and head, Department of Structural Engineering, Malaviya Regional Engineering College, Jaipur, India. He received the degree of Bachelor of Engineering (Honors) in 1953. Since then he has been teaching structural engineering. Author of several papers in the field of structural engineering, Dr. Pandit received the Commonwealth award for study and research at the University of Alberta in 1962 and obtained MSc and PhD degrees in civil engineering from that University in 1963 and 1965, respectively. Dr. Pandit has contributed to ACI previously.

INTRODUCTION

The interconnected girders of a bridge deck are invariably subjected to a combination of bending, torsion and transverse shear. The distribution of bending and twisting moments between these interconnected girders depends upon the flexural and torsional stiffnesses at different load levels. Klus and Wang[1] in their theoretical and experimental studies on reinforced concrete grid frames found that if torsion is neglected in the analysis, large errors may occur for certain loading conditions.

At present there is no accepted procedure for the computation of torsional stiffness or angle of twist for a reinforced concrete member subjected to combined loading although there have been a few tests in recent years. Chinenkov[2] reported that the effect of co-existing flexure in the case of combined bending and torsion of rectangular reinforced concrete beams was to reduce the torsional stiffness. Thus he found that the angle of twist for the same level of torque was greater for a higher level of bending moment. He, however, neither reported the angles of twist nor gave any formula for computing the angle of twist in combined bending and torsion. The author[3] reported on the basis of his tests on 14 reinforced concrete rectangular beams that the effect of flexure was to reduce the torsional stiffness and presented an expression for the initial torsional stiffness of a rectangular reinforced concrete beam subjected to combined bending and torsion. The author's observation received a further corroboration by the study of grid frames carried out by Klus and Wang[1] who observed that a more accurate prediction of moment distribution may be obtained if the torsional stiffness is decreased by 35 percent. Ramkrishnan and Vijaya Rangan[4] have reported tests for the torque-twist characteristics of beams subjected to pure torsion. Tests by Victor and Ferguson[5] seem to indicate a reduction in torsional stiffness due to the presence of bending moment for reinforced concrete T-beams without web reinforcement.

PURE TORSION

For a homogeneous, isotropic and linearly elastic material, the angle of twist per unit length of the beam is given by Eq.(1).

$$\theta = \frac{T}{KG} \qquad (1)$$

where T = twisting moment

K = torsion constant which depends on the geometry of the cross-section

$= \frac{2}{G\theta} \iint \phi_e \, dx \, dy$

G = shear modulus of elasticity

ϕ_e = elastic stress function.

The torsional stiffness of a beam may be defined as the twisting moment required for a unit angle of twist per unit length.

$$S = \frac{T}{\theta} = KG \qquad (2)$$

where S = torsional stiffness.

For a linearly elastic material KG is a constant. Hence the torque-twist relationship is represented by a straight line. The torsional stiffness is the slope of this straight line.

The above equations cannot be applied to the concrete beams because the stress-strain relationship for concrete is non-linear. Hence the torque-twist relationship is also non-linear represented by a curve rather than a strai-ght line. Using the analogy between the stress-strain curve and the torque-twist curve, the torsional stiffness S is analogous to the modulus of elasticity. Hence similar to the tangent and secant modulii of elasticity, the tangent and secant torsional stiffness S_t and S_s may be defined as indicated in Fig.1. The initial torsional stiffness S_o is defined as the initial slope of the torque-twist curve:

$$S_o = \lim_{T \to 0} \left(\frac{dT}{d\theta} \right) = \lim_{T \to 0} (KG) = K_o G_o \qquad (3)$$

Similar to Hognestad's[6] stress-strain curve, the torqe-twist relationship may be assumed to be a second-degree parabola so that the angle of twist at any level of torque may be expressed by Eq.(4).

$$\theta = \frac{T}{S_s} = \frac{T}{S_o}\left(1+\beta\frac{T}{T_{cr}}\right) \tag{4}$$

where T_{cr} = cracking torque

β = a dimensionless constant

Eq.(4) implies that the secant torsional stiffness may be expressed by Eq.(5).

$$S_s = S_o / \left(1+\beta\frac{T}{T_{cr}}\right) \tag{5}$$

The reduction in the torsional stiffness as the torque increases may be attributed to the reduction in the shear modulus of elasticity as well as in the torsion constant due to the micro-cracking of concrete. For the lower limit $T = o$, Eq.(4) defines the initial torsional stiffness S_o as given by Eq.(3). The upper limit of validity of Eq.(4) is restricted to the cracking torque, $T = T_{cr}$. For a torque greater than the cracking torque, the torsional stiffness drops abruptly and is a function of the amount and disposition of the reinforcement.

COMBINED BENDING AND TORSION

The author reported on the basis of his tests on 14 reinforced concrete beams of rectangular cross-section that the initial torsional stiffness is reduced by the fraction $1/(1 + M/M_u)$ due to the presence of flexural moment:

$$S_o \text{ (combined bending and torsion)} = S_o /(1+M/M_u) \quad (6)$$

where M = flexural moment

M_u = ultimate strength in pure flexure

Combining Eq.(6) with Eq.(4), the angle of twist in the case of combined bending and torsion may be expressed by Eq.(7):

$$\theta = \frac{T}{S_o} \left(1 + \beta \frac{T}{T_{cr}} \right) \left(1 + \frac{M}{M_u} \right) \quad (7)$$

Eq.(7) is valid for $T < T_{cr}$ and $M < M_u$. For the limiting case of pure torsion Eq.(7) reverts to Eq.(4).

COMBINED BENDING, TORSION AND SHEAR

The shearing stresses due to torsion and flexural shear add up on one side of the cross-section. Hence the flexural shear assists torsion in producing diagonal cracking at the critical point. The presence of flexural shear, therefore, reduces the twisting moment necessary for diagonal cracking. The effect of flexural shear may consequently be expected to reduce the torsional stiffness and increase the angle of twist. Hence to include the effect of flexural shear, Eq.(7) may be modified as:

$$\theta = \frac{T}{S_o}\left(1+\beta \frac{T}{T_{cr}\left(1-\sqrt{T_{eq}/T_{cr}}\right)}\right)\left(1+\frac{M}{M_u}\right) \quad (8)$$

where T_{eq} = equivalent torque necessary to produce the same shearing stress at the critical point as that produced by the flexural shear

Eq.(8) may be rewritten as:

$$\theta = \frac{T}{S_o}\left(1+\beta' \frac{T}{T_{cr}}\right)\left(1+\frac{M}{M_u}\right) \quad (9)$$

where $\beta' = \beta / \left(1 - \sqrt{T_{eq}/T_{cr}}\right)$ (10)

which shows that the effect of flexural shear has been assumed to increase the constant β by the factor $1/\left(1-\sqrt{T_{eq}/T_{cr}}\right)$. Eq. (9) is valid for $T < T_{cr}$, $T_{eq} < T_{cr}$ and $M < M_u$. For the limiting case of combined bending and torsion, $T_{eq} = 0$ and $\beta' = \beta$. Hence Eq.(9) reverts to Eq.(7). For the limiting case of pure torsion, $T_{eq} = M = 0$. Hence Eq. (9) reverts to Eq. (4).

TEST PROGRAM

The test program comprised of tests on 31 reinforced concrete beams. The nominal cross-section of 26 beams was 6 x 12-in. (nom. 15 x 30 -cm.) whereas that of the remaining 5 beams was 6 x 9 -in. (nom. 15 x 22.5 cm.). Twelve beams were tested in pure torsion, 10 beams in combined bending and torsion and 9 beams in combined bending, torsion and shear. The method of testing was to apply the desired flexural moment and flexural shear before applying torsion. The details of test setup are given elsewhere[7] The angle of twist over the gage-length was measured after each increment of torsional load by means of twistmeters whose construction details are given elsewhere[8].

The specimen properties are given in Table 1 in which the reinforcement details, actual size of specimens and the concrete strength have been listed. The strength properties of the reinforcing steel are presented in Table 2. The flexural moment M before application of torque and the ratio M/M_u for beams tested in combined bending and torsion are listed in Table 3. The ultimate flexural strength, Mu has been computed using Eq.(11).

$$M_u = 0.9\ A_s\ f_y\ d_e \qquad (11)$$

where A_s = area of the tension steel

f_y = yield stress of tension steel

d_e = effective depth of the section.

The flexural moment M and the flexural shear V_u applied to the specimen before it was twisted are listed in Table 4. The specimens were tested with a single point loading applied at the center of a 116-in. (nom. 295-cm.) span for beams in combined bending, torsion and shear. Since flexural moment gradient was unavoidable in this type of loading, the average flexural moment over 18-in. (nom. 45-cm.) gage-length located between 10 inches (nom. 25 cm.) and 28 inches (nom. 70 cm.) from the center-line of the support has been listed in the table. The ultimate flexural moment M_u and the ratio M/M_u have been computed as for Table 3. The nominal shear stress due to flexural shear, v_u has been computed using Eq.(12).

$$v_u = \frac{V_u}{bd} \tag{12}$$

where b = width of the rectangular section

d = depth of the rectangular section

The equivalent torque, T_{eq} introduced in Eq. (8) and listed in Table 4 has been computed using Eq.(13).

$$T_{eq} = k_2 \, b^2 \, d \, v_u \tag{13}$$

where k_2 = a constant which depends on the ratio d/b

= 0.231 and 0.246 for d/b = 1.5 and 2.0 respectively. For values of k_2 for other values of d/b, refer Timoshenko and Goodier[9].

CORRELATION OF TEST RESULTS

(i) Pure Torsion

At zero stress the relationship between the shear modulus of elasticity, G_o and the modulus of elasticity, E_o is given by Eq. (14).

$$G_o = \frac{E_o}{2(1+\mu)} \qquad (14)$$

where μ = Poisson's ratio

Taking E_o = $1000\ f'_c$ where f'_c is the compressive strength

and μ = 0 and noting that for a rectangular section the torsion constant $K_o = k_1\ b^3\ d$, Eq. (4) for beams of rectangular cross-section may be written as:

$$\theta = T(1+\beta\ T/T_{cr})/(500\ f'_c\ k_1\ b^3\ d) \qquad (15)$$

where k_1 = a constant which depends on the ratio d/b

= 0.196 and 0.229 for d/b = 1.5 and 2.0 respectively. For values of k_1 for other values of d/b, refer Timoshenko and Goodier[9].

The cracking torque may be computed using Eq. (16).

$$T_{cr} = k_2\ b^2\ d\ \tau_o \qquad (16)$$

where τ_o = unit torsional strength of concrete

= tensile strength of concrete

Taking the tensile strength of concrete equal to two-third of the modulus of repture in accordance with Wright's[10] findings and using Eq.(17) recommended by the European Concrete Committee:

$$\text{Modulus of repture} = 9.5\sqrt{f'_c} \qquad (17)$$

the relationship between τ_o and f'_c is given by Eq. (18).

$$\tau_o = 6.33\sqrt{f'_c} \qquad (18)$$

Hence the cracking torque may be expressed as:

$$T_{cr} = k_2\, b^2\, d\,(6.33\sqrt{f'_c}) \qquad (19)$$

The angles of twist, θ_a computed using Eq. (15) and (19) for twisting moments equal to 12, 22, 33 and 43 in-kips (14, 25 38 and 50 cm-tons) are listed in table 5 for the seven 6 x 12-in. (nom. 15 x 30-cm.) beams tested in pure torsion. The value of the constant β was taken equal to 2.3 which gave complete agreement between the mean computed and observed angle of twist at the torque of 43 in-kips (50 cm-tons). The value of $\beta = 2.3$ is further checked in Table 6 using the mean values of K_oG_o and T_{cr} from Table 5. The computed and observed angles of twist for 6 x 9-in. (nom. 15 x 22.5-cm.) beams are compared in Table 7. The average value of the ratio of the computed and observed angles of twist θ_a / θ_t and the mean deviation are also given in Tables 5 and 7.

(ii) Combined Bending and Torsion

Proceeding as for the derivation of Eq.(15), Eq.(7) for the angle of twist in the case of combined bending and torsion may be written as:

$$\theta = T(1+\beta\, T/T_{cr})\ (1+M/M_u)/(500\ f'_c\ k_1 b^3 d) \tag{20}$$

The angles of twist, θ_a computed using Eq.(20) and the observed angles of twist, θ_t are compared in Table 8 for the ten beams tested in combined bending and torsion. The average value and the mean deviation of the ratio θ_a / θ_t are also given in Table 8.

(iii) Combined Bending, Torsion and Shear

Proceeding in the same manner as for the derivation of Eq.(15), Eq.(8) for the angle of twist in the case of combined bending, torsion and shear may be expressed as:

$$\theta = T\left(1+\beta \frac{T}{T_{cr}(1-\sqrt{T_{eq}/T_{cr}})}\right)\left(1+\frac{M}{M_u}\right)/\left(500 f'_c k_1 b^3 d\right) \tag{21}$$

The angles of twist, θ_a computed from Eq.(21) and the observed angles of twist, θ_t are compared in Table 9 for the nine beams tested in combined bending, torsion and shear. The average value and the mean deviation of the ratio θ_a / θ_t are also given in Table 9.

DISCUSSION

Considering the usual scatter in the deformation measurements in reinforced concrete, the correlation between the computed and observed angles of twist is very satisfactory. A still better correlation could probably be achieved by adopting a more complicated torque-twist relationship. But due to the availability of limited test results at present, the simple torque-twist relationship of Eq.(4) was adopted. It is probable that certain factors like concrete strength and d/b ratio affect the torque-twist relationship. As regards the effect of the ratio d/b, it may be noted that for a larger d/b ratio, there is a greater redistribution of stress due to a higher stress gradient. Hence the actual maximum stress is lower than that predicted by the elastic theory resulting in a smaller deformation. This reasoning appears to be supported by the tests in pure torsion in this investigation since the average value of θ_a / θ_t for 6 x 12-in. (nom. 15 x 30 -cm.) beams was 1.22 whereas its average value for 6 x 9-in (nom. 15 x 22.5-cm.) beams was 1.12.

The tests show that the torsional stiffness is lower in the case of combined loading. This is of importance in the analysis of grid frames used for bridge decks. Assuming that the working flexural moments are half of the ultimate flexural strengths of the members of the grid, the torsional stiffness is reduced by 33.3 percent due to the presence of flexural moments according to Eq.(6). Tests by Klus and Wang[1] showed that a more accurate prediction of moment distribution may be obtained by reducing the torsional stiffness by 35 percent. This appears to support Eq.(6) and the author's observation that the torsional stiffness is lower in combined loading than in the case of pure torsion.

CONCLUSIONS

Within the limitations of the tests and the type of specimens in this investigation, the following conclusions may be drawn:

1. The average value of the ratio of the computed and observed angles of twist θ_a / θ_t in pure torsion tests was 1.22 and 1.12 and the mean deviation 0.33 and 0.17 for the larger and the smaller beams respectively. In the tests involving combined bending and torsion, average value of θ_a / θ_t was 1.08 and the mean deviation was 0.20. The average value of θ_a / θ_t and the mean deviation in the tests in combined bending, torsion and shear were 1.03 and 0.28. This represents a fair correlation.

2. The torsional stiffness is lower in the case of combined loading as compared to that in pure torsion. The angle of twist for the beams of rectangular cross-section may be calculated using Eq.(15), (20) or (21) depending on the type of loading.

3. A better computation of the moment distribution in grid frames may be achieved by making due allowance for the effect of combined loading on the torsional stiffness.

More tests are called for to establish the effects of factors like b/d ratio, concrete strength and the shape of the cross-section on the torque-twist relationship.

REFERENCES

1. Klus, J.P., and Wang, C.K., "Torsion in Grid Frames," Torsion of Structural Concrete, Special Publication No.18, American Concrete Institute, Detroit, 1968, pp. 89-101.

2. Chinenkov, Yu. V., "Investigation of Behavior of Reinforced Concrete Elements Subjected to Combined Bending and Torsion", Proceedings of the Concrete and Reinforced Concrete Institute, Moscow, Vol.5, 1959, (in Russian). Translated by Margaret Corbin as Foreign Literature Study No.370, Portland Cement Association, Research and Development Laboratories, Skokie, Illinois.

3. Pandit G.S., and Warwaruk, J. "Effect of Flexure on the Initial Torsional Stiffness of Reinforced Concrete Beams of Rectangular Cross-Section," Indian Concrete Journal, Vol.41, No.9, September, 1967 pp.355-358.

4. Ramakrishnan, V., and Rangan, B.V., "The Torque-Twist Relationship for Rectangular Beams," CONCRETE, Vol. 1, No.11, November, 1967 pp.383-386.

5. Victor, D.J., and Ferguson, P.M. "Reinforced Concrete T-beams Without Stirrups Under Combined Moment and Torsion," ACI Journal, Proceedings V.65 No.1, January 1968, pp. 29-36.

6. Hognestad, E., " A Study of the Combined Bending and Axial Load in Reinforced Concrete Members," Bulletin No.399, Engineering Experiment Station, University of Illinois, Urbana, November, 1951, 128 pp.

7. Pandit, G.S., and Warwaruk, J., "Reinforced Concrete Beams in Combined Bending and Torsion -Part I: Ultimate Strength Analysis -Part II: Experiments," Torsion of Structural Concrete, SP 18, American Concrete Institute, Detroit, 1968, pp.133-163.

8. Pandit, G.S., "Torsion in Concrete Sections", M.Sc. Thesis, University of Alberta, September, 1963.

9. Timoshenko, S., and Goodier, J.N., "Theory of Elasticity," McGraw-Hill Book Company, Inc. Second Edition, 1951.

10. Wright, P.J.F., "Comments on an Indirect Tensile Test on Concrete Cylinders", Magazine of Concrete Research, Vol. 7, No.20, July, 1955.

APPENDIX - NOTATION

T = twisting moment

T_{cr} = cracking torque

T_{eq} = equivalent torque necessary to produce the same shearing stress at the critical point as that produced by the flexural shear

M = flexural moment

M_u = ultimate strength in pure flexure

V_u = flexural shear

v_u = nominal shear stress due to flexural shear

f_y = yield stress of tension steel

f'_c = compressive strength of concrete

τ_o = unit torsional strength of concrete
= tensile strength of concrete

E_o = Modulus of elasticity of concrete at zero stress

G = shear modulus of elasticity

G_o = shear modulus of elasticity of concrete at zero stress

b = width of the rectangular section

d = depth of the rectangular section

d_e = effective depth of the rectangular section

A_s = area of the tension steel

K = torsion constant

K_o = torsion constant for a concrete section at zero torque

θ = angle of twist

θ_a = computed angle of twist

θ_t = observed angle of twist

ϕ_e = elastic stress function

S = torsional stiffness

S_o = initial torsional stiffness

S_t = tangent torsional stiffness

S_s = secant torsional stiffness

μ = Poisson's ratio

β, β', k_1, k_2 = constants

TABLE 1 SPECIMEN PROPERTIES

Beam	Longitudinal bars				Stirrups**		Concrete strength***	Actual size	
	At top		At bottom		Size in(mm)	Spacing in(mm)	psi(kg/cm^2)	Width in(mm)	Depth in(mm)
	No.	Size in(mm)	No.	Size in(mm)					
B-2	2	3/8(9.5)	2	1/2(12.7)	3/8(9.5)	6.0(152)	4640(326)	6.20(157)	12.20(310)
B-3	2	3/8(9.5)	2	1/2(12.7)	3/8(9.5)	6.0(152)	4690(330)	6.05(154)	12.20(310)
B-4	2	3/8(9.5)	2	1/2(12.7)	3/8(9.5)	6.0(152)	5070(355)	6.10(155)	12.20(310)
C-1	2	3/8(9.5)	2	5/8(15.9)	3/8(9.5)	4.5(114)	4980(350)	6.00(152)	12.20(310)
C-2	2	3/8(9.5)	2	5/8(15.9)	3/8(9.5)	4.5(114)	4820(339)	6.15(156)	12.20(310)
C-3	2	3/8(9.5)	2	5/8(15.9)	3/8(9.5)	4.5(114)	5340(374)	6.10(155)	12.20(310)
C-4	2	3/8(9.5)	2	5/8(15.9)	3/8(9.5)	4.5(114)	5800(408)	6.50(165)	12.20(310)
D-1	2	5/8(15.9)	4*	3/4(19.1)	3/8(9.5)	4.5(114)	4880(343)	6.20(157)	12.20(310)
D-2	2	5/8(15.9)	4*	3/4(19.1)	3/8(9.5)	4.5(114)	5100(359)	6.20(157)	12.20(310)
D-3	2	5/8(15.9)	4*	3/4(19.1)	3/8(9.5)	4.5(114)	4650(327)	6.20(157)	12.20(310)
D-4	2	5/8(15.9)	4*	3/4(19.1)	3/8(9.5)	4.5(114)	5080(357)	6.20(157)	12.20(310)

TABLE 1 SPECIMEN PROPERTIES (CONTINUED)

E-1	2	1/2(12.7)	2	1/2(12.7)	3/8(9.5)	4.5(114)	4910(345)	6.20(157)	12.20(310)
E-2	2	1/2(12.7)	2	1/2(12.7)	3/8(9.5)	4.5(114)	5100(359)	6.20(157)	12.20(310)
E-3	2	1/2(12.7)	2	1/2(12.7)	3/8(9.5)	4.5(114)	4700(330)	6.20(157)	12.20(310)
F-1	3	3/8(9.5)	3	3/8(9.5)	3/8(9.5)	8.0(203)	5060(356)	6.10(155)	12.20(310)
F-2	3	3/8(9.5)	3	3/8(9.5)	3/8(9.5)	8.0(203)	5060(356)	6.10(155)	12.20(310)
F-3	3	3/8(9.5)	3	3/8(9.5)	3/8(9.5)	8.0(203)	4650(327)	6.15(156)	12.20(310)
F-4	3	3/8(9.5)	3	3/8(9.5)	3/8(9.5)	8.0(203)	4650(327)	6.10(155)	12.20(310)
G-1	3	3/8(9.5)	3	3/8(9.5)	1/4(6.4)	3.5(89)	4560(321)	6.20(157)	12.20(310)
G-2	3	3/8(9.5)	3	3/8(9.5)	1/4(6.4)	3.5(89)	4560(321)	6.20(157)	12.20(310)
G-3	3	3/8(9.5)	3	3/8(9.5)	1/4(6.4)	3.5(89)	4920(346)	6.15(156)	12.20(310)
G-4	3	3/8(9.5)	3	3/8(9.5)	1/4(6.4)	3.5(89)	4920(346)	6.20(157)	12.20(310)
H-1	Nil	-	2 & 1	3/8(9.5) 3/4(19.1)	1/4(6.4)	3.5(89)	4450(313)	6.10(155)	12.20(310)
H-2	Nil	-	2 & 1	3/8(9.5) 3/4(19.1)	1/4(6.4)	3.5(89)	4450(313)	6.10(155)	12.20(310)
H-3	Nil	-	2 & 1	3/8(9.5) 3/4(19.1)	1/4(6.4)	3.5(89)	4830(340)	6.25(159)	12.20(310)
H-4	Nil	-	2 & 1	3/8(9.5) 3/4(19.1)	1/4(6.4)	3.5(89)	4830(340)	6.25(159)	12.20(310)

TABLE 1 SPECIMEN PROPERTIES (CONTINUED)

2	2	1/2(12.7)	2	1/2(12.7)	1/4(6.4)	2 (51)	4160(292)	6.00(152)	9.10(310)
3	2	1/2(12.7)	2	1/2(12.7)	3/8(9.5)	4.5(114)	4050(285)	6.00(152)	9.10(310)
4	2	1/4(6.4)	2* & 3	1/4(6.4) 1/2(12.7)	3/8(9.5)	4.5(114)	5020(353)	6.00(152)	9.10(310)
5	2	1/2(12.7)	2	1/2(12.7)	1/2(12.7)	8.0(203)	5020(353)	6.00(152)	9.10(310)
7	2	1/2(12.7)	2	1/2(12.7)	1/4(6.4)	2 (51)	4160(292)	6.00(152)	9.10(310)

* Arranged in two layers

** Size of stirrups of 6 x 12-in(nom. 15 x 30 -cm) beams 5 x 11-in.(nom. 12.5 x 27.5 -cm) and of the 6 x 9 -in(nom. 15 x 22.5-cm) beams 4.5 x 7.5-in. (nom. 11.25 x 18.75 -cm) on the outside.

*** Based on the compression test on 6 x 12-in (nom. 15 x 30-cm) cylinders.

TABLE 2 STRENGTH PROPERTIES OF REINFORCING STEEL

Size of bar in. (mm)	Average yield stress psi (kg/cm^2)	Average ultimate stress psi (kg/cm^2)	Type
1/4(6.4)	45,000 (3160)	58,300(4100)	Plain
3/8(9.5)	57,300 (4030)	82,500(5800)	Deformed
1/2(12.7)	58,300 (4100)	88,400(6210)	Deformed
5/8(15.9)	49,500 (3480)	75,400(5300)	Deformed
3/4(19.1)	51,300 (3610)	73,900(5200)	Deformed

TABLE 3 BEAMS IN COMBINED BENDING AND TORSION

Beam	M	M_u	M/M_u
	in-kips (cm-tons)		
B-2	195(225)	228(263)	0.86
B-3	110(127)	228(263)	0.48
C-1	280(322)	297(342)	0.94
C-2	195(225)	297(342)	0.66
C-3	110(127)	297(342)	0.37
D-1	637(734)	823(948)	0.77
D-2	365(420)	823(948)	0.44
D-3	195(225)	823(948)	0.24
E-1	195(225)	228(263)	0.86
E-2	110(127)	228(263)	0.48

TABLE 4 BEAMS IN COMBINED BENDING, SHEAR AND TORSION

Beam	M*	M_u	M/M_u	V_u	v_u	T_{eq}
	in-kips(	cm-tons)		kips(tons)	psi(kg/cm²)	in-kips (cm-tons)
F-1	140(161)	187(215)	0.75	9.2(4.2)	137(9.6)	15(17)
F-2	95(109)	187(215)	0.51	6.2(2.8)	92(6.5)	10(12)
F-3	50(58)	187(215)	0.27	3.2(1.5)	47(3.3)	5(6)
G-1	155(179)	190(219)	0.82	10.2(4.6)	147(10.3)	17(20)
G-2	95(109)	190(219)	0.50	6.2(2.8)	89(6.3)	10(12)
G-3	50(58)	190(219)	0.26	3.2(1.5)	47(3.3)	5(6)
H-1	245(282)	348(401)	0.70	16.2(7.3)	242(17.0)	27(31)
H-2	155(179)	348(401)	0.45	10.2(4.6)	152(10.7)	17(20)
H-3	80(92)	348(401)	0.23	5.2(2.4)	76(5.3)	9(10)

*Average over the gage length.

TABLE 5 ANGLE OF TWIST OF BEAMS IN PURE TORSION, RADIANS/INCH* $\times 10^6$.

Beam	$K_o G_o \times 10^6$	T_{cr}	T=12 in-kips (14 cm-tons)			T=22 in-kips (25 cm-tons)			T=33 in-kips (38 cm-tons)			T=43 in-kips (50cm-tons)		
			θ_a	θ_t	θ_a/θ_t	θ_a	θ_t	θ_a/θ_t	θ_a	θ_t	θ_a/θ_t	θ_a	θ_t	θ_a/θ_t
	lb-in² ton- cm²	in-kips (cm-tons)		Radians per inch* $\times 10^6$										
B-4	1620(4.7)	50(58)	12	18	0.67	-	-	-	51	51	1.00	80	80	1.00
C-4	2230(6.5)	61(70)	-	-	-	18	24	0.75	-	-	-	51	51	1.00
D-4	1690(4.9)	52(60)	-	-	-	26	29	0.90	-	-	-	74	105	0.70
E-3	1560(4.6)	50(58)	-	-	-	28	29	0.97	-	-	-	82	80	1.03
F-4	1480(4.3)	48(55)	13	8	1.63	30	21	1.43	57	38	1.50	90	75	1.20
G-4	1640(4.5)	51(59)	11	8	1.38	27	21	1.29	50	46	1.09	77	88	0.88
H-4	1650(4.5)	52(60)	11	4	2.75	26	17	1.53	49	33	1.48	75	54	1.39
Total	11870 (34.0)	364 (420)	47	38	6.43	155	141	6.87	207	168	5.07	529	533	7.20
Mean	1700 (4.9)	52 (60)	12	10	1.61	26	24	1.15	52	42	1.27	76	76	1.03
Average value of (θ_a / θ_t) = **1.22** Mean deviation = 0.33														

*Multiply by 0.3937 to get the angle of twist in radians/cm $\times 10^6$

TABLE 6 CHECK ON VALUE OF $\beta = 2.3$ USING MEAN VALUES* OF K_oG_o AND T_{cr} FROM TABLE 5

T in-kips (cm-tons)	$2.3T/T_{cr}$	θ_a	θ_t (mean)	θ_a / θ_t
		Radians/inch** x 10^6		
12 (14)	0.53	11	10	1.10
22 (25)	0.97	25	24	1.04
33 (38)	1.46	48	42	1.14
43 (50)	1.90	73	76	0.96
Total		157	152	4.24
Mean		39	38	1.06

* K_oG_o = 1700 x 10^6 lb-in^2 (4.9 x 10^6 ton-cm^2) and
T_{cr} = 52 in-kips (60 cm-tons).

** Multiply by 0.3937 to get the angle of twist in radians/cm x 10^6

TABLE 7 ANGLE OF TWIST OF BEAMS IN PURE TORSION, RADIANS/INCH* x 10^6

Beam	T = 13 in-kips (15 cm-tons)			T= 19 in-kips (22 cm-tons)			T= 24 in-kips (28 cm-tons)			T=30 in-kips (35 cm-tons)		
	θ_a	θ_t	θ_a/θ_t	θ_a	θ_t	θ_a/θ_t	θ_a	θ_t	θ_a/θ_t	θ_a	θ_t	θ_a/θ_t
2	32	30	1.07	57	42	1.36	83	60	1.38	121	82	1.48
3.	33	33	1.00	59	48	1.23	85	67	1.27	124	113	1.10
4	25	33	0.76	45	46	0.98	65	62	1.05	94	83	1.13
5	25	32	0.78	45	45	1.00	65	58	1.12	94	78	1.21
7	32	30	1.07	-	-	-	83	67	1.24	121	107	1.13
Total			4.68			4.57			6.06			6.05
Mean			0.94			1.14			1.21			1.21
Average value of (θ_a / θ_t) = 1.12 Mean deviation = 0.17												

* Multiply by 0.3937 to get the angle of twist in radians/cm x 10^6

TABLE 8 ANGLE OF TWIST OF BEAMS IN COMBINED BENDING AND TORSION, RADIANS/INCH* $\times 10^6$

Beam	T=12 in-kips (14 cm-tons)			T= 22 in-kips (25 cm-tons)			T=23 in-kips (26 cm-tons)			T= 33 in-kips (38 cm-tons)			T=43 in-kips (50 cm-tons)		
	θ_a	θ_t	θ_a/θ_t	θ_a	θ_t	θ_a/θ_t	θ_a	θ_t	θ_a/θ_t	θ_a	θ_t	θ_a/θ_t	θ_a	θ_t	θ_a/θ_t
B-2	-	-	-	-	-	-	57	56	1.02	-	-	-	155	167	0.93
B-3	19	16	1.19	-	-	-	48	40	1.20	85	67	1.27	131	107	1.22
C-1	24	16	1.50	-	-	-	62	53	1.17	110	118	0.93	170	189	0.90
C-2	-	-	-	-	-	-	50	40	1.25	-	-	-	136	102	1.33
C-3	-	-	-	35	31	1.13	-	-	-	-	-	-	100	111	0.90
D-1	-	-	-	48	80	0.60	-	-	-	-	-	-	138	211	0.65
D-2	-	-	-	37	27	1.37	-	-	-	-	-	-	106	69	1.54
D-3	-	-	-	35	36	0.97	-	-	-	-	-	-	103	98	1.05
E-1	-	-	-	50	53	0.94	-	-	-	-	-	-	143	160	0.89
E-2				38	36	1.06	-	-	-	-	-	-	108	131	0.82
Total			2.69			6.07			4.64			2.20			10.23
Mean			1.35			1.01			1.16			1.10			1.02

Average value of $(\theta_a / \theta_t) = 1.08$ Mean Deviation = 0.20

* Multiply by 0.3937 to get the angle of twist in radians/cm $\times 10^6$

TABLE 9 ANGLE OF TWIST OF BEAMS IN COMBINED BENDING, TORSION AND SHEAR, RADIANS/INCH* x 10^6

Beam	T= 12 in-kips (14 cm-tons)			T=22 in-kips (25 cm-tons)			T= 33 in-kips (38 cm-tons)			T=43 in-kips (50 cm- tons)		
	θ_a	θ_t	θ_a/θ_t	θ_a	θ_t	θ_a/θ_t	θ_a	θ_t	θ_a/θ_t	θ_a	θ_t	θ_a/θ_t
F-1	29	67	0.43	77	150	0.51	156	267	0.58	-	-	-
F-2	22	21	1.05	58	46	1.26	116	108	1.07	134	172	1.07
F-3	18	21	0.86	46	54	0.85	90	100	0.90	142	150	0.95
G-1	34	42	0.81	93	133	0.70	189	225	0.84	305	425	0.72
G-2	24	33	0.73	63	67	0.94	124	117	1.06	198	175	1.13
G-3	17	23	0.74	43	50	0.86	84	113	0.74	131	163	0.80
H-1	49	33	1.48	143	92	1.56	302	171	1.77	499	278	1.79
H-2	30	42	0.71	83	96	0.86	170	159	1.07	275	246	1.12
H-3	17	8	2.13	44	33	1.33	86	67	1.28	136	104	1.31
Total			8.94			8.87			9.31			8.89
Mean			0.99			0.99			1.03			1.11

Average value of (θ_a / θ_t) = 1.03 Mean Deviation = 0.28

*Multiply by 0.3937 to get the angle of twist in radians/cm x 10^6

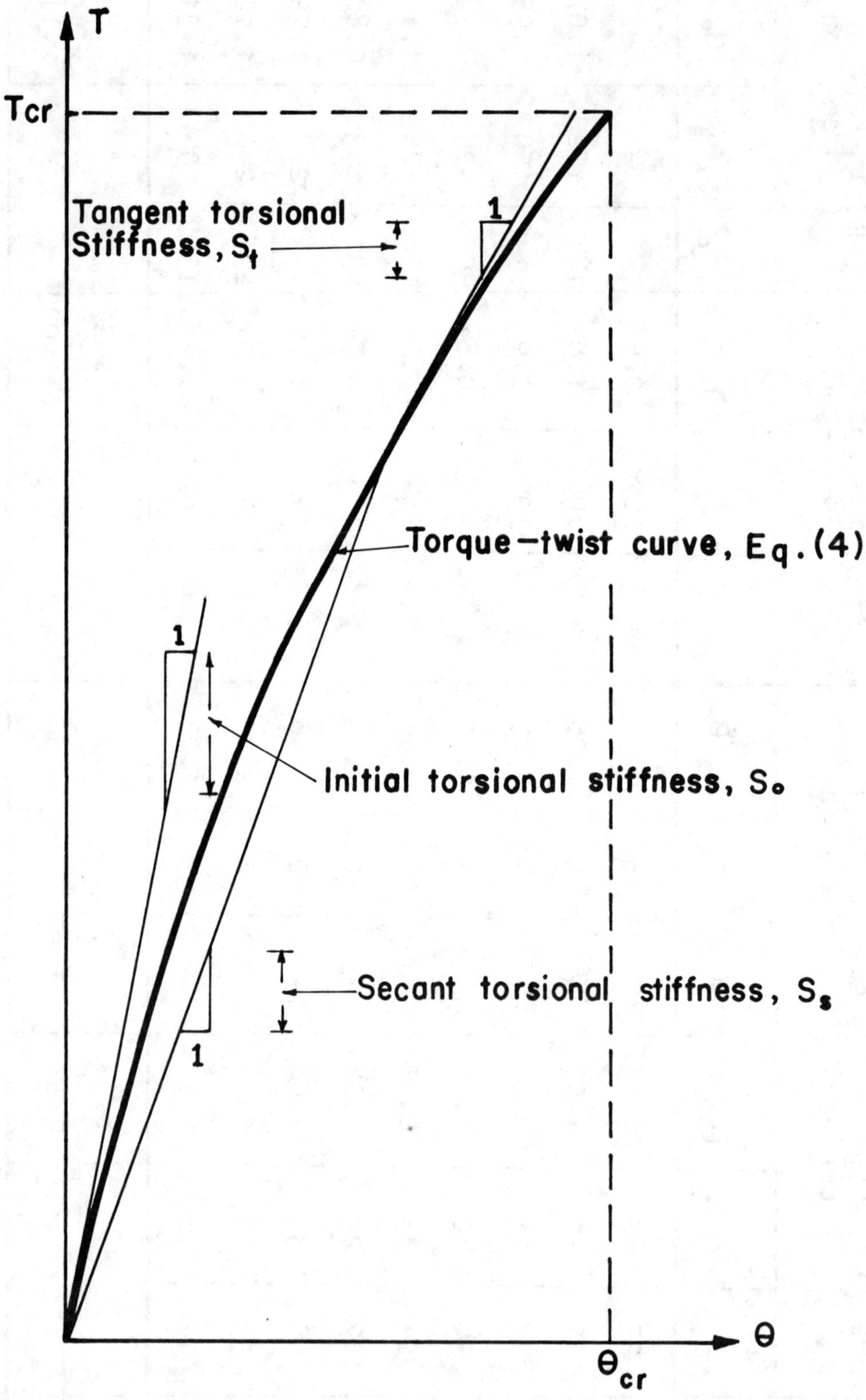

Fig. 1 Torque-twist characteristics